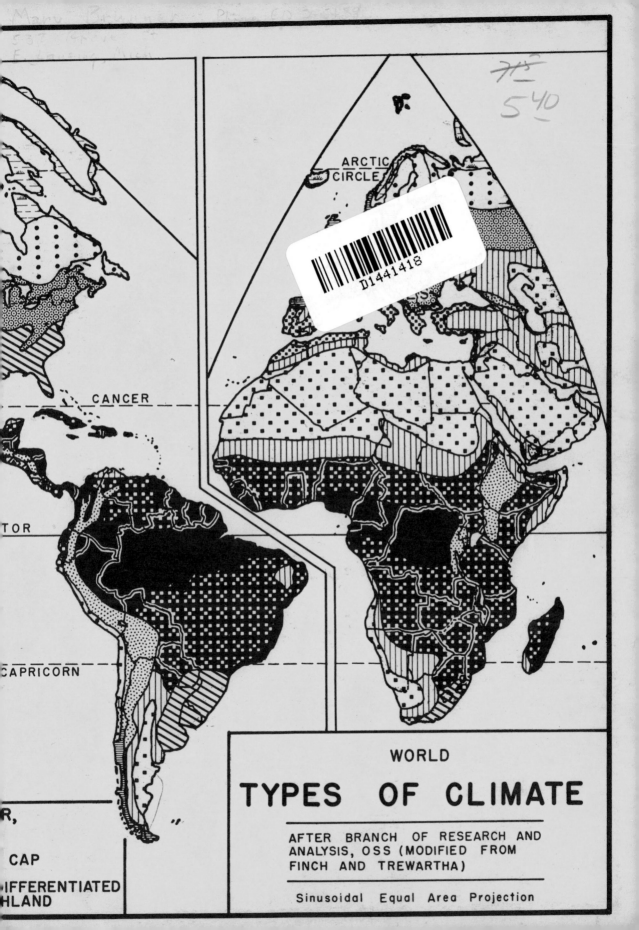

WORLD

TYPES OF CLIMATE

AFTER BRANCH OF RESEARCH AND
ANALYSIS, OSS (MODIFIED FROM
FINCH AND TREWARTHA)

Sinusoidal Equal Area Projection

Regional Geography of The World

REGIONAL

GEOGRAPHY

OF THE WORLD

An Introductory Survey

JESSE H. WHEELER, JR.
UNIVERSITY OF MISSOURI

J. TRENTON KOSTBADE

RICHARD S. THOMAN
UNIVERSITY OF CHICAGO

HENRY HOLT AND COMPANY · NEW YORK

29342–0115

Printed in the United States of America

Preface

This volume seeks to assist college and university students in acquiring certain basic ideas and supporting facts about contemporary world geography which a person with a college education might reasonably be expected to know. Its aim, in short, is general education in world geography.

It surveys the world importance, geographical characteristics, and major problems of eight world regions—Europe, the Soviet Union, the Middle East, the Orient, the Pacific World, Africa, Latin America, and Anglo-America. Attention is also given to important individual countries and regional groups of countries within each world region. Pertinent background material on systematic physical and cultural geography is presented at appropriate places. A general introduction to geography as a field of study is presented in Chapter 1.

The book is designed as a text for courses in world regional geography on an introductory college level. It is believed to be suitable either for one-semester courses or, with supplementary reading, additional map work, and expanded class discussion, for two-semester courses. In the preparation of the book, no previous training in systematic physical and cultural geography on the part of the prospective student users has been assumed. However, the authors feel that some teachers and departments employing the traditional arrangement of an "elements" or "principles" course followed by a world regional course may find the volume suitable for the second course.

Instructors may not find it necessary to require students to purchase an atlas. Nearly all of the place names mentioned in the text are shown on maps. A considerable number of maps showing the world or regional distribution of population, types of climate, major crops, and other elements of geographical significance are included. Students should be encouraged to use atlases as essential reference tools.

The photographs in the volume are not intended to give a comprehensive coverage, although it is hoped that each photo will convey at least one significant idea about the country or region portrayed. Teachers are urged to make such use as time permits of movies, slides, and film strips to illustrate, amplify, and supplement the ideas contained in the text and to give students the "feel" of the areas considered.

Statistics have been employed in various places to reinforce important concepts. It has not been felt necessary in an introductory textbook to give full documentation for all statistics. With a few major exceptions, population figures cited for cities represent late estimates as given in either the 1954 *Britannica Book of the Year* or the 1954 *Americana Annual*. The *Columbia-Lippincott Gazetteer of the World* (1952) has been used as the principal source for areas of political units and the 1953 *United Nations Statistical Yearbook* as the major source for populations of political units. Climatic and economic data have been taken from a variety of standard sources.

Although the major portion of the text has been specially written, a variety of readings, mostly short, are included. It was hoped by this means to provide a diversity of viewpoints and, by selecting especially well-written materials, to add to the over-all readability. In editing the readings, minor changes in spelling, capitalization, and punctuation have been made in order to give uniformity with the remainder of the book. Most of the sectional headings within the body of the readings represent editorial additions. Elision marks are not used at the beginning of an opening paragraph or the end of a selection.

The senior author has carried the over-all editorial responsibility for the book and was chiefly responsible for the planning and supervision of the cartography and the selection and captioning of photographs. Chapters 1, 2, 6, 11, 12, 13, 14, 15, 16, 19, 23, and 24 were prepared by the senior author. Mr. Kostbade prepared Chapters 7, 8, 9, 10, 17, 18, 22, 27, and 28, and Chapters 3, 4, 5, 20, and 21 were prepared jointly by Mr. Kostbade and the senior author. Chapters 25 and 26 were prepared by Mr. Thoman, who also rendered important assistance with the maps, including the actual drafting of a number of the more complicated ones. The basic core of ideas in the book was to a large degree a product of many hours of discussion among the three authors during a fruitful association at the University of Missouri extending over a period of several years.

The authors extend sincere thanks to a number of other geographers who were kind enough to offer their comments on portions of the manuscript submitted for criticism, or who otherwise rendered assistance. Their suggestions proved exceedingly useful and were heeded in the great majority of cases. They are, of course, absolved of any responsibility for errors of fact or interpretation in the book. The men to whom acknowledgment is due include the following:

John E. Brush, Rutgers University; Wesley Calef, University of Chicago; Charles C. Colby, University of Chicago (Emeritus); Jerome D. Fellman, University of Illinois; Gerard Foster, University of California, Los Angeles; Norton S. Ginsburg, University of Chicago; William A. Hance, Columbia University; Robert A. Harper, Southern Illinois University; Chauncy D. Harris, University of Chicago; Howard F. Hirt, University of Missouri; William Horbaly; Rayburn W. Johnson, Memphis State College; H. Louis Kostanick, University of California, Los Angeles; Trevor Lloyd, Dartmouth College; James S. Matthews, Memphis State College; Edwin S. Munger, University of Chicago and American Universities Field Staff; Howard J. Nelson, University of California, Los Angeles; Jerome P. Pickard, Washington, D. C.; Robert S. Platt, University of Chicago; Paul H. Sisco, Memphis State College; Joseph E. Spencer, University of California, Los Angeles; Edward J. Taaffe, Loyola University, Chicago; Philip True;

Philip Wagner, University of Chicago; and James R. Wray, University of Chicago.

Acknowledgment is made to the following persons who assisted in the drafting of maps: Fumie Shimazu, Ray Mathews, James Sommerer, Mrs. Edith Bond Thompson, James B. Kenyon, R. Kenton Wibking, Barbara Conway, Mrs. Evelyn Thoman, Mrs. Llyn Tamantini, and Mrs. Henrietta Bock.

The senior author expresses his sincere and deep appreciation to the Fund for the Advancement of Education of the Ford Foundation for its award of a Faculty Study Fellowship in 1951–1952. This grant made possible a school year of work devoted to organizing a new general education course in world regional geography at the University of Missouri and led eventually to the preparation of the present book.

Thanks are expressed to the individuals, firms, and government agencies or other organizations who permitted the use of copyrighted textual matter, photographs, and maps. Such permissions are separately acknowledged. Design did not permit specific acknowledgment along with the illustra-

tions for the part titles. Therefore, the authors wish to thank the following organizations at this point: Standard Oil Company (N. J.) for Parts 1, 4, and 8; French Government Tourist Office, Part 2; Sovfoto, Part 3; Technical Cooperation Administration, U. S. Department of State, Part 5; British Information Services, Parts 6 and 7; and Price Brothers & Company Limited, Part 9.

The authors are aware of the pitfalls involved in preparing a book on the regional geography of the entire world in the midst of changing times and with source materials so varied as to accuracy, recency, and completeness. Nevertheless, they believe the enterprise was worth attempting, and sincerely hope the finished product will be of service in raising the level of geographic knowledge, understanding, and appreciation among the college and university students to whom it is addressed.

J. H. W., Jr.
J. T. K.
R. S. T.

Columbia, Mo.
February 1, 1955

Contents

PART 9: ANGLO-AMERICA

PART 1
Introductory Concepts

Some Introductory Concepts of Geography

The main reason for studying geography is to gain a better understanding and appreciation of the world in which we live. Of course, many other subjects besides geography contribute to this end. In fact, most school subjects are concerned in one way or another with enhancing our understanding and appreciation of the world about us. Geography, however, has one characteristic which tends to distinguish it from most other subjects, namely, that it centers attention on the study and interpretation of particular *areas* in the world.

A well-known geographer, George B. Cressey, has stated this idea as follows: "It is the task of geography . . . to draw information from widely scattered sources, and to give it a new significance as applied to the understanding of specific areas."[1]

The term "area," as used by geographers, may refer to any portion of the earth's surface. The largest of all areas is, of course, the entire world. However, in most respects the world is much too large and complicated to be readily comprehended all at once. For purposes of study it is generally

[1] By permission from *Asia's Lands and Peoples*, by George B. Cressey. Copyright, 1944, 1951. New York: McGraw-Hill Book Company, Inc. Pp. 34–35.

Excessive crowding in the lowlands of overpopulated regions leads to the tilling of steep slopes, such as the Puerto Rican tobacco field shown in the above view. Erosion by heavy tropical downpours will soon destroy the soil and render this land worthless. (*Government of Puerto Rico.*)

3

necessary to subdivide it into areas of a smaller size. In this book primary attention is given to two kinds of areas, the *countries* as outlined on an ordinary political map and the *major world regions* in which the individual countries lie.

The Major World Regions

As customarily used by geographers, the term "region" refers to an area of considerable size which has some degree of internal unity or homogeneity and which differs in significant respects from adjoining areas. A region may be wholly contained within a single country, or it may include several different countries or parts of countries. This book is organized in terms of eight major world regions: Europe, the Soviet Union, the Middle East, the Orient, the Pacific World, Africa, Latin America, and Anglo-America. Although these regions are commonly recognized as grand divisions of the world, authorities differ as to the precise area which should be included in each. In this book the eight world regions are delimited as blocks of countries, and thus the outer limits of the respective regions follow political boundary lines. This method of regional division has been adopted for convenience in using statistical materials and for sharpness in presenting regional concepts on an introductory level. However, the student should not assume that the political lines which are employed as regional boundaries necessarily represent sharp lines of cleavage in other respects. In physical, cultural, and economic terms the major world regions tend to be separated by zones of transition where the characteristics of one region change gradually to those of the next. This tendency to merge gradually rather than to be separated by sharp lines is also true of regions of a smaller order of size. Since regions are merely convenient devices useful in generalizing about the world, it is more important to grasp the particular set of features which characterizes the core of a region than it is to search for an exact line where the characteristics of one region end and the characteristics of another region begin.

The scheme of eight major world regions employed in this book is only one among various alternative methods of subdividing the world for purposes of study. However, it is believed to be especially well suited as an organizing device for accomplishing the major objective of the book, which is simply to assist the student in acquiring a fund of concepts about the geography of the contemporary world that any educated person might reasonably be expected to know. The regional names employed already have some familiarity for the student and are in common use in published writing and news reporting about world affairs. Thus the student can proceed from the known to the unknown in acquiring the new perspectives which a sound knowledge of world geography is able to give.

Each of the major world regions has certain well-defined characteristics which tend to give it a unity or personality of its own.

Europe is a busy industrial, commercial, and agricultural region in middle latitudes.[2] It includes a larger number of individual countries than any other area of comparable size. These countries are small, being generally comparable in extent to American states. However, many of them

[2] For the guidance of students who have had no previous course work in college or high school geography, a limited number of important technical terms are explained in bracketed sections in the text following the paragraph in which they first appear.

This map delineates the eight major world regions forming the basic framework of organization for this text. (*Boggs Equal Area Projection, used by courtesy of A. J. Nystrom and Co.*)

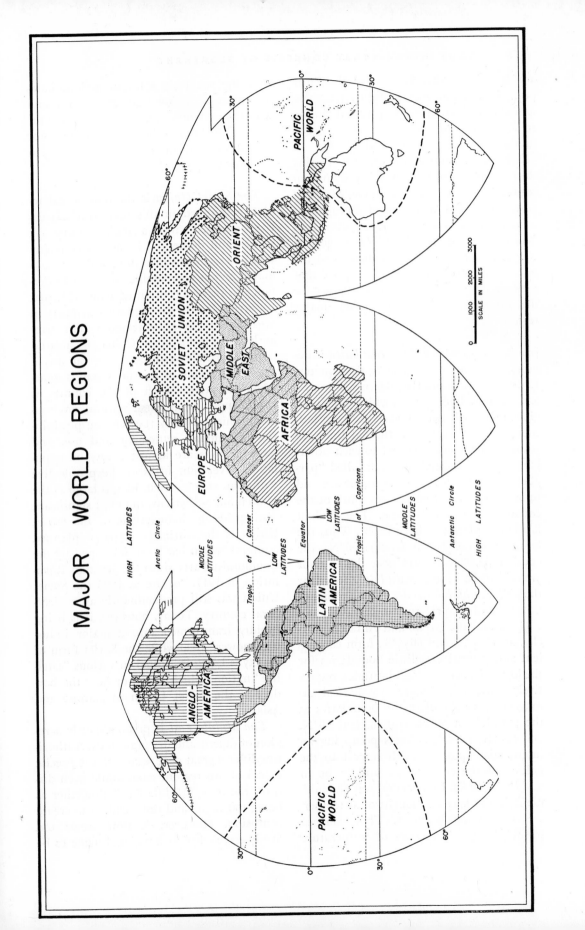

MAJOR WORLD REGIONS

are densely populated. Some of the European countries have extensive overseas possessions. The latter were acquired during an age of oceanic expansion which began in the fifteenth century and reached its height in the nineteenth century. During this period Europe became the dominant region in world affairs. However, in recent years the world influence of Europe has waned, partly as a result of two disastrous World Wars in less than half a century. Nevertheless, the European impact on the rest of the world has been so great that some knowledge of Europe is a necessity for the understanding of any other major region.

[EDITORIAL COMMENT. The term *latitude* denotes position with respect to the equator. Latitude is measured in degrees, minutes, and seconds. The equator, which circles the globe midway between the poles, has a latitude of 0°. All other latitudinal lines are parallel to the equator and to each other. Hence all latitudinal lines are called "parallels." Places north of the equator are said to be in north latitude; places south of the equator, in south latitude. The highest latitude a place can have is 90°. Thus the latitude of the North Pole is 90°N., the South Pole, 90°S. Places near the equator are said to be in *low latitudes;* places near the poles, in *high latitudes.* The Tropics of Cancer and Capricorn, at 23½°N. and 23½°S., and the Arctic and Antarctic Circles, at 66½°N. and 66½°S., form convenient and generally realistic boundaries for the low latitudes and high latitudes, respectively (although a more symmetrical arrangement would place the boundaries at the parallels of 30°N. and S., and 60°N. and S., respectively). Places occupying an intermediate position with respect to the poles and the equator are said to be in *middle latitudes.* In a general way the middle latitudes may be thought of as temperate or seasonal latitudes. They contrast strongly in yearly regimes of temperature

with the relatively constant and monotonous heat of the low latitude lowlands and with the extremes of cold which prevail for most of the year in the high latitudes. (For a definition of longitude, see page 226 in Chapter 12.)]

The Soviet Union is the only world region considered in this text which is entirely enclosed within a single country. Yet so vast and influential is the Soviet Union that one seems justified in regarding it as a major region comparable in world importance to regions containing many different countries. It is by far the largest country in area on the globe, being more than twice as large as Canada or China, its nearest competitors. Nevertheless, the great size of the Soviet Union as seen on a map is somewhat deceptive. Much of the country is handicapped by a harsh natural environment which severely restricts the possibilities for human settlement and use, and large sections are almost empty of population. Over four fifths of the people live within an area less than half as large as the United States. Perhaps the most significant distinguishing characteristic of the Soviet Union is the distinctive type of planned economy which has been developed by the Communist Party since the Russian Revolution of 1917. As late as 1928 the Soviet Union was still predominantly an agricultural country. Today, however, it is being rapidly transformed into a major industrial power. Meanwhile the Soviet form of society is being instituted in various "satellite" nations which lie on or near the borders of the Soviet Union in Europe and Asia.

The Middle East is predominantly a region of deserts and dry grasslands. Authorities differ a great deal regarding the precise extent of this region; some would even disavow the term "Middle East" altogether as being too vague and thus tending to create confusion. However, it now seems too firmly established as a regional name to be easily dislodged. In this book the Middle East is considered to include an area stretching across northern Africa and southwestern Asia from Morocco and Spanish Sahara to West Pakistan. In most parts of this region human settlement is discouraged by lack of moisture. Industrial resources are not outstanding, and modern types of manufacturing are poorly developed. The majority of the people are farmers or nomadic herdsmen. Field agriculture is mostly confined to irrigated oases and to areas bordering the Mediterranean Sea where winter rains bring more moisture than is customary in the region. Although the Middle East is not well supplied with most types of natural resources, it has an abundance of one vital commodity, oil. One of the most significant characteristics of the Middle East is the dominance of the Moslem or Mohammedan religion. This region forms the heart of the Moslem World. Until recently a colonial region, this area is today mainly composed of small and relatively weak national states, although a number of European dependencies still exist.

The Orient, a region extending around the southern and eastern margins of Asia from India and Pakistan to Korea and Japan, is the home of about half of the human race. Two thirds or more of all Orientals are farmers. The majority eke out a bare subsistence from tiny plots of land averaging perhaps 3 acres in size and seldom being larger than 5 or 10 acres. In many parts of the Orient the pressure of population on the available resources is extremely severe. In fact, the adjective "overpopulated" can probably be applied to this region with greater justice than to any other area of comparable size. Most of the people live in tropical or subtropical climates, although parts of the region extend outside of these climatic zones. Agri-

culture is facilitated by monsoon rains, which bring abundant moisture to most farming areas during the summer months. Many millions of people in the Orient are vitally dependent on these rains; when the monsoon fails, or is weak, famine may result. Home of some of the earliest-known civilizations, the Orient has long been distinguished by stable patterns of culture and by ancient contemplative religions. Like the Middle East, this region is mainly composed of young national states which have recently emerged from a colonial status to become self-governing members of the family of nations. The passing of the colonial age with its heritage of bitterness toward the white man, and the advent of world communism as a powerful force in international affairs, have combined in recent years to make the Orient an area of profound unrest and a major focus of world tension.

The Pacific World embraces the island continent of Australia, together with a host of islands, large and small, scattered about in the vast reaches of the Pacific Ocean. This region is entirely composed of dependent territories except for Australia and New Zealand, which are self-governing countries.[3] The Pacific World lies mainly in the tropics, with the exception of New Zealand and southern Australia, which are in middle latitudes. The island peoples of this region long led a simple, self-sufficient existence built around fishing, primitive forms of agriculture, and the utilization of the coconut palm. But the coming of the white man and disturbances wrought by the two World Wars have brought great changes, not always propitious, to the trade-wind isles of the "South Seas."

Africa is the only world region considered in this book which is coextensive with a continent. It will be noted that "Africa" overlaps the "Middle East," since North

---

[3] Statehood for the Territory of Hawaii, long debated in the American Congress, still seemed somewhat problematical at the time of writing. The independent island nations of Indonesia, the Philippines, and Japan are considered in this text to lie within the Orient rather than the Pacific World.

Africa is included in both regions. This should occasion no difficulty so long as one conceives of regions simply as useful tools designed to further geographic understanding and appreciation. For various reasons it seems desirable to consider North Africa in the context of both "Africa" and the "Middle East." This procedure appears clearly to enhance our understanding and appreciation of both world regions, and thus to be consistent with the aims of geographic study. By far the greater part of Africa is a tropical region composed of European colonial dependencies. There are only a handful of self-governing nations. White men of European descent are found principally in the extreme north and far south, where Africa extends into subtropical latitudes, and in some parts of the tropical highlands of the continent. Negroid peoples form the overwhelming majority nearly everywhere in tropical Africa; in North Africa the Arabs, Berbers, and related Semitic and Hamitic peoples are the main population elements. In the economic world Africa is principally important as a producer of strategic minerals and tropical and subtropical agricultural commodities, as a market for European manufactured goods, and as a promising field for outside investment. In the immediate past Africa has exerted little direct influence on the course of world affairs, its destinies being mainly controlled by forces outside the region. But today the peoples and countries of Africa are being increasingly affected by currents of colonial unrest so that this region must be regarded as an awakening part of the political world.

Latin America is predominantly a region of small independent nations, together with such European colonial possessions as survived the revolutionary period of the nineteenth century. The independent countries of Latin America were originally colonies of either Spain, Portugal, or France. Today the predominance of Roman Catholicism and the widespread use of the Spanish, Portuguese, and French languages reflect the former importance of the European colonial powers in this region. Like Africa, Latin America is mainly tropical or subtropical, its natural environment being similar to that of Africa in a number of respects. However, in the far south Latin America extends much further into the middle latitudes than does Africa. This region is perhaps most important to the outside world as a storehouse of important minerals, as a producer of specialized tropical agricultural commodities, and as a market for manufactured goods and investment capital from the United States and Europe.

Anglo-America consists of the United States, Canada, Alaska, and, as a marginal appendage, Greenland. Like Europe and the Soviet Union, this region lies completely within the middle or high latitudes in the Northern Hemisphere. Basically English in language and culture, though much affected by other cultural influences, the people of Anglo-America have an exceptionally high degree of cultural unity. Of all the major world regions, Anglo-America is probably the richest in natural resources. On this resource base the United States and Canada have developed an extraordinarily productive "triple economy" of industry, agriculture, and trade. These two nations lead all others in productivity per person and general prosperity. They exercise great influence in world affairs.

Of the eight world regions, two, Anglo-America and Europe, are today primarily industrial, although in each of these regions agriculture is highly developed and important. A third region, the Soviet Union, is rapidly industrializing. The remaining five regions are, generally speaking, the great "underdeveloped" areas of the world. In these latter regions modern types of manufacturing have been little developed, with conspicuous exceptions in the case of Japan, southeastern Australia, southeastern Brazil, and other scattered industrialized areas. Agricultural methods are often backward and inefficient, pressure of population on available resources is very great in many areas, and the general standard of living is low. But progress is slowly being made in these areas; with assistance from the industrialized regions they may be expected to experience many changes for the better. Especially fortunate are areas with enough minerals to attract foreign capital.

Key Topics in Geographic Study

To the student embarking on a study of world geography, the mass of detail to be mastered may seem at first to be overwhelming. However, the observant student will note that certain topics tend to recur as different regions and countries are studied. These key topics include (1) Location, (2) Population, (3) Political Status, (4) Natural Environment, (5) Type of Economy, (6) Potentialities, and (7) Problems. In the following pages each of these topics will be briefly discussed.

▶ Location

One of the purposes for which one studies geography is to learn the location of important features on the earth's surface— in other words, to learn where things are in the world. One tries to acquire a sort of mental map, on which countries, important cities, rivers, mountain ranges, climatic zones, and other features are plotted in their correct relation to each other. No person can claim to be truly educated who does not carry such a map in his head. However, it is not enough to simply know the *facts* of location; one also needs to develop an understanding and appreciation of the *significance* of location. To a considerable degree the geographic characteristics of any area are due, directly or indirectly, to its location. For the most part, location is a concept which must be discussed with regard to particular areas. There is relatively little of real significance which can be said about location in general. Each area has a different location and must be separately evaluated.

Perhaps an illustration will point up the foregoing remarks. Let us compare the location of Great Britain with that of New Zealand (see page 11). Each is an island area, Great Britain consisting of a single large island, while New Zealand has two main islands about equal in size. Both areas are located in the middle latitudes. Both come within the influence of westerly winds which, blowing off the surrounding seas, bring abundant rain and moderate temperatures throughout the year. The climates of Great Britain and New Zealand are remarkably similar, in spite of the fact that these areas are located in opposite hemispheres and are about as far from each other as it is possible for two places on the earth to be.

Thus in certain ways the locations of Great Britain and New Zealand are similar. In other respects, however, their locations are vastly different. Great Britain is located in the Northern Hemisphere, which contains the bulk of the world's land and all of the principal centers of population and industry; New Zealand is on the other side of the equator in the Southern Hemisphere. Great Britain is located near the center of the world's land masses and is separated by only a narrow channel from the densely populated industrial areas of western continental Europe; New Zealand is surrounded by vast expanses of ocean. Great Britain is located in the western seaboard area of Europe where the major ocean routes of the world converge; New Zealand is far away from the centers of world commerce, at the very end of the commercial sea lanes. For more than four centuries Great Britain has shared in the development of northwestern Europe as a great organizing center for the world's economic and political life; New Zealand, meanwhile, has lived in comparative isolation. These differences of location help to account for the fact that Great Britain has become a densely populated industrial area and a major center of political and economic power, while New Zealand has remained a sparsely populated pastoral country of much less significance in world affairs.

The student should realize that factors of location are not constant, but are relative to the circumstances of a particular time. In other words, *the significance of location changes as circumstances change.* During the early centuries when the borderlands of the Mediterranean Sea contained the principal centers of European culture and political power, Great Britain was an unimportant area situated on the very edge of the known world, its location being scarcely more advantageous than that of New Zealand. Not until much later, when the European center of gravity had shifted from the Mediterranean region to the shores of the North Sea and the age of oceanic expansion had commenced, did the location of Great Britain become highly advantageous.

▶ Population

Population is a topic of major importance in geographic study. More than any other element, it is human life which gives character and geographic significance to areas. The numbers, density, distribution, and qualities of the population, together with population changes or trends, supply an essential background or focus in studying the geography of any area. These aspects of population will be illustrated in an introductory way through a brief consideration of world population as a whole.

• **Population Numbers.** In 1954 the total number of people in the world was estimated at 2.6 billions. This figure represents a calculation based on the best available data, but cannot be regarded as truly accurate. No reliable total for world population is yet possible due to a lack of census data for a number of countries which have not taken a census in recent years. Indeed some of the world's countries have never had a complete census at all, prominent examples being Iran (Persia), Afghanistan, Saudi Arabia, Ethiopia, Anglo-Egyptian Sudan, Liberia, and Nepal. In view of the lack of reliable data, any attempt to secure a world population total at present can be little

TABLE 1

THE MAJOR WORLD REGIONS: AREA AND POPULATION DATA

REGION	AREA (MILLION SQUARE MILES)	ESTIMATED POPULATION IN MILLIONS, 1953	POPULATION DENSITY (PER SQUARE MILE)
Europe	1.9	400	210
Soviet Union	8.6	210	24
Middle East [a]	7.0	192	27
Orient [a]	8.0	1350	169
Pacific World [a]	3.3	14	4
Africa [a]	11.7	210	18
Latin America	7.9	172	22
Anglo-America	8.4	176	21

[a] Areas and populations of certain countries are included in two different regional totals. For example, Egypt is included under both Africa and Middle East.

Great Britain and New Zealand compared in location on the map to the right.

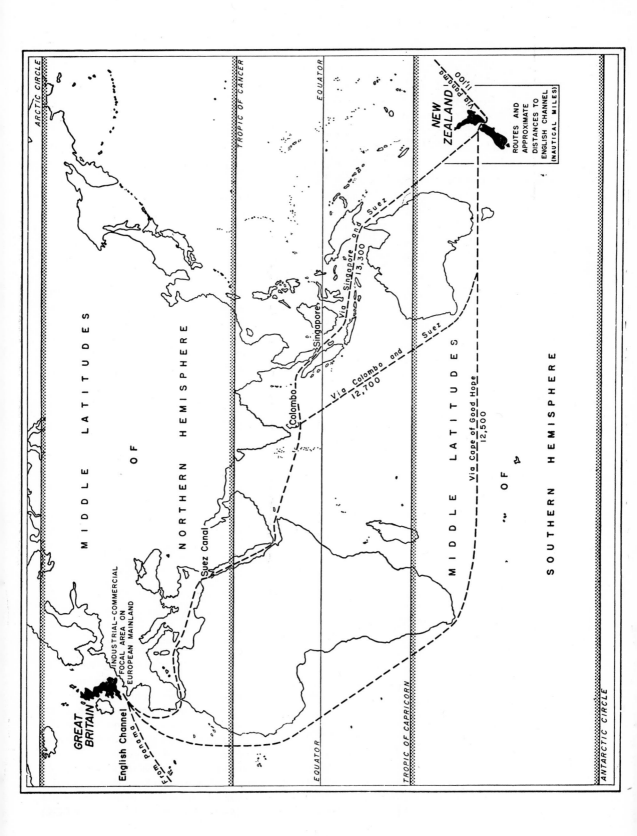

ROUTES AND
APPROXIMATE
DISTANCES TO
ENGLISH CHANNEL
(NAUTICAL MILES)

Great areas of the earth's surface are either deserts (to the left) or excessively cold arctic and subarctic lands (facing page). These difficult regions are very sparsely populated. In the view to the left of the Sahara Desert in the political unit of the Sudan, south of Egypt, the camels are laden with bags of cotton from a near-by oasis. (*British Information Services.*)

more than educated guesswork.

Total populations of the eight major world regions based on the latest available census figures or estimates are given in Table 1. A few important points to be noted from this table are: (1) the tremendous population total of the Orient, which has three times as many people as Europe, the region ranking second in total numbers; (2) the striking correspondence in population totals among five of the eight regions —the Soviet Union, the Middle East, Africa, Latin America, and Anglo-America— each having a total of between 172 and 210 millions; (3) the extremely small number of people in the Pacific World as compared with other world regions.

• *Population Density.* The total area of the earth's surface is approximately 197 million square miles. The land surface, however, including inland waters, comprises only about 57.4 million square miles, or slightly more than 29 percent of the total. Since the estimated population of the earth is 2.6 billions, the average density of population for the entire world is approximately

45 per square mile. If ice-covered and unpopulated Antarctica is excluded, the average density is approximately 50 per square mile. This figure compares fairly closely with the estimated density of 53 per square mile for continental United States at the beginning of 1954.

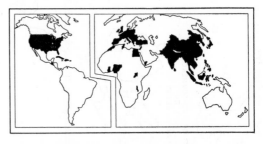

The political units shown in black have an *overall* population density greater than the estimated world average of 50 per square mile (excluding Antarctica). Note the preponderance of black in the Orient and Europe. Only recently has the population density in the United States become greater than the world average. Many small islands not shown exceed the world average, as do many sizable parts of mainland countries whose over-all density is below the world average. (*Boggs Projection* © A. J. Nystrom & Co.)

A winter scene in the Canadian subarctic west of Hudson Bay. The black dots in the foreground are a herd of caribou on a frozen lake. (*Canadian Wildlife Service.*)

Figures on population density for the world as a whole are practically meaningless, due to the extremely uneven distribution of population, resources, and productive facilities over the earth. However, such figures do furnish a rough yardstick with which to measure the densities of various countries and regions. The individual countries of the world vary tremendously in over-all population density, from the Netherlands, let us say, with 812 per square mile, and Belgium, with 744, to huge but almost empty Australia with only 3 per square mile.

• *Population Distribution.* The distribution of population over the earth is extraordinarily uneven. Most of the world's people are concentrated in three major population clusters. The largest of these occurs in the Orient. It includes portions of China, Japan, India, Pakistan, Indonesia, and other lands bordering these populous countries. The people of this Oriental cluster comprise about half of the human race. A second major population cluster including Europe and portions of the Soviet Union contains over a fifth of the world's people. The third major cluster is considerably smaller. It includes the eastern half of the United States and adjoining parts of Canada. Elsewhere in the world small clusters of population are scattered about here and there, separated from each other by vast stretches of sparsely settled or unoccupied land.

Areas in which population is extremely sparse or altogether absent make up more than three fourths of the earth's land surface. Such areas fall into four principal categories, as follows: (1) arctic and subarctic areas where settlement is hampered by excessive cold, (2) areas of desert and dry grassland which are handicapped by lack of moisture, (3) areas of rugged highland where settlement is restricted by steep slopes and high altitudes, and (4) areas of tropical rain forest and tropical grassland (savanna), where excessive heat and moisture, dense forest growth or rank grasses, and infertile soils discourage fixed settlements. Of the four main types of "negative areas," the tropical forests and grasslands seem to offer the best possibilities for large future increases in population. Indeed, some areas of this type in the Orient already support extremely large and dense populations. However, corresponding areas in Latin America, Africa, and Southeast Asia are still quite sparsely populated. Future spread of settlement in these tropical areas seems conditional on further advances in tropical medicine and in methods of utilizing tropical soils.

• *Population Trends.* Various periods of history have witnessed great changes in the numbers, density, and distribution of people over the earth and in the different countries and regions. Some of the most significant changes have occurred during the past three or four centuries. This period has witnessed an unparalleled increase in total population numbers. Since 1650 the population of the world has more than quadrupled, from an estimated 545 million to 2.6 billion. At the present time this increase is continuing at the rate of about 25 million a year. Fears are often expressed that mankind may eventually outrun its food supply unless the steady increase in population numbers can somehow be checked. However, some optimistic students of this problem believe that the earth could support several times its present population if all the available resources were more intensively and scientifically managed.

The tremendous increases in population during the past three centuries appear to be mainly the result of a declining death rate. The latter has resulted partly from improved medical and sanitary facilities and partly from the more abundant, varied, and dependable food supply made possible by improved agricultural techniques, better transportation facilities, and the opening of vast new lands for cultivation in such areas as the Americas, Australia, Africa, Asiatic Russia, and Manchuria.

At the present time population is increasing in nearly all of the world's countries, but the rate of increase is much greater in some countries than in others. Sharp upward trends of population in such countries as India, the Soviet Union, and the United States contrast strikingly with the slow rate of population growth in France.

A fact not often appreciated is the rapid rate at which the European peoples, as well as the colored races, have been reproducing themselves. In fact, the Europeans appear to have an edge in this regard over other

A French geographer, the late Jean Brunhes, maintained that the two most significant maps were the map of men, or population, and the map of rainfall. Much geography can be read or inferred from the map of men to the right. Among other things, the map shows that the areas where large numbers of them have found it desirable to live are quite limited in extent. There are striking concentrations in the industrialized regions of Europe and northeastern United States and in the intensively cultivated farming regions of southern and eastern Asia. Note the tendency of men to congregate on the margins of continents, near the sea. Most parts of the vast continental interiors are sparsely populated or uninhabited. Geographers are students of *regions*, but they are also students of *distributions*—not only of men, but of crops, animals, rainfall, minerals, and other features on the earth. They are particularly interested in the various ways that different distributions *are related* to each other. Compare this map with the map of cultivated land on page 16 for similarities and differences in the *pattern* of distribution. Note the small maps of land and water hemispheres. The land hemisphere comprises 80 percent of the world's total land area and has some 95 percent of the population. The water hemisphere has only 20 percent of the land area and 5 percent of the population. The main map, modified from one issued by the Office of Foreign Agricultural Relations, was prepared from prewar data, but reflects essentially the postwar pattern of population distribution. The graphs at the lower left are based on postwar data.

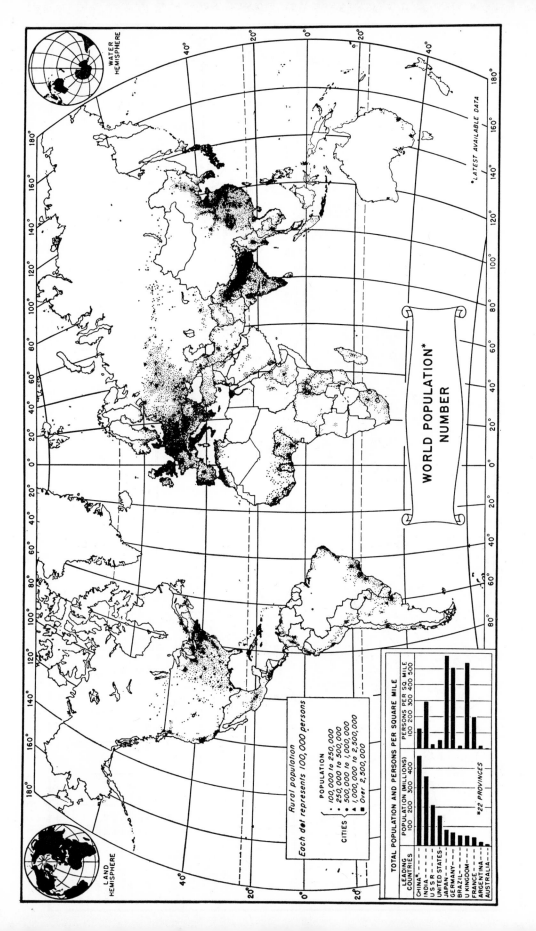

WATER
HEMISPHERE

LAND
HEMISPHERE

WORLD POPULATION*
NUMBER

*LATEST AVAILABLE DATA

POPULATION

Rural population
Each dot represents 100,000 persons

· 100,000 to 250,000
· 250,000 to 500,000
● 500,000 to 1,000,000
▲ 1,000,000 to 2,500,000
■ Over 2,500,000

CITIES

TOTAL POPULATION AND PERSONS PER SQUARE MILE

LEADING COUNTRIES	POPULATION (MILLIONS)				PERSONS PER SQ. MILE				
	100	200	300	400	100	200	300	400	500
CHINA*									
INDIA									
U S S R									
UNITED STATES									
JAPAN									
GERMANY									
BRAZIL									
U KINGDOM									
FRANCE									
ARGENTINA									
AUSTRALIA									

*22 PROVINCES

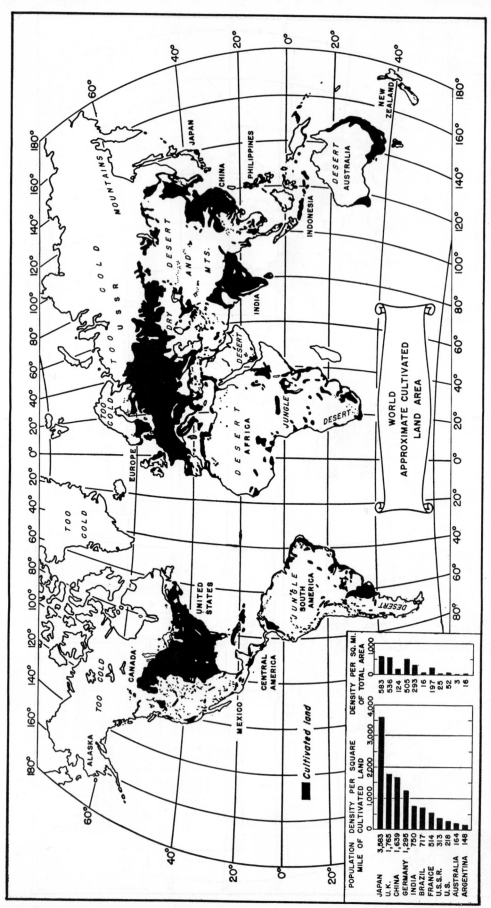

Generalized map showing the distribution of the world's cultivated land. (*Slightly modified from a map by the Office of Foreign Agricultural Relations.*)

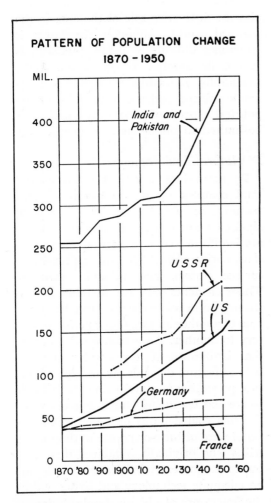

PATTERN OF POPULATION CHANGE
1870 – 1950

Note the population "explosion" in India-Pakistan since 1930. Unless this rapid population increase can be slowed, the peoples of these countries are in a race with disaster. (*Modified from a graph by the Office of Foreign Agricultural Relations.*)

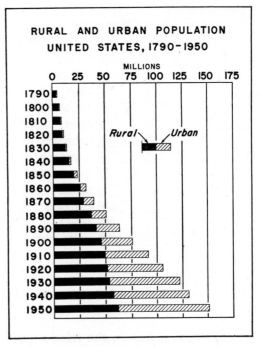

RURAL AND URBAN POPULATION
UNITED STATES, 1790–1950

In the United States, as in the Soviet Union and many other countries, people are migrating in large numbers to the cities. This new Urban Revolution is a significant feature of our times. (*From the Office of Foreign Agricultural Relations.*)

racial groups. It is estimated that in 1800 less than an eighth of the world's people were of European descent, whereas today nearly a third of all people fall in this category. At present some of the most rapid rates of population increase are occurring in the overseas areas to which Europeans have migrated in large numbers.

During the past three or four centuries the world pattern of population distribution has also been altered considerably.

This was brought about principally by two great movements of population: the migration of Europeans to new lands overseas and the migration of rural dwellers to the cities.

• *Other Aspects of Population.* The general topic of population encompasses not only numbers, density, distribution, and movements or trends, but also the *qualities* of the population—in other words, such characteristics as skin color, language, religion, food habits, educational levels, health, and general cultural heritage. The peoples of various areas are vastly different in these respects. Such differences are of fundamental concern and interest to the student of geography.

An extremely significant aspect of population not yet mentioned is the comparative age structure of populations in dif-

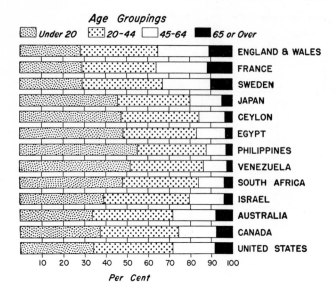

The age composition of the population in selected countries.

ferent countries; that is, the relative proportion of young, middle-aged, and old people in the population. Particularly in time of war, it is a great advantage for a nation to have a relatively youthful population affording the maximum numbers for service in the armed forces or employment in war industries.

▶ Political Status

We are living in a world which has been subdivided into a multitude of political units—national states, subdivisions of national states (provinces, states, departments, counties, etc.), and various types of dependent political units (colonies, protectorates, trusteeships, etc.) and their subdivisions. Separated by boundaries drawn on maps and in many cases marked out on the ground, these political divisions form a complicated patchwork enclosing nearly all of the land surface of the earth.

The political status of any area is an important feature of its geography. In a broad sense, political status includes not only the political organization of the area in terms of functional political units, but

also the distinctive role of the area in the political world. Although the latter is sometimes difficult to define precisely, it cannot be ignored in geographic study. Geography, rightfully conceived, is a dynamic subject, and a consideration of the political aspects of geography should not be limited to purely static elements.

▶ Natural Environment

By natural environment is meant the total complex of natural conditions and resources occurring in an area. The principal elements of the natural environment are landforms, climate, natural vegetation, soils, native animal life, underground and surface waters, and mineral resources. These elements vary considerably among themselves in relative significance from one area to another and from one period of history to another. To a considerable degree the significance of a particular environmental feature depends on the type of culture prevailing at a given time in the area where the feature is found. For example, the rich coal deposits of western Pennsylvania were of little or no use to the Indian tribes who originally inhabited that area, but to the present inhabitants, armed with an adequate technology and living within the framework of a highly developed industrial civilization, these same coal deposits are of the utmost significance.

One should beware of easy generalizations about the "influence" of the natural environment on human life. The connections or relationships which exist between people and their environment are often extremely complicated. Any particular set of environmental features offers various possibilities for human use. Social, economic, psychological, and historical factors will condition the actual employment to which such features will be put by a human group.

An American geographer, Robert S. Platt, has summed up the foregoing ideas effectively in the section quoted below: [4]

The importance of our natural environment is obvious. People have been, and still are, conscious of the significance to them in everyday life of the weather, the soil, minerals, mountains, and plains. Travelers long ago observed, and still do, that differences from place to place in natural environment are associated with differences in the lives of people: that mountaineers live differently from plainsmen, jungle savages differently from Arctic Eskimos. . . .

[However] it is misleading to advance the hypothesis of an active influence of natural environment tending to shape human life in the natural and proper way and to look for coincidences between environment and life as evidence confirming this hypothesis. Increasing evidence shows that the hypothesis of a simple and direct relationship is not thus confirmed, that there is no proper natural way of shaping life but innumerable ways, not sorted out by nature but reduced by man's choices past and present. *People live differently in similar environments and differently at different times in the same environment*, without feeling any environmental pressure to lessen these differences.

In equatorial regions savage life is natural, but all the other forms of life there are natural also. There are not only jungle savages living in many different ways but also . . . many people who are not savages and are under no inducement to become so. On the contrary, some of them are engaged in horticultural enterprises as highly developed as any in the world. In addition, there are innumerable untried possibilities for other ways of living, some of which would require thousands of years for full realization through the development of plant or animal resources. *In any given type of regional environment, people have alternative ways of living, apparently many in some places and few in others.* Probably everywhere the conceivable number of possibilities is far greater than people can imagine and far beyond the range of choice now open to them.

Actually, people are limited by things other than natural environment, though set within the confines of that environment. Particularly are they limited by habits they have learned and facilities available to them, accumulated through an unbroken series of choices and rejections in the entire course of their history—in other words, by the cultural heritage of the group to which they belong, by their culture defined in the broadest sense. The choices made in the past which now limit people in their activities have been impelled not by natural environment but by the play of history thereafter embodied in their culture.

For example, in the Great Lakes region farmers have been limited agriculturally to a certain range of possibilities, mainly involving cereals and livestock. But if some of our ancestors at the dawn of civilization had not chosen to domesticate certain grasses as cereals and certain four-footed animals as livestock but, instead, had chosen to develop fungus growths or edible insects as a basis of productive culture, our mode of life might be now utterly different in ways which the natural environment might support as well as it does our present agriculture, or conceivably better.

▶ *Type of Economy*

One of the most significant characteristics of an area is its type of economy—in other words, the kind of mechanism which human beings have developed in the area as a means of satisfying their needs and wants for economic goods and services. A particularly important aspect of an area's economy is its *occupational structure,* or the numbers and proportion of people employed in each of the principal means of livelihood. In most countries a larger proportion of the people are employed in *agriculture* than in any other occupation. Heavy dependence on agriculture is espe-

[4] Robert S. Platt, "Environmentalism Versus Geography." *American Journal of Sociology,* v. 53 (1948), pp. 351–352. Used by permission of the author and the University of Chicago Press. Some portions italicized in editing.

cially characteristic of underdeveloped countries. In more advanced countries a considerable proportion of the people are engaged in *manufacturing, transportation, trade,* and *personal and professional services.* Nevertheless, even in highly industrialized countries agriculture is an important means of livelihood. However, the proportion of the population engaged in this occupation is significantly less than in the underdeveloped countries, although agricultural production per worker and per unit of land is often much higher.

The more sparsely settled regions of the world are characterized by such occupations as *grazing (nomadic herding* or *livestock ranching), hunting, fishing, trapping,* or *the forest industries.* In scattered areas *mining* serves as a source of livelihood. Mining areas are distributed irregularly over the earth wherever commercial deposits of minerals are found.

Besides the occupational structure, it is also important to consider the characteristic *units of economic organization* in an area (farms, factories, stores, etc.), together with the lines of transportation and communication which connect these units. Other pertinent questions regarding the economy of the area would be:

1. What is the general status of technology—advanced, moderately developed, primitive, or a mixture of these?

2. What are the principal commodities produced, and in what quantities?

3. Is production primarily of a commercial or a subsistence character?

4. Is the economy largely self-contained, or is there a significant dependence on trade with other areas?

5. What are the principal imports and exports?

6. Have the productive facilities of the area been largely financed by domestic capital, or by outside capital?

▶ *Potentialities*

As a field of study, geography is primarily concerned with the interpretation of areas as they are. But geography also gives attention to the *potentialities* of areas—that is, to areas as they may be, or could be, in the future. In this connection it needs to be re-emphasized that every area offers alternative possibilities for human use. For example, the interior grasslands of North America were originally the habitat of Indian tribes pursuing a mode of life based on the hunting of buffalo and other herbivorous animals. Later, however, the Indians were displaced by ranchers who utilized for the grazing of domesticated livestock the grasses that previously had supported the native wild animals. The ranchers, in their turn, have now given place in many parts of the grasslands to farmers who are growing crops on the deep, black, fertile grassland soils that previously lay undisturbed and unused. Each successive group of occupants has used this area in a way consistent with its particular cultural heritage and with the circumstances of a particular time. In all probability the potentialities of the area have by no means been exhausted, and centuries or even decades hence its occupants may use it in ways that are entirely unforeseen at present.

By and large, it seems idle to discuss the potentialities of an area in purely general terms. Potentialities have meaning only with reference to a particular human group having a certain set of objectives, attitudes, and abilities, and only in the light of a specific set of future historical circumstances.

Perhaps the two most fundamental questions that can be asked concerning the potentialities of an area are:

1. How many people can the area support?

2. What possibilities does the area afford for improving the present standard of living of the inhabitants?

Geographers, as well as scholars in many other fields, are constantly looking for answers to these questions, both for the world as a whole and for particular countries and regions.

▶ Problems

The people of almost any area are beset by many serious problems which must be solved if the potentialities of the area are to be realized. Most of these problems fall under the head of political problems, economic problems, social problems, or a mixture of these. Space will not permit an extended discussion of the endless variety which they assume. The following are a few specific categories of problems which are of major importance on a world basis:

1. *Problems of severe population pressure* are found in many different parts of the world, but are perhaps most acute in India, Japan, China, and other areas of the Orient where rapidly increasing populations are pressing hard on the available food supply.

2. *Problems of landownership* are particularly acute in underdeveloped areas where the bulk of the productive land is held by a relatively few individuals and the mass of the people are either tenants or owners of only modest plots of land.

3. *Problems of racial and religious antagonism* are best exemplified in such areas as the Union of South Africa (whites versus nonwhites), India-Pakistan (Hindus versus Moslems), and Israel (Moslems versus Jews).

4. *Problems of unrest in colonial areas,* arising from local dissatisfaction over outside rule, are present to some degree in nearly all parts of the colonial world.

The four categories of problems listed above are not entirely distinct from each other, but are interconnected. For example, unrest in the world's colonial areas is partly due to population pressure, unequal distribution of land, and racial and religious antagonisms, as well as to other circumstances.

Explanation in Geography

It is important for the student to realize that the geographic study of an area is not confined merely to consideration of an isolated list of topics. In geographic study one tries to understand and appreciate the various ways in which the features of an area *are related* to each other. However, the student should be warned that to fully *explain* the geography of an area may be very difficult or impossible.

▶ Argentina as an Example

The following excerpts from an article by Robert S. Platt will serve to illustrate the foregoing points: [5]

Consider the geography of Argentina from an explanatory viewpoint. . . . Argentina may be characterized as a virile South American nation having a productive territory of over a million square miles, a vigorous population of about [18,000,-000] people, a rich landed gentry, a highly commercialized economy, a centralized dictatorial government, and a militant nationalism at odds with the United States.

In explanation of these phenomena the following major factors may be cited:

(1) A fundament [6] of fertile mid-latitude plains bordering on the Atlantic, and territorial unity unbroken by physiographic barriers from the east coast to the Andes.

(2) A racial heritage of white people from Europe, of colonial plus recent immigrant stock.

(3) A cultural heritage of Spanish land tenure and social organization.

(4) A reciprocal trade relation with Europe owing to the industrial revolution,

---

[5] Robert S. Platt, "Determinism in Geography." *Annals of the Association of American Geographers,* v. 38 (1948), pp. 126–128. Used by permission of the author and the Association of American Geographers. Author's population figure for Argentina has been replaced by a 1953 estimate, shown in brackets. One editorial footnote has been added.

[6] *Editorial Note.* The fundament is the original natural environment of an area.

particularly to the European demand for food in exchange for manufactured goods, and to steam transportation and refrigeration.

(5) A competitive relation with the United States, owing primarily to similar mid-latitude production.

(6) Military and political affiliations with Fascism in Spain, Italy, and Germany.

• *Failure to Explain*

These factors are in effect and of significance. As historical and geographical circumstances associated with Argentine development, they may help toward an understanding of the country. But will this list or any similar list, however amplified, or any such approach to the subject explain Argentina or reveal cause and effect relations?

The approach is misleading rather than revealing. The value of the specified factors is unmeasured and immeasurable; multitudes of other factors also are present, many of them different, some of them opposite in effect; countless incidents and decisions of critical value are largely unknown and unknowable; and alternative tendencies are ignored.

Some factors of the Argentine fundament provide a basis for unity, but there is no self-evident pre-existent unity, and some natural features provide bases for disunity. Even the natural barrier of the Andes is not an unequivocal factor as an international boundary. At one time the line between Argentine and Chilean jurisdiction was drawn in the dry plains far east of the Andes, and western provinces of modern Argentina were eastern communities of colonial Chile.

White racial stock provides a basis for vigorous development, but factors other than immigration from Europe seem largely responsible for recent advance; and there are other significant racial strains.

The factor of Spanish culture is expressed in a landed gentry. But other factors are expressed in agrarian movements which have modified and may obliterate the old system.

Trade connection with Europe is a prominent factor in Argentine economy. But American big business has played a leading role in Argentine development; and the trade of the United States with Argentina is greater than with most other Latin American countries.

European fascism is an obvious factor in Argentine government and politics. But French, British, and American democracy has been another factor. Democracy has developed more in Argentina than in most other countries of Latin America, and is as much alive as fascism, and more deeply rooted. . . .

So other factors appear, still without explaining Argentina fully. Minor incidents and critical decisions with their alternative possibilities pile up endlessly in the pursuit of causes.

Thus full explanation of the geography of an area is seen to be extremely difficult or impossible, due to the presence of factors whose effects cannot be known with certainty. However, this should not be allowed to deter a search for such understanding as the available data will permit. Much that is useful and enlightening can be learned about the geography of areas, even if all the facts that are observed cannot be fully explained.

Differences in Areas

Since early times, geography as a field of study has found its essential basis in the easily observed fact that places on the earth are not alike. In the ancient world geography first developed as a normal outgrowth of the curiosity of people regarding lands which were different from their own. As knowledge of the world has increased through the progress of discovery and exploration, an almost endless variety of landscapes and modes of life have been found to exist. Scholars have been intrigued by these differences in areas, and they have sought to describe and account for them. Thus through observation, description, and analysis has grown the modern science of geography.

► Differences between America and Other Areas: A Geographer's View of America's Queerness

In the modern world great differences in areas still exist and continue to form a basis for geographic study. In the following selection an American geographer, the late Ellsworth Huntington, has illustrated this fact by showing some of the ways in which modern America is different from other parts of the world: [7]

One of the greatest troubles with Americans is that they cannot recognize their own queerness. In spite of all our geographical instruction, the average American fails to appreciate the fact that in most respects it is we who are queer and not the people of China, India, Japan, or even Russia. We realize, to be sure, that we are queer in the sense of being extremely prosperous. Outside of the United States not one-tenth of the world's . . . people live as comfortably as does the average skilled laborer in the United States. . . . We are the great exception because we carry watches, ride in automobiles, listen to the radio, use washing machines, electric irons, electric vacuum cleaners, electric toasters and refrigerators. Since not one person in ten among all the people of the world does these things, it must be we who are queer and not the others.

Another way in which the uniqueness of America is apparent is illustrated by fences. In most parts of the world fences are built around houses, but there are no fences around the fields. With us the opposite is

the case. There are few fences around houses, but practically all our fields are fenced. England and some of the neighboring regions of northwestern Europe have many hedges, but that condition prevails in only a relatively small area compared with the world as a whole. In most parts of the world the normal thing is to see field after field in unbroken succession covering all the land between the villages. The only thing to separate one field from another is a change in the crops or a little line, a foot or two wide, where an unsown strip separates one field of wheat, beets, or some other crop from another.

This lack of fences is symbolic of two far greater differences between America and the rest of the world. The first of these differences is that the size of land holdings is far smaller in most parts of the world than in the new lands in the temperate parts of North and South America and Australia. Among us the average size of the farms is about 150 acres.[8] Even in the older parts of the country the average farmer in most states has well toward 100 acres. In Europe, Asia, and Africa, however, where the overwhelming majority of the earth's people now dwell, the average farm is a tiny affair of not more than 10 or 15 acres. In many parts of China the size drops to 3 or 4 acres. . . . [Only a small proportion of European farms are larger than 25 acres.] This means that in most parts of the world by far the largest occupational group of people is inevitably doomed to poverty so long as the present system prevails. It also means incidentally that fences are a very expensive luxury. This is not only because the farms are so small, but also because as a general rule the farmers of the Old World do not have all of their land in one place. Each man usually owns several small separate parcels. If fences were built around every individual field, the cost would be prohibitive. Because our fields are so large it is relatively cheap to fence

[7] Ellsworth Huntington, "A Geographer's View of America's Queerness." *Education*, v. 52 (1932), pp. 254–257. Used by permission of The Palmer Company, Boston, Mass., publishers of *Education*. One editorial footnote has been added.

[8] *Editorial Note.* Since the early 1930's, when this article was written, the tendency has been for American farms to increase in average size. The 1950 census reported 215 acres as the average size of farm in the United States.

Village settlement in an intensively farmed section of the Old World. The farmers go out to the fields each day from their homes in the two villages shown in the view. The photo was taken in southern Luxembourg near Luxembourg city. (*U. S. Air Force Photo.*)

them.

The other thing illustrated by the absence of fences is that in the world as a whole materials are relatively more expensive than labor, but with us the reverse is the case. In the parts of the world inhabited by at least a billion and a half people, the place of fences is taken by people. A small boy or an old man or woman can be hired to herd the sheep or cattle far more cheaply than a fence can be made. This same cheapness of labor in contrast to the expensiveness of materials is illustrated by the way in which in many parts of the Old World . . . elaborate and beautiful handwork is applied to boxes made of poor thin boards which soon crack, or to coarse or sleasy cloth which is not at all appropriate for the beautiful embroidery which it bears.

Another of our queer habits is that even among our urban population a vast number of us live in detached houses set among grass and green trees. It is hard for us to realize that there is anything strange about this, but the facts are clear. Even in our larger cities, like New York or Chicago, there are large areas where this type of detached dwelling prevails. Such houses sometimes contain two or three families but usually only one. In smaller cities, especially in those with less than 100,000 people, a large fraction of the population lives in such houses. And of course this is also true of our millions of suburban people. This seems to us so much a matter of course that we fail to appreciate the fact that it is very uncommon when the world as a whole is considered. In Italy, India, China, and most other countries, such houses are practically unknown. In Germany, and the neighboring parts of Europe, only a very few people live in single houses surrounded by lawns. . . . In cities like Madrid, Rome, Vienna, and . . . Berlin, big apartment houses built up solidly on regular city streets often adjoin the fields. Almost the only important parts of the Old World where there are large numbers of detached suburban houses are Great Britain, Holland, and Scandinavia. Yet, even in England, the industrial worker who lives outside the central part of a town is usually housed in a little two-story house of brick or stone which forms part of a long monotonous row. He may have a bit of lawn as big as a tablecloth in front of his house, but the chances are that his house is part of a solid row. Even where such houses are separate from one another, they usually have merely a narrow paved walk between them.

An even more striking evidence of the queerness of the people of the United States is the fact that the vast majority of our farmers live on farms. This may seem absurd. It seems to us so natural and convenient for a farmer to live on his farm that we call anything else stupid. . . . In Canada, Australia, and New Zealand the same habits and opinions prevail. Yet, strange to say, in all the rest of the world there are probably not much more than another 30 or 40 million farming people who live in this isolated way. In Scandinavia, to be sure, and in mountainous regions in many parts of the world, the farmers do live by themselves on their own land. In England this is true to a slight degree, but even there the great majority of farmers live in villages and go out to their work each day. In other countries, such as Spain [and] Italy . . . the wealthier land owners may live in isolated houses on their own land, but the bulk of the agricultural population lives in compact villages. The hundreds of millions of farming people in India, China, Japan, and most other parts of the world practically all live in compact villages. . . .

In many ways such agricultural villages are the most characteristic feature of human geography. This is because they re-

tain a stronger individuality than does either the land on which there are no houses or the land that is covered with houses in cities. Grain fields, pastures, forests, and gardens have a strong family resemblance all over the world. Of course, a field of cabbages is very different from a field of potatoes, and an apple orchard is not at all like a banana patch. Nevertheless, cabbages look much the same everywhere no matter who raises them, and so do potatoes, apples, and bananas. Then, too, all over the world the cities tend gradually to become more and more alike. When Yokohama and Tokyo suffered from earthquake and fire, large sections were rebuilt in a purely Western style. Street cars, electric lights, steel frames, modern processes of using concrete, and a thousand other new methods tend constantly to become standardized all over the world. Cotton factories and hotels in Bombay are almost like those in North Carolina. A railroad station or moving picture house is much the same thing in Jerusalem and in Montevideo. Cities like Constantinople, Cairo, Madras, and Hankow still possess a high degree of individuality, to be sure. Nevertheless, even in those cities some sections are so thoroughly modernized that the mere appearance of the streets scarcely tells a stranger whether he is in America, Europe, Asia, or Africa. On the other hand, the farming villages all over the world still display a persistent individuality. The flat-roofed, mud villages near Smyrna in Turkey could never be confused with the palm-thatched huts near Madras or with the thatched houses of a wholly different type near Kyoto. Everywhere the farming villages, far more than almost any other feature of the surroundings, reflect the characteristics of the local geography. Since three-fifths of all the world's people live in such villages, we may well say that they are one of the most fundamental features of human geography. Yet in this respect as well as in wealth, transportation, use of machinery, and the use of fences with all that they imply as to the size of land holdings and the value of labor, we are so unique that we well deserve to be called queer.

PART 2
Europe

Introduction to Europe

For the purposes of this book, "Europe" is defined as the group of countries in Eurasia lying west of the Soviet Union and Turkey. This definition is somewhat at variance with traditional ideas. Europe has customarily been considered as one of the continents, separated from Asia by the "line of the Urals" (Ural Mountains and Ural River), Caspian Sea, Caucasus Mountains, Black Sea, Turkish Straits (Bosporus, Sea of Marmara, and Dardanelles), and Aegean Sea. Thus Europe has been considered to include parts of the Soviet Union and Turkey, often referred to as "European Russia" and "European Turkey," respectively. For various reasons, including important differences in culture and environment, it has been thought desirable to exclude the Soviet Union and Turkey entirely from "Europe" as that region is conceived of and discussed in this book. To avoid confusion, a name such as "Europe Exclusive of the Soviet Union and Turkey" might have been employed. However, there seems no great need for this cumbersome title so long as the student keeps in mind the precise area to which the term "Europe" is meant to apply. There is actually an increasing tendency in current usage for the name to be employed in much the same sense as in this volume.

Essentially a great peninsula fringed by lesser peninsulas and islands, Europe is bounded on the west and north by the Atlantic and Arctic Oceans and on the south by the Mediterranean Sea. Eastward, Europe merges with the main continental mass of Eurasia.

A view of the great industrial seaport of Glasgow on the River Clyde. (*British Information Services.*)

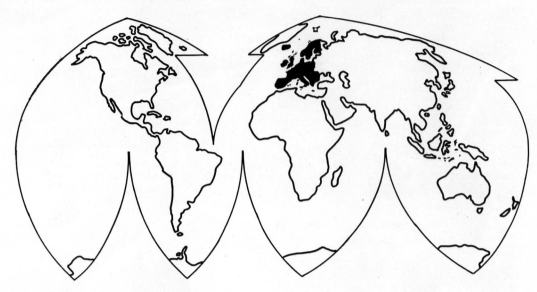

World location of Europe. (*Boggs Equal Area Projection, copyright A. J. Nystrom and Co.*)

Regional Groups of Countries in Europe

The countries of Europe can be divided into a number of fairly distinct regional groups.

At the northwest, separated from the mainland by the English Channel and North Sea, are the *countries of the British Isles.* They include the United Kingdom of Great Britain and Northern Ireland, and the Republic of Ireland (Eire). These two island countries are now entirely separate from each other in a political sense. However, they have been closely associated historically and are still closely linked by bonds of trade.

The *countries of West Central Europe* lie on the mainland opposite the British Isles. Germany and France are the major countries in this group. Other countries in the group include the small but highly important Benelux nations of Belgium, the Netherlands, and Luxembourg; the mountainous countries of Switzerland and Austria; and the tiny semi-independent political units of Liechtenstein, Andorra, Monaco, and the Saar. The countries of West Central Europe, considered as a group, are

dominantly industrial and commercial in their activities and outlook. Together with the United Kingdom, they constitute the industrial and commercial core of Europe. In these productive countries agriculture is by no means neglected, although its overall importance is less than that of industry and trade. Indeed, large sections in some of these countries are dominantly agricultural. Generally speaking, the farmers of West Central Europe pursue a highly commercialized form of agriculture characterized by intensive and scientific methods and exceptionally high yields per acre. The countries of this area carry on a complex interchange of goods and services, and thus tend to function together as an economic unit. They form a well-knit group, to which the phrase "highly developed" may properly be applied.

The *countries of Northern Europe,* often referred to as the Scandinavian or Fennoscandic countries, include Denmark, Sweden, Norway, Finland, and Iceland. Relatively small in numbers, but industrious, thrifty, and progressive, the peoples

ARCTIC OCEAN

Reykjavik
ICELAND

ATLANTIC

North
Sea

NORWAY
Oslo ⊙

SWEDEN
Stockholm ⊙

FINLAND
Helsinki ⊙

Baltic
Sea

UNITED

REPUBLIC
OF
IRELAND
Dublin ⊙

KINGDOM

London ⊙

OCEAN

DENMARK

Copenhagen ⊙

Amsterdam ⊙
The Hague ⊙
NETH.
Brussels ⊙
BELG.
Bonn ○
LUX.

Hamburg ●

Berlin ⊙
EAST
GERMANY

WEST
GERMANY

Paris ⊙

SOVIET

UNION

POLAND
Warsaw ⊙

Prague ⊙
CZECHOSLOVAKIA

Zurich ●
Bern ○
SWITZ.

Vienna ⊙
AUSTRIA

Budapest ⊙

HUNGARY

RUMANIA
Bucharest ⊙

Black

Sea

FRANCE

ITALY

YUGOSLAVIA

Belgrade ⊙

Lisbon ⊙
PORTUGAL

Madrid ⊙

SPAIN

Rome ⊙

BULGARIA
Sofia ⊙

Tirana ⊙
ALBANIA

GREECE

TURKEY

Mediterranean

Athens ⊙

Sea

EUROPE

INTRODUCTORY LOCATION MAP

○ CAPITAL OF COUNTRY
● LARGEST CITY OF COUNTRY
⊙ CAPITAL & LARGEST CITY

0   100 200 300 400 500

MILES

Introductory place location map of Europe showing political units as of January 1, 1955. Note the fact that in most European countries the political capital is also the largest city.

of Northern Europe have made skillful use of a restricted resource base in achieving general levels of health, education, and welfare which are exceeded by few nations. The different countries of this regional group have many environmental and cultural similarities and have had close historical ties with each other.

Very different from the cool, northerly countries just described are the warm and sunny *countries of Southern Europe,* often called the Mediterranean countries. This group includes Italy, Spain, Portugal, and Greece, together with the micro-states of San Marino and Vatican City State, and the British possessions of Gibraltar and Malta. These countries considered as a group are mountainous, generally poor in natural resources, and dominantly rural and agricultural rather than urban and industrial. In spite of a historic past and ancient cultures, they are today relatively

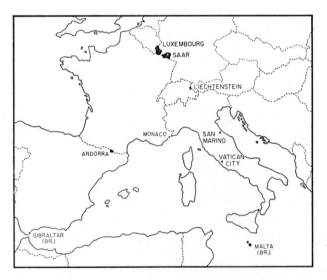

Europe: micro-states and Mediterranean dependencies.

poor and less advanced socially and economically than the countries of northwestern Europe. Extensive areas in Southern Europe have standards of living which are probably as low as any to be found in Europe. Some areas, however, are better off,

the most notable example being northern Italy, where a considerable amount of industry has been developed and conditions for agriculture are more favorable than in most parts of Southern Europe.

Along or near the borders of the Soviet Union are the *countries of East Central Europe*—Poland, Czechoslovakia, Hungary, Rumania, Bulgaria, Albania, and Yugoslavia. Germany and Austria have had close historical connections with the East Central European countries, but in other respects do not fit well with this group. Following World War II the countries of East Central Europe, with the exception of Yugoslavia, became political "satellites" of the Soviet Union. As this book went to press, it seemed impossible to forecast how long the new Soviet-instituted political order was likely to last. Such uncertainty has long been characteristic of this region. Through the centuries political boundaries have fluctuated violently, and the various national groups have been repeatedly submerged by the great powers bordering the region. The pattern of peoples, languages, religions, and cultures is more complicated than anywhere else in Europe. Most of the people speak Slavic languages, although Hungarian, Albanian, and certain other languages are significant exceptions. Taken as a whole, East Central Europe, like Southern Europe, is mainly agricultural, although a considerable amount of industry exists in certain areas and more is being developed. In many parts of this region the rural populations have been extremely backward. Since World War II the political, economic, and social life of the satellite countries has been remodeled along Communist lines. This fact is also true of Yugoslavia, although the latter nation has been pursuing an independent course, having broken away from Russian control.

Combining countries into regional groups in the manner of the preceding paragraphs is a useful device for securing an introductory general picture of an area as complicated as Europe. However, two points need to be emphasized: first, that each regional group is composed of countries having definite "personalities" of their own, and worthy of study as individual units despite broad physical and cultural similarities; and second, that the various regional groups are not entirely separate and distinct from each other in all respects, but tend to be separated by zones of transition rather than sharp lines. The core areas, however, are reasonably distinct.

The Importance of Europe

In recent centuries the peoples of Europe have exerted a profound influence on the rest of mankind. In fact, these centuries have been in many ways a European Age, characterized by great migrations of Europeans to overseas areas, establishment of European political control over vast territories peopled by non-Europeans, and penetration of European trade and cultural influence into all quarters of the globe. "For centuries Europe was at the root of every important world trend: modern civilization stemmed from it; science, art, trade, and migrations fanned out of it and imposed European supremacy on the other parts of the world; standards were set according to European normality." [1]

The interaction of European and non-European peoples and cultures resulting from European expansion has been one of the most significant developments, not only of modern times, but of all human history. Multitudes of people outside of Europe have had their ways of living profoundly altered by the spread of European goods, institutions, languages, customs, beliefs, ideas, and ideals, and the Europeans themselves have been deeply affected by their contacts with other lands.

Modern European expansion had its principal beginnings in the fifteenth and sixteenth centuries, when a series of great voyages of discovery and exploration opened the way to vast new areas previously unknown or only dimly realized. However, the early stages of expansion were somewhat tentative, and the movement did not reach its height until the eighteenth and nineteenth centuries. During these centuries, especially in the nineteenth, Europe stood unchallenged as the dominant region in world affairs. Most countries outside of Europe were dependent on Europe in either a political or an economic sense, or both. Europe served as a great focus, or center of organization, for the world's economic and political life. From the European core, lines of trade and political influence extended to outlying territories in all parts of the world. This world-wide economic and political system was mainly designed to facilitate the exchange of European manufactured goods for foodstuffs and industrial raw materials (as well as certain manufactures of a luxury character) produced in other parts of the world. Modern techniques of manufacturing were first developed in Europe, and for many decades the manufacturers of Europe had little effective competition in world markets. Most of the world's people depended primarily on Europe for such manufactured items as they were able to afford. Europe, in turn, was dependent on other areas for a considerable part of its food supply and for various minerals, fibers, and other materials not produced in Europe, or produced in insufficient quantities to meet the needs of European industry.

In the twentieth century Europe has lost much of its former predominance. The reasons for this turn of events are complicated,

---

[1] Jean Gottmann, *A Geography of Europe*, rev. ed. New York: Holt, 1954. P. 1. Used by permission of the author and the publisher.

but certain relevant factors can be cited. Among these are: (1) the weakening effects of two World Wars, both of which were initiated and mainly fought in Europe; (2) the emergence of the United States and the Soviet Union as world powers, and the failure of Europe to keep pace with these nations in rate of economic development; (3) the rise of nationalist movements in the colonial world; and (4) an increasing decentralization in the world of modern types of manufacturing, hence a lessening of the former dependence on Europe for manufactured goods.

Whatever the causes, there can be no doubt that the relative importance of Europe has declined. However, this should not be taken to mean that Europe is now unimportant, for this region is still tremendously significant. Essentially, the continuing importance of Europe seems mainly connected with four factors: (1) its large, dense, and highly skilled population; (2) its large annual production of goods and services; (3) the political, economic, and cultural ties which it still retains with various overseas areas; and (4) its great potentialities for future development, provided certain political obstacles can be overcome.

▶ The Population of Europe

Although Europe is the smallest in area of the major world regions considered in this book, it is the second largest in population, being exceeded only by the Orient. In a space about two thirds as large as the United States are concentrated some 400 million people, many of them highly skilled in manufacturing, agriculture, and other economic pursuits. Despite the reverses of recent decades, these masses of people, long accustomed to political, economic, and cultural leadership, must still be reckoned with as a highly significant factor in world affairs.

The only countries of Europe with a population density of less than the 53 per square mile estimated for continental

United States in 1954 are Sweden, Finland, Norway, Iceland, and the little country of Andorra in the Pyrenees Mountains. In over-all population density Europe leads all other world regions. It has an average density of about 210 per square mile, as compared with a world average, excluding Antarctica, of about 50 per square mile.

The greatest congestion is found along two major population axes—an east-west axis extending from Great Britain across northeastern France, Belgium, the Netherlands, Germany, and western Czechoslovakia to southern Poland; and a less continuous north-south axis from Great Britain to Switzerland and northern Italy. These axes of population correspond to the major axes of European industry. In Europe the densest populations are found in or near the great industrial districts and mainly depend on manufacturing and associated activities for a livelihood. This situation is quite different from that of the densely populated sections in the Orient where agriculture is the main occupation and population has tended to congregate on fertile lowlands suitable for intensive farming.

▶ The Outstanding Productivity of Europe

One of the most significant reasons for the continuing importance of Europe is its immense yearly production of economic goods and services. Over the centuries the peoples of Europe have developed a complex array of farms, fisheries, mines, and factories which are capable of producing a tremendous volume of foodstuffs, industrial raw materials, and finished manufactures. At present Europe, exclusive of the Soviet Union, produces about one fourth of the world's wheat, one third of the oats and two fifths of the rye, three fifths of the potatoes, half of the coal, and one third of the iron ore and finished steel, as well as large amounts of many other important commodities.

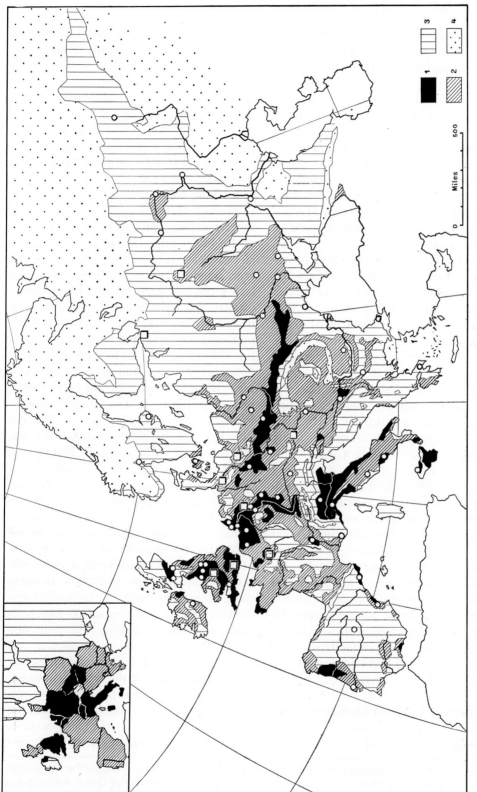

Generalized pattern of population densities in Europe and adjoining parts of the Soviet Union. Shade 1 (black—see legend at lower right) indicates areas having an average density of more than 250 inhabitants per square mile; shade 2, densities of 125 to 250; shade 3, densities of 25 to 125; shade 4, densities of less than 25. Note the clearly defined east-west and north-south axes of densest population. Urban agglomerations of more than 2,000,000 inhabitants are indicated by small squares; agglomerations of 500,000 to 2,000,000 are shown by small circles. The inset map at upper left shows over-all densities of political units according to scale of shades at lower right. (Reprinted from Jean Gottmann, A Geography of Europe [Holt, 1954], by permission of the author and the publisher.)

Especially significant on a world scale is Europe's production of manufactured goods. Although the relative importance of European manufacturing is less than it formerly was, this region continues to be one of the three greatest concentrations of industry on the globe. Only Anglo-America and the Soviet Union are in a class with Europe as manufacturing regions.

European production is not confined merely to production of commodities. In a broad sense the term production also includes services of various kinds, such as transport and communication services, banking, insurance, and investment services, and others. Europe has long been the center of a world-wide network of service facilities, and still retains great importance in this regard, although the United States has offered increasing competition in recent decades, especially in financial services.

In the era of tension between Communist and non-Communist countries which developed following World War II, European productive capacity became a highly strategic factor, representing a sort of economic balance between the contending groups of countries. The importance of Europe in this regard was evidenced by the strenuous attempts which were made by both the Soviet Union and the United States to influence the direction of European affairs after the war. Aided by financial assistance from the United States and other outside countries, Europe has made a remarkable economic recovery from the war. Many European countries have attained postwar levels of productivity equaling or surpassing the highest levels of prewar years.

▶ Continuing Ties with Overseas Areas

Although their influence in overseas areas has declined, various European countries do have strong political, economic, and cultural ties with countries outside of Europe. For example, the United Kingdom, which has been historically the most important of the colonizing powers, still forms the political, economic, and to some degree the cultural center of a great Commonwealth of Nations comprising about a fourth of the world's land and people. Several other European countries are centers of far-flung political associations. In recent years many colonial possessions of the European nations have become increasingly restive under imperial rule, and a number of them have secured independence. However, some of the latter have retained at least a nominal political tie with the home country. Such ties are exemplified by voluntary "commonwealth" bonds still connecting India, Pakistan, and Ceylon with the United Kingdom. In line with these developments the traditional term "empire" is rapidly going out of favor and is being replaced by terms such as "commonwealth" or "union." Thus the British Empire has now become officially the Commonwealth of Nations and the French Empire has become the French Union.

Many countries outside of Europe, whether associated politically with European nations or not, still look to Europe as a market for their surplus foodstuffs and industrial raw materials and as a supplier of manufactured goods which they do not produce in sufficient quantities to meet their needs. The bulk of the world's seaborne commerce still moves in European ships, and the world-wide European network of communication, insurance, and banking facilities is still vitally important to the transaction of the world's business.

Less tangible than political and economic ties, but nevertheless important, are cultural ties between European nations and overseas countries. Such ties are espe-

Map showing world production of major cereals and soybeans based on averages for the period 1935–1939. Note the importance of Europe and adjoining areas of the Soviet Union. Although the production of individual European countries is relative small, the total production for Europe as a whole is very great. (Modified from a map by the Office of Foreign Agricultural Relations.)

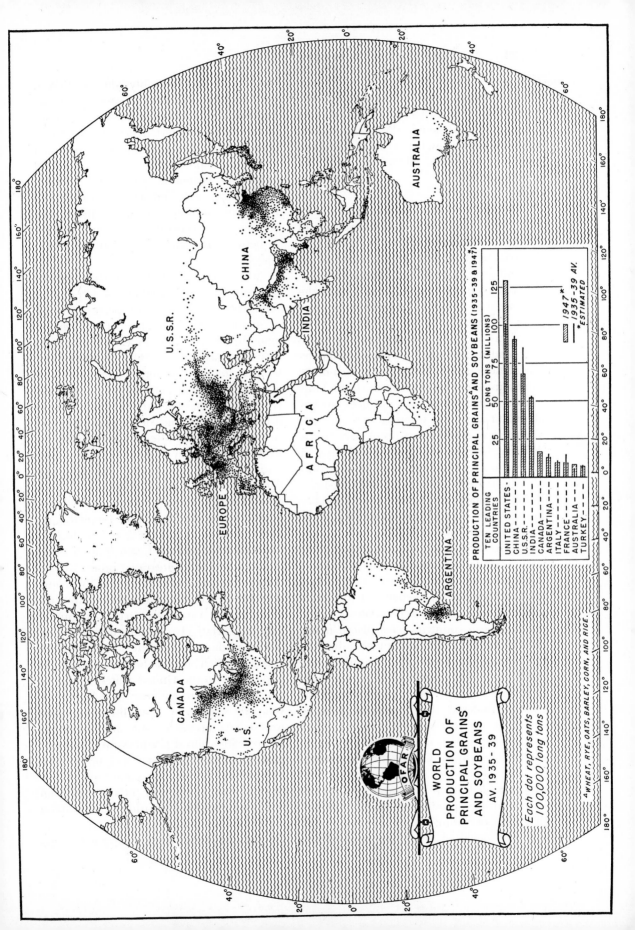

WORLD
PRODUCTION OF
PRINCIPAL GRAINS△
AND SOYBEANS
AV. 1935 - 39

Each dot represents
100,000 long tons

△ WHEAT, RYE, OATS, BARLEY, CORN, AND RICE.

PRODUCTION OF PRINCIPAL GRAINS△ AND SOYBEANS (1935-39 & 1947)

TEN LEADING COUNTRIES	LONG TONS (MILLIONS)
	25 50 75 100 125
UNITED STATES -	
CHINA - - - - -	
U.S.S.R. - - - -	
INDIA - - - - -	
CANADA - - - -	
ARGENTINA - - -	
ITALY - - - - -	
FRANCE - - - -	
AUSTRALIA - - -	
TURKEY - - - -	

1947 *
1935-39 AV.
* ESTIMATED

cially well exemplified by the close cultural bonds between Great Britain and its former colonies of Australia, New Zealand, and Canada. Although the latter nations are now entirely self-governing, their cultures reflect many affiliations with the home country.

▶ Potentialities of Europe

It seems very likely that Europe could achieve considerably higher levels of productivity and perhaps regain some of its lost influence if certain problems of political and economic organization within the region could be solved. At present Europe is divided politically into a large number of relatively small independent or semi-independent nations. To a considerable degree these countries complement each other in resources and types of production. Thus France is deficient in coal and steel but has abundant iron ore, whereas Germany has abundant coal and a surplus of steel, but is deficient in iron ore. Italy is deficient in coal, iron ore, and steel, but has a surplus of citrus fruits and wine—commodities which Germany and France have normally imported in considerable quantities. Were such comparisons extended to include other countries and commodities, and were statistics of intra-European trade examined, it would be seen that the nations of Europe are economically interdependent to a high degree. Despite this fact, however, the various European countries have placed many restrictions on the movement of industrial raw materials, foodstuffs, manufactured products, workers, and capital across their respective frontiers. Such restrictions have greatly hindered the development of a large internal market area comparable to the internal market of the United States or the Soviet Union. Could such a market area be achieved, it seems likely that Europe would develop large-scale, integrated industrial mass production on the order of that now prevailing in the United States and the Soviet Union, and agriculture would also be favorably affected. Thus, with lowered unit costs of production and expanded opportunities for sales of goods in an enlarged internal market, the European peoples could achieve more rational and efficient production, increase the total output of economic goods and services, make more goods and services available to European consumers at a lower price, thus adding to the general welfare, and achieve a better competitive position in world trade.

Full realization of these goals seems dependent on an increased degree of political unification among the European countries, involving the surrender of a certain amount of sovereignty by each nation concerned. Since World War II several attempts toward greater unification have actually been made. One of the most promising of these has been the establishment of a European Coal and Steel Community, set in motion in 1953 after a considerable period of preliminary negotiation. This Community, organized under the so-called "Schuman Plan," includes as member nations France, West Germany, Italy, Belgium, the Netherlands, and Luxembourg. Its purpose is to provide a free-trade area for coal, iron, and steel, and thus to foster an expanded and integrated production of these vital commodities within the countries concerned. Could the six member nations of the Coal and Steel Community achieve a relatively complete degree of economic unification, a unit would thus be created which would be comparable in population to the United States, would be equipped with an extensive and highly developed industrial establishment, and would have access to large and varied resources. Such a unit would stand in the first rank of industrial powers and might well provide the nucleus for some type of federation embracing still other European countries. However, creation of a common market for coal, iron, and steel among the six nations immediately concerned represents only a beginning, and these countries still have far to go before attaining a really noteworthy degree of economic and political unification.

Movements toward European unity face many obstacles. Strong feelings of nationalism developed over a period of centuries work against the surrender of national sovereignty, even on a limited scale. Hatreds engendered by wars are hindrances, especially to cooperation between the Germans and other European peoples who have endured German military attack and occupation. Overseas commitments of certain countries—the United Kingdom in particular—have made these countries reluctant to merge their interests with nations not possessing colonies or commonwealth ties. In every country special groups whose particular interests might be jeopardized are opposed to unification—farmers, for instance, now protected by tariff barriers, who would be obliged to compete with lower-cost producers in other countries. The European nations are currently operating under a considerable variety of political and economic systems, and it would be extremely difficult to make political and economic arrangements which would satisfy all concerned.

Not the least of the obstacles to European unification is separateness feeling which tends to characterize each of the different nationalities. National consciousness is highly developed among Englishmen, Frenchmen, Germans, Danes, Swedes, Poles, and the other national groups. Each group would have misgivings about merging its identity with that of other groups in a common European nationality. Although many Europeans, particularly the intellectuals, are keenly aware of the urgent need for greater unity, the existence of strong feelings of nationalism among the rank and file of the people, and exploitation of these feelings by politicians and special interest groups are major hindrances at present.

▶ The Diversity of European Languages

Many different languages are spoken in Europe. This would in itself present difficulties for a European federation, though such difficulties would be lessened by the fact that many Europeans are able to converse in more than one language. In addition, great progress has been made during recent decades in the development of communication techniques for parliamentary bodies, such as the United Nations, which are composed of representatives speaking different languages.

Languages spoken in Europe include three major groups, the Germanic, Romance, and Slavic languages, plus a great many minor languages and dialects.

The *Germanic languages* include German (spoken in Germany, Austria, and parts of Switzerland and eastern France), Dutch, Flemish (similar to Dutch and spoken in the northern half of Belgium), Frisian (also akin to Dutch, spoken in the Frisian Islands and along the northwest coast of Germany), Danish (spoken in parts of Germany adjoining Denmark, as well as in Denmark itself), Norwegian, Swedish (spoken in Sweden and parts of western Finland), and Icelandic. English is basically a Germanic language, although it contains many words from French, Latin, and Greek. The Germanic languages are principally spoken in countries bordering the North and Baltic Seas. They are derived from ancient languages of the Teutonic tribes who overran Europe during the early centuries of the Christian era.

The *Romance languages,* derived from Latin, are mainly spoken in countries bordering the Mediterranean Sea. They include French (spoken in parts of Switzerland as well as in France; Walloon, a dialect of French, is the principal language of southern Belgium), Italian (principally spoken in Italy, parts of Switzerland, and Corsica), Spanish, Catalan (mainly spoken in northeastern Spain and the Balearic Islands), and Portuguese. Rumanian, also, is often classified as a Romance language, though spoken in an area considerably removed from the main area of Romance speech, and containing many Slavic words and expressions.

The *Slavic languages,* which include Russian, are predominant in East Central Europe, the principal languages spoken being Polish, Czech, Slovak, the Yugoslav languages of Serbo-Croat, Slovene, and Macedonian (the latter spoken in parts of Greece and Bulgaria, as well as Yugoslavia), and Bulgarian.

Modern Greek is derived from classical Greek.

Celtic languages, once widely spoken, are now restricted to parts of Wales, Ireland, Scotland, and the peninsula of Brittany in western France.

Other languages belonging to none of the groups named above, but spoken by considerable numbers of people are Hungarian, Finnish, Albanian, and Basque. Turkish is spoken in parts of Bulgaria.

Within the major language areas are many enclaves where distinctive dialects or other languages are spoken. Such enclaves are especially common in East Central Europe, an area which has long been characterized by a confused mixture of tongues.

A diversity of languages does not necessarily preclude a reasonable degree of political unity. This fact has been demonstrated by a number of European countries in which two or more major languages are spoken. Perhaps the best example is Switzerland, which has no national language, but has a high degree of national unity despite the fact that it includes three fairly distinct language areas in which German, French, and Italian, respectively, are spoken, plus a small area in the Alps where Romansch, an old language closely related to Latin, is used. Finland, also, is a unified nation, although it has two official languages, Finnish and Swedish, that are entirely distinct from one another.

▶ Religious Divisions

Religious differences are undoubtedly a hindrance to a European union, although the precise effects of such differences would be difficult to forecast. Most Europeans who profess any religion are Christians, and modern European civilization owes much to Christian influence. However, the Christians of Europe, like Christians elsewhere, are divided among many different churches and sects. Members of Protestant denominations form a majority in the United Kingdom, northern Germany, and the Scandinavian countries, including Finland. Important Protestant groups are also found in the Netherlands, Czechoslovakia, and Switzerland, and smaller groups in various other European countries. The Roman Catholic Church claims a majority in Italy, Spain, Portugal, France, rural Switzerland, Belgium, the Republic of Ireland, southern Germany, Austria, Poland, much of Czechoslovakia, Hungary, and the Croat and Slovene areas of Yugoslavia. Large Roman Catholic minorities are found in the United Kingdom and other European countries. The Greeks, Serbs, Rumanians, and Bulgars are mainly adherents of the Orthodox Eastern Church. Islam (Mohammedanism) has been the dominant religious faith in Albania, parts of southern Yugoslavia, and some areas in Bulgaria. Jews are found in considerable numbers in many European countries, although the Jewish populations have been decimated by persecution in Nazi Germany as well as in Poland and other areas formerly controlled by the Nazis. The effects of the official Communist philosophy of atheism in the satellite nations are difficult or impossible to determine with any degree of accuracy at the present time.

One area in which religious differences have led to political friction is Ireland. The Protestant north forms part of the United Kingdom but is claimed by the adjoining Irish Republic, a Roman Catholic country.

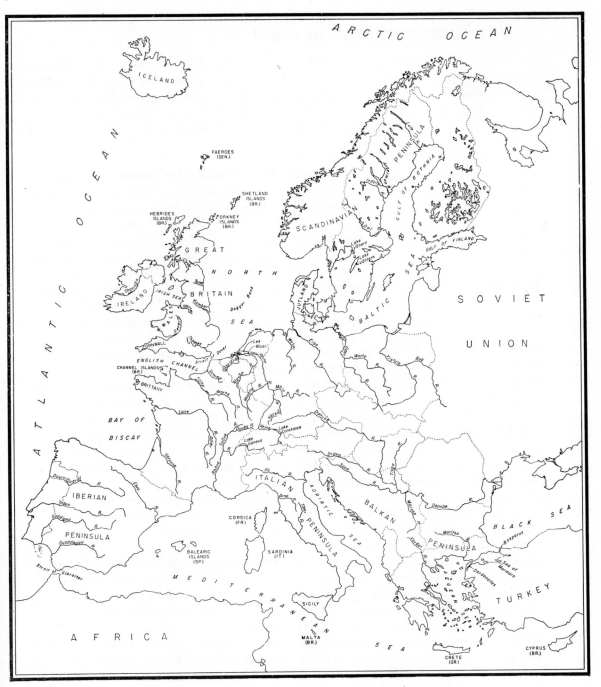

The main islands, seas, peninsulas, and rivers of Europe.

The European Environment

The diversity of Europe is not limited to cultural diversity. The natural environment of Europe also is diverse. Probably no area of equal size in the entire world exhibits such a variety of natural conditions and resources. On the whole, this environment has proved quite favorable for human settlement and use. No other world region contains such a small proportion of unproductive land. In the following paragraphs certain significant features of the European environment are briefly discussed.

▶ The Irregular Outline of Europe

One of the most noticeable characteristics of Europe as seen on a map is its extremely irregular outline. The main peninsula of Europe is fringed by numerous smaller peninsulas, including the Scandinavian, Iberian, Italian, and Balkan Peninsulas of the second order of size, the still smaller peninsulas of Denmark, Brittany, and Cornwall, and many others. Offshore are a multitude of islands, including such large and well-known islands as Great Britain, Ireland, Iceland, Sicily, Sardinia, Corsica, and Crete. Around the indented shores of Europe long arms of the sea penetrate the land and countless harbors offer a protection for shipping. The complex mingling of land and water has created an environment which provides many opportunities for maritime activity, and almost every European nation possessing a stretch of coast has turned extensively to the sea for a part of its livelihood. Excluding a few of the semi-independent micro-states, only four European countries—Switzerland, Austria, Czechoslovakia, and Hungary—lack direct access to the sea. Even these countries, however, are connected with the sea by rivers navigable for barges. The Rhine River provides access to the North Sea for Switzerland, as does the Elbe River for Czechoslovakia. The Danube River gives access to the Black Sea for Austria, Czechoslovakia, and Hungary. Few places in Europe are located more than 300 miles from waters navigable by ocean-going vessels.

▶ The Northerly Location of Europe

A circumstance of European geography which is not always appreciated is the northerly location of this world region. Much of Europe, including some of the most densely populated areas, lies farther north than the United States. We are so accustomed to thinking of these northern lands as bleak and forbidding that it comes as a considerable surprise to realize that Scotland lies in the same general latitude as Hudson Bay and that Norway has many thriving communities located as far north as the northern mainland of Canada. The British Isles, the Scandinavian countries, Belgium, the Netherlands, and most of Germany and Poland lie entirely north of the United States. Only in Spain, Italy, and Greece do European latitudes reach as far south as North Carolina or Tennessee. The most southerly point on the European mainland is in the general latitude of Nashville, Tennessee.

▶ The Temperate European Climate

As might be inferred from the presence of some of the world's most densely populated areas in latitudes corresponding to those of Canada, the climate of Europe is more temperate than the northerly location would suggest. Winter temperatures, in particular, are very mild for the latitude. For example, London, England, has approximately the same average temperature in January as Richmond, Virginia, which is 950 miles farther south. Reykjavik, the capital of Iceland, is nearly as warm in January as St. Louis, 1750 miles to the

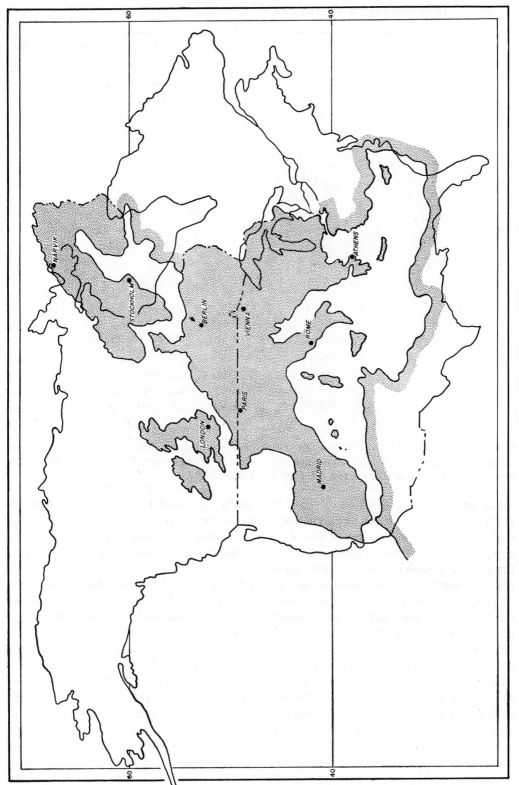

Europe and the Mediterranean Sea compared in latitude and area with the United States and Canada. (Goode's Homolosine Equal Area Projection, copyright The University of Chicago Press.)

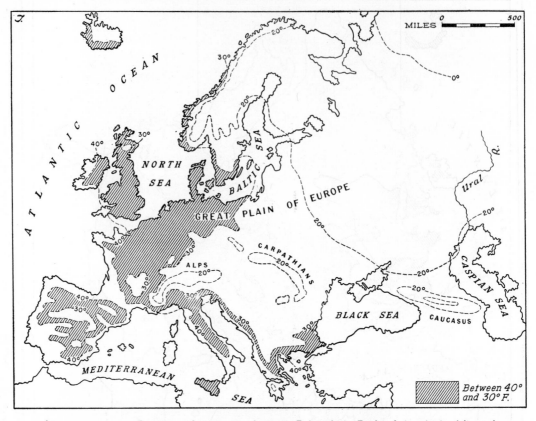

Actual temperatures in Europe in January in degrees Fahrenheit. Each of the dashed lines, known as an isotherm, connects places having the same average January temperature. (*From Jean Gottmann,* A Geography of Europe, *rev. ed. New York: Holt, 1954.*

south, and Tromsö, located on the coast of Norway 3° north of the Arctic Circle, has a slightly higher January average than Chicago, which is 1900 miles farther south. (In the preceding comparisons, distances given are approximate and the places named lie at generally comparable elevations above sea level.) Such anomalies of temperature are largely due to the influence of relatively warm currents of ocean water which wash the western shores of Europe during the winter season. These currents, originating in tropical parts of the Atlantic Ocean, drift to the north and east, and make the waters around Europe in winter much warmer than the latitude would warrant. Westerly winds, blowing across these waters, bring considerable amounts of warmth to the land, making temperatures abnor-

mally high, even in midwinter. Such effects are naturally most striking in places on or near the sea, although the moderating influence of the westerly winds and warm ocean waters is felt to some degree in all parts of Europe. In summer the ocean tends to have a cooling effect so that the seaward parts of Europe seldom experience excessively high summer temperatures.

Most large bodies of water temper the climate of adjoining land areas to some degree. Water gains and loses heat more slowly than land, and thus the oceans, seas, gulfs, and even large lakes have a moderating or stabilizing influence on the climate of lands which they border. The climate of Europe is affected not only by the open Atlantic, but also by the many arms of the Atlantic, such as the North Sea, Baltic Sea,

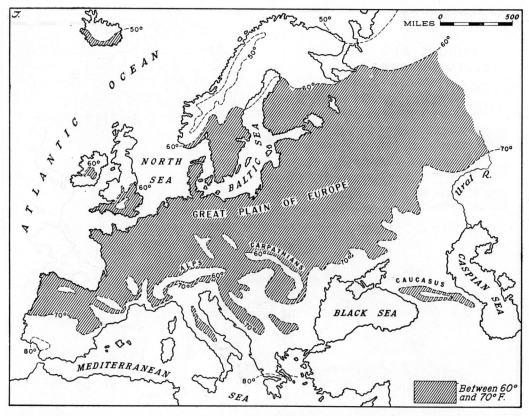

Actual temperatures in Europe in July. (*From Jean Gottmann, A Geography of Europe, rev. ed. New York: Holt, 1954.*)

and Mediterranean Sea, which penetrate deeply into the land. However, it is the Atlantic itself which has the most profound influence on European climate.

The same winds which bring warmth in winter and coolness in summer also bring abundant moisture to the land. Most of this falls in the form of rain, although the higher mountains and more northerly areas have considerable snow. Most European lowlands receive 20 inches or more of precipitation a year, and a few highland areas receive 100 inches or more. The general average of precipitation in the lowlands is 20 to 35 inches; few areas receive more than 40 inches a year. Although in some parts of the world 20 to 30 inches of precipitation would be distinctly marginal for agriculture, in western and northern Europe this amount is ample for a wide range of crops. The latter is essentially due to the effect of mild temperatures and high atmospheric humidity, which lessen the rate of evaporation and thus increase the effectiveness of the precipitation for crop growth. However, in Mediterranean Europe conditions are more unfavorable. In this area high summer temperatures cause excessive evaporation, and the yearly regime of rainfall concentrates most of the rain in the winter half-year. Thus moisture is most deficient during the summer season when it is needed most by growing crops.

• *Types of Climate.* Geographers and climatologists have observed, primarily on the basis of records kept by weather stations, that climate tends to be fairly uniform over considerable areas. Various systems have been devised for classifying climates into

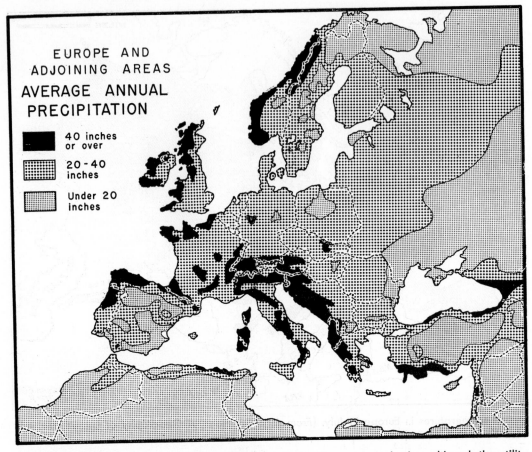

EUROPE AND
ADJOINING AREAS
AVERAGE ANNUAL
PRECIPITATION

■ 40 inches
   or over

▦ 20 - 40
   inches

▨ Under 20
   inches

Most parts of Europe receive sufficient total precipitation for crop production, although the utility of the rainfall in areas of mediterranean climate is lessened by its concentration into the colder half of the year. Highlands along windward coasts often receive excessively heavy precipitation. (*After a map by the Office of Foreign Agricultural Relations.*)

"types," to which descriptive names have often been applied, varying with the particular climate system. Each climate type has certain characteristics of temperature, precipitation, wind behavior, and so forth, which tend to distinguish it from other types. In addition, each type has certain associated features of vegetation, soil, and, to some degree, landforms, which tend to occur wherever the type is found. An area characterized by a particular climate type is known as a climatic region. Maps have been made showing the distribution of climatic types and regions on a world basis. Although such maps are somewhat inac-

curate, due to lack of data for certain areas, they are extremely useful in geographic study. (See end-paper climatic map.)

Marine West Coast Climate. Climatic effects of the ocean are most pronounced in areas along the northwestern seaboard of Europe. The climate of these areas is often referred to as the *marine west coast* or *humid marine* climate. This type of climate is characterized by relatively mild winters and relatively cool summers, with ample precipitation for crops at all seasons, a high proportion of cloudy weather, especially in winter, and considerable fog. Throughout the year, changes of weather follow each other in rapid succession. Rainfall in the marine west coast climate tends to come in slow drizzles, often lasting for days. London has experienced as many as 72 successive rainy days. There are a large proportion of rainy days during the year. On the average London has 164 rainy days and Paris 188; parts of the Shetland Islands, north of Scotland, have 260 rainy days a year.[2] Winter days are characteristically short, cloudy, dull, and humid. In the lowlands winter snowfall is light, and the ground is seldom covered for more than a few days at a time. Summer days are longer, brighter, and more pleasant, but even in summer a good many chilly and overcast days occur. The frost-free season of 175 to 250 days is sufficiently long for most crops grown in the middle latitudes to mature. However, excessively cool and/or rainy summers in some areas are a handicap to certain crops such as corn and wheat. Regions of marine west coast climate are found in other parts of the world besides northwestern Europe, a notable example being the Pacific coast of Anglo-America from San Francisco northward to southern Alaska.

Humid Continental Climate. Inland from the coast in western and central Europe, the marine climate gradually changes. Winters become colder, summers hotter; the annual precipitation becomes somewhat less, with more precipitation in summer than in winter; and the percentage of cloudiness and fog decreases. At a considerable distance inland the climate becomes sufficiently different to be considered a separate type —the *humid continental* climate. This type of climate, which prevails in most of East Central Europe, is similar in many ways to the climate of east central United States.

Mediterranean Climate. Southern Europe has an unusually distinctive type of climate —the *dry-summer subtropical* or *mediterranean climate.* The most characteristic feature of this climate type is the occurrence of a pronounced autumn and winter maximum of precipitation. The total yearly precipitation is less, on the average, than in the marine west coast and humid continental climates, and very little precipitation occurs during the summer months, when temperatures are most advantageous for crop growth. Mediterranean summers are warm to hot, and winters are mild. In the lowlands snow is rare, although it may accumulate to considerable depths on adjacent mountains. The frost-free season is very long, lasting practically the entire year in some of the more southerly lowlands. Winters in this climatic region are famous for their mild, bright, sunny weather—a great attraction to tourists from the damper, cloudier, cooler regions to the north. In the United States a mediterranean type of climate occurs in parts of central and southern California.

Subarctic, Tundra, and Highland Climates. The greater part of Northern Europe has a *subarctic climate* characterized by long, severe winters and short, rather cool summers. Due to the shortness of the frost-free season, only the hardier crops can be grown. Most of the land in the subarctic areas is covered by coniferous forest.

The *tundra climate* is found in northerly areas where conditions are too severe for a normal stand of trees. In such areas the vegetation is composed of moss, lichens, grass, low bushes, and a scattering of stunted trees. Conditions are even less favorable for agriculture than in the subarctic zone. Frost is apt to occur at any time during the year. The principal areas of tundra climate in Europe are found along the Arctic shore of the European mainland and on the island of Iceland. Both the subarctic climate and the tundra climate

---

[2] Glenn T. Trewartha, *An Introduction to Climate.* New York: McGraw-Hill, 1954. P. 319.

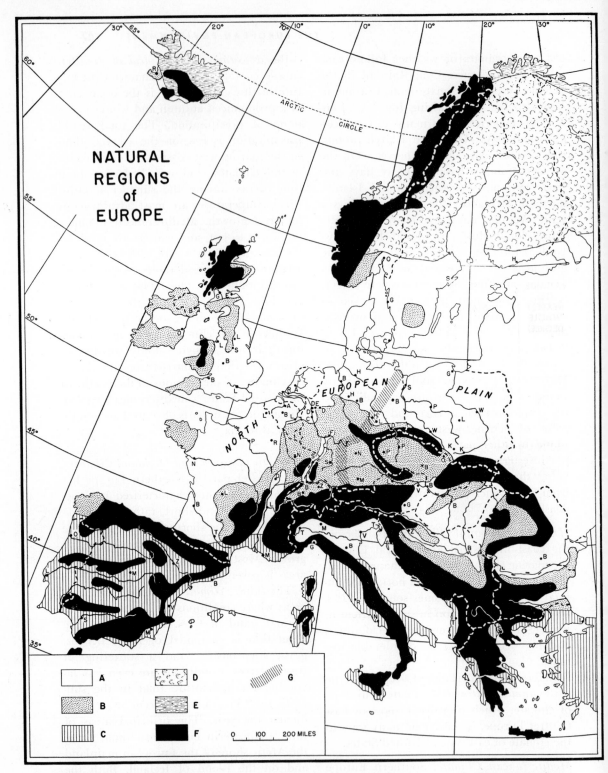

NATURAL
REGIONS
of
EUROPE

The meaning of the symbols in the legend at lower left is as follows: A—humid mid-latitude plains; B—humid mid-latitude hill lands; C—mediterranean (dry-summer) subtropical hills, tablelands, and small plains; D—glacially scoured subarctic plains and hills forested in conifers; E—Arctic tundra; F—mountains; G—approximate boundary between marine west coast climate (west of line) and humid continental climate (east of line) between Alps and Baltic Sea. Prominent cities are shown as reference points by dot and capital letter.

of Europe are duplicated, on a much larger scale, in the Soviet Union and Canada. These climate zones are among the most sparsely settled parts of Europe.

The higher mountains of Europe, like high mountains in other parts of the world, have a *highland climate* varying in character according to altitude. In the Alps, for

instance, a range of climates is found which varies from subtropical at the base of the mountains to tundra and ice-cap climates at the highest elevations.

Temperature and precipitation data for selected European climatic stations are given in Table 2.

Taken as a whole, the climates of Eu-

TABLE 2

CLIMATIC DATA FOR SELECTED EUROPEAN STATIONS

LATITUDE (TO NEAREST WHOLE DEGREE)	STATION	ELEVA-TION ABOVE SEA LEVEL (FEET)	TYPE OF CLIMATE	AVERAGE TEMPERATURE (DEGREES F. TO NEAREST WHOLE DEGREE)			PRECIPITATION	
				ANNUAL	JANU-ARY	JULY	ANNUAL AVER-AGE (TO NEAREST INCH)	PERCENT OCCUR-ING APRIL –SEPTEM-BER (TO NEAREST WHOLE PERCENT)
53°N.	Dublin (Ireland)	155	Marine West Coast	48°	41°	59°	28″	50%
56°N.	Glasgow (Scotland)	180	Marine West Coast	47°	39°	58°	37″	46%
52°N.	London (England)	18	Marine West Coast	50°	41°	63°	24″	48%
49°N.	Paris (France)	164	Marine West Coast	50°	37°	65°	22″	52%
51°N.	Brussels (Belgium)	328	Marine West Coast	50°	36°	64°	33″	51%
56°N.	Copenhagen (Denmark)	16	Marine West Coast	46°	31°	63°	21″	54%
60°N.	Bergen (Norway)	72	Marine West Coast	45°	34°	58°	84″	42%
53°N.	Berlin (Germany)	131	Humid Continental	49°	32°	66°	23″	56%
52°N.	Warsaw (Poland)	399	Humid Continental	46°	26°	66°	21″	61%
45°N.	Belgrade (Yugoslavia)	453	Humid Continental	52°	31°	71°	25″	58%
43°N.	Marseilles (France)	246	Mediterranean	57°	43°	72°	23″	38%
42°N.	Rome (Italy)	208	Mediterranean	60°	45°	76°	33″	32%
38°N.	Athens (Greece)	326	Mediterranean	63°	48°	80°	16″	24%
66°N.	Haparanda (Sweden)	30	Subarctic	34°	14°	60°	21″	51%
70°N.	Vardö (Norway)	33	Tundra	33°	22°	48°	26″	42%
47°N.	Santis (Switzerland)	8202	Highland	28°	16°	41°	110″	56%

rope are temperate, humid, seasonal climates which have proved favorable for human settlement. The general range of climates in Europe is duplicated in other parts of the world, most notably in Anglo-America. It is to overseas areas having climates generally similar to those of Europe that Europeans have migrated in the largest numbers.

► The Varied Topography of Europe

The surface features of Europe are extremely diversified. It is safe to say that no other area of equal size exhibits so much variety. Plains, plateaus, hill lands, and mountains form a complex pattern, and together with associated vegetation, water bodies, and works of man, produce a variegated and often highly scenic landscape.

[EDITORIAL COMMENT. Geographers are not in agreement regarding the precise meaning of plains, plateaus, hill lands, and mountains. In general, a *plain* is a relatively level area of slight elevation (although the "High Plains" of western United States reach elevations of 5000 feet above sea level). Some plains, particularly those developed by rivers, are quite flat, but most plains exhibit gentle to moderate slopes. However, it is the horizontal rather than the vertical dimension which predominates in plains country. Most of the world's people live on plains, so that consideration of plains and their significance becomes a highly important facet of geographic study. Geographers constantly speak of "land level enough" for farming, transportation, and the like.

To a degree, a *plateau* is simply an elevated plain. Most areas recognized as plateaus lie at elevations of 2000 feet or more, although some are considerably lower. To qualify as plateaus in the strictest sense, such areas should be terminated on at least one side by a steep edge, or *escarpment,* marking an abrupt transition from the plateau surface to areas at a lower elevation.

However, the word "plateau" is often used loosely in referring to relatively level areas lying at considerable heights, whether terminated by a definite escarpment or not. Well-defined plateaus are often spoken of as "tablelands." Plateaus of arid or semi-arid regions are frequently trenched by deep canyons, a classic example being the mile-deep Grand Canyon of the Colorado River, cut in the level surface of the Colorado Plateau in northern Arizona. In Europe, probably the best example of a plateau is the Spanish *Meseta,* a great tabular upland which occupies most of the Iberian Peninsula.

In *hill lands* and *mountains* the vertical dimension predominates. No sure way has been devised to distinguish between these two classes of landforms. In general, mountains are higher and more rugged than hill lands, are more of a barrier to movement, and offer fewer possibilities for human settlement and use. Whereas many areas of hill land support moderate to dense populations, most mountain areas are sparsely populated. Local usage of the term "mountain" varies greatly from place to place over the earth. In plains country, areas of a few hundred feet elevation which stand out conspicuously above their surroundings may be called "mountains" by the local inhabitants. However, the term is most commonly used in reference to comparatively rugged areas lying at least 2000 to 3000 feet above sea level.]

Probably the most significant of all European surface features is a continuous plain which extends from the Pyrenees Mountains across western and northern France, central and northern Belgium, the Netherlands, northern Germany, Denmark, and northern Poland, and stretches without a break far into the Soviet Union. Outliers of this plain are found in Great Britain, southern Sweden, and southern Finland. On this North European Plain are found the largest expanses of arable land in Eu-

A glaciated landscape in Northern Europe. The town in the view is Strängnäs, situated on the shore of Lake Mälaren in central Sweden. (*Swedish National Travel Office.*)

rope. In addition, there are large deposits of coal, potash, salt, and other economic minerals. For many centuries this plain has formed a major avenue of movement between east and west in Europe. Today it forms the principal focus of European industrial, commercial, and agricultural activity. For the most part the North European Plain is not flat, except in certain areas, but contains great stretches of undulating or rolling land, with many gentle hills.

South of the northern plain, Europe is predominantly mountainous or hilly, although the mountains and hill masses enclose many relatively level areas. The mountains of southern Europe are mostly rugged alpine mountains, with many jagged peaks and snowcapped summits. The highest peaks are found in the Alps, a massive snowclad range containing many summits of 12,000 feet or higher. These mountains constitute a considerable barrier to traffic, though on the whole a less formidable barrier than their appearance on a map would suggest, since they are cut through by many passes, river valleys, and tunnels. To the countries in which they lie, the mountains are valuable as sources of hydroelectric power, as tourist attractions, and as defensive ramparts in wartime. In some areas, particularly the Balkan Peninsula, the mountains have tended to isolate small groups of people, and thus have aided in the development of many small, distinctive regions within the mountain zone.

The hill lands of Europe are lower and less rugged than the mountains. Generally speaking, the hill lands are older than the mountains in point of geologic time. Having been formed earlier, they have been exposed to weathering and erosion for a longer period and thus have a smoother and more rounded aspect. Many of the important deposits of metals in Europe are found in the hill lands.

At the north the North European Plain is fringed by glaciated lowlands and hill lands in eastern Sweden and Finland, and by rugged, ice-scoured (though not very high) mountains in western Sweden and Norway. In the British Isles a few sizable areas of lowland are fringed by hill country and low mountains.

[EDITORIAL COMMENT. During the Great Ice Age, a massive continental ice sheet formed over the Scandinavian Peninsula and Scotland, from which it moved outward into Germany, Poland, the Netherlands, England, and Russia. Over a period of perhaps a million years the ice sheets alternately advanced and retreated as glacial and interglacial ages succeeded each other. The latest retreat of the ice is thought to have begun at least 35,000 years ago. Continental ice sheets still cover about 10 percent of the earth's land surface in Greenland and Antarctica, as compared with an estimated 28 percent of the lands when the glaciers were at their maximum extent.

In some of the glaciated areas the ice sheets scoured deeply, removing most of the surface soil and gouging hollows which became lakes when the ice melted. Elsewhere the glaciers deposited the materials accumulated on their under side, either in the form of outwash carried by sheets of water issuing from under the ice, or else in the form of morainal materials dropped in place as the ice melted. In Norway, most of

Finland, much of Sweden, parts of the British Isles, and Iceland (which had a local ice sheet of its own) scouring predominated over deposition. The present landscape of these areas is dominated by thin soil, bare rock, and a multitude of lakes. The ice sheets interfered with the pre-existing drainage pattern so that the present streams tend to wander about aimlessly, with many rapids and waterfalls. Thus many natural sites for the development of hydroelectric power have been created. The latter is an important circumstance in Norway, Sweden, Finland, and Iceland, which are poor in the mineral fuels and consequently place much dependence on hydroelectricity as a source of power.

Glacial deposits of varying thickness were laid down on the North European Plain. Unfortunately, many of the deposits were excessively sandy so that the present soils are not very fertile on the whole, although they have often been made productive by careful handling and large additions of fertilizer. Immediately south of the glaciated areas, deposits of a windblown material known as _loess_ appear. This material appears to have been transported from the glaciated areas by winds after the surface was dry. A relatively continuous band of loess extends along the southern edge of the North European Plain, from northeastern France to southern Poland and southern Russia. Loess tends to weather into good soils, and the loess belt represents one of the most fertile and productive farming areas in Europe.]

▶ *River Systems*

[EDITORIAL COMMENT. Some terminology regarding rivers may be in order at this point. A *river system* is a river together with its tributaries. A *river basin* is the area drained by a river system. The *source* of a river is its place of origin; the *mouth* is the point where it empties into another body of water. As they near the sea, many rivers become rather sluggish, depositing great quantities of sediments to form *deltas,* and often dividing into a number of separate channels, known as *distributaries.* The Rhine divides in this manner, its two principal distributaries being the Lek and the Waal.]

In the mountains and hill lands of Europe many important rivers rise. Most of the rivers that are the chief transportation arteries empty into the seas which border Europe on the north and west. Among the most important of these commercial waterways are the Rhine, Scheldt, Seine, Thames, Mersey, Clyde, Weser, Elbe, Oder, and Vistula. Along the lower courses of many streams deep *estuaries* have been formed by the sinking of the river mouths. Such estuaries are often capable of admitting ocean vessels for considerable distances. The seaward portions of many rivers experience tides of considerable height. The daily ebb and flow of tidal waters helps to keep navigation channels scoured free of sediments, although the action of the tides must often be supplemented by dredging. Were it not for the tides, it would be very difficult for many of the smaller ports located some distance upstream to keep open. However, in certain rivers the range of tides is so great as to constitute a distinct handicap for the ports, requiring expensive installations to offset the rise and fall of the water level and thus permit continuous use of the wharves. The foregoing statements do not apply to the Mediterranean, Baltic, and Black Seas, which are nearly tideless.

Many of the major seaports of Europe are located along the lower courses of rivers. Among the largest and most important of these ports are London, on the Thames; Rotterdam, on the Lek distributary of the Rhine; Antwerp, on the Scheldt; and Hamburg, on the Elbe.

The most important inland waterway of Europe is the Rhine. This river, together with tributary rivers and canals, is equaled in economic significance only by the Great Lakes–St. Lawrence waterway of North America. The longest river of Europe, however, is the Danube. Although it is used considerably for navigation, it carries a much smaller volume of traffic than the Rhine. Flowing eastward to the Black Sea through regions which are primarily agricultural rather than industrial, the Danube is largely lacking in the cargoes of coal, iron ore, steel, and other bulky industrial materials which constitute the major tonnage on the Rhine.

The rivers of Mediterranean Europe, in Italy, Iberia, extreme southern France, and the Balkans, are used very little for navigation. Flowing mostly through hilly or mountainous country, they are typically steep and swift with many rapids and waterfalls (the sluggish Po River in northern Italy is a conspicuous exception). Due to the unbalanced yearly distribution of rainfall in the mediterranean climate, these streams are less regular in flow than the rivers of northwestern Europe. They are often choked with water during periods of heavy rain in the autumn and winter, but may become mere trickles in the drought of midsummer.

The rivers of the Scandinavian Peninsula, Finland, and Iceland, like those of Mediterranean Europe, are mostly short, rock-strewn, and swift. However, they are more even in flow, partly as a consequence of the more balanced distribution of precipitation and partly as a result of the fact that many of these streams originate in lakes which serve as natural reservoirs and release water gradually throughout the year. These rivers, with their many rapids and waterfalls, are not very useful for navigation, except for the transportation of logs. However, many of them are harnessed for the production of hydroelectric power.

The usefulness of rivers emptying into the Baltic Sea is somewhat lessened by the fact that they are ordinarily frozen for a considerable period in midwinter. Parts of the Baltic margins freeze in winter; indeed the Gulfs of Bothnia and Finland are normally frozen for 3 months or more. In some winters the extreme north of the Gulf of Bothnia is frozen for 7 months. The Baltic and its gulfs, being almost completely enclosed by land and continuously supplied with fresh water by a large number of rivers, are less saline than the ocean and so are especially susceptible to freezing.

In other parts of Europe sea ice is uncommon. The shores of the North and Irish Seas, the Bay of Biscay, and the Mediterranean are normally ice free throughout the winter. On the open coast of Norway ice is rare. This is true even north of the Arctic Circle.

The Diversified Economy of Europe

Diversity is the keynote of the European economy, as it is of the European environment. Agriculture, fishing, manufacturing, mining, the forest industries, transportation, trade, and other forms of economic activity are highly developed. Much variety exists from one country and region to another, both in the relative emphasis given to each of the major pursuits and in the relative intensity of development.

▶ Agriculture and Fisheries

Agriculture finds its highest development in the countries bordering the North Sea. Scientific methods of farming are employed, and yields per acre are high. However, the different countries vary considerably among themselves. Belgium, for example, consistently obtains higher yields than France, mainly as a result of more intensive methods. In the North Sea countries, agriculture is more highly commercialized than in other parts of Europe, a fact principally due to the close proximity of large and dependable urban markets for surplus foodstuffs.

• *Types of Farming.* Almost everywhere in Europe livestock are important in the farm economy. However, the emphasis on livestock raising is proportionately greatest in northwestern Europe. Two principal types or systems of farming are especially characteristic of the latter area—*dairy farming* and *commercial crop and livestock farming.* In dairy farming, cows are kept for the production of milk, butter, and cheese; calves not needed for the dairy herd are sold; and the income from dairying is often supplemented by production of hogs and poultry. A high proportion of the available land is occupied by temporary or permanent pasture, and crop land is devoted principally to hay, feed grains, and root crops suitable for feed. In Denmark, the Netherlands, and England dairying is particularly prominent. Several other countries of northwestern Europe also contain significant dairy districts. In commercial crop and livestock farming, cattle and other animals, especially hogs, sheep, and poultry, are raised primarily for meat. The farm income results principally from the sale of livestock, although crop surpluses may be sold. The ratio of cropped land to pasture is higher than in dairy farming, with a good balance being maintained among grains, root crops, and hay.

In East Central Europe agriculture has been characterized in the past by poorer methods and lower yields than in the North Sea countries. Much of the farming has been of a subsistence nature, with a high proportion of the products being used at home rather than sold. Collective farming on the Russian model has been instituted in many parts of East Central Europe since the end of World War II.

In Southern Europe agriculture is both favored and hindered by the climate. Mild winter temperatures and a long growing season make possible the production of specialized subtropical crops, such as citrus fruits, olives, and early vegetables. However, lack of rain severely restricts the growing of crops in the summer, except for deep-rooted, drought-resistant perennials such as olives, grapes, dates, and figs, or crops grown by irrigation. Summer is the difficult season for most farmers in this part of Europe. Fall-sown grains (wheat, barley, or rye) are extensively grown with the aid of fall and winter rains. In Southern Europe, as in East Central Europe, much of the agriculture is of a subsistence character. Farmers in this region are handicapped not only by a lack of summer rain, but also by a dearth of land sufficiently level to grow crops. The most important exception to these generalizations is the Po Valley, which has summer rain coupled with wide stretches of level land.

Generally speaking, agricultural methods in Europe are most backward and yields are lowest in areas where the largest proportion of the people depend directly on agriculture for a livelihood. Such areas, found mostly in Southern and East Central Europe, are frequently characterized by a serious degree of rural overpopulation.

• *The Major Crops.* Approximately half of the crop land in Europe is devoted to cereals. Wheat, the leading cereal, both in acreage and yield, is grown to some degree in nearly all parts of Europe, and tends to occupy the best soils. A map of wheat acreage probably comes closer to a map of general crop distribution than a map of any other single crop.

On the sandy plains of northern Germany and Poland, rye is grown in larger quantities than wheat. It is the principal bread grain for the majority of rural people on the North European Plain east of the Rhine. Most of the world's rye is grown in Europe and the Soviet Union.

Growing of corn (maize) for grain is mainly restricted to areas having long, hot summers and a summer maximum of rainfall. Such conditions are found in the Danubian plains of Hungary, Rumania, and Yugoslavia, and in the Po Valley of northern Italy. The four countries named grow most of Europe's corn.

Considerable quantities of oats and barley are grown in various parts of Europe, both being used mainly for livestock feed. Rice is grown in the Po Valley and also in some irrigated areas of Spain and Portugal.

Root crops are far more important in European agriculture than in the agriculture of the United States. Potatoes are grown in enormous quantities, particularly in Germany and Poland; they are used for human food, stock feed, and the production of alcohol. Sugar beets are extensively grown on the better soils; the beet tops are fed to stock, as are the residues after the juice has been extracted for the production of sugar. Turnips, mangels, rutabagas, carrots, and other root crops are very important for stock feed, especially in the North Sea countries.

Many important areas of market gardening and specialized horticulture are found in Europe, particularly in the zone of mediterranean climate and in the vicinity of the larger cities.

• *European Fisheries.* The products of European agriculture are supplemented by products of the fisheries. Europeans eat more fish per capita than do Americans, and fishing is intensively developed in a number of European countries. The most important fishing nations are the North Sea countries and Iceland. The shallow seas which border Europe on the northwest, especially the North Sea, are rich in small marine organisms known collectively as *plankton.* Such organisms are the principal food for schools of cod, herring, mackerel, and other fish of economic value. Many thousands of fishermen gain their

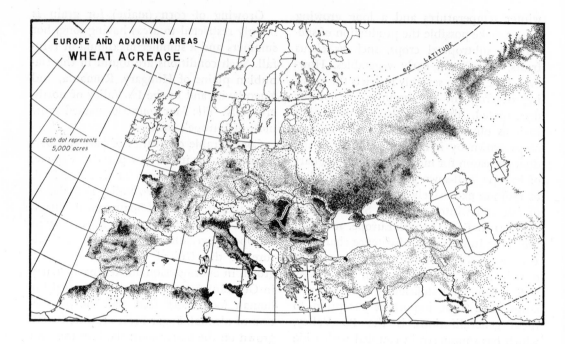

The short dashes on the maps on these pages indicate prewar political boundaries. Some of the postwar boundaries shown by solid lines are not officially recognized by the United States Government. (*Modified from maps prepared by the Office of Foreign Agricultural Relations on the basis of prewar data.*)

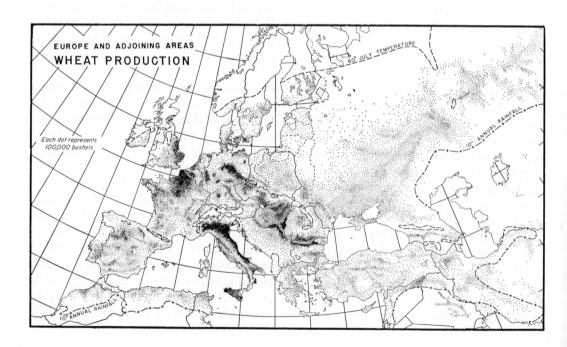

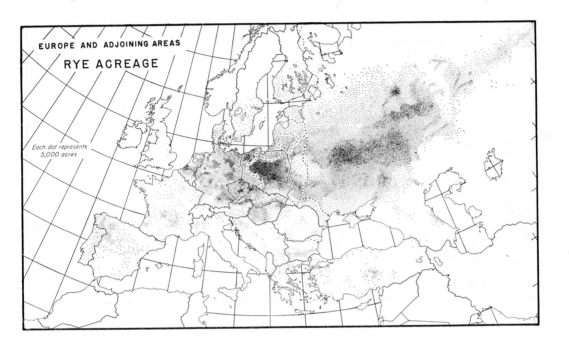

EUROPE AND ADJOINING AREAS
RYE ACREAGE

Each dot represents
5,000 acres

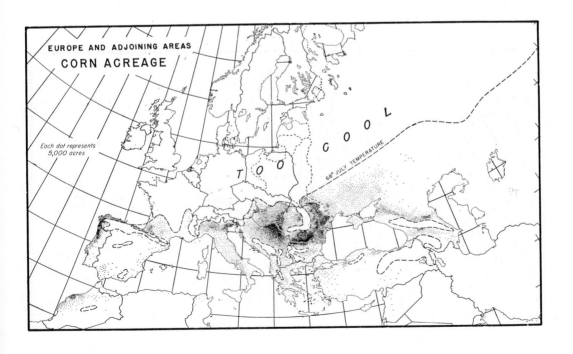

EUROPE AND ADJOINING AREAS
CORN ACREAGE

Each dot represents
5,000 acres

TOO COOL

68° JULY TEMPERATURE

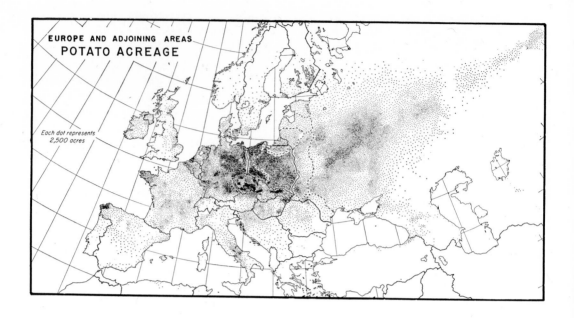

Short dashes indicate prewar political boundaries. Some of the postwar boundaries shown by solid lines are not officially recognized by the United States Government. (*Modified from maps prepared by the Office of Foreign Agricultural Relations on the basis of prewar data.*)

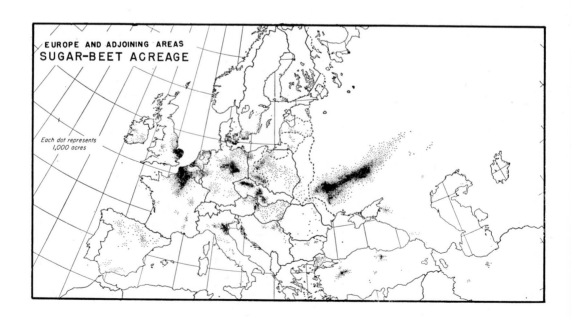

principal livelihood from these waters. The Dogger Bank in the North Sea is famous as a fishing ground. Norway and the United Kingdom lead other European nations in total quantity of fish caught, although fishing is of greatest relative importance in the economy of Iceland, a country so notoriously poor in land resources that it must depend mainly on the sea for support.

• *Dependence on Food Imports.* In spite of its great production from agriculture and the fisheries, Europe is not self-sufficient in most foodstuffs. In fact, among the principal foodstuffs it is 99–100 percent self-sufficient only in whole milk, potatoes, and rye. Domestic production of the remaining foods must be supplemented by imports from other parts of the world. Among the more prominent food imports are wheat, corn, oil cake (for stock feed and fertilizer), animal and vegetable fats and oils, chilled and frozen meats, cane sugar, cocoa, tea, coffee, and tobacco. Europe also imports large quantities of fibers (cotton and wool predominantly) and natural rubber. As for many decades past, this region still remains the greatest market for the world's surplus agricultural commodities. However, the individual countries of Europe vary a great deal in their degree of dependence on agricultural imports. The United Kingdom is vitally dependent on such imports, but for such countries as Hungary, Rumania, and Bulgaria they are relatively unimportant. There is a great deal of intra-European trade in foodstuffs, particularly in livestock products and fresh fruits and vegetables. Denmark, the Netherlands, Ireland, and Iceland are notable examples of European nations which gain a large share of their national income from sales of food surpluses to other European countries.

▶ Manufacturing and Mining

The products of European factories run the gamut of industrial commodities, from pig iron and steel to the finest textiles, ceramics, optical goods, and metal wares.

• *Metalworking.* European industries produce three main types of commodities: metal goods, chemicals, and textiles. The most important of the metalworking industries is the iron and steel industry, which is mainly concentrated in a few major districts in Germany, the United Kingdom, France, Belgium, Luxembourg, Poland, and Czechoslovakia. These districts are located in close proximity to deposits of coal, iron ore, or both. Of the latter commodities, coal is the more abundant and widespread. It is tremendously significant, not only to the iron and steel industry, but also to many other European industries which depend on it as their principal source of fuel and power. Europe has few deposits of petroleum or natural gas, and consequently places a very heavy dependence on coal, and, to a lesser degree, on hydroelectric power. The chief coal fields are found in an east-west line extending from the United Kingdom to southern Poland. This axis of coal deposits corresponds generally with the main axis of population and industry described earlier. In Europe, as in other industrialized parts of the world, there has been a pronounced tendency for industrial plants and workers to gravitate to coal.

Iron ore is less plentiful than coal, and many of the smaller deposits have been exhausted. However, two major reserves of iron ore still remain—the ore deposits of Lorraine in eastern France and the Kiruna district of northern Sweden. The French ores are larger in amount, but the Swedish ores are of better quality. Smaller reserves of ore are found in Germany, the United Kingdom, Austria, Luxembourg, Czechoslovakia, northern Spain, and elsewhere.

The known deposits of nonferrous metals in Europe have been worked for a long period, some of them for thousands of years. Today these deposits can no longer supply the demand, and large quantities of copper, zinc, lead, bauxite, and tin must be imported. Smelting of foreign nonferrous ores is an important specialty of Belgium, the United Kingdom, and certain other European countries. In addition, Europe requires large imports of the ferro-alloys, including manganese, nickel, chromium, tungsten, cobalt, molybdenum, and vanadium. The latter are used to impart special qualities of hardness, toughness, resistance to heat, or other desirable properties to steel.

• *The Manufacture of Chemicals.* All industrial nations use large quantities of chemicals—acids, alkalis, dyes, and a host of others. This is due to the fact that most industrial processes require chemicals of some type. Fortunately, the chemicals

needed in the largest amounts by modern industry can be manufactured from raw materials which are relatively abundant. Among the latter, salt, limestone, sulfur, and coal are important. Europe is well supplied with these materials, and it was in this region that the modern chemical industry was born, Great Britain and Germany being the early leaders in the industry.

The United States has now become the leading nation in chemical manufacture, but the European chemical industry remains significant. One of the most important branches of this industry is the manufacture of chemical fertilizers. Most European soils are not particularly fertile by nature, and it has taken large applications of commercial fertilizer (along with animal manures) to make them productive. The

A small industrial town located in the important coal-mining and steel-producing Saar district on the border between France and Germany. An important share of European manufacturing is conducted in towns such as the one shown in this view. (*French Embassy Press and Information Division.*)

principal raw materials for fertilizer manufacture are available in Europe in large quantities: potash from huge natural deposits in Germany and France; phosphates from blast furnace wastes and from deposits of phosphatic rock in French North Africa; and nitrates secured by the fixation of atmospheric nitrogen and also as a by-product of coke manufacture. Europe uses more chemical fertilizer than any other world region, with Anglo-America a close second.

• *Textile Manufacture.* The manufacture of textiles is the most widespread major branch of European industry. Although in many areas textile milling is the main industry, there is also an extensive development of textile manufacture employing chiefly women and girls in some areas where the male workers are principally employed in other enterprises—coal mining, steel milling, shipbuilding, and the like. Woolen and cotton textiles are mainly produced from imported fibers, although a considerable amount of raw wool is available from the United Kingdom and lesser amounts from several other European countries. Linen manufacture, particularly important in Northern Ireland, relies on European and Russian flax, and the synthetic fiber industry (rayon, nylon, etc.) mainly depends on European materials. The manufacture of silk is less important than formerly, although the city of Lyons in France still has a considerable silk industry. Some raw silk is produced in the Po Valley and a few other areas.

Europe continues to lead other manufacturing regions in the production of highly finished types of goods requiring painstaking care and a high degree of skill in manufacture. Swiss watches, English woolens, German chinaware and cameras, Bohemian glassware, Irish linens, and the best French wines and liquers are famous, and unsurpassed in quality. Such products find a ready sale in export markets.

Most European manufacturing is carried on within the area enclosed by the heavy black line. (*From J. Russell Smith and M. Ogden Phillips,* Industrial and Commercial Geography, *3d ed. New York: Holt, 1946.*)

▶ *The Forest Industries*

The principal forest stands of commercial value are found in the Scandinavian Peninsula and Finland. Smaller commercial forest tracts are scattered throughout continental Europe, particularly in the mountains and hill lands. Despite an extensive development of lumbering in certain areas, the existing forests cannot fully supply the demand for timber products so that sizable imports from other world regions are required. A number of the European countries have developed scientific forestry to a high degree in an effort to conserve their remaining stands of timber. The present commercial forests are principally composed of softwood trees (spruce, fir, pine, etc.), although sizable stands of oak, beech, and other hardwoods occur in some areas. Among the European nations, Sweden, Finland, Norway, and Austria lead as exporters of lumber and wood pulp, the main types of forest exports. Most of these exports go to other European countries.

► The Pattern of Internal Transportation

Europe is equipped with an elaborate network of rail lines, water routes, highways, and airways over which flows a vast amount of freight and passenger traffic. Some of the principal features of this transportation system have been described as follows by two American geographers, J. Russell Smith and M. Ogden Phillips: [3]

The trade of the different European countries with each other is of great extent and closely resembles the trade of temperate North America. Each of these continents has, in the region of middle temperature facing the Atlantic, a large territory with tens of millions of manufacturing people buying food and raw materials. In America this manufacturing region may be said to be bounded by a line connecting St. Louis, Milwaukee, Montreal, Portland, Maine, and Baltimore, and extending back to St. Louis. In Europe the manufacturing belt extends from Stockholm, Budapest, and Florence westward to the ocean, including Great Britain, the birthplace of the modern factory system. Farther in the interior of Europe and America lie the grain- and meat-producing plains; in the north are water power and forests with their wood and paper output; in the south, the land of fruits and early vegetables. Europe has only a small corn belt and almost no vestige of a cotton belt, but has instead a great extent of potato, barley, oats, and rye belts in her mid-region. . . .

European commerce has developed two sets of commercial routes: first, the heavy traffic routes, which are chiefly water routes; and, second, the fast traffic routes, which are chiefly overland routes. The distinction between the two cannot always be sharply drawn, and the commerce of the first sometimes uses parts of the routes of the second; but, broadly taken, there is a distinct division. In each group there are two classes, primary and secondary, or trunk lines and branches. Most of the trade routes radiate from the populous industrial region of northwest Europe to the less populous regions in the northeast, east, and south.

• The Heavy Traffic Routes

Two great heavy traffic trunk routes are furnished by the southern and northern seas—the sea routes skirting southern Europe to the Black Sea and northern Europe to the Gulfs of Finland and Bothnia and the White Sea. The secondary heavy traffic routes, the feeders to these main water routes, are the navigable bays and rivers and the railroads, which, like the rivers, run in most cases toward the sea, and carry inland products down to the ports. . . .

The heavy traffic routes of European commerce, skirting the continent and fed by . . . secondary routes . . . are served by a multitude of coasting vessels, large and small, giving access to every port of Europe and to every country except Switzerland, Czechoslovakia, Austria, and Hungary; Switzerland has Rhine boats, Czechoslovakia has Elbe and Danube boats, and Austria and Hungary have Danube boats. It is by ship that the heavy freight of Europe is carried, the traffic in which economy of cost is more important than economy of time—the wines, fruits, and oil of Spain, France, and Italy; sulfur from Sicily; dried fruits from Greece; wool and figs from Turkey; grain from Hungary and the Black Sea . . . British coal; Belgian cement, glass, and iron; and the machinery and the heavy manufactures of Great Brit-

[3] J. Russell Smith and M. Ogden Phillips, *Industrial and Commercial Geography*, 3d ed. New York: Holt, 1946. Pp. 816–824. Used by permission of the authors and the publisher. One of the authors' headings has been altered and several headings omitted.

ain, Germany, Belgium, and France.

The manufacturing region of Europe is either the origin or destination of most of this water-borne commerce. It is a region threaded by canals and navigable rivers giving to every capital except Bern and to almost every manufacturing city of importance the advantage of barge transportation to and from the seaports, thus affording very cheap rates on such industrial fundamentals as coal, iron, wood, stone, ore, cement, cotton, grain, and heavy manufactures. . . .

• The Fast Traffic on Overland Routes

The water routes that surround western and central Europe afford an excellent basis for the heavy commerce upon which industry rests. But these cheap and therefore important routes are slow, and in a region so populous and so advanced in industry there is a large traffic that requires the most expeditious routes—the railroads.

Passengers, mail, and valuable or urgent freight use these routes. For through traffic of this character, there is a well-organized system of railway trunk lines performing a service which is quite distinct from that of the heavy system with its feeders. The fast traffic routes connect the great centers of population, and the quickest time is therefore often made over somewhat circuitous routes that happen to pass a number of large cities. The configuration of the country sometimes helps population centers to locate the fast traffic routes of Europe with some disregard of distances.

In addition to water and rail transportation, Europe also has a well-developed system of highways and air services. The routes of internal transportation in this region are tied in with world transportation by major ocean routes and airways extending to all parts of the globe.

The British Isles

The British Isles lie off the northwest coast of Europe. There are approximately 5500 separate islands in the group, but most of these are very small, and only two islands, Great Britain and Ireland, are of major consequence. The largest island, Great Britain, lies only 22 miles across the Strait of Dover from France. Relations with the European continent have always been close, and the islands have always been considered an integral part of the continent.

Two sovereign countries occupy the islands. The lesser of the two in size and world importance is the Republic of Ireland, which occupies all of the island of Ireland except for the counties of Northern Ireland. The Republic of Ireland and Northern Ireland are considered briefly at the end of Chapter 4.

The other sovereign country of the British Isles is the United Kingdom of Great Britain and Northern Ireland. Many common substitutes are in use for this unwieldy name, including "United Kingdom," "UK," "Britain," and "Great Britain." The United Kingdom occupies the island of Great Britain and includes the six counties of Northern Ireland, plus a great number of small islands, of which the Isle of Wight, Isle of Man, Hebrides, Orkneys, Shetlands, and Channel Islands are among the best known. Altogether the United Kingdom contains approximately four fifths of the area and 95 percent of the population of the British Isles.

An agricultural landscape near the western edge of the Central Lowlands of Scotland. Most British lowlands are undulating or rolling rather than flat. (*British Information Services.*)

Political Subdivisions of the United Kingdom

The United Kingdom is sometimes incorrectly referred to as "England." However, England is merely the largest of four main subdivisions of the country, the others being Scotland, Wales, and Northern Ireland. These were originally independent territories. Wales was conquered by England in the Middle Ages, but preserves some cultural distinctiveness associated with the Welsh language, still spoken by about a third of its population. Northern Ireland, together with the rest of Ireland, was twice conquered by England. The earlier conquest in the later Middle Ages was followed by a lapse of English control during the Wars of the Roses in the second half of the fifteenth century. A second conquest was completed in the seventeenth century. Although a part of the United Kingdom, Northern Ireland has a certain amount of political autonomy. It has its own parliament, which meets at Belfast and legislates in matters of local concern. However, Northern Ireland is also represented in the Parliament of the United Kingdom at London. Scotland was first joined to England when a Scottish king inherited the English throne in 1603, and the

two became one country under the Act of Union passed in 1707. Scotland sends representatives to the Parliament at London, but has no separate parliament of its own. It does, however, have special administrative agencies in Edinburgh which deal with Scottish affairs. It also has its own system of courts and law, although the House

The two main islands and the major political divisions of the British Isles.

TABLE 3

BRITISH ISLES: AREA AND POPULATION DATA

POLITICAL UNIT	AREA (THOUSAND SQUARE MILES)		POPULATION (MILLIONS: 1951 CENSUS)		DENSITY (PER SQUARE MILE: TO NEAREST WHOLE NUMBER)	
United Kingdom	94.3		50.37		534	
England		50.3		41.14		818
Wales		8.0		2.60		324
Scotland		30.4		5.10		168
Northern Ireland		5.2		1.37		262
Isle of Man		0.2		0.06		250
Channel Islands		0.1		0.10		1370
Republic of Ireland	26.6		2.96		111	
British Isles	120.9		53.33		441	

of Lords, in Parliament, is the highest court of appeal for Scotland as well as the remainder of the United Kingdom. Areas and populations of the various political subdivisions of the British Isles are given in Table 3.

Size and World Importance of the United Kingdom

In terms of area and even of population the United Kingdom is a relatively small country, hardly comparable to such giants as the Soviet Union, the United States, China, or India. The total area of slightly less than 95,000 square miles is about the same as the combined areas of New York and Pennsylvania. Even the population of slightly more than 50 million is less than a third the population of the United States. In area and population the United Kingdom fits in a general class with the larger nations of continental Europe, but not with the larger nations of the world.

The international importance which this small country has attained is one of the more amazing aspects of the modern world. Probably no nation has exercised a greater influence on modern history. When British power and prestige were at their peak in the century between 1815 and 1914, the United Kingdom was generally considered the world's greatest power. During most of that period it was the world's foremost manufacturing nation. Its navy dominated the seas, and its merchant ships carried the major part of the world's ocean trade. Its manufacturers and merchants dominated international commerce, and its investors financed the development of much of the rest of the world. All this was not accomplished without monetary profit, and some classes of the British population became extremely prosperous.

Since World War I, however, the United Kingdom has experienced serious difficulties and it has definitely lost its former pre-eminence. This process of relative decline was well underway even before 1914. Nevertheless, Britain still has great influence in world affairs. No nation, not even the United States or the Soviet Union, takes any important international action without considering carefully its probable effect on the United Kingdom. The world's economic affairs are conditioned by the fact that Britain is second only to the United States as a trading nation, and its political affairs by the fact that, with Germany divided and its military establishment diminished, Britain is still the third greatest military and political power.

The Commonwealth of Nations

One of the main reasons for the current importance of the United Kingdom lies in the fact that it forms the center of a great and complex political association, the Commonwealth of Nations, which ranks with the United States and the Soviet Union as one of the "Big Three" in world power and influence. The Commonwealth of Nations is composed partly of sovereign nations and partly of dependent territories.

The sovereign nations of the Commonwealth fall into two principal groups. In one group are the older self-governing countries, lying principally in middle latitudes, and having populations which are dominantly British, or at least European, in descent and culture. Besides the United Kingdom itself, this group includes Canada, Australia, and New Zealand. It also includes the Union of South Africa, although South Africa's population is dominantly European only in a political and

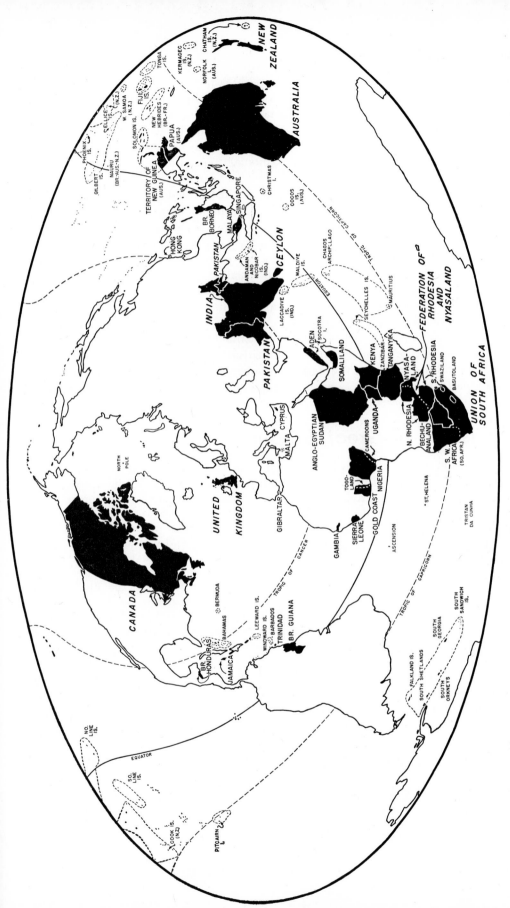

The Commonwealth of Nations. Areas in black are political units included in the Commonwealth as of January 1, 1955. (Anglo-Egyptian Sudan, a condominium under British and Egyptian rule, will decide in 1956 what its political association with the Commonwealth will be.) Small island dependencies are encircled by dashes. Names in largest type indicate sovereign states, except for the new Federation of Rhodesia and Nyasaland, which has an elected parliament and prime minister but is not completely self-governing. Dependencies not otherwise identified as to ownership are possessions of the United Kingdom. (Briesemeister Elliptical Equal Area Projection, copyright American Geographical Society of New York.)

social sense. White South Africans of European descent are outnumbered five to one by native Africans and members of other racial groups. A second group of self-governing countries in the Commonwealth is composed of three Asian nations, India, Pakistan, and Ceylon. These lie principally in tropical latitudes, are peopled by non-Europeans, and have only lately evolved from a colonial status. Although each nation is completely free to manage its own affairs, the sovereign countries of the Commonwealth are held together by bonds of sentiment and economic and political self-interest. These bonds are probably strongest in the case of the United Kingdom, New Zealand, Australia, and Canada, somewhat weaker in the case of South Africa, and weakest of all in the case of the Asian nations. By participation in the Common-

wealth each member nation, including the United Kingdom, magnifies its own importance and influence.

The dependent territories of the Commonwealth encompass a great variety of colonial possessions scattered over the globe. The majority are dependencies of the United Kingdom. They differ widely in size, population, and political status. The largest is Nigeria, in West Africa, a country larger in area than France and having a population of some 30 millions; the smallest territories are mere specks of land (though often highly strategic), such as Gibraltar, Malta, Hong Kong, and Singapore. Only the dependent territories of the United Kingdom can now be called the "British Empire" in a strict sense, and a number of these dependencies are evolving rapidly toward complete self-government.

The Island of Great Britain

The land from which this world-wide political association grew and which is still its heart, giving it life and unity, is Great Britain, an island about 600 miles in length and less than 300 miles across at its widest point. This island, despite its comparatively small size, has a remarkable variety of landscapes and modes of life.

▶ *Highland and Lowland Britain*

The diversity of Great Britain is connected with a fundamental division of the island into two contrasting parts: Highland and Lowland Britain. Each of the latter is briefly described in the following selection by a British geographer, L. Dudley Stamp: [1]

A line joining the mouth of the Tees on the east coast of England to the mouth of

the Exe or Tor Bay in Devonshire divides approximately Highland Britain from Lowland Britain. There are many fundamental distinctions between these two divisions. Not only do all the major highland masses lie to the north and west of the line whilst the chief lowlands are to the south and east, but the rocks which make up Highland Britain are mostly the older rocks which break down but slowly into somewhat poor, stony soils, whilst the rocks of Lowland Britain are younger, less resistant to weathering, and afford richer soils. As a result man has been able to utilise effectively only the better parts of Highland Britain—the valleys, the coastal plains, and the lowlands—and his farms or his villages are often separated from one another by wide stretches of uninhabited upland moors. [2] . . .

In Lowland Britain, on the other hand,

[1] L. Dudley Stamp, *The Face of Britain.* Published for The British Council by Longmans, Green and Co. Copyright 1940, 1944 by The British Council. Pp. 8–9. Used by permission. Two editorial foot-

notes have been added.

[2] *Editorial Note.* In its most common usage the term *moor* means a deforested upland, usually covered with grass or heather.

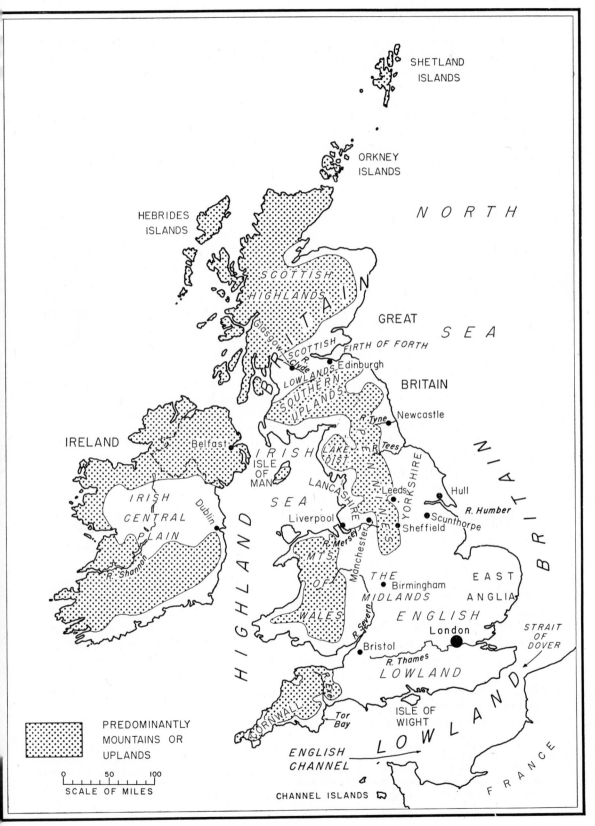

SHETLAND
ISLANDS

ORKNEY
ISLANDS

HEBRIDES
ISLANDS

N O R T H

S E A

SCOTTISH
HIGHLANDS

GREAT

Glasgow
SCOTTISH
LOWLANDS
R. Clyde
FIRTH OF FORTH
Edinburgh

BRITAIN

SOUTHERN
UPLANDS

Newcastle
R. Tyne

IRELAND

Belfast

IRISH
ISLE
OF
MAN

SEA

LAKE
DIST.

R. Tees

B   R   I   T   A   I   N

IRISH
CENTRAL
PLAIN

Dublin

LANCASHIRE

Leeds

Hull

YORKSHIRE

R. Humber

R. Shannon

Liverpool

R. Mersey
Manchester

Sheffield
Scunthorpe

PENNINES

HIGHLAND

MTS.
OF

WALES

R. Severn

THE
MIDLANDS

Birmingham

EAST
ANGLIA

ENGLISH

London

STRAIT
OF
DOVER

Bristol

R. Thames

LOWLAND

CORNWALL

Tor
Bay

ISLE OF
WIGHT

L   O   W   L   A   N   D

R. Exe

ENGLISH
CHANNEL

FRANCE

CHANNEL ISLANDS

PREDOMINANTLY
MOUNTAINS OR
UPLANDS

0   50   100
SCALE OF MILES

Highland and Lowland Britain. (*Based in part on a map by L. Dudley Stamp.*)

the land is more kindly, gently rolling and undulating rather than flat, though rarely reaching a thousand feet above sea level. Ploughed lands and grass fields, farms and villages, form an intricate but continuous pattern. Land unsuitable for farming and settlement is limited in extent, and occurs as isolated islands. Human settlement is essentially continuous, and individuals form members of communities which are but rarely isolated.

It is not surprising that Lowland Britain, essentially Anglo-Saxon, has had an entirely different history from the Celtic fringe [3] or Highland Britain. To this day the Highland peoples—the Scots, the Welsh, the Cornish, and indeed the Irish—are distinct in traditions, dialect, and outlook from the Lowland English. . . .

Highland Britain includes the whole of Scotland, which itself comprises three contrasted parts. The northern half of Scotland is formed by the Highlands, to the south of which are the Central Lowlands, in turn cut off from England by the Southern Uplands. Although the Highlands and Southern Uplands cover three-quarters of the country, they have less than a quarter of the people: the Central Lowlands, which most closely approach Lowland Britain in

many characters, have only a fifth of the area but four-fifths of the people. The Southern Uplands are continued by highlands across the border into northern England, where the broad upland of the Pennines forms the so-called backbone of England . . . and where also is England's mountain playground, the Lake District. The Lake District forms actually the northernmost of three westward-projecting peninsulas. The central and largest one is Wales; the southern one is occupied by the counties of Devon and Cornwall.

Lowland Britain comprises the hill and valley land of the southeast; the rich farming land of the east, and the rolling grassy plain of the Midlands. The latter has a northwesterly prolongation into the plain of Lancastria, and a northeasterly one into the plains of Yorkshire.

Almost everywhere in Britain the major coal fields occur in the borderlands between Highland and Lowland Britain—where mountain or hill-mass gives place to the plain. In some areas, notably in South Wales, coal has been the magnet which has drawn a dense population, largely of Lowland origin, into the otherwise unattractive valleys of the great moorlands.

Insularity as a Factor in the Early Rise of Britain

The rise of Great Britain to world importance began after Europe established contact by sea with the Americas and the Orient. Following the voyages of Columbus and Vasco da Gama at the end of the fifteenth century, the nations along the western seaboard of Europe launched an intense competition for trade and colonies in overseas areas. By the eighteenth century Britain had distanced her continental rivals in this struggle. In so doing the island was able to exploit certain geographic advantages as against its continental competitors.

Perhaps the greatest of these advantages was the fact that Britain had no land frontiers to defend. A strong navy was sufficient to protect the island and thus to allow Britain to choose the time and place in which to engage in land fighting. In contrast, the continental powers had to maintain constant watchfulness over exposed land frontiers and to be constantly on the alert against possible military moves by

---

[3] *Editorial Note.* Peoples speaking Celtic languages inhabited the British Isles when the islands emerged into the light of history with the Roman invasions. When Roman power waned in the fifth century, A.D., peoples speaking Germanic tongues, the Angles and Saxons, invaded Great Britain and drove the Celtic inhabitants into the more remote and defensible Highland Britain, where their descendants still live. Hence we have the term "Celtic fringe."

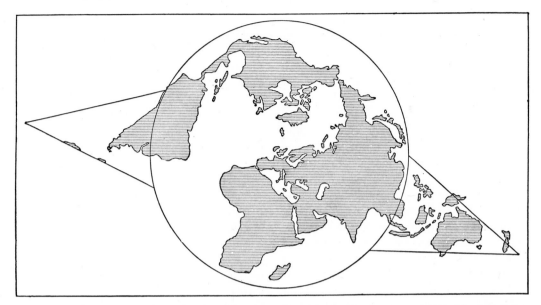

Map of the world centered on London. Note how the major land masses are grouped around the margins of the Atlantic and Arctic Oceans. The northwestern coast of Europe lies in the center of the "land hemisphere." (*Reprinted from J. Russell Smith and M. Ogden Phillips*, Industrial and Commercial Geography, *3d ed. New York: Holt, 1946.*)

their neighbors. Of necessity their attention was strongly divided between Europe itself and the colonial areas, whereas Britain's island security made possible a greater concentration of effort in the colonial field. Whenever one of the continental powers became a threat to Britain, the latter sought allies among the other continental nations. Thus in a series of wars extending over most of two centuries Spanish ambitions were thwarted by a coalition of Britain, France, and the Netherlands; the Netherlands was checkmated by Britain and France; and France was checkmated by Britain and a series of continental allies in shifting combinations. The rebellious American colonies secured their independence at a time when Britain lacked a continental ally against France, Spain, and the Netherlands.

The Age of Discovery changed immensely the significance of Britain's location. Previously Great Britain had been an island outpost on the edge of the known world. During the Middle Ages the island was mainly a pastoral area supplying raw and semifinished wool to continental industries. Its peripheral location and type of economy has caused Britain to be described as the Australia of the time. Following the great discoveries in the fifteenth and sixteenth centuries, however, Great Britain found itself at the front door of Europe opening toward the new lands overseas. Britain's position between the coast of northwestern Europe and the open Atlantic meant that continental shipping would have to pass by at close range, especially since most ships preferred the narrow English Channel to the stormy ocean outlet of the North Sea between Scotland and Norway. Thus Britain lay across or near the lines of communication connecting the continent with overseas areas, while the continental countries had no similar advantage with respect to Britain. This advantage of position could be exploited either peaceably to expand trade, or militarily to intercept and harry the overseas shipping of continental rivals.

Britain and the Industrial Revolution

The commercial supremacy which Great Britain enjoyed by the eighteenth century laid the groundwork for its leadership in what has commonly been called the Industrial Revolution. Expanded markets and commercial opportunities stimulated men to work out means whereby goods could be produced in larger quantities and at a faster rate. The result was a series of inventions which transformed manufacturing, trade, and the general conditions of life.

These inventions allowed men to produce goods cheaply and on a relatively large scale. New machines multiplied the amount of work one man could do. They were run by water power and then by coal in place of the relatively puny muscles of men and animals, and consequently, the amount of energy available was multiplied. The industries which led the way in the Industrial Revolution were coal mining, which furnished the power; ironmaking, which supplied the material for the machines; and textile production, which was the most important manufacturing business of the time. Eventually iron and coal led to revolutionary developments in transportation with the appearance of the iron steamship and the railroad. Still later, iron gave way largely to steel. Most of the early inventions in these fields were first made and applied in Great Britain. Thus invention and large-scale industry in Britain were fostered by the needs and opportunities of an expanding commerce, the comparative security and freedom of the British people, and the availability of certain key resources, notably coal and iron.

As Great Britain industrialized, consequences of great magnitude, both at home and abroad, soon followed. In the island itself population grew rapidly and settle-

ments began to concentrate on the coal fields in or along the margins of Highland Britain. There mining and factory towns and adjoining seaports experienced a mushroom growth, while the agricultural southeast became relatively less important. In the world at large Britain's preeminence throughout most of the nineteenth century was assured by the advantages derived from its early leadership in modern industry. Britain became the world's principal supplier of manufactured goods and the principal market for raw materials and food. Later, however, the advantages of an early start accounted for significantly less. Other countries, often possessing superior resources, adopted the new techniques developed in Britain and began to offer increasing competition in world markets. Meanwhile, Britain was finding that some of its early industrial equipment had become obsolete and some of its best mineral deposits depleted. In addition, the British economy had become so overbalanced in the direction of industry that buying and selling abroad was a matter of life and death. This was not necessarily a disadvantage in itself, but became so in the twentieth century, when excessive nationalism began to result in world wars, high peacetime tariffs, and other hindrances to the free flow of trade.

▶ Rise of the Traditional British Industries

The preceding discussion of industrial development in Britain is considerably amplified and illustrated in the following selections by Smith and Phillips describing the rise and significance of the British coal, iron and steel, shipbuilding, and cotton and woolen textile industries: [4]

---

[4] J. Russell Smith and M. Ogden Phillips, *Industrial and Commercial Geography*, 3d ed. New York: Holt, 1946. Pp. 70–73, 143–144, 165, 284–286, 700–702, 709–710. Authors' footnotes are omitted. Two editorial comments and six editorial footnotes have been added. A few of the authors' headings have been omitted or altered. Used by permission of the authors and the publisher.

Cities and industries of the United Kingdom, 1951. Key: 1, iron; 2, steel; 3, cotton; 4, wool; 5, linen; 6, silk; 7, chemicals; 8, commercial ports; 9, fishing ports; 10, shipyards; 11, tin; 12, lead; 13, principal railroads. The size of population is indicated by the type of lettering for the names of cities: block capitals mean over 1,000,000 inhabitants; slanted capitals, 500,000 to 1,000,000; block letters, 100,000 to 500,000. The widespread mechanical and food-processing industries are not shown. (*Map and caption from Gottmann,* A Geography of Europe, *rev. ed. New York: Holt, 1954.*)

• *British Coal Production and Trade*

While it is generally believed that coal was dug up and burned as fuel by the ancient Britons before the Roman conquest, it is definitely known that during the thirteenth century coal was commonly used in manufacturing in Great Britain by brewers and smiths and that substantial shipments were carried by sailing vessels from Newcastle to London, where part was consumed in the city and part was reshipped to the continent. In those early days coal mines were generally shallow holes in the ground which rapidly filled with water and were usually abandoned after a short period of use. The first great impetus to Brit-

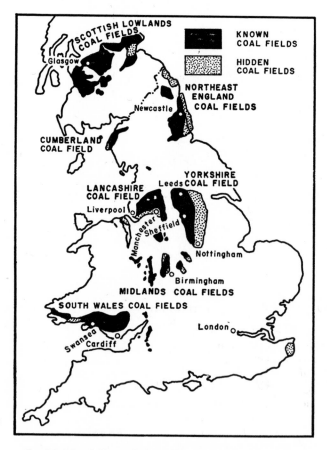

Coal fields of Great Britain. The "known" coal fields outcrop at the surface. The "hidden" fields lie concealed under later formations than those containing the coal measures. (*After U. S. Bureau of Mines.*)

ish coal mining came in 1709 with the discovery of a practical method of using coal in the smelting and manufacture of iron, a development that liberated forges and foundries from dependence upon the waning supply of wood and charcoal. Thus, Great Britain was already a user of coal before the steam engine was invented. The perfection of the steam engine proved to be a second and tremendous stimulus to the coal industry, for it was then possible to pump water out of the mines and to increase their depth, thereby increasing the supply of coal; furthermore the steam engine together with other inventions in time led to a great increase in the demand for coal.

Great Britain was particularly fortunate in having coal fields near the sea and near to iron, which is necessary for the harnessing of power derived from coal. England had, in addition to power, an adequate labor supply, a stable government, and peace. With these advantages the modern factory system quickly originated. It came after a number of mechanical inventions in the latter part of the eighteenth century made it possible to assemble many workers in one building where their machines could be run by a common engine. Previously, the English manufacturing had been done by hand machines in the cottages of people who lived in populous country districts and tilled some land. But coal and steam made easy the establishment of the factory system, and condensed these people into cities often to their physical injury, changed Britain from an agricultural to a manufacturing country, and transferred the center of population and power from the agricultural southeastern plains to the rougher, more mountainous north-northwest and west with their coal and iron. . . .

Leading British Coal Fields. The location of British coal fields favored this early development. The coal is good, although it is almost all bituminous, and the fields are well distributed, some on the east coast at Newcastle, some on the west coast in Cumberland, some in Scotland near Glasgow, some in Wales near Cardiff, and some inland near Sheffield and Birmingham and Manchester, making possible a varied development of industry. Each coal field has developed an industrial district. . . .

[EDITORIAL COMMENT. Bituminous coal is one of the major ranks into which coal is customarily divided. Coal is the residue from organic matter which has been compressed for a long period under overlying layers of the earth. Different original materials and different degrees and lengths of compression have given a variety of coals rather than a single uniform substance. The common ranks of coal as classified on the basis of hardness and heating value (caloric content) are anthracite, bituminous, lignite, and brown coal. Peat, which is coal in the earliest stages of formation, may be added at the lower end of the scale, since it can be burned if dried. Anthracite and bituminous coals are customarily divided into subranks. Lignite and brown coal are mostly used in areas where adequate deposits of bituminous and anthracite coal are lacking, being principally employed as household fuel and for raising steam—which may be used in generating electricity. The main difference between them is that brown coal is powdery, while lignite is solidified. Bituminous coals are used in larger quantities than any other rank. Gas is manufactured from them, and they are used for raising steam. Some bituminous coals can be used for making coke, which is coal with the volatile elements baked out, leaving pure carbon. Coke is essential in manufacturing iron on a large scale in blast furnaces. Access to a good supply of "coking coal" is a major necessity for a modern industrial nation. Anthracite coal burns with a hot flame and almost no smoke. It is excellent for domestic heating and can be used to produce gas and raise steam. It is not ordinarily used for coking. Often coals are referred to according to the uses for which their special properties fit them, as flame coals, gas coals, or coking coals. Not only the amount of coal, but the *kind of coal* available is very important to a country's industries. In recent times coal has become very important as a raw material in the modern chemical industry.]

The British Coal Export Trade. While coal has been exported from Great Britain for 700 years or more, it was the development of the ocean steamship during the nineteenth century that gave rise to the great British coal trade of modern times. Steamships arriving in northwestern Europe gladly filled their bunkers with the high grade steam coals of Cardiff and Newcastle. Many of these ships were tramp steamers bringing to Britain and nearby lands full cargoes of grain, timber, ores, and many other foodstuffs and raw materials. Since few bulky outbound cargoes were available, they gladly took on full cargoes of British coal destined for ports and coaling stations scattered throughout the world. These outbound coal cargoes meant profits for the owners of coal mines, the exporters of coal, and vessel owners; they also meant that lower freight rates were charged on raw materials and foodstuffs inbound to Great Britain and northwestern Europe, an advantage accruing to manufacturers and consumers in general. So extensive was the British coal trade in the late decades of the nineteenth century that there was scarcely a port in the world that was not served with British coal, excepting only the ports of eastern United States and some nearby Caribbean ports where American coal was sold. . . . Among the advantages that contributed to the predominance of Great Britain in the world's coal trade were the long experience of the British people in coal mining and exporting; the variety and high quality of British coals; the short rail haul from mine mouth to seaboard, averaging less than 25 miles; proximity to industrial northwestern Europe and the coal-barren Mediterranean area, the two greatest markets; ownership of the world's largest navy and merchant marine, the greatest consumers of bunker coal; political control of 40 percent of the world's coaling stations so strategically located that they supplied 80 percent of the bunker coal used by all the steamships in the world; and financial control of many railroads and other coal consuming industries in the vast British Empire and in foreign lands.

Since World War I the British coal export trade has suffered a drastic decline, decreasing from an all-time peak of 79.5 million tons in 1923 to 61 millions in 1929 and to 36.9 millions in 1939.[5] The causes of this decline are of a serious and permanent nature. As other countries began to produce and export coal, British coal decreased in one market after another. For example, scarcely a cargo of British coal is now shipped east of Suez because of keen competition from South African, Indian, Australian, and Japanese coal, and between World War I and World War II much less was sold in the big European markets because of growing competition from German, Polish, and Russian coal. As one country after another turned to the use of petroleum and water power wherever available, their imports of British coal declined or ceased entirely, as happened along the west coast of North and South America.[6] . . .

By exporting coal under any circumstances Britain has been selling the foundation stones of the house in which she lives. . . .

• *Rise of the Iron and Steel Industry*

The fuel of the early blast furnace, like that of the forge it succeeded, was charcoal, and the iron industry in England came into disrepute in Queen Elizabeth's time and was subjected to restrictive legislation, because it devoured so much wood that, to keep itself going, it followed the vanishing forests of England from place to place. In the eighteenth century English iron output declined, and it seemed that the English iron industry was doomed because of the limitation of the fuel. There was large iron import from the pine forest districts of Germany, imports from the new American colonies across the Atlantic had begun, and the basis for a great trade was visible between the forested colonies with abundant charcoal material and the bare mother country. But this trade was shattered by a number of improvements in the technology of iron manufacture. One was the substitution of coke for charcoal. As early as 1709 Abraham Darby established the commercial use of coke in smelting, but it was not until sixty years later that coke came into general use, in spite of Britain's need for a better and more abundant fuel. As long as charcoal was used, the size of the blast furnace was limited, because it was impossible to pile up a charge of iron ore and charcoal very high, as the weight of the iron would crush the soft charcoal and smother the fire. By removing this limitation, the use of coke helped to make possible the manufacture of iron on a larger scale. However, the only way that the pig iron of the blast furnace could be formed into useful articles was by pouring the liquid iron into molds of the desired shape, and the finished products were brittle. In 1784 Henry Cort perfected the puddling furnace, heated by coal, which removed most of the carbon from the pig iron, thereby making it malleable. The product, puddled wrought iron, was processed in a rolling mill and shaped for many uses. Thus, pig iron acquired greater utility, and between 1784 and 1830 the puddling furnace was so improved that its output was increased from 10 to 200 tons per week. The old-fashioned bellows of blast furnaces were replaced by improved blowing apparatus, which was first operated by steam in 1790. These and other improvements liberated iron manufacture from the tyranny of charcoal and water power, thereby facilitating a great increase in output. Hence the British iron manufacturing

[5] *Editorial Note.* Coal exports were only 1.2 million tons in 1947 and 11.7 million in 1952.

[6] *Editorial Note.* Most of the world's ships and an increasing number of railway locomotives now burn petroleum rather than coal. Increased efficiency of coal-burning engines has also tended to reduce the demand for coal. In Britain itself the coal industry has encountered serious difficulties due to higher costs caused by increasing depths of mining, outmoded equipment, the prevalence of thin and broken seams difficult to work with machinery, and the lack of a really adequate supply of labor willing to work under the rather unattractive conditions of the mines. In recent years, securing an adequate supply of coal for domestic needs rather than export has been the key problem.

industry received a new lease on life and prospered greatly during the growth of the factory system in the early nineteenth century when no other country had industrial access to such resources of fuel, ore, and labor.

In the middle of the nineteenth century, the railroad, the steamship, the modern factory with its great use of machinery, caused a rapid increase in the demand for iron, and Britain with her good resources of coal and iron ore lying side by side became the world's leading manufacturer of iron. Iron manufacturing, in common with other great industries, was concentrated in and near the coal fields of England, Scotland, and Wales. Their location along or near the sea greatly facilitated the export of iron manufactures, and later, when the ore supplies ran low in Great Britain, it was easy for the British iron industry to turn to a supply of imported ore from the mountains near the north coasts of Spain and from northern Sweden. Sheffield and Birmingham, in particular, became world famous producers of iron and steel. . . . Following the discoveries of Bessemer, Siemens, Martin, Gilchrist, Thomas, and others, it was Great Britain that led the world out of the age of wrought iron and high-cost steel into the modern era of large-scale steel production. The British output of steel ingots and castings increased rapidly from 220,000 tons in 1870 to 4.9 million tons in 1900, and to 13.5 million tons in 1939. . . . Yet in spite of the great increase in production, British dominance was soon shattered by the development of iron and steel manufacturing in other countries.[7] . . .

[EDITORIAL COMMENT. The Bessemer converter, introducing a blast of oxygen through molten iron to burn out impurities, was patented in 1855 and first allowed cheap, large-scale production of steel. Siemens' open-hearth furnace, patented in 1856, uses a gas or oil flame to burn out impurities in the molten iron, and is now the chief instrument in steel making. Thomas and Gilchrist introduced a process in 1878 to make use of iron ores with a high phosphorus content (such as the Lorraine ores of France) through employment of limestone to neutralize the phosphorus. Somewhat later the Martin brothers, of Anteuil, France, found that scrap iron, scrap steel, and iron ore could be added to the charge in the steel furnace.]

• *British Leadership in Shipbuilding*

Great Britain has long led the world in shipbuilding, and as late as 1893 her shipyards launched four-fifths of the world's merchant vessel tonnage. With the development of shipbuilding in other countries, the British share of the world's output declined to about three-fifths in 1914 and to less than one-half in 1938. Britain's leadership since the latter part of the nineteenth century is due partly to unusually cheap iron and steel produced close to the sea, partly to cheaper skilled labor, partly to the availability of capital and the limitations of home opportunities, partly to the habit of seamanship and to long experience in shipbuilding, but also largely because she is a world trading nation and needs shipping to import her raw materials and export her manufactured products. . . . During and shortly after World War I, and again during World War II, Britain temporarily lost her shipbuilding supremacy to the United States, when American yards broke all ship-

---

[7] *Editorial Note.* In 1952 the United Kingdom produced 18.4 million tons of steel. This was much smaller than the production of the United States (93.2 million tons) or the Soviet Union (an estimated 38.6 million tons), and a little smaller than that of a reviving Germany, which produced 19.6 million tons. France and the Saar together produced 15.1 million tons. At present the countries named produce about four fifths of the world's steel. The iron and steel industry of Great Britain is now mainly concentrated in the following areas: (1) Northeast England, around Middlesbrough, (2) South Wales, around Swansea and Cardiff, (3) the industrial regions of South Yorkshire, the Midlands, and Lancashire, surrounding the southern end of the Pennine Range, (4) the vicinity of the great iron-mining center of Scunthorpe, between Sheffield and Hull, and (5) the Scottish Lowlands, around Glasgow. Scattered deposits of low-grade iron ore in eastern England are supplemented by imports of higher grade ores, principally from North Africa, Sweden, France, Spain, Sierra Leone, and Newfoundland. About one third to one half of all ore requirements are imported.

building records with mass production of standardized ships.[8] . . .

While shipbuilding is carried on in many areas, the northeast coast . . . centering about Newcastle-on-Tyne and Sunderland, and the Clyde estuary below Glasgow, Scotland, generally produce about four-fifths of all British merchant tonnage. . . .

• British Cotton Manufacture

For more than a century the name of Manchester has been synonymous throughout the commercial world with cotton cloth. That city, the metropolis of Lancashire, long was the center of the greatest cotton-manufacturing district in the world. The industry, established there as early as 1640, was partly due to the Atlantic winds which gave the moisture necessary to the best cotton manufacturing. Later these same Atlantic winds influenced the industry through the water power of numerous small streams that descended from the central highlands (known as the Pennine Chain) and led to quick development after the invention of the new machines. Both of these advantages have now passed away. The moisture, like the temperature of the factory air, can be controlled, and the factories of Lancashire have long since outgrown the water power and turned to steam, for which the local coal fields are very convenient. The third factor in Lancashire's start was the convenient harbor of Liverpool, which has long had wide ship connections with regions producing and consuming raw cotton. The city of Manchester itself has now ceased to be so strictly a manufacturing city, and has become the sale and storage center for the product of many surrounding towns. Liverpool, the natural port of entry for this region, is one of the greatest cotton ports in the world because back of it lies the great cotton-manufacturing district.[9] . . .

Great Britain has led all countries in the manufacture of cotton goods because she had the great advantage of an early start, no wars on her home soil, the ready use of capital while others had to borrow, the most wide-reaching shipping connections, and the local advantages of unrivaled coal, iron, and harbors. Because of her tariff policy, she had cheaper food than any continental country,[10] and she had cheaper cash wages than America. As a result of all these advantages, the equipment and also the operation of a cotton mill was much cheaper in Lancashire than in Massachusetts. Hence the United States like many other countries, places a tariff against the import of foreign cotton goods.

However, the British cotton-manufacturing industry which reached its peak before World War I has declined, due to competition from newer areas, and the fact that former outstanding advantages no longer are important. . . . Artificial humidifiers can moisten the driest of air. Inventions and mechanical improvements lessen the significance of skilled labor. Power may be transmitted from distant areas to make fuel deposits unessential. Only by abandoning general cotton manufacturing and specializing in high-grade textiles has Britain been able to maintain an important position in the world picture. . . .

• British Woolen Manufacture

[During the Middle Ages wool was the staple export of England. Most of it went to the industrial area of Flanders, across the Strait of Dover, which was the great leader in wool manufacturing at that time.]

---

[8] *Editorial Note.* Approximately 40 percent of the gross tonnage of all merchant ships under construction as of July 1953 was accounted for by shipyards in the United Kingdom, as against only 6.7 percent in the United States. Most of the remaining ships were being built by Germany, Sweden, the Netherlands, France, Norway, and Japan, aside from an unknown number in the Soviet Union. The latter nation was excluded in determining the percentages given for the United Kingdom and the United States.

[9] *Editorial Note.* Liverpool rose to the position of Great Britain's second most important port, after London, as trade with America grew. Tobacco, slaves, and British textiles and trinkets were important in its commerce before the cotton trade grew large. Manchester is also a seaport, being connected with the Mersey estuary by the Manchester Ship Canal.

[10] *Editorial Note.* Great Britain allowed free import of foodstuffs after 1846. This policy nearly ruined British agriculture, due to competition from new lands overseas, but it reduced the cost of living in the industrial areas.

The English kings introduced Flemish weavers into England during the eleventh, fourteenth, and fifteenth centuries, but for a long time unfinished English woolen cloth went to Flanders to be finished and dyed. This practice seems to have ended about 1650, and England has now surpassed her old teacher, Flanders, in quality of output. English woolen cloths have been much famed during the period since power-driven spinning and weaving machinery has been adapted to woolen manufacture, an occurrence that soon followed their application to cotton manufacture. England, long a wool exporter, now uses over four times as much as she grows, and leads other countries in the excellence of her wool cloth. The towns of Bradford, Leeds, and Huddersfield in Yorkshire . . . are known wherever fine woolen cloths are bought and sold. . . .

Britain has been unable to secure such leadership in the world's supply of woolens as has been the case with cottons, nor has the industry been so important. It employs less than half the number of workers employed in the cotton industry. There is considerable equality in the amount of woolen goods produced in Britain, the United States, Germany, Italy, and France, while the rest of the world produces lesser but increasing amounts. . . . The explanation of this greater equality . . . is to be found in the fact that wool manufacturing was a world-wide domestic industry. The Industrial Revolution found wool an established industry and merely transformed it. . . . Cotton manufacturing was . . . almost a new business, resulting from practically the rediscovery of cotton when Whitney's cotton gin made its production cheap. This came after the textile machines were established in England. That country, being in much the best position to manufacture textiles in factories, seized the new raw material and built up a world's trade in cotton, while wool, an industry as old as history, was still being made upon hand looms in millions of farmhouses and in every textile village of Europe and America.

A Land of Cities

The industries described above, together with a multitude of engineering and fabricating activities subsidiary to them, have dominated British economic life for a century and a half. The rise of the cities associated with these industries has made Britain a nation of city dwellers. In 1951 no less than 52 percent of the people of the United Kingdom lived in cities of over 50,000 inhabitants, and 43 percent in cities of over 100,000. Comparable figures for the United States in 1950 were 35 percent in cities of over 50,000 and 29 percent in cities of over 100,000. With only about 10 percent of its population falling outside the classification of town dwellers and only about 5 percent of its workers engaged in agriculture, the United Kingdom is probably the world's most highly urbanized and industrialized country.

During the nineteenth century the coalfield industrial districts of South Wales, the Midlands, Lancashire, Yorkshire, Northeast England, and the Scottish Lowlands were spectacular centers of urbanization. Whole clusters of industrial cities in these areas, as well as the ports to serve them, rose from village status. During the twentieth century, however, a trend of population and industry back toward Lowland Britain in the southeast has set in. Since the use of electricity permits power generated from coal to be transmitted over considerable distances, factories no longer have to be located so near the coal fields, and many of the newer industrial developments in Great Britain, such as the manufacture of automobiles and airplanes, have located in the less congested or more attractive southeast.

Nevertheless, most of the larger urban centers are still found in the older indus-

Royal pageantry in the heart of London. The coronation procession of Queen Elizabeth II passing Trafalgar Square. The Admiralty Arch, symbol of British sea power, is at the left center. (*United Press.*)

trial districts. Birmingham, the industrial capital of the Midlands, had a population of 1,112,000 according to the 1951 census, and formed the center of a conurbation [11] numbering 2,237,000. In Lancashire the great cotton-milling center of Manchester and the major seaport of Liverpool on the Mersey River had populations of 703,000 and 790,000, respectively, and formed conurbations of 2,421,000 and 1,382,000. Glasgow, the great shipbuilding center on the Clyde River, at the western end of the Scottish Lowlands, had 1,090,000 people,

and its conurbation included 1,758,000. In Yorkshire the metalworking center of Sheffield numbered 513,000, while the woolen-manufacturing city of Leeds had 505,000 and its conurbation, including Bradford (292,000) and smaller cities, aggregated 1,692,000 people. Newcastle, the principal city of the Northeast England industrial district, had only 292,000 in the city proper, but the entire conurbation along the River Tyne reached a total of 835,000. The remaining cities of 200,000 or over included the Scottish capital of Edinburgh

[11] A *conurbation* is a group of cities grown together into a single larger urban area.

(467,000) on the Firth of Forth; Belfast (444,000), the capital, main port, and main industrial center of Northern Ireland; the seaports of Bristol (442,000) on the River Severn, Hull (299,000) on the Humber, Cardiff (244,000) in South Wales, and the English Channel ports of Portsmouth (233,000) and Plymouth (209,000); and finally, the Midlands industrial cities of Nottingham (306,000), Leicester (285,000), Stoke-on-Trent (275,000), and Coventry (258,000). Two additional cities of more than 200,000, Croydon (250,000) and Harrow 219,000), form part of the great conurbation of London, the largest urban center of the British Isles and second largest in the world.

▶ London

In 1951 the population of London proper was 3,348,000, but the entire conurbation numbered 8,346,000. Although it is the only major city in Great Britain which is not located on or near a coal field, the ancient English capital has more than held its own during Britain's industrial age. It is the greatest seaport of Britain, and its multitude of diversified industries make it the most important single industrial center. It is briefly described in the following passage by a French geographer, Jean Gottmann: [12]

In the rural southeast of Great Britain, away from coal and iron mines, has been erected the largest conurbation of Britain and Europe—London—only recently outstripped by New York as the greatest city in the world. At the head of the Thames tidal estuary, London was also on the old Roman road crossing the river at the Westminster Ford. Tacitus [13] spoke of the town as being active in commerce, but the maritime vocation arose when the merchants of the Hanseatic League [14] established there a port trading with the continent; in the sixteenth century local merchants began going abroad. Until then London's fortune had been based on the export of wool of the English sheep—the Speaker of the House of Commons still sits on the woolsack, thus symbolizing the foundation of English wealth and power. But with the maritime discoveries and expansion, London began trading with remote lands and importing all kinds of tropical products that were resold in Britain or re-exported to the continent. In the eighteenth century London achieved the part of the greatest emporium of colonial goods in the world, becoming the hub of world trade. Most of the European transactions in coffee, tea, rice, cotton, wool, silk, indigo, furs, sugar, hardwood, and gold passed through London. In the nineteenth century the Industrial Revolution boosted the volume of international trade to such an extent that no one port could handle it; the rise of nationalism in Europe led also to direct transportation from producing to consuming areas.

Still London continued to grow. Its population reached 670,000 in 1682, passed the million mark soon after 1800, rose to 2,800,000 in 1861, and Greater London counted 8.3 million people in 1951. Its port rivaled New York for the heaviest traffic in the world,[15] its docks stretching along the banks of the Thames for over 25 miles. Merchandise from all over the world was gathered here, but less often for redistribution to consuming markets than to feed the

---

[12] Jean Gottmann, *A Geography of Europe,* rev. ed. New York: Holt, 1954. Pp. 214–215. An editorial comment and four editorial footnotes have been added. Used by permission of the author and the publisher.

[13] *Editorial Note.* A Roman historian of the first century, A.D.

[14] *Editorial Note.* In the Middle Ages the Hanse towns, or Hanseatic League, composed a loose federation of trading communities around the shores of the North and Baltic Seas. Although German in origin, the Hanseatic League also came to include towns in Scandinavia, Flanders, and England. Most of the Hanse towns were seaports, among the more important being Lübeck, Hamburg, Bremen, Bruges, London, Danzig, Stockholm, and Bergen. Some, however, were inland (notably Cologne, Magdeburg, Breslau, Cracow). The Hanse merchants played a leading role in the revival of European commerce which took place after the Dark Ages.

[15] *Editorial Note.* In tonnage of *vessels,* not of goods. London's tidal range has required that closed basins be built in which the larger ships dock.

population and factories of London itself and a part of England. Something of the *entrepôt* trade and redistribution function survives here, especially for wool, tea, and rubber. In the midst of World War II, a manufacturer in New York could get a shipload of Australian wool more easily from London than from Melbourne.

[EDITORIAL COMMENT. *Entrepôt* trade is import of commodities for the purpose of resale in other countries; in other words, re-export or intermediary trade. It often involves some processing, or at least repackaging of the commodities handled.]

Such a tremendous accumulation of stockpiled materials meant a permanent long-range investment of huge sums of money. From its commerce and trade Lon-

don had a capitalization which its brokers and banks used with great art, making of the City [16] the clearinghouse of the world's financial accounts. The Bank of England for money and Lloyd's for insurance were until the beginning of the twentieth century the apex of the pyramid of international financing. Anything could be bought, sold, insured, or rented through London, and the offices in the City took a commission on every one of the innumerable businesses they helped to transact directly or indirectly; goods and ships did not need to clear through the docks or warehouses of London or even Britain to bring some income to the Londoners. In the human and economic structure of Britain, London is indeed a region by itself, a special and essential one.

---

[16] *Editorial Note.* The "City" is the original nucleus around which London has grown. It is today pre-eminently a financial district, ranking with the Wall Street district of New York City as one of the two major centers of world finance. In the heart of The City stands the Bank of England.

4

Economic Problems of Contemporary Britain

The discussion of the major British industries and industrial districts in the previous chapter ended generally on a pessimistic note. Coal production in Britain is now less adequate and more expensive than formerly, and coal exports are only a fraction of what they were a generation ago. Steel production has come to depend more heavily on imported raw materials, has ceased to expand rapidly, and has been far surpassed by production in other nations. British shipyards are turning out a smaller proportion of the world's ships than before.

The virtual monopoly in cotton textiles which Britain formerly enjoyed has long since been broken, and other nations are offering telling competition to Lancashire. These industrial difficulties are important manifestations of a collection of problems which brought Britain to a state of almost continuous economic crisis following World War II. Indeed, it is apparent that the crisis existed even before the war, if the mass unemployment which afflicted Britain along with other countries in the 1930's is taken into account.

A picture symbolic of Britain's world-wide trading interests. The 281st annual meeting of officials and stockholders of the Hudson's Bay Company, held in the City of London. (*British Information Services*.)

Factors in the Altered Situation of Britain

The problems of modern Britain stem from the change in the world conditions in which the country rose to wealth and power. Britain rose to greatness by building an economy which rested on trade and industry. Its income was largely derived from the sale to the rest of the world of goods, such as coal and manufactures; of services, such as cargo carrying, banking, and insurance; and of capital, in the form of British loans and investments throughout the world. In return Britain required of the rest of the world mainly food, to maintain a population swollen beyond the capacity of the island's agriculture to support, and a tremendous variety of raw materials, not present at home, to be processed by British industry. This economy thrived in a world where few nations produced large amounts of cheap manufactured goods, and many nations had surpluses of food and raw materials available for export. Political and military circumstances of the time made possible the necessary security for the system to operate. A massive navy and a small army were sufficient to look after British interests over the world and to protect the home islands from any threat of invasion. None of the other nations in Europe was sufficiently advanced to pose a military or economic threat to Britain by itself, and these nations were so balanced in power that none could gain the continental dominance necessary to pose a threat.

Britain's situation was undermined by the industrialization of other countries, the rise of nationalism in its various forms over the world, the collapse of the European balance of power, the rise of new methods of warfare, and the two World Wars which followed on these events. The industrialization of other countries provided competition in the markets where Britain sold its exports and in the markets where it bought its imports. Often countries shut out British goods from their national and colonial territories in order to protect their own industries from competition. The collapse of the European balance of power took place with the development of a unified and powerful Germany after 1871. Eventually Britain had to fight in two World Wars against the threat of continental domination by Germany, just as it had fought in previous centuries against a similar threat by France. Defeat of Germany in 1945 did not restore a balance on the continent, but merely allowed the Soviet Union to emerge, temporarily at least, as the potential ruler of all Europe. The appearance on the military scene of the airplane, the guided missile, and, more recently, the atomic bomb, has come close to nullifying the protective value of the English Channel, although it was still sufficient to frustrate German armies in World War II. In addition, the submarine has nearly succeeded in starving Britain in both World Wars. Victory in the wars of the twentieth century has been extremely costly to Britain. Many interest-earning overseas investments have had to be liquidated to help finance the war efforts, exports have been temporarily halted during the war periods, and overseas markets have been lost to noncombatant or less involved countries. Huge quantities of British shipping have been destroyed, to say nothing of physical destruction of British cities from the air and large casualties, civilian as well as military. Thus in the twentieth century a deteriorating competitive position in international trade has been accompanied by, and partly a consequence of, a drastic reduction in security, great wartime destruction, and a heavy burden of armaments.

Yet in this changed world the United Kingdom must continue to support itself in somewhat the same way that it did in the past. Behind this necessity is the fact that about half of the country's food must be imported. To pay for this food large exports must be sold, and to allow production for export almost every raw material except coal must be imported and paid for. For many years Britain's exports of goods have not paid for the necessary imports, but the difference was previously made good by the "invisible" exports of capital and services. Both of the latter have been sharply reduced by the two World Wars, and thus Britain has had difficulty in striking a financial balance despite a phenomenal postwar increase of around 60 percent in the export of goods. The latter increase might have been considerably greater had it not been necessary for Britain to divert much of her production to military purposes in the face of unsettled world conditions.

Increase of production and exports over prewar years indicates that the British have attacked their problems vigorously. Two main approaches have been employed: (1) restriction of home consumption and imports, with concomitant increases in domestic agricultural production; and (2) stimulation of industrial production and exports, with accompanying reorientation of trade toward the Commonwealth.

The Role of Agriculture

Rationing has been one major means toward restricting home consumption and imports. Although progressively lessened in the early 1950's, rationing was in full force during the decade following 1939. Applied to goods largely imported, it facilitated the reduction of imports. Applied to goods produced in Britain, it enabled an increased share of the production to be reserved for export. It also tended to lessen inflation of prices, give everyone a share of scarce goods, and thus to balance somewhat the sacrifices made by various segments of the population. In 1954 all rationing in Britain was ended.

As a further means of lessening imports, British agriculture was stimulated to produce more food at home. The basic fact behind the past and present inability of agriculture to feed the population is simply that there is not enough good land in Britain to fully support so many millions of people, despite very high production per acre. The chief limiting factors are excessive moisture, cool summers, rough terrain, and poor soils. Highland Britain suffers the most on all of these counts, but various parts of Lowland Britain are also affected. The result is that about half of the total area of the United Kingdom is kept in permanent pasture and meadow, the bulk of which lies in Highland Britain. The pastures and meadows of Britain, together with forage crops, furnish the basis for a considerable livestock industry which is the chief element in British agriculture. Fluid milk is the most important single product, and in this food Britain is entirely self-sufficient. Beef cattle and sheep are also important, the latter particularly in the more difficult highland areas. Production is far from satisfying British requirements for beef and mutton, however. The emphasis on livestock in British agriculture was intensified in the nineteenth century when it became government policy to allow the import of foodstuffs free of duty and a flood of cheap foreign grain, particularly wheat, poured into British markets. Under such competition only a few of the drier and more fertile areas, such as East Anglia to the north and northeast of London, were able to continue large-scale wheat production. Consequently oats, well adapted to dampness and cool summers, became the main grain crop, es-

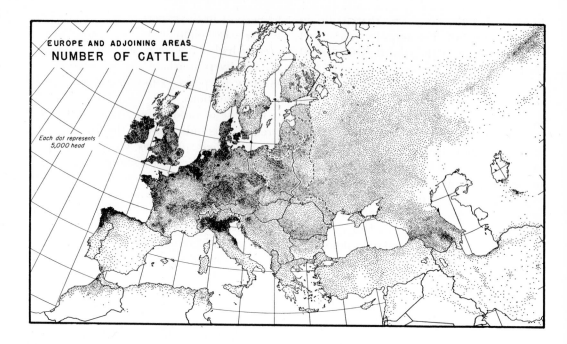

Distribution of cattle and sheep in Europe and adjoining areas. Note the prominence of the British Isles in both types of livestock. Most European countries emphasize one or the other, but seldom both. Short dashes indicate prewar boundaries. Some of the postwar boundaries shown by solid lines are not officially recognized by the United States Government. (*Modified from maps by the Office of Foreign Agricultural Relations based on prewar data.*)

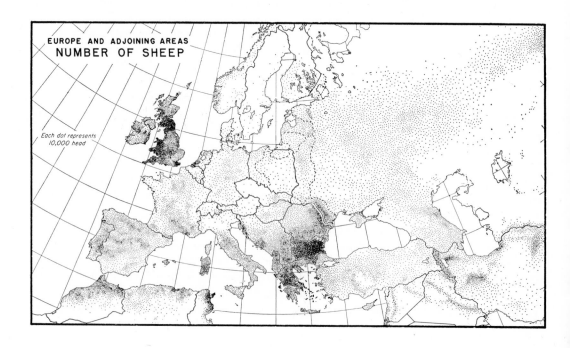

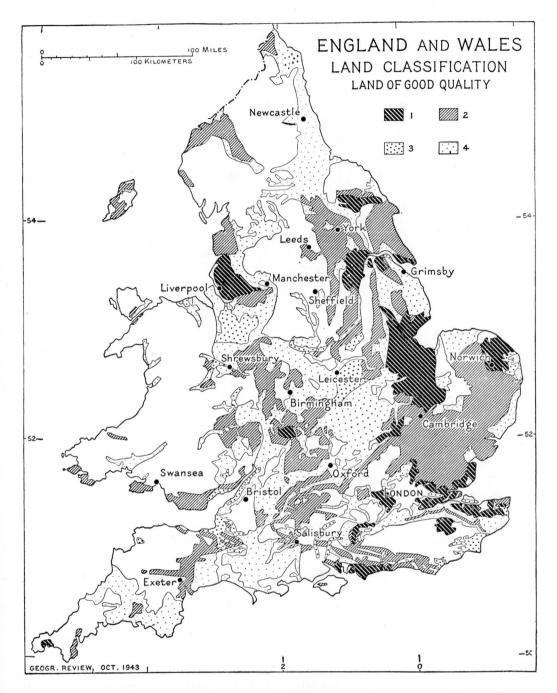

ENGLAND AND WALES
LAND CLASSIFICATION
LAND OF GOOD QUALITY

1   2
3   4

100 MILES
100 KILOMETERS

Newcastle

York
Leeds
Manchester   Grimsby
Liverpool
Sheffield
Shrewsbury
Norwich
Leicester
Birmingham
Cambridge
Swansea
Oxford
Bristol   LONDON
Salisbury
Exeter

GEOGR. REVIEW, OCT. 1943

Tentative land classification map of England and Wales prepared by the Land Utilization Survey.
Key: 1, first-class arable land; 2, good arable land; 3, first-class grassland; 4, good grassland
and other areas with pockets of good land. Note the concentration of good to excellent arable
land in eastern England.

pecially in Highland Britain, where the Scots are one of the few peoples to use oats as a staple food.

Only about one third of the United Kingdom can be classed as arable land, suited under present natural and economic conditions to producing cultivated crops. This third lies mainly in Lowland Britain, and that part of the country produces the major portion of all crops except grass and oats. During and since World War II the British government has attempted, through subsidies and the planning and control of land use, to increase the amount of land plowed and the production of food crops. These efforts have met with some success. In the early 1950's wheat production was about half again as great as in the middle 1930's and was nearly equal to the production of oats, with barley a close third. The latter grain, used principally as a feedstuff

and in the brewing and distilling industry, showed a phenomenal increase of nearly 200 percent. Increased emphasis on potatoes had about doubled their production and the production of sugar beets was up by approximately 50 percent or more. Dairy production had also increased, although the production of meat had declined.

Despite the considerable improvement over the prewar situation, Britain is at present self-sufficient only in fluid milk and potatoes among the major foods. It is still necessary to import around half of its total food supply, with food imports accounting for about a third of all British imports by value. In addition, the improvement has been achieved partly by the substitution in the British diet of more bread and potatoes for such "luxury" foods as meat and sugar.

The Role of Industry

If the United Kingdom is to fully recover from its long economic crisis, industrial production must not only be expanded, but must also be made more efficient so that British goods may be sold more easily and in greater volume on world markets. A vital factor is power supply. Inadequate supplies of coal, or coal selling at too high a price, could undermine the whole effort. A spectacular step taken with the object of curing the ills of the coal industry has been nationalization of the mines. Private ownership was deemed by the government to be incapable of taking the necessary measures. These included closing the most uneconomical mines and concentrating production in the better ones, investing large sums in the industry to mechanize it and modernize it as far as possible, eliminating profits beyond the break-even point, and attempting to cure an acute labor shortage by making the work safer and more attractive. Since nationalization there

has been a sizable increase in production, but by 1953 the production peaks of the industry at its height had not been reattained, costs remained relatively high, and many long-standing problems were still essentially unsolved. The long-range possibilities of underground gasification (burning of coal in the mine to obtain energy) and of atomic energy on a commercial basis are being explored.

Considerable stimulus has been given to exports by expanded production of goods with which other countries cannot compete so easily as they can with the products of the older British industries. In general the tendency is toward goods whose value is derived less from the power and material, and more from the labor skill and technical ability used in their manufacture. Thus the older industries are concentrating more on high-quality merchandise, and newer industries are growing rapidly in such fields as automobiles, jet aircraft, electronics, and motion pictures. In these lines Britain finds fewer capable competitors in world markets than in cheap textiles or crude steel.

Reorientation of British Trade

Another approach to solving the problem of exports has been the reorientation of British trade with increased emphasis on trade between the United Kingdom and the Commonwealth. This has essentially been an attempt to compensate for increased international competition and the tariff discriminations of other countries by making the Commonwealth more of an economic unit, with the Commonwealth countries furnishing assured markets for each other. The latter policy was initiated in the depression years of the early 1930's when many countries increasingly restricted the importation of British products while damaging British industry and threatening British currency reserves by dumping goods on the free British market. Faced with this situation, the United Kingdom abandoned its century-old policy of free trade and began to impose tariffs on imports. This procedure gave Britain an opportunity to bargain with other nations on the basis of privileged treatment for British exports to these nations in return for privileged admittance of their goods into the British market. Such mutual privileges were granted mostly among the Commonwealth nations under the designation of "imperial preferences." The proportion of the United Kingdom's exports which go to the Commonwealth has increased considerably in recent years and stood at 45 percent in 1950.

Extension of Governmental Authority

In order to plan and carry out the various measures considered necessary for Britain's economic survival, a wide extension of government authority over the British economy and the lives of the British people has been effected. Some of the manifestations of extended governmental powers have been rationing, agricultural subsidies, control of land use, and controlled allocation of materials in industry. Particularly important has been the nationalization of important sectors of the British economy, including the Bank of England, the coal mines, the electric power stations, the gas industry, railroads and trucking lines, and the iron and steel industry. Nationalization of these enterprises was carried out by the Labor (Socialist) government elected in 1945 and up to 1954 had not been reversed, except for truck transport and the iron and steel industry, by the Conservative government which came to power in 1951. Radio and telephone communication were government monopolies in the United Kingdom long before these recent nationalizations. The specific purposes of nationalization varied from industry to industry, but were in general rather similar to the purposes of coal nationalization already described. Their background was Britain's desperate situation and the feeling on the part of the government and widespread sectors of public opinion that privately owned industry in Britain had proven unable to cure the country's longstanding economic ills.

Accompanying these changes, one of the world's most comprehensive systems of social security has been instituted (security "from the cradle to the grave"), including various forms of state aid for the individual and compulsory insurance, such as health insurance. Strenuous efforts toward rehabilitation of the economy, security for the individual, and continued military strength have necessitated an extremely high level of taxation. Income taxes are particularly high and are sharply graduated to bear heavily on the highest incomes, so that class differences in the population are being greatly scaled down. This procedure has been considered necessary to

secure revenue and to conform to the idea that national hardship should be shared with some degree of equality. The broad governmental powers described above have been exercised by both Laborites and Conservatives, with only minor differences, and both have maintained the traditions of responsible government and political liberty which have become marked features of British life.

Military Expenditures a Handicap to Recovery

Particularly critical in Britain's situation since World War II has been the necessity for high military expenditures to maintain national security. The withdrawal of British forces from Burma, India, Pakistan, Ceylon, and Palestine may be interpreted partly as an attempt to bring imperial military commitments within more reasonable limits. In addition, when Greece was threatened with Communist domination shortly after World War II,

Britain turned over to the United States its former role as unofficial protector of that country. These withdrawals, however, were more than offset by military demands on Britain for the defense of Western Europe and the home islands against possible attack. As a result, military expenditures have been at very high levels since World War II, and they have been a major handicap to the strenuous British effort toward economic recovery.

The Problem of American Trade

The United States has been both a great friend and a great problem to the United Kingdom, as to many countries, since World War II. As a friend, the United States has extended to Britain billions of dollars in economic and military aid. This generous action has not been completely altruistic, however, since Britain has been seen as the most valuable ally of the United States in a potential third World War and hence could not be allowed to fall into possible economic decay and chaos. In addition, American aid programs have served on occasion as forms of indirect subsidization to American agriculture and industry. British gratitude for American aid has been tempered by knowledge of these factors and also by the feeling that Britain suffered more than the United States in

both World Wars while fighting enemies that the United States only belatedly came to recognize as its own enemies.

The United States is a problem to Britain in that it is a country with which Britain finds it extremely necessary but also somewhat difficult to trade. Since 1945 the loss of alternative sources of food imports in countries behind the Russian "Iron Curtain," plus the necessity for replacing equipment which was damaged or worn out during the war has forced Britain to import more than ever from the United States. At the same time, the ability of Britain to pay for imports from the United States has declined as a consequence of wartime liquidation of British investments in that country to pay for war materials. To make up for the loss of dollar income from investments, Britain has needed to increase its exports of goods to the United States. But the scale and efficiency of many American industries has made competition difficult, and even when British goods could compete favorably, they have often been excluded from the American market by protective tariffs. Thus Britain has been faced with a continuing deficit in trade with the United States.

A number of solutions to the latter problem seem possible. (1) The United States could lower tariffs in order to admit more British goods. Such a step would react unfavorably on certain American industries. (2) Britain could find alternative sources for imports now obtained from the United States. At present, such sources would be difficult or impossible to find. Some areas of the world might be developed as sources, but only with difficulty and large capital investments to stimulate production, as the British found when they attempted to develop large-scale production of peanuts and peanut oil in Africa following World War II. (3) Britain could obtain a surplus in trade with third countries which in turn had a surplus in trade with the United States. Such a situation already exists with regard to some countries, but countries having a surplus in trade with the United States are usually poor nations which produce a few important foodstuffs or raw materials and do not furnish large markets for manufactures. A further hindrance to this solution would be restrictions on the free exchange of one currency for another. (4) The United States could continue to give Britain dollars to cover its deficits. This solution has little appeal for either nation. In any case, Britain's deficits have notably lessened since 1951.

Emigration as a Possibility

One radical solution to Britain's difficulties which has often been suggested of late years is the emigration of a sizable proportion of the British people. Some have suggested that emigration up to 20 percent of the United Kingdom's total population would be desirable. However, Britain's accomplishments in economic recovery since World War II indicate that such drastic measures should hardly be necessary if the affairs of the world in which Britain lives are handled with any intelligence. Wholesale emigration might ameliorate British problems, temporarily at least, but few nations are encouraging mass immigration today, and the practical difficulties are such that without much greater need this step hardly seems a real alternative.

Ireland

The island of Ireland, separated from Great Britain by the Irish Sea, consists essentially of a central plain bordered on the north, south, and west by hills and low, rounded mountains. Most of the central plain is below 500 feet in elevation, and the highest summit in the entire island only reaches 3414 feet. Glaciation has disorganized the drainage of central and western Ireland, resulting in a multitude of lakes. The latter are connected by sluggish rivers, of which the largest is the River Shannon. Marshes and peat bogs abound: dried peat is a major fuel in a land which has little coal, no petroleum, and almost no wood. The hills and mountains of Ireland, like those of Great Britain, are essentially treeless; open moorland rather than forest is

An Irish landscape—the village of Cahersiveen in southwestern Ireland. Rounded, treeless hills, such as those depicted, are characteristic of the British Isles. (*Irish Tourist Bureau.*)

characteristic of the uplands and part of the central plain as well. True forest covers less than 2 percent of Ireland. The mild, humid climate of the island sponsors a luxuriant growth of grass; consequently green is the prevailing and proverbial color of the Irish countryside.

▶ Political and Religious Divisions of Ireland

Ireland is divided politically into two principal parts. To the north is Northern Ireland, a part of the United Kingdom, with an area of 5238 square miles and a population (1951) of about 1.4 million. To the south is the independent Republic of Ireland (known as Eire in the native Gaelic language, not so much used as English), with an area of 26,600 square miles and a population in 1951 of nearly 3 million.

The division of the island between two political units is based principally on re-ligion. The population of the Republic of Ireland is almost solidly Roman Catholic, whereas Northern Ireland is predominantly Protestant. This situation arose when the English government fostered the settlement of Scottish Protestants in the north of Ireland during the seventeenth century. They were intended to form a nucleus of population loyal to the Crown in a hostile conquered country. When the Roman Catholic portions of the island gained full self-government and dominion status in 1921 as the Irish Free State, the Protestant majority in Northern Ireland elected to remain with the United Kingdom. Today, as in the past, the Irish Republic claims Northern Ireland as its rightful territory, and the political separation continues to be a source of friction between the two parts of the island and between the Republic of Ireland and the United Kingdom.

▶ Political Antagonism and Economic Interdependence

The two sovereign states of the British Isles present some very sharp contrasts. The United Kingdom is dominantly Protestant, the Republic of Ireland overwhelmingly Roman Catholic. The United Kingdom is many times larger in population, having 50 million people as against 3 million for its neighbor. The intensive urban and industrial development of the United Kingdom contrasts sharply with the predominantly rural and agricultural character of the Irish Republic.

Perhaps the most striking contrast, however, is found in the political antagonism of the two countries, as opposed to their close economic relations. The antagonism stems from nearly 800 years of Irish struggle against British domination. In World War II when the United Kingdom was engaged in a desperate fight for survival against Germany, the Republic of Ireland remained neutral, thus expressing Irish feelings of resentment against Britain. Following the war the government of the Irish Republic elected to withdraw from the Commonwealth of Nations and in 1949 severed its last remaining political ties with the United Kingdom.

Political antagonism has not led to a severance of economic relations, however. Few areas in the world are more closely linked by bonds of trade than the two sovereign countries of the British Isles. In 1952 the United Kingdom took 86 percent of all exports by value from the Irish Republic and provided 51 percent of all imports entering the latter country.

▶ Importance of Livestock in the Irish Economy

Livestock provide the principal exports of the Republic of Ireland and are the major element in the agriculture of Northern Ireland as well. Cattle outrank other types of livestock in importance, although poultry, horses, sheep, and hogs are significant sources of income. One of the characteristic features of the Irish export trade is a large annual movement of live animals, mainly cattle, to England for slaughter. In 1952 live animals constituted about a third of all exports from the Irish Republic by value.

Livestock husbandry was a major specialty on the large estates, mainly British-owned, which dominated the Irish countryside before World War I. Today most of the estates have been broken up, and Ireland is predominantly a land of small landowning farmers. Permanent pastures and meadows occupy nearly three times the acreage of tilled crop land on the island, and the cropping system is geared to the needs of a livestock economy. In acreage and production oats is the leading grain crop, followed by wheat and barley; the major root crops are potatoes, turnips, mangels, and sugar beets. Since World War I the government of the Irish Republic has fostered an increase in the production of wheat and sugar beets as a means of achieving greater self-sufficiency in foodstuffs, although the climate and soils of Ireland are not particularly suited to either crop. Growing of wheat and sugar beets is mainly confined to the warmer and drier eastern portion of the island.

▶ Industrial Development in Ireland

The government of the Republic of Ireland has also attempted to foster an increased development of industry, although lack of capital and markets as well as deficiencies in raw materials have proved serious handicaps to large-scale industrialization. The main industrial center is Dublin (635,000 with suburbs), which is also the political capital, main seaport, and by far the largest city in population. More than a fifth of the entire population of the Irish Republic is concentrated in the Dublin metropolitan area. Dublin is mainly a center of light, diversified industries, including such specialties as brewing and distilling, flour milling, baking, sugar refining, butter making, and other food-processing industries, as well as the manufacture of textiles, clothing, leather goods, glass, cement, and chemicals. The city is also the major Irish center for printing and publishing.

Northern Ireland is more industrialized than the Irish Republic. Belfast (444,000), the major industrial center, has important shipbuilding industries and is the principal center of Irish linen manufacture. In addition, Belfast has a variety of other metallurgical, textile, chemical, and food-processing industries.

▶ The Problem of Depopulation

Today the Irish are recovering from their disastrous history of the past several centuries. They are small in numbers, however the island of Ireland being one of the few sizable areas in the world with a smaller population today than it had a century ago. The population of the island was about 8.2 million in 1841, as against 4.3 million in 1951. The decline in population followed the appearance of a blight which caused the potato crop to fail for several years in succession and resulted in more than a million Irish deaths between 1846 and 1850. During the decade beginning with 1846, more than 1½ million Irishmen emigrated, principally to the United States. Continued emigration and a falling birth rate steadily decreased the population over the next several decades until relative stability was achieved in the second quarter of the twentieth century. In the Irish Republic, where depopulation has been somewhat more severe than in Northern Ireland, the 1951 census revealed a rise of some 5500 over the 1946 census figure—the first intercensal increase in population to be recorded since 1841.

France

The west central portions of the European mainland across the English Channel from the British Isles are occupied by a group of highly developed industrial nations which have long had close political and economic relations with each other. Germany and France are the largest nations in the group and the only ones which have ranked as Great Powers in the twentieth century. Most of the remaining countries are found in a historic buffer zone separating the two major nations. From north to south they include the Netherlands, Belgium, Luxembourg, the Saar, and Switzerland. Austria, though less developed industrially than the other countries, may be included because of its close relationships with Germany. Monaco and Andorra, ad-

joining France, and Liechtenstein, between Switzerland and Austria, are insignificant micro-states with a semi-independent status; only proximity entitles them to be numbered with the countries of this group. Luxembourg and the Saar, likewise, are small and not completely independent, but the mineral resources and metallurgical industries of these political units give them an importance out of proportion to their size.

Topographic variety, economic interdependence, and political antagonism are key phrases describing the countries of West Central Europe as a group. In physical terms the area they occupy may be thought of as consisting of three concentric and widely different arcs of land: an outer arc

A large potash mine on the level plain of the Rhine in Alsace. (*French Embassy Press and Information Division.*)

95

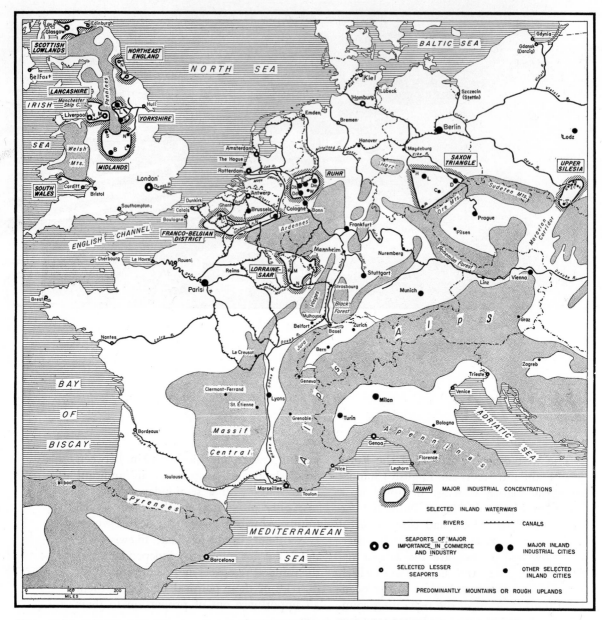

Cities, industrial concentrations, waterways, and highlands in West Central Europe and adjoining areas. Most sections of the internal waterways shown are navigable for barge traffic. The "major industrial concentrations" are relatively continuous industrialized areas. All of the industrial concentrations except the Saxon Triangle contain large deposits of bituminous coal. Note the clustering of industrial concentrations in the border zone between the highlands and the North European Plain. Cities indicated by letter are as follows: Northeast England —N, Newcastle, M, Middlesbrough; Yorkshire—L, Leeds-Bradford, S, Sheffield; Lancashire—M, Manchester; Midlands—B, Birmingham, L, Leicester, N, Nottingham, S, Stoke-on-Trent; Franco-Belgian District—L, Lille, R, Roubaix, C, Charleroi, N, Namur, L, Liége; Lorraine-Saar—M, Metz, N, Nancy, S, Saarbrücken; Ruhr—Db, Duisburg, Dd, Düsseldorf, E, Essen, Dm, Dortmund, W, Wuppertal; Saxon Triangle—H, Halle, L, Leipzig, D, Dresden, C, Chemnitz, P, Plauen; Upper Silesia—K, Katowice, B, Bytom, C, Chorzow, Z, Zabrze, G, Gliwice, O, Ostrava. Dotted areas represent highlands offering some hindrance to transportation and being sufficiently steep, rugged, or infertile to discourage dense agricultural settlement.

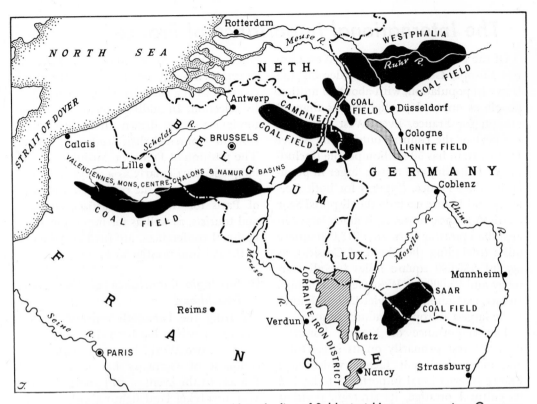

Major coal fields of West Central Europe. Note the line of fields stretching across western Germany, the Low Countries, and northeastern France. (*U. S. Geological Survey.*)

of lowland plains bordering the Atlantic; a central arc of hills, low mountains, small plains, and basins; and an inner arc of high, rugged mountains. France and Germany include portions of all three arcs, the Netherlands and Belgium lie mostly within the outer arc of plains, Luxembourg and the Saar are within the central hilly zone, and Switzerland and Austria lie principally within the inner zone of Alpine mountains.

The largest deposits of coal and iron in Europe provide a major basis for an industrial development of the first magnitude. An almost continuous series of great industrial concentrations stretches across this area from northeastern France to southwestern Poland, following the major axis of coal deposits. Smaller industrialized areas exist by the score. Coal and iron also furnish an important basis for trade among the countries of the group, most of which are deficient in one or both of these vital commodities. Germany and the Saar export coal in large quantities to the other countries, while France and Luxembourg export iron ore. Many other bases for trade exist, and all of the countries concerned have close economic relations with other countries of the group.

Political relations are troubled, however, by antagonisms of long standing. The countries of this group have fought each other repeatedly in past wars. In the twentieth century the principal antagonists have been Germany and France, but only Switzerland among the other sovereign countries has escaped embroilment in the quarrels and conflicts of these larger nations. Avoiding further strife is today a major preoccupation of these countries.

The International Importance of France

Of the two major countries in West Central Europe, Germany is considerably the larger in population, with about 70 million people as opposed to slightly less than 43 million for France. Even West Germany, the part of the country outside the Soviet Iron Curtain has 50 million people (including West Berlin) and thus is larger in population than France. (Figures for both Germany and France exclude the disputed Saar district.) France, however, is much larger in area than postwar Germany: 213,000 square miles (including the island of Corsica), as against 136,000 square miles for all Germany and 95,000 for West Germany alone. In fact, excluding the Soviet Union, France is the largest European country in area.

The importance of France, however, does not rest primarily on its size. Other and more significant factors which give France international importance today are its cultural prestige, its strategic position in Europe, and its possession of the world's largest colonial empire in area and second largest in population.

▶ Achievements of French Culture

France was conquered for Rome by Julius Caesar in the first century, B.C., and thereafter became thoroughly Romanized. It has thus been a highly civilized land longer than any other European country except Greece and Italy. During the Middle Ages Paris, the French capital, became the main center of Roman Catholic scholarship and culture. In modern times the French have made eminent contributions in all fields of scholarship and art, and Paris has generally been regarded as the world's foremost artistic and cultural center. Such names as Pasteur and Curie in science; Descartes, Pascal, Voltaire, Rousseau, and Bergson in philosophy; Molière, Racine, Hugo, Balzac, Zola, and Proust in literature; Matisse and Gauguin in art

come readily to mind as evidence of France's contributions to civilization. Even to make such a short list is almost to falsify by selection. In addition, many illustrious foreigners have drawn their inspiration from and pursued their studies in France. The position of French as an international language, particularly as a major language of diplomacy, and the continued attraction of Paris for the world's artists, students, and tourists, as well as for important international conferences, are further evidences of the cultural prestige of France.

▶ Strategic Importance of the French Beachhead

During the twentieth century France's strategic position has been that of a beachhead. In two World Wars the path to the conquest of Germany has lain through France. In the event of still another World War involving land fighting on the European continent, it seems quite possible that France would again play a similar role. Location at the western end of Europe (except for Spain and Portugal, which are militarily weak and relatively isolated behind the Pyrenees), sea frontage on three sides, proximity to Great Britain, and good communications with the continent to the east combine to make France a critical area in war and hence a critical area in politics.

▶ The French Union

The significance of France in the modern world is heightened by French control of a world-wide colonial empire, the French Union. Overseas areas held by France in late 1954 totaled about 4½ million square miles (21 times the size of France itself), with an estimated population of 70 to 75 million. The most important of these areas —Algeria, Morocco, and Tunisia—lie just across the Mediterranean in North Africa. To the south, French territory extends

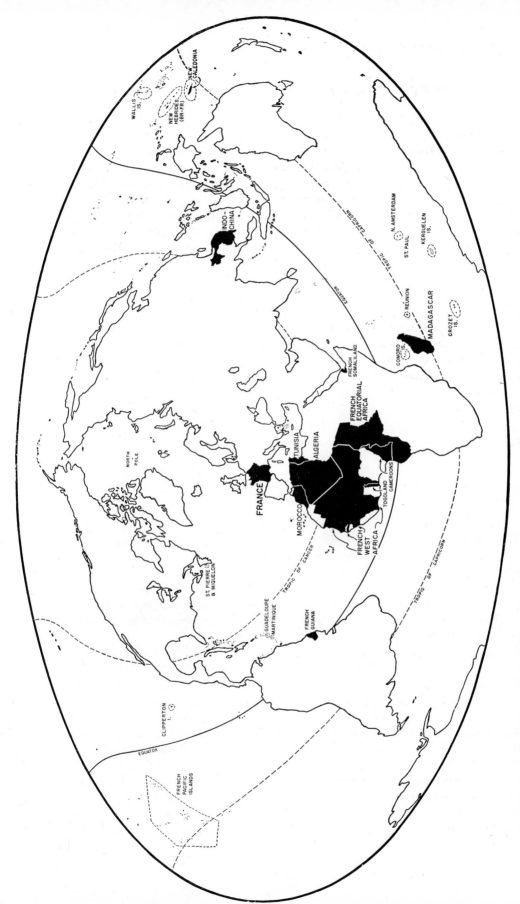

The French Union, January 1, 1955, shown in black. Small island possessions are encircled with dashes. (*Briesemeister Elliptical Equal Area Projection, copyright American Geographical Society of New York.*)

The following labels appear on the map:

WALLIS IS.

NEW CALEDONIA

NEW HEBRIDES (BR.-FR.)

INDO-CHINA

N. AMSTERDAM

ST. PAUL

KERGUELEN IS.

TROPIC OF CAPRICORN

RÉUNION

MADAGASCAR

CROZET IS.

COMORO IS.

FRENCH SOMALILAND

EQUATOR

FRENCH EQUATORIAL AFRICA

TUNISIA

ALGERIA

FRANCE

NORTH POLE

MOROCCO

CAMEROONS

TOGOLAND

FRENCH WEST AFRICA

TROPIC OF CANCER

TROPIC OF CAPRICORN

ST. PIERRE & MIQUELON

GUADELOUPE

MARTINIQUE

FRENCH GUIANA

CLIPPERTON I.

EQUATOR

FRENCH PACIFIC ISLANDS

across the Sahara Desert and into equatorial regions of Africa. Other large and important holdings are the island of Madagascar and French Indochina. Scattered bits of territory are held on the coasts of Africa and South America, as well as islands in the Pacific, the Caribbean, and elsewhere. With minor exceptions, none of the overseas areas are predominantly French in population, but they add considerably to the economic and political stature of France.

Since World War II the struggle of a number of French-held areas to achieve independence, or at least a greater degree of self-government, has been a factor helping to undermine world peace and stability. The French have attempted to allay colonial discontent by giving a few territories the status of Overseas Departments (Algeria, Martinique, Guadeloupe, French Guiana, Réunion) administered in a manner similar to the departments of France itself. (The department is the basic territorial-administrative subdivision of France, corresponding roughly to the American state, although having smaller powers of self-government.) Another move in this direction was to give the three Indochinese states of Vietnam, Laos, and Cambodia the status of Associated States of the French Union, with the expectation that they would develop broad powers of self-government. Actual representation in the French Parliament has been granted to the Overseas Departments and on a lesser scale to the other overseas territories, though not to the Associated States or the North African protectorates of Morocco and Tunisia. At the time of writing, strong elements in Indochina, Morocco, and Tunisia were demanding immediate independence from France, and conditions in these areas were very unsettled. In July, 1954, France was forced to cede the northern part of Vietnam to Communist rebels following a civil war of eight years, and her hold on the rest of Indochina seemed increasingly tenuous.

A Great Power in Decline

France has declined considerably from the peak of power and importance it once attained. An advantageous topography facilitated early unification of the country under a powerful central government, and before the age of modern industry the agriculture of France was able to support the largest population in Europe. For centuries France was the most powerful military nation in Europe and probably in the world. It dominated Europe under Louis XIV, and came near to subjugating the entire continent under Napoleon I. In each case French expansion was eventually checked by a combination of continental powers allied with Britain.

France's modern decline has been accompanied by the emergence of such giants as the United States and the Soviet Union, but has been most closely associated with the rise of Germany. Defeat in the Franco-Prussian War of 1870–1871, victory at a tremendous cost in the First World War of 1914–1918, stunning conquest in the spring of 1940, and occupation until 1944 have left the French a nation whose main concern often seems to be security from Germany.

The threat of invasion from the east is magnified by the character of France's northeastern frontier. Here inferior natural defenses leave open relatively easy routes of invasion; mixed cultures engender conflict and uncertainty; and the proximity of vital areas, including Paris itself, to the frontier weakens the French position. The Franco-German frontier zone has been for a long period one of the world's more critical problem areas, and the relations between the two countries which face each other there still remain of vital concern to the world at large.

Much of France's importance and many of its problems, especially the German problem, can be related to the geographical circumstances of the country. These circumstances are briefly analyzed in the following selection: [1]

France proper, or "metropolitan" France, embraces a compact, squarish country somewhat smaller than Texas. The maximum north-south and east-west dimensions are almost equal, just under 600 miles. . . . The compactness of France and its configuration facilitated the early unification of the nation and contributed materially to its defensibility before the age of air power and mechanized armies. The speed with which the Germans overran the country in 1940, however, shows that in the warfare of today no country as small as France has sufficient depth to give protection against a stronger and more resolute enemy.

France is well favored by its climate. In the northern two-thirds of the country, the winters are warmer and the summers cooler than in Central Europe, and the rainfall is well distributed throughout the year. Southern France, especially the southeast, has the hot, dry summers characteristic of the Mediterranean region. The soils of France, on the whole, are fertile; and droughts during the growing season are nowhere as serious a problem as in countries like Russia, the United States, and Spain. The climate and soils have made possible an agricultural production unusually rich and diverse for a country no larger than France—a decided national asset. . . .

Major Areal Divisions

► North and South

The climatic and topographical differences between the northern half of France and the South, or Midi, give rise to marked differences in agriculture. The lowlands of the Midi specialize in the production of wine, fruits, vegetables, and some cereals; its mountain ranges (Alps, Pyrenees, and Massif Central) are devoted mostly to cattle raising. In the northern half of France, plains or low hills, with richer soils, predominate; these support a more intensive and often mechanized form of agriculture. Wheat, oats, sugar beets, and vegetables are the main crops; the northwestern region, checkered with hedges, is a rich dairy country. Some flax is grown in the North; and on easterly facing slopes the grapevine is cultivated. Cider and beer largely take the place of wine in northwestern France. The four main centers of the mining and manufacturing industries are outside of the Midi, mostly in the northeastern part of the country.

Fully as important as these differences are persistent differences between the Midi and the rest of France in dialects, traditions, and customs. The Midi has inherited far more from ancient Rome than has northern France, which was incorporated into the Roman Empire much later and came under more powerful Teutonic influences in the Middle Ages.

The rapid economic development of the North in recent times contrasts with conditions in the South. According to a popular French saying "The North pays the taxes; the South runs the politics."

► Lowlands and Highlands

A number of diverse regions that were politically separate in the Middle Ages have been joined together and closely integrated to make modern France. Never-

---

[1] *Geographical Foundations of National Power* (Army Service Forces Manual M 103–1). Washington: Government Printing Office, 1944. Pp. 35–48. Several of the original headings have been eliminated and others added. One editorial comment has been added. Several changes in italicizing have been made in editing.

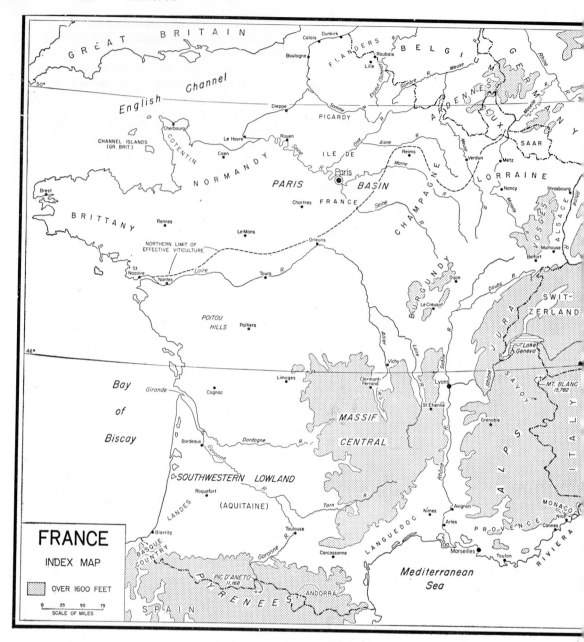

FRANCE

INDEX MAP

OVER 1600 FEET

0   25   50   75
SCALE OF MILES

theless, the different regions still retain their individuality. Apart from the mountains on the Spanish and Italian frontiers, which rise to heights of more than 12,000 feet, the country consists of three principal lowlands—the Paris Basin, the Southwestern Lowland, and the Rhône-Saône Valley —underlain by limestone and other sedi-mentary rocks and separated by highlands, underlain for the most part by crystalline rocks. The central highland, appropriately named *Massif Central* (Central Mountain Mass), though rugged, and indeed mountainous along its eastern side, is not particularly high (an average altitude of 3000 feet) and is cut almost asunder along stream valleys. However, it tends to deflect ordinary transportation, whether commercial or military. The three lowlands are connected with each other by broad lowland gaps around the margins of the Massif Central. A smaller lower upland area forms the two peninsulas, Brittany and Normandy, that jut out from northwestern France.

In general, the lowlands consist of fertile river basins, and most parts of them are under cultivation. There are extensive marshes in the center and sandy heaths in the southwest. The highlands, by and large, are rugged and covered with relatively poor soils, derived from the disintegration of crystalline rocks.

[EDITORIAL COMMENT. *Sedimentary rocks* have been formed from sediments (sand, gravel, clay, or lime) deposited by running water, wind, or wave action either on land or in bodies of water, and consolidated into rock over a span of geologic time by pressure of the accumulated deposits or the cementing action of chemicals contained in waters percolating through the rock materials. The main classes of sedimentary rocks are sandstone, shale (formed principally of clay), and limestone. *Crystalline rocks* are of two main kinds: igneous and metamorphic. Igneous, or volcanic, rocks are formed by the cooling and solidifying of molten materials, either within the earth or poured out on the surface by volcanic action. Granite is a well-known type of igneous rock. Metamorphic rocks are formed from igneous or sedimentary rocks through changes occurring in the rock structure as a result of heat, pressure, or the chemical action of infiltrating waters. Marble, formed from pure limestone, is a common example of a metamorphic rock. Crystalline rocks, being harder and more closely compacted than sedimentary rocks, are usually more resistant to weathering and erosion, and thus tend to form uplands or highlands in areas where the sedimentary rocks have been weathered into lowlands. In general, sedimentary rocks weather into more fertile types of soil than crystalline rocks, although certain types of volcanic rock break down into extremely fertile soils, and within the sedimentaries themselves there are great variations in this respect, with limestone usually forming soils of greater fertility than shale or sandstone. The two main classes of rock are also significantly different with respect to associated economic minerals. Coal and petroleum, for example, are customarily found in sedimentary areas, whereas the metal-bearing ores are found in crystalline areas, except for certain deposits (particularly of iron ore) formed of materials removed from crystalline areas by percolating waters and redeposited in sedimentary areas.]

As might be expected, the most productive croplands are the coastal lowlands and the river basins. A considerable fraction of the highlands is also planted to crops, but there the output is generally smaller. Drainage and nearness to the ocean also affect the distribution of crops. The coasts of Brittany and Normandy favor dairying, because meadows and pasture do better than most crops in the moist, cool oceanic climate. Conversely, wheat is best grown on the well-drained limestone plains in the north. Horticulture, including vineyards and market gardens, dominates all the more fertile areas facing the Mediterranean Sea.

▶ Importance and Regional Setting of Paris

French life is tied up with the capital, not only politically and socially, but also physically and economically. It is the hub of the communications system and the center of the finishing industries, banking, and commerce. The conquest of Paris by a foreign army paralyzes the national life. Lyons is, in an economic sense, the capital of the Center, and Marseilles the capital of the Midi; but the environmental setting and social ramifications of these cities are relatively limited. Politically they have no distinction beyond being local administrative centers.

France was unified from Paris and a small surrounding district called the *Ile de France* (Island of France), which forms the heart of the Paris Basin and for cen-

Paris. A tug and barges on the Seine. Notre Dame Cathedral at left. (*Standard Oil Company* [N. J.].)

turies was the only territory dependably loyal to the French kings. Today that district, though far from central with respect to France as a whole, remains the core of the country politically, economically, and socially. Paris lies on the Seine, near the center of the Paris Basin, the most productive and diverse of the French lowlands. The river is navigable at all times of the year, and its tributaries give direct access by low passes to the Rhône-Saône Valley and the Southwestern Lowland. The numerous right-bank tributaries lead toward the Lorraine Gate and the Belgian Plain. Paris and the Ile de France, however, are somewhat protected toward the east and southeast by a series of ridges that curve concentrically around the Ile de France

and are separated from each other by similarly curving belts of lower land. The inner slopes of the ridges, those toward Paris, are often so gentle as to be almost imperceptible; but those facing outward, toward the east and southeast, fall off sharply some scores of feet and in places form pronounced escarpments or lines of cliffs. Several such concentric barriers present their steep faces to invaders coming from the east and provide good terrain for the ground defense of Paris. The Seine and its tributaries cut through these successive ridges and lowland belts in narrow valleys. In many a war of the past, the ridges have helped the French armies to protect Paris. The ridges have seldom been breached and only when the government at Paris has been inadequately equipped as compared with its enemies.

Two islands in the Seine are stepping stones on a major north-south route, which crosses the valley by low gradients. The first settlement of Paris was on the easily defended islands, and the city has grown up around the original site. When a capital is firmly established, its influence spreads out in all directions. This has been notably true of Paris, which is far more than the political and economic center of the nation. It is the epitome of the national life. In few nations is the prestige of the capital so great as in France.

► The Southern Lowlands

An open lowland gate, near the town of Poitiers, connects the Paris Basin with the Southwestern Lowland, largely a country of wheat fields and vineyards. In 732, the French king, Charles Martel, defeated the Moors in this gate, where other battles decisive in world history have since been fought.

The Rhône-Saône Valley and neighboring Mediterranean coasts produce the ordinary wine (vin ordinaire), the winter vegetables, and many of the fruits consumed all over France. The valley has a further, and perhaps greater, importance as the main line of communication between north and south Europe west of the Balkans. It is connected by a narrow but easy saddle (near the town of Carcassonne) with the Southwestern Lowland also. . . .

Paris. Sidewalk cafes on the Boulevard St. Germain. (*Standard Oil Company* [N. J.].)

Land Frontiers

France has two land boundaries, the Pyrenees boundary with Spain, and the eastern boundary with Italy, Switzerland, Germany, Luxembourg, and Belgium.

The Pyrenees are a formidable barrier. The range extends unbroken from sea to sea, with steeper slopes to the north than to the south. While the range is only 20 to 60 miles wide and none of its peaks much exceed 11,000 feet, the general level is continuously high (over 5000 feet), there being but one pass lower than 5000 feet (Perthus, some 30 miles from the eastern end). Aside from shepherds' trails, only six motor roads and three railroads connect the two sides of the mountains. France has maintained no major fortifications along the Pyrenees, partly because of the natural defensive strength of the mountains and partly because France has not felt menaced by Spain, a nation that has been much weaker than its northern neighbor throughout modern times.

Of the eastern boundary of France only the segments fronting Italy and Switzerland conform to mountain barriers. In the south the boundary with Italy follows the crestline of the Alps for 330 miles. While the western Alps are several times as wide as the Pyrenees, they constitute a less effective barrier. They are very high, culminating in Mt. Blanc near the north end (nearly 16,000 feet), but are broken by deeply cut passes which have been military and trade routes from the earliest historical times. . . .

Beginning with Mt. Blanc, the boundary with Switzerland first follows the Alps to a point near the eastern end of Lake Geneva; thence it is formed by the lake almost to the latter's southwestern end; next it skirts Geneva, leaving that city in Switzerland, and finally, it runs northeast some 150 miles along the Jura Mountains to the Rhine. This range, less lofty than the Alps, has for centuries been the political border, although the language boundary between German-speaking and French-speaking peoples lies some distance to the eastward,

except near the northern end of the mountains, where it cuts across them. One railroad and a few roads traverse the range.

▶ The Vulnerable Northeastern Frontier

In modern times France has not feared invasion from Switzerland and did not fear it from Italy until 1940. Hence the southern half of its eastern frontier has been far less critically important from the strategic point of view than the northern half, over which the Germans swept into France in 1870, in 1914, and again in 1940.

This border zone is traversed by three natural avenues for invading armies, separated by two natural barriers. The southern and central avenues, known as the Belfort Gap, or Burgundian Gate, and the Lorraine Gate, respectively, lead directly from southern and central Germany into the eastern part of the Paris Basin. The northern avenue, or Belgian Plain, leads from northern Germany across Belgium into the northeastern corner of the Paris Basin. Between the Belfort Gap and the Lorraine Gate, the Vosges Mountains form the southern of the two natural barriers. The second natural barrier, between the Lorraine Gate and the Belgian Plain, is the western part of an upland region that extends westward from Germany across southern Belgium and a short distance into France and is known in France and Belgium as the Ardennes.

The Belfort Gap, strongly fortified before the war, is a lowland gate only a few miles wide, which permits easy movement from southwestern Germany and Switzerland into both the Rhône-Saône Valley and the Paris Basin. . . . North of the Belfort Gap, the Vosges Mountains form a substantial barrier for about 75 miles. Although only 3500 to 4500 feet high and 20 to 30 miles wide, they are unbroken by low passes. They rise gently from the west and fall off sharply on the east into the rich, flat-floored valley of Alsace. . . .

The Lorraine Gate, between the Vosges and the Ardennes, is a broad expanse of gently rolling country across which many armies have throughout history marched west into France or east into Germany. . . .

From Switzerland to the northern side of the Lorraine Gate, France directly faces Germany. From the Ardennes to the North Sea, however, the French frontier faces . . . Belgium and Luxembourg, on whose neutrality France has too much relied for safety. The Ardennes, a wooded hilly land, offers only slight obstructions. German armies passed through it readily enough in 1914 and in May 1940.

The Belgian Plain, between the Ardennes and the North Sea, is by far the most open and vulnerable of the three natural avenues between France and Germany. Parts of it were originally marshy; and reclamation has produced a network of canals somewhat hampering the movement of armies. Nevertheless, armies have so frequently passed across it and through the corridor valley of the Sambre and Meuse,

a short distance to the south, that Belgium has been called "the cockpit of Europe." From it a vast lowland spreads northeastward across Germany, flat and easily traversed. In and on the margins of this lowland lie the populous lower Rhineland and the Ruhr region with its mighty industries; farther east, the lowland broadens into the North German Plain in which stands Berlin. Southwestward the Belgian Plain opens into the Paris Basin, the economic and political core of France. Although the country between the Belgian Plain and Paris is not flat, it is relatively uninterrupted. Here the ridges which, as we have seen, help protect Paris on the east in the direction of the Lorraine Gate, fade out into a more level country. Thus the Belgian Plain forms the broadest and most direct highway leading to the vital core of France from those parts of Germany from which the most powerful blows can be struck, as demonstrated by the German armies in 1914 and 1940. . . .

Critical Areas from the Political Point of View

The entire eastern frontier region of France might well be considered a critical area, except perhaps for the part facing Switzerland, whose traditional neutrality and high mountains have been considered safeguards to France. The world has learned by bitter experience that the neutrality of small buffer states is but a feeble guarantee against invasion from across their territory when it is to the military advantage of an aggressor power to come that way.

▶ Alsace and Lorraine

By far the most critical part of the eastern frontier region is the part that directly borders on Germany, the provinces of Alsace and Lorraine. We have already seen that two of the three principal avenues from Germany into France lead through here. . . . Thus, even if Alsace and Lorraine were devoid of natural resources and inhabitants, they would nevertheless be of strategic importance. Their resources, their

history, and their people enormously increase the political instability of these provinces.

Alsace and Lorraine are among the most productive provinces of France. The valley of Alsace is extremely fertile, producing cereals, tobacco, vegetables, and dairy products, and supporting textile industries. It also has [one of] the most important known potash deposits in the world. . . . Lorraine possesses the largest deposit of iron ore in Europe, a resource on which the industrial strength of France partly depends. The lack of iron ore in substantial quantities is one of the chief economic weaknesses of Germany. Iron ore is useless without coking coal for smelting it. The [largest and best] coal fields in France lie nearly 200 miles away on the Belgian border beyond the Ardennes; but just across the boundary from Lorraine in the Saar district . . . there is some suitable coal. Farther down the Rhine, the Ruhr region of Germany is one of the largest and richest coal fields in Europe; and the Rhine River and its tributaries, as well as railroads and canals, connect the iron of Lorraine with the coal of the Ruhr. . . .

In Alsace and the eastern part of Lorraine a German dialect is spoken; French is the tongue of western Lorraine only. The two provinces were annexed to France piecemeal in the 16th and 17th centuries. While they were largely Germanic in culture and were included in the loose federation of German states known as the Holy Roman Empire, they became a part of France at a time when there was little or no feeling of national unity in Germany, and the German people, as a whole, were probably not much concerned over their loss. In 1871 when the new and strongly nationalistic German Empire, welded together by Bismarck, annexed Alsace and the northern part of Lorraine where iron deposits had recently been discovered, much was made of Germany's historic claim to the provinces, even though they had formed an integral part of France for more than 200 years. And when France regained them after the First World War, many German patriots felt that an integral part of Germany had been cut off. However, it is likely that the vast majority of the people of Alsace and Lorraine would prefer to remain with France. . . .

► *Minor Critical Areas*

The other critical areas need only brief mention. In 1860 Savoy, a district at the north end of the French Alps, and Nice, on the Mediterranean, were ceded to France by the little state of Piedmont in northern Italy (the so-called Kingdom of Sardinia), which was then taking the lead in bringing about the unification of Italy. Although Savoy is purely French and the French outnumber the Italian population of Nice, Fascist Italy clamored for their return, as well as for Corsica, where most of the people speak Italian although the island has belonged to France since 1769.

The inhabitants of certain other small areas around the margins of France speak other languages than French, but only among the Basques and the Bretons has there been any notable agitation for self-rule. The Basques, whose extraordinary tongue is unrelated, so far as is known, to any other language in Europe, occupy a small area about the size of New Jersey on both sides of the western Pyrenees, but for the most part in Spain. The Bretons of outer Brittany speak a Celtic language, akin to Welsh, Irish, and Gaelic.

Neither the Catalans, on the French side of the eastern Pyrenees, nor the Flemish of the extreme north of France have shown any particular desire to join their linguistic kinsfolk beyond the frontiers. Nor have the French-speaking Walloons of southern Belgium or the French-speaking people of western Switzerland desired annexation by France. . . .

Individualism and Political Unity in France

The vast majority of the people of France speak French and share a common cultural heritage. France was one of the first countries of Europe to emerge from the political welter of the Middle Ages as a powerful, proud, unified nation. The governmental administration and the economic control of the country have been strongly centralized in Paris since the French Revolution. Agitation for autonomy, to be sure, has existed in certain regions, such as Alsace and Brittany, and among the Basques. . . . Metropolitan France, however, has no large territories occupied by minorities of alien speech and customs.

Though the French people "speak the same language" in the literal sense, many of them do not do so in the figurative sense. They differ widely among themselves in character and outlook. They are pronounced individualists, extraordinarily tenacious of their personal, local, regional, and class rights and interests. Hence they have often tended to work at cross purposes, as their turbulent internal politics bear witness. Their difficulty in seeing eye to eye with each other has often been a source of weakness, but their love of country is so deep-seated and intense that it has enabled them at times, as in the Napoleonic wars or during the First World War, to put aside their internal differences and rise to extraordinary heights of united effort.

The Population Problem of France

The relative decline of France as a world power has been closely related to the failure of the country's population and economy to develop at rates comparable to those of a number of other nations during the past century. Especially critical has been the failure of France to keep pace with her arch enemy, Germany, in population growth. In 1870 these nations were approximately equal in population, each having about 38 million people. The loss to Germany of the 2 million inhabitants of Alsace-Lorraine following the Franco-Prussian War put France at a population disadvantage, and the lower French birth rate caused a further widening of the gap. By World War I the population of Germany had reached 68 million, as contrasted with only 40 million for France. Approximately the same difference in population obtained immediately prior to World War II. The growth of the French population since 1800, as compared with that of certain other countries, is shown in Table 4. Some of the figures given are estimates. This table goes a long way toward telling the story of France's decline in military power and security.

TABLE 4

COMPARATIVE POPULATION DATA: FRANCE AND SELECTED COUNTRIES

YEAR	APPROXIMATE POPULATION IN MILLIONS					
	FRANCE	GERMANY	UNITED KINGDOM	ITALY	RUSSIA	UNITED STATES
Approx. 1800	27	25	11	18	39	5
Approx. 1850	36	35	27	23	62	23
Approx. 1900	38	56	37	32	129	76
Pre-World War I (1910–1913)	40	68	41	35	—	92
Pre-World War II (1936–1940)	41	70	46	43	170	132
Approx. 1950	42	70	49	47	201	151
Approximate increase, 1850–1950 (Millions)	6	35	22	24	139	128

The immediate cause of France's relatively stable population is a low birth rate. Falling birth rates are characteristic of countries as they become industrialized and urbanized and as their standard of living rises. But the falling birth rate affected France before other countries, and affected not only the urban but also the rural population to a greater degree than is usual. In France, as in other countries, the larger families are generally found on farms, but French farm families tend to be smaller than in most countries, and this tendency showed itself at a relatively early date. It was an important factor in the comparatively early slackening of France's population growth.

No one can say for certain what has

caused the early and extreme decline in French natality, although many hypotheses have been advanced. Among the more plausible hypotheses are the following:

1. Since the French Revolution the law has required a farmer to divide most of his property evenly among his children when he made his will. The hypothesis is that French peasants, in order to avoid the enforced subdivision of their family farms, have limited themselves to small families.

2. French society has placed a premium on the education of children. This has increased their expensiveness and decreased their economic value to the parents, thus, it is asserted, leading to smaller families.

3. The French Revolution proclaimed the equality of all men and the right of all to rise socially and economically to the highest levels their talents could attain. It is asserted that emphasis on climbing the social ladder has led to limitation of families in order for the adults to be less burdened for the climb.

4. The family has exercised great control over the choice of the marriage partner in France. It is asserted that marriages which have often been little more than economic arrangements have not been conducive to large families where the means were available to avoid them.

5. Though nominally Catholic by 90 percent or more, much of the French population is "anticlerical" or nonreligious. It is asserted that weakening of religious ties has had much to do with the rise of birth control.

6. It is asserted that increasing urbanization has had an adverse effect on the birth rate, since children are less convenient in an urban environment. Although this is undoubtedly true, France has been much less urbanized than a number of other countries which began considerably later to follow the same path of population development.

Probably all of the aforementioned factors have been operative against the French birth rate, and none fully explains the matter. Another factor that might be mentioned is the failure of the French economy to develop new opportunities for employment as rapidly as the economies of a number of other industrialized countries. At any rate, the small population increases that did occur from the middle of the nineteenth century were largely due to immigration. After World War II the French birth rate took a sudden and unexpected upward spurt, but expert opinion does not believe this will continue. The total increase 1946–1953 was about 2 million.

The National Economy of France

The relative decline of French power in the twentieth century is partly associated with the nature of the French national economy. Both the agriculture and the industry of France are characterized by small-scale units of production and relatively inefficient methods as compared with other advanced nations. More hand labor is employed per unit of output than is true of such nations as the United States, Germany, or Great Britain. In agriculture France has failed to utilize adequately the advantages afforded by a favorable climate and good soils; in industry she has concentrated on light consumer items, especially of a luxury character, rather than heavy manufactures. From the standpoint of national power these characteristics have been a disadvantage to France in an age which trends increasingly toward large-scale, mechanized mass production and in which the most powerful nations tend to be those with the greatest development of the heavier types of industry.

▶ Characteristics of French Agriculture

Although France is one of the more important industrial nations, agriculture predominates over industry in terms of employment. In 1946 36 percent of the labor force was employed in agriculture, forestry, and fishing, as against only 23 percent in manufacturing. Agriculture is relatively more important as a source of employment in France than in any of the other industrialized nations bordering the North Sea.

France emerged from the French Revolution as a nation of small peasant farmers, most of whom owned their farms. The proverbial industry and thrift of the French peasant have been a great asset to the country, but his often narrow and unreasoning individualism and conservatism have been on occasion a provoking source of national weakness.

In 1947, 25 percent of all French farms were less than 2.5 acres in size and 72 percent were less than 24.8 acres. These farms, however, accounted for only 23 percent of the total farm land of France. Only 28 percent of all farms were larger than 24.8 acres, but these larger farms represented 77 percent of all French farm land. In other words, most French farms are small, but most French farm land is in fairly large holdings. The considerable inequality thus revealed is also characteristic of the distribution of other forms of wealth in France.

About 40 percent of all French land is cultivated. This is approximately equal to the proportion of cultivated land in Germany and is higher than the proportion in any other country of northwestern Europe except Denmark. Excluding the Soviet Union, France has a greater total acreage of arable land than any other European country and a greater acreage per capita than any of the North Sea countries except Denmark and Sweden. Farming methods, however, are not so advanced as in some of the neighboring countries. The French peasant, despite the relative abundance of land and definite advantages of climate and soil, gets lower yields on the average than his compatriot in Denmark, the Netherlands, Belgium, the United Kingdom, or Germany. For example, the average yield of wheat per acre in Denmark, the Netherlands, or Belgium is ordinarily about double the average yield in France.

Nevertheless, France is a sizable producer of a varied list of agricultural commodities. Wheat leads in acreage. Other major crops are oats, barley, potatoes, sugar beets, grapes, orchard fruits, and vegetables. France is the largest producer of wheat in Europe, exclusive of the Soviet Union, and is the world's largest producer of grapes and apples, used principally for making wine and cider, respectively. Livestock totals also are impressive: excluding the Soviet Union, France raises more cattle than any other European country, more horses than any country except Poland, and more hogs than any country except Germany and Poland. In sheep production France is exceeded only by Spain, the United Kingdom, Italy, Yugoslavia, Rumania, and Bulgaria.

France is the only nation of Western Europe which is normally self-sufficient in wheat, and France comes the closest of any to being completely self-sufficient in food. Some food is regularly imported, however. The high degree of French self-sufficiency in agricultural products is due to the large proportion of arable land and the relatively low density of population; it is achieved in spite of the relative inefficiency of the French farmer. The lack of efficiency in French agriculture, and the great importance of wheat as well, are probably due in good part to the protection from foreign competition which high tariffs have afforded. At the same time no such scientific and nationalistically motivated attempt to increase the productivity of the land has been made in France as in Germany, which also has protected its agriculture from outside competition.

▶ Relation of the Economy to Urbanization

As compared with other nations bordering the North Sea, France has a relatively low degree of urbanization. According to the census of 1946 the population of France was 53 percent urban. Comparative urban percentages for the other North Sea nations in the period 1946–1951 were: Norway 51, Netherlands 55, Sweden 56, Belgium 63, Denmark 67, Germany 72, and the United Kingdom 80. France is especially noteworthy for the small number of large cities in proportion to the size of the national population. Only three French cities have a population of approximately half a million or more: Paris (2,853,000, or about 5,500,000 with suburbs), Marseilles, and Lyons. Each of the latter cities has a population of more than 600,000 including suburbs. The next largest cities are Toulouse and Bordeaux, each with a population of well over 250,000.

The dearth of large cities in France is partly a reflection of the predominant position of agriculture in French life. It is also partly due to the failure of French industry to develop enterprises of a sufficient scale to foster the growth of large industrial cities. The high degree of centralization in the French government has been an additional factor tending to favor the growth of Paris at the expense of other French cities. In few other countries is so large a proportion of the urban population contained in the largest city.

▶ *Characteristics of French Industry*

The small family-owned factory or shop is the characteristic type of manufacturing enterprise in France. Individual manufacturing establishments are more numerous in France than in the United States, but the average American establishment employs several times as many workers. France is basically a producer of light consumer goods requiring a considerable amount of hand labor. Products of this nature, emphasizing quality, elegance, and taste, do not lend themselves well to modern techniques of mechanized mass production. Wine making is a characteristic industry in which France leads the world. French production of wine in 1953 amounted to

A view of a characteristic French industry. Decorating chinaware by hand at Limoges. (*French Embassy Press and Information Division.*)

1,410,000,000 gallons, one fourth of the world total. The bulk of the production is consumed within the country, and only the best wines, bearing famous names like Champagne or Cognac, are exported. Other characteristic products of French consumer industries are perfumes and cosmetics, fine laces and other expensive fabrics, jewelry, cut glass, and fine porcelain. Paris is a world center for the manufacture of fashionable women's clothing and millinery. Although such products ordinarily command a good sale in export markets, they do not provide a solid basis for large-scale industrialization. In the strenuous economic, political, and military competition among nations in the twentieth century, France has been handicapped by an overemphasis on goods of a luxury character and an underemphasis on volume production of iron and steel, machinery, and other basic commodities which underlie national strength.

The lack of large-scale industrial development in France is to be explained partly by the strong individualism of the French worker, who has often preferred to work alone or in company with a few others rather than risk the loss of his identity among several hundred or several thousand employees in a large plant. It has also been partly due to a lack of capital for financing large-scale enterprises. The Frenchman has been notoriously conservative as an investor, being inclined to hoard his money or to purchase government securities rather than invest in common stocks. In addition, the French family-owned business has ordinarily been reluctant to seek capital outside the family, since this would admit outsiders to a share of ownership and perhaps of control and management. Thus expansion of family-owned enterprises has often had to depend on accumulated profits. The development of large-scale, efficient industries in France has probably been hampered also by the high degree of protection given by tariffs. Furthermore, with its relatively low population density and high degree of self-sufficiency in foodstuffs, it has not been so necessary for France to compete in world markets as for nations like the United Kingdom or Belgium. Thus French industry has been able, and has chosen, to concentrate mainly on supplying the French home and colonial market. This market is relatively small and has been slow to expand; it cannot support a really large scale of operations. The industry of a country can afford to be inefficient if competition need not be feared.

Since World War II a number of the major economic enterprises have been nationalized, including the Bank of France, most of the major insurance companies, the coal industry, and the gas and electric power industries. The major part of the French communication and transportation systems has long been government-owned. Belief that French private enterprise was incapable of improving the country's economic position and the fact that certain industrialists had collaborated with the Germans during the occupation period were major factors behind the postwar nationalizations.

▶ Mineral Resources and Heavy Industrial Development

It should not be inferred from the foregoing discussion that France is entirely lacking in large-scale industrial facilities capable of mass producing iron and steel, metal wares, basic chemicals, and the cheaper grades of textiles. France is distinguished not by a complete lack of such facilities, but only by a lack relative as compared to other advanced industrial nations. Substantial industrial progress has been made since World War I, based principally on the utilization of a group of key mineral resources, including iron ore, coal, potash, and bauxite, as well as on increased development of France's large reserves of hydroelectric power. Industrial development after 1914 was stimulated first by the need for munitions and military equipment during the war, and later by the necesity for large-scale rebuilding in the devastated areas adjoining the northeastern frontier. Mechanization of industry was stimulated by a severe shortage of labor, which also resulted in an influx of several million foreign workers (mainly Italian, Belgian, Spanish, and Portuguese) following the war.

Reacquisition of Lorraine and Alsace from Germany gave access to major deposits of iron ore, potash, and salt. In addition, France controlled the coal production of the Saar from 1919 until 1935 and again following World War II. These resources, plus the coal of northern France adjoining the Belgian frontier, provided the basis for heavy industry. Today France is the fifth nation in iron and steel production, although her output of 12 million tons of steel in 1952 (excluding 3 million tons produced by the Saar) was only two thirds as large as the production of Germany or the United Kingdom, less than one third as large as the production of the Soviet Union, and only about an eighth as large as the production of the United States. The main centers of iron and steel production are in Lorraine, where the principal iron deposits are found. The Lorraine ores are fairly low-grade, averaging only 32 percent iron content and having a high content of phosphorus impurities. However, the reserves, among the largest in the world, are probably adequate in quantity for all foreseeable French needs, and the Thomas-Gilchrist process of iron manufacture makes possible the economical removal of the phosphorus. Smaller centers of iron and steel production are found in northern France in the coal field and in the eastern margins of the Massif Central, where minor local deposits of coal occur. Lorraine and neighboring Alsace are important centers of chemical manufacture, based on immense deposits of rock salt in Lorraine and potash and salt in Alsace. These provinces, in association with the Saar, represent the core of heavy industry in France.

Despite substantial reserves in the north, France suffers from a shortage of coal, especially high-grade coal suitable for coking. The northern field, which produces about two thirds of the French total, consists mainly of thin seams which are deeply buried, often broken or tilted, and consequently expensive and difficult to mine. In addition, France, like Britain, has lacked an adequate supply of coal miners during recent decades, and the methods of extraction have frequently been antiquated and inefficient. Since World War II the French have made energetic efforts to increase the volume and efficiency of their coal production. Considerable progress has been made toward developing a commercially feasible process for coking the low-grade coals of Lorraine. These coals, an extension of the Saar deposits, exist in thick seams which are relatively easy to work. Production has been increasing, and the Lorraine field accounts for a fifth or more of the French total. Since World War II France has secured a 50-year lease on the coal mines of the Saar. This small German-speaking area has been a major bone of contention between France and Germany. It was German territory prior to World War I, but was placed under League of Nations jurisdiction in 1919, with France having access to the coal deposits by virtue of a customs union. Following a plebiscite in 1935 the Saar was returned to German control. However, it became a French zone of occupation at the end of World War II, and the mines were leased to France as stated above. At the time of writing in 1954 the Saar was an autonomous territory with a government of its own. Proposals were afoot to make it the first "European" political unit by placing it under the jurisdiction of the six-nation European Coal and Steel Community or some other supranational body. Access to Saar production greatly alleviates the French coal problem but does not completely solve it, since the Saar coals must be mixed with higher-grade coking coals, supplied principally by the Ruhr, in order to be satisfactorily used in iron and steel manufacture. Unless the French effort to utilize low-grade coals for coking proves a success, it seems likely that a considerable amount of coal will continue to be imported from Germany. Such imports are being facilitated by a lowering of customs barriers under the Schuman Plan.

France has some petroleum and natural gas in the southwest, but hydroelectricity is the principal alternative to coal as a source of power. The hydroelectric potential of the country is mainly localized in the Alps, Pyrenees, Vosges, and Massif Central. A number of major schemes of hydroelectric development have been undertaken in the Alps since World War II, and power production in that area has been greatly expanded. As a consequence, an increase in manufacturing activity is to be expected, both in the Alps and in the near-by Rhône Valley. France and Italy lead all European countries in hydroelectric power production and are exceeded in the world only by the United States, Canada, and Japan. One of France's principal mineral resources, bauxite, is conveniently located in the far south adjoining the Mediterranean Sea and relatively near to the electric power stations of the Alps. Bauxite, the ore from which aluminum is extracted, requires large amounts of electric power for processing. France is the largest producer of bauxite in Europe, and her aluminum production is fourth in the world, being surpassed by that of the United States, Canada, and the Soviet Union.

With the few important exceptions already noted, the mineral position of France is not very strong. Not only is France itself deficient in most of the major minerals, but the French overseas possessions are poorer in this respect than are the possessions of Britain. The most valuable mineral reserves of the overseas areas are found in French North Africa, which contains some of the world's largest deposits of phosphate rock, plus a fair amount of high-grade iron ore.

▶ The Major Industrial Concentrations

Large concentrations of industry in France are few in number. The Lorraine-Saar district has already been described as the major center of heavy industry. However, in value and variety of production, as well as in number of workers employed, the Paris metropolitan area overshadows other industrial districts in importance. Paris is the main center of the French automobile industry. It has an extremely wide variety of other finishing industries. In the north of France the city of Lille adjoining the Belgian border is the largest of several contiguous textile-milling cities producing woolens, linens, and cottons. The conurbation of Lille contains nearly three quarters of a million people and another half-million live near by in a group of small to medium-sized mining and metallurgical centers on the northern coal field. The industrial area of northern France is continued across the border in Belgium.

Still another important industrial district surrounds the city of Lyons in the Rhône Valley. About a million people live in the conurbation which includes Lyons, St. Étienne, and smaller satellite cities and suburbs. Textile production, emphasizing silk and rayon, is the best-known of a varied group of industries in Lyons and its environs, while St. Étienne is a coal-mining and metallurgical center. France has many industrial areas which are secondary in importance to those already described; possibly the most noteworthy are the Marseilles district, which has the diversified collection of industries customarily associated with a great seaport, and the cotton-milling district centering on the city of Mulhouse (87,000) in southern Alsace between the Rhine and the Belfort Gap.

► Transportation Facilities

The French economy is served by an excellent network of internal transportation and port facilities. Paris is the center of a spiderweb of railroads, paved highways, and navigable waterways radiating outward toward the seaports and land frontiers of France. The most important rail lines run south to Lyons and Marseilles, north to Lille, Calais, and Belgium, east to Lorraine and Germany, northwest to the Seine ports of Rouen and Le Havre, and southwest to Bordeaux and Toulouse. The Seine River and its tributaries provide the principal system of internal waterways; Paris, at the junction of the Seine and its major tributary, the Marne, handles by far the largest tonnage of any inland port in France. Canals connect the Seine system with the Rhine, Rhône, Meuse, Scheldt, and Loire.

France faces the sea on three sides. Marseilles is the principal Mediterranean port and the major port for traffic with the French colonies. Bordeaux, on the deep estuary of the Garonne River (known as the Gironde), is the sea outlet of the Southwestern Lowland and the main port facing the Bay of Biscay. Le Havre and Rouen are the major ports on the English Channel. Rouen, located upstream on the Seine River at the head of ocean navigation, is mainly a freight port, while Le Havre, at the mouth of the Seine, accommodates large passenger liners as well as cargo vessels. Le Havre vies with Marseilles for leadership among French seaports. The two Seine ports are about equal in size, each having slightly more than 100,000 people. Seaports of lesser importance than those named include the shipbuilding centers of Nantes (200,000) and its smaller outport of St. Nazaire, on the estuary of the Loire River; the transatlantic passenger port of Cherbourg (40,000), on the Cotentin peninsula; and the small but busy Channel ports of Boulogne, Calais, and Dunkirk, each a city with a population of 50,000 to 100,000.

France is a mature nation which has made great contributions to the world. Its unfortunate history in the twentieth century has been marked by one internal crisis after another; more than most nations France can be said to have lived in a constant atmosphere of crisis since the outbreak of World War I. The difficulties of France in this century have arisen from a variety of causes: military defeat in World War II and near-defeat with tremendous casualties in World War I, severe inflation and economic depression in the 1920's and 1930's, unrest in colonial areas, especially since World War II, and internal political instability associated with these and other factors. The friends and well-wishers of France in other lands will watch anxiously in the coming decades to see whether this nation, with its historic past and great traditions, can somehow manage to solve its multitude of problems and again achieve the stability and prosperity it has enjoyed in past times.

The Iron Curtain. Soviet troops returning through the Brandenburg Gate after placing wreaths on a war memorial in the British-occupied sector of Berlin. (*U. S. Army Photograph.*)

Germany

In the magazine *Foreign Affairs* Germany was once referred to as "The Problem Child of Europe." [1] The expression is apt, for modern Germany has been a problem to its neighbors ever since its unification in the middle decades of last century.

Historical Introduction

Prior to the year 1866, "Germany" was little more than a territorial expression referring to a loosely connected group of independent or semi-independent states, mostly small, in Central Europe. This group of states, a holdover from feudal times, possessed a certain amount of economic unity resulting from the gradual abolition of customs barriers after the Napoleonic wars. But political unity was not achieved until the period 1866–1871, when all of the states were combined into a single country which shortly emerged as the most powerful nation on the mainland of Europe.

▶ Background of German Unification

The historical background of German unification has been briefly sketched as follows: [2]

[1] Dorothy Thompson, "The Problem Child of Europe." *Foreign Affairs*, v. 18 (1940), pp. 389–412.

[2] *Geographical Foundations of National Power* (Army Service Forces Manual M 103–1). Washington: Government Printing Office, 1944. P. 63.

In ancient and medieval times Germanic peoples overran large parts of Europe. Having invaded the ancient Roman Empire, they settled down in various parts of the conquered lands and were eventually absorbed by the native populace. Later conquests led in the ninth century to the creation of the Holy Roman Empire of the German Nation. This loose congeries of petty German states finally expired at the time of Napoleon (1806) because of internal weaknesses. Voltaire said it was "neither holy, nor Roman, nor an Empire," and despite its name it was certainly not a national state in the modern sense.

Except for Italy, Germany was the last of the Great Powers to achieve national unity. During the centuries from the close of the Middle Ages down to 1870, while Great Britain, France, and Russia were strong and united, Germany remained subdivided among petty states, and its people as a whole felt little national consciousness. In political loyalty they were Prussians or Bavarians or Saxons, and Germans only in speech and culture.

Unification was a slow process, accomplished under the leadership of Prussia, which from about 1740 on gradually extended its own territories to include the whole of northern Germany. In 1871 Bismarck's statesmanship brought South Germany also into a new state, over which the King of Prussia was crowned as Emperor William I. Thus was created the Second German Empire, a firmly knit federation under Prussian domination.

From the beginning the new nation assumed an aggressive military posture. Even before final unification the German states, led by Prussia, had defeated France in the short Franco-Prussian War of 1870–1871. In 1914 and again in 1939 Germany embarked on ambitious schemes of military conquest, but in both of the resulting World Wars the German armies, after initial successes, eventually succumbed to the combined strength of their opponents. Few nations in Europe have escaped invasion by German military forces since 1870. Some,

particularly France and Belgium, have been invaded repeatedly. These recurrent invasions, with their attendant destruction, loss of liberty, and loss of life, have made a deep impression on all the invaded peoples, so that fear of German armed strength is today a powerful force in European thought and politics.

▶ German Leadership in Industry and Commerce

Although Germany was defeated in both World Wars, it was only after years of conflict in which the German armies, with some assistance from weaker allies, withstood the combined forces of many nations. The staying power of Germany, as manifested in these wars, was among other things a reflection of German industrial strength. The period 1871 to 1914 witnessed a rapid development of large-scale industry, so that by the outbreak of World War I German industrial production exceeded that of any other nation in continental Europe. German leadership was particularly marked in coal, steel, and chemicals—critical commodities in which German production rivaled or surpassed even that of the foremost European industrial power, Great Britain.

Industrial development in Germany came to be largely dominated by great monopolistic combinations or trusts: I. G. Farben in chemicals, the Krupp and Thyssen interests in iron and steel, and many others. Through efficient organization these industrial combines, fostered by the state and allied with German science, were able to overcome many of the handicaps created by a rather mediocre domestic base of industrial resources. The industrial mag-

Cities, internal waterways, landform divisions, mineral resources, and iron and steel and chemical industries of Germany. Political capitals of German Federal Republic and German Democratic Republic are underlined. City symbols for Map 2 duplicate larger cities of Map 1. (*Based in part on two maps in* Focus.)

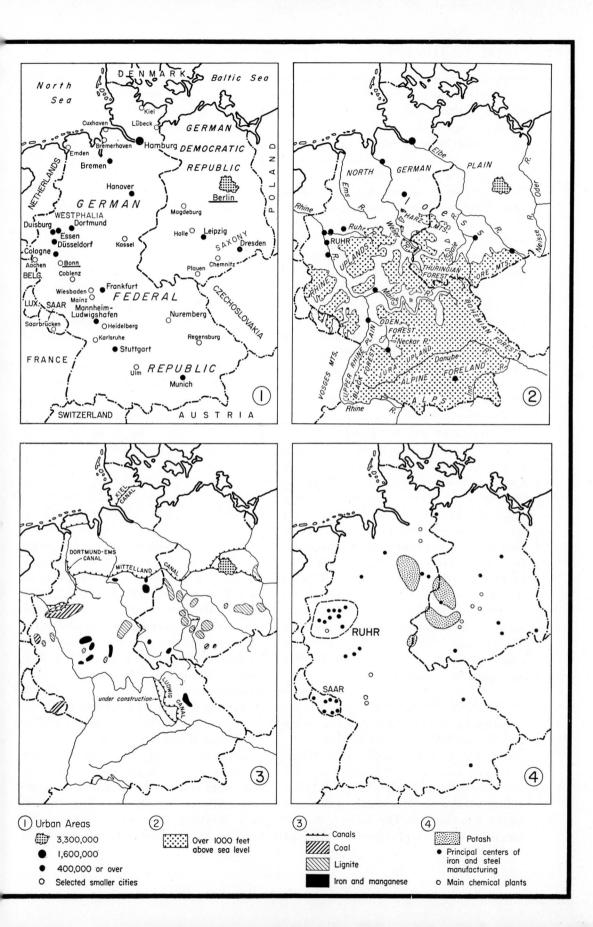

Map 1

North Sea
DENMARK
Baltic Sea
Kiel
Lübeck
Cuxhaven
GERMAN
Bremerhaven
Emden
Hamburg
DEMOCRATIC
Bremen
REPUBLIC
Hanover
POLAND
GERMAN
Magdeburg
Berlin
WESTPHALIA
Dortmund
Duisburg
Halle
Leipzig
Essen
SAXONY
Düsseldorf
Kassel
Dresden
Cologne
Plauen
Chemnitz
Aachen
Bonn
BELG.
Coblenz
CZECHOSLOVAKIA
Wiesbaden
Frankfurt
LUX.
SAAR
Mainz
FEDERAL
Mannheim-
Saarbrücken
Ludwigshafen
Nuremberg
Heidelberg
Regensburg
Karlsruhe
FRANCE
Stuttgart
Ulm
REPUBLIC
Munich
SWITZERLAND
AUSTRIA
①

Map 2

NORTH
GERMAN
PLAIN
Ems R.
Elbe R.
Rhine
Oder R.
HARZ MTS.
Weser R.
Neisse R.
RUHR
Ruhr R.
Saale R.
UPLANDS
THURINGIAN
FOREST
ORE MTS.
RHINE
Main R.
BOHEMIAN FOREST
VOSGES MTS.
ODEN
FOREST
Neckar R.
UPPER RHINE PLAIN
JURA UPLAND
Danube R.
Isar R.
BLACK FOREST
ALPINE FORELAND
Rhine R.
A L P S
Inn R.
②

Map 3

KIEL CANAL
DORTMUND-EMS CANAL
MITTELLAND CANAL
LUDWIG CANAL
under construction
③

Map 4

RUHR
SAAR
④

① Urban Areas

- 3,300,000
- 1,600,000
- 400,000 or over
- ○ Selected smaller cities

② ▒ Over 1000 feet above sea level

③
- Canals
- ▨ Coal
- ▨ Lignite
- ■ Iron and manganese

④
- ▒ Potash
- ● Principal centers of iron and steel manufacturing
- ○ Main chemical plants

nates who headed these enterprises came to exercise great influence on the political as well as the economic life of Germany. To some degree the trend toward monopoly was offset by agitation among the working classes for increased social control of industry. However, the ultimate results of the latter movement were not very impressive, although a certain amount of legislation favorable to labor was enacted prior to 1890.

Development of industry was accompanied by a great expansion of commerce. The Germans built a large merchant marine and a sizable navy, and by 1914 were actively contesting with the British in overseas trade. However, the bulk of German trade was carried on with other countries of Europe.

▶ The Short-Lived German Colonial Empire

Between 1884 and 1900 Germany built a colonial empire, mainly in Africa, but also including island territories in the Pacific Ocean and certain holdings in China. All of these overseas possessions were lost as a result of World War I, and Germany today has no colonies. Most of the former German colonial territories are at present being administered as trusteeships under supervision of the United Nations. Between the two World Wars German politicians repeatedly demanded the return of the colonies on the basis of German need for "Lebensraum" (living space)—a phrase eventually used as an excuse for German aggression in continental Europe.

▶ The Nazi Dictatorship

Following World War I, Germany was a republic until 1933, when the National Socialist or Nazi Party, under Adolf Hitler, came to power and established a dictatorship, the Third Reich (Third Empire), which endured until the defeat of Germany by the Allies in 1945. The Nazis, with their fantastic doctrines of German racial superiority, Pan-Germanism, and exaggerated devotion to the dictator, found allies in German big business and the Prussian military clique. Under the Nazi regime democratic traditions and practices, never too strong in Germany, were thoroughly submerged.

▶ Postwar Territorial Arrangements

Following the German surrender in 1945, the part of the country immediately east of the Oder and Neisse Rivers was placed under Polish administration. East Prussia was divided and occupied by Russia and Poland. The Saarland was made quasi-independent politically, but was meshed into the French economy. The remainder of prewar Germany was divided into four zones of occupation administered, respectively, by the United States, Britain, France, and the Soviet Union. The capital city of Berlin, deep within the Soviet Zone, was placed under joint administration of the four powers. As a result of postwar tensions between the Soviet Union and the three Western powers, the western boundary of the Soviet Zone gradually crystallized into a dividing line between two separate republics. This boundary now forms the German segment of the highly publicized "Iron Curtain." To the west of the boundary is the German Federal Republic, or West Germany, with approximately 95,000 square miles and 50 million people. To the east is the Soviet-inspired German Democratic Republic, or East Germany, with about 42,000 square miles and 20 million people. Population figures given for both republics include figures for Berlin, amounting to more than 2.1 million in the Western zones of the city and more than 1.1 million in the Soviet zone.

Thus the question arises, what is meant by "Germany"? The present political divisions were reached on the basis of expediency and may or may not endure. In German thinking they are not necessarily permanent: present-day German-compiled statistics almost invariably include all of the territory occupied by the nation in 1936, although such figures may be classified under the headings of "Federal Republic," "Democratic Republic," "West Berlin," "The section administered by Poland," "East Prussia," and "The Saar Territory." In this chapter the word "Germany" will be used to designate the territory occupied by the German Federal Republic, the German Democratic Republic, and the whole of Berlin. The term "prewar Germany" will be used to designate the country as delimited in 1936.

The Diversified German Environment

Whether viewed with respect to natural or cultural features Germany is not a simple land, although it does not have quite as much variety as its neighbor, France. Broadly conceived, the terrain of Germany can be divided at the approximate latitudinal center into a low-lying, undulating plain at the north, and higher country to the south.

► The North German Plain

The lowland of northern Germany is a part of the much larger North European Plain. The German segment of the plain seldom rises much above 500 feet in elevation and is mostly below 300 feet. It is predominantly an area of former glaciation, and the present topography bears much evidence of glacial action. Among the more prominent glacial features are the low ridges or *terminal moraines,* formed by continued deposition at the front of an ice sheet during times when melting balanced the ice movement to such an extent that the ice front remained stationary for a considerable period. These moraines rise intermittently above a surface that is fairly level but seldom flat and is principally composed of infertile sandy or gravelly land punctuated here and there by stretches of heavy clay, a considerable number of bogs, and, in the northeast, many lakes. Along the coasts and river estuaries, especially in the northwest, are found expanses of flat, somewhat more fertile land that in most instances had to be drained artificially before use and resembles the diked lands of the adjoining Netherlands and Belgium.

► The Varied Terrain of Southern Germany

The southern countryside is much less uniform than the northern plain. To the extreme south are the high German Alps, fringed by a rolling piedmont or foreland that slopes gradually toward the east-flowing upper Danube River. Between the Danube and the northern plain is a complex series of uplands and depressions. The uplands are predominantly composed of rounded, forested hills or low mountains: they include (1) the Bohemian Forest, Ore Mountains (Erzgebirge), and Uplands of Saxony at the east, bordering Czechoslovakia; (2) the Black Forest, Oden Forest, and Rhine Uplands at the west, bordering the Rhine River; (3) the famed Harz Mountains and Thuringian Forest at the north center; and (4) the low Jura Upland at the south, bordering the Danube on the northern side of the river. Interspersed with these uplands are broad agricultural depressions or basins draining to the Rhine, Danube, Weser, or Elbe.

► The Major Rivers

The latter streams, together with the Oder, are the principal German rivers. Three of them, however—the Rhine, Elbe, and Oder—rise outside the borders of Germany, and three—the Rhine, Danube, and Oder—enter the sea via a foreign country. Only the Weser is a purely German stream. The Rhine, which is by far the most im-

A winter scene in the Harz Mountains. (*German Tourist Information Office.*)

portant internal waterway of Germany, rises in Switzerland. From the Swiss border to the junction with its major right-bank tributary the Main River, the Rhine flows in a flat-floored valley bordered on the east by the Black and Oden Forests and on the west by the Vosges Mountains of France. Downstream, the river follows a narrow gorge through the Rhine Uplands before it emerges upon the North German Plain in the vicinity of the industrial Ruhr district. Nearly all of the lower course of the Rhine from the Ruhr to the North Sea lies in the Netherlands. The Weser also flows to the North Sea, as does the Elbe, which rises in Czechoslovakia. The Oder, formerly German for almost its entire length, now lies mostly in Poland, although it forms the boundary for a distance between Poland and East Germany. The Oder enters the Baltic Sea through Polish territory. The Danube River rises in the Black Forest of southwestern Germany, although several important tributaries enter the upper river from Austria. The Danube

flows eastward to the Black Sea. Most of the course of the river lies outside Germany.

▶ Climate, Soils, and Vegetation

The climate of Germany is maritime in the northwest and becomes increasingly continental toward the east and south. Along the North and Baltic Seas temperatures are generally similar to those of coastal British Columbia, whereas in Westphalia they are more like those of western Oregon or Washington. In the higher country to the south and southeast, temperatures are generally comparable to those of northern Idaho. On the whole, the climate of Germany, like that of other countries of northwestern Europe, is characterized by rather mild temperatures. The January average temperature is 36.3°F. at Cologne, 33.8° at Bremen, 31.6° at Berlin, and 28.2° at Munich. July average temperatures are 65.1° at Cologne, 63.3° at Bremen, 66.4° at Berlin, and 63.9° at Munich. The annual precipitation is adequate but not excessive, with most places in the lowlands receiving an average of 20 to 30 inches per year. Distribution of the rainfall is fairly uniform throughout the year, although there does exist a tendency for a summer maximum toward the south and east.

The soils of Germany, while extremely varied in type, are rather acid and infertile by nature. Soils significantly higher than average in fertility are found mainly in a discontinuous belt along the southern margins of the North German Plain. Here a cover of loess (wind-blown silt) has provided parent material for the most productive large group of soils in Germany. Another region possessing soils of comparatively high natural fertility is the alluvial upper Rhine Valley, between the city of Mainz and the Swiss border. The remainder of the country has soils that tend to be, at best, of moderate quality; many, especially those of the hilly or mountainous sections, are poor.

The original virgin forest is thought to have been a mixture of coniferous and deciduous trees; today conifers predominate, although deciduous species are relatively abundant. Tracts of forest are distributed irregularly throughout the country on the rougher lands and the better-drained areas of poor soil. Germany has long been famous for its state-administered and rigidly controlled program of forest management and conservation. About a fifth of the country is forested—the same proportion as in France.

▶ Coal, Potash and Other Minerals

Among Germany's mineral resources, coal is by far the most abundant and vital to the national economy. The reserves, while amounting to much less than those of either the United States or the Soviet Union, are nevertheless extremely large, and seem adequate in quantity and quality for all foreseeable German and Western European needs. The largest and best deposits of bituminous coal, together with some anthracite, are found in the Ruhr coal basin and the near-by, but much smaller, Aachen field. Lignite is mined extensively in the industrialized province of Saxony, located in East Germany adjoining Czechoslovakia. Smaller deposits of coal and lignite are found in a number of places, especially in the border zone which is situated between the North German Plain and the southern uplands.

Potash, a vital material in the chemical industry, is another mineral which Germany is known to possess in outstanding quantities. The deposits, situated mainly between the city of Hanover and the upper Elbe River, coincide in location rather closely with the fertile belt of loess soils. The postwar division of the country has placed the bulk of German potash deposits within the German Democratic Republic and thus within the economic orbit of the Soviet Union.

Aside from coal and potash, and substantial deposits of common salt worked in Saxony and the lower Rhineland, Germany is not well provided with minerals. The country has some low-grade iron ore and small deposits of a number of other metals, but the reserves and production are far from adequate. The deficiency in iron is particularly noteworthy. The German steel industry, third largest in the world, must rely mainly on imported iron ore, which is principally secured from France and Sweden.

Regional Differences in Culture

The German people as a whole form a cohesive national group, and they have evinced a rather strong loyalty to the German nation during recent times. Nevertheless, certain regional differences in culture are worthy of note. There are important differences between the North German Plain and southern Germany. "Southern Germany is today largely Catholic, northern Germany predominantly Protestant. There are marked differences in dialect between the two areas. Northern Germany was unified under Prussia long before the unification of the whole German nation in 1871. Under the Second Empire, from 1871 to 1918, the many petty states into which South Germany had for centuries been broken retained a considerable measure of autonomy, and even under the republic the different parts of southern Germany maintained political individuality as administrative districts."[3]

The sandy plains east of the Elbe River, mainly agricultural rather than industrial, and formerly dominated by the large estates of the Prussian military caste (Junkers), have also differed in historical, cultural, and economic respects from the rest of the country. "In the early Middle Ages eastern Germany was a Slavic domain into which the Germans pushed forward their frontiers. Here Prussia first took form, a military state warring with Poles, Russians, and Baltic peoples, at a time when western Germany could enjoy longer periods of peace and security."[4] Today this area is being Communized under the auspices of the Soviet Union.

Population and Economy of Germany

Germany is one of the most densely populated countries in the world. Excluding a few of the micro-states, its over-all density of approximately 511 per square mile is exceeded in Europe only by the Netherlands (812), Belgium (744), and the United Kingdom (534). The German Federal Republic, with approximately 526 per square mile, is somewhat more densely populated than the German Democratic Republic, with about 476 per square mile.

▶ Distribution of Population and Cities

The distribution of rural population is fairly uniform throughout the country. The lightest densities are found in the more rugged parts of the southern uplands and in some of the more infertile areas of the northern plain. The heaviest densities tend to occur in the zone of loess soils and in the southwestern depressions draining to the Rhine.

Germany is a highly urbanized country, though less so than the United Kingdom. Of the total population of the Federal Republic, about 30 percent live in the 46 cities (excluding West Berlin) with populations of 100,000 or more. In the more rural Democratic Republic approximately 20 percent are in the nine cities (excluding East Berlin) of 100,000 or more. The primary axis of city development in Germany tends to follow the border zone between the North German Plain and the southern uplands. This axis is anchored on the west by the great cluster of industrial cities in the Ruhr and on the east by a smaller, less concentrated cluster of manufacturing cities in Saxony. In the center are the relatively isolated industrial and transportation centers of Hanover (468,000) and Magdeburg (252,000). Berlin, the largest city of Germany, is situated slightly to the north of the main urban axis at its eastern end. The population of Berlin was 3,300,000 according to the 1950 census. Other major German cities outside the main urban axis include (1) the North Sea ports of Hamburg (1,658,000) and Bremen (463,000); (2) the widely spaced cities along the Rhine and its tributaries, including (besides the Ruhr cities) Cologne (629,000), Mannheim (256,-

---

[3] *Geographical Foundations of National Power, op. cit.,* p. 67.

[4] *Ibid.,* p. 68.

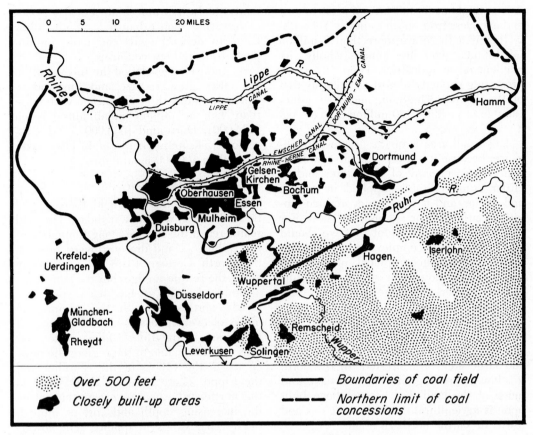

The Ruhr. (After two maps in Focus.)

000; including suburbs, more than 400,-
000), Frankfurt-on-the-Main (564,000; including suburbs, more than 600,000), and
Stuttgart (522,000); and (3) the important,
though isolated, Bavarian cities of Munich
(870,000) and Nuremberg (382,000).

▶ Germany's Premier Industrial District —The Ruhr

The urban dwellers of Germany, and
many of the rural inhabitants as well, are
primarily dependent upon manufacturing
for a livelihood. Germany is beyond question the third or fourth manufacturing nation of the world, being outranked only by
the United States, the Soviet Union, and
possibly the United Kingdom. As in all

great manufacturing countries, industrial
development primarily rests on three basic
lines of goods: (1) metals, particularly iron
and steel, (2) textiles, and (3) chemicals.
The largest single concentration of industry is found in the Ruhr, an industrial district so important as to have no real
counterpart in all of Europe. The Ruhr is
the principal seat of the German iron and
steel and coal-mining industries, and has
important metal-fabricating, textile, and
chemical industries as well. It is briefly described and analyzed in the following selection by a British geographer, Norman
J. G. Pounds: [5]

The Ruhr is a very small area to have
figured so prominently in the news. At most

---

[5] Norman J. G. Pounds, "The Ruhr," *Focus*, v. 1,
no. 3 (1950), pp. 1–3. Three subheads and populations of cities have been added. Used by permission

of the author and *Focus*, which is published by
the American Geographical Society of New
York.

it is only about 50 miles from west to east and even less from south to north. Yet within this area there are more than 6 million inhabitants, who are almost wholly dependent on its industries. There is a steel-producing capacity almost as great as that of the United Kingdom, and coal mines capable of yielding 120 million tons of coal a year.

This small area is of the greatest significance, because it has been the arsenal from which the Germany of the Kaiser and of Hitler equipped and supplied its armies and navies, and it may again produce munitions either for or against the West. For this reason it is important that we should know how this complex industrial area operates, what geographical problems it presents, and how their solution will further or hinder the cause of the Western democracies. . . .

[The Ruhr is located] in northwest Germany, close to the Belgian and Dutch frontiers. In the south the Ruhr is hilly, and large areas are forested. In the north it is low and rolling; movement is easy, and much of the land that has not been built upon is agricultural. Most of the cities and towns lie on the northern plain. . . .

Across the western edge of the Ruhr flows the Rhine, a great highway of trade between South Germany and the Netherlands. The industrial area is drained by the Ruhr, Emscher, and Lippe Rivers. . . . Canals have been built along the Emscher and Lippe valleys and at their east ends are joined to the Dortmund-Ems Canal, by which they are linked with the German North Sea ports of Emden and Bremen.

The Ruhr industrial area has grown up within the last 100 years. Its origins lay in the primitive iron refining carried on in the hills, where there were small deposits of iron ore, as well as charcoal for the furnaces and running streams to power the machines and the hammers. It was not until after 1850 that industry spread on any considerable scale from this early center into the area that we now call the Ruhr. It was attracted by the beds of coal, much of which was suitable for coking and thus for the iron furnace. In the years 1850 to 1870

many steelworks were built. Local supplies of ore were soon exhausted and the Ruhr came to depend more and more on imports from foreign countries.

As industry developed in this area, so the cities grew in size and importance. There are today three cities each with more than half a million inhabitants: Essen [624,000], Dortmund [535,000], and Düsseldorf [540,000]. There are 14 cities with more than 100,000 inhabitants.

• *The Coal-Mining Industry*

But without the coal field there would be no Ruhr as we know it today. The coal seams reach the surface along the valley of the Ruhr . . . and dip northward beneath the North German Plain. Mining began along the southern edge, but for more than a hundred years it has been spreading slowly northward, with the opening of mines of ever-increasing depth. The oldest mines are in the Ruhr Valley, which has thus given its name to the region; the newer are in the valleys of the Emscher and the Lippe. There seems to be no limit to this northward expansion except that set by the increasing depth and cost of mining.

The coal varies in quality. The lowermost seams, which come to the surface in the south, are anthracitic. Above them are, in order, coking, gas, and flame coals. Of these the coking coals, which are mined in the Emscher Valley, are of the greatest industrial importance.

Between the two wars the Germans concentrated production in a reduced number of larger mines. At many of these, coking furnaces were erected. Here the coal is pulverized, blended, and coked. The coke is sent to the blast-furnaces, and the gas from the retorts is used for various heating purposes in the steelworks; the exhaust gases from the furnaces go to fire the retorts in the cokeries. Coal mining and steel-working have thus been integrated geographically, not merely in the balance sheets of the operating companies.

The abundance of coal has led to the erection of synthetic-fuel plants, whose production of fuel oil from coal was of vital importance to the German military machine during the last war.

Before the Second World War, nearly 40 per cent of the coal mined was used within the Ruhr, about 30 per cent was sent to other parts of Germany, and about 30 per cent was exported. Exports went chiefly to France, Italy, the Netherlands, Belgium, Luxembourg, Scandinavia, and Switzerland, countries with small or inadequate coal reserves of their own. . . .

• The Iron and Steel Industry

The second great industry of the Ruhr is the manufacture of iron and steel. Germany has little iron ore, and the Ruhr relies to the extent of three-quarters of its requirements on imports from Sweden, France, Spain, North Africa, and elsewhere. Some comes in through the German North Sea ports, but most through the Dutch ports, whose prosperity depends greatly on the trade of the Ruhr. Most of the steelworks are well placed on the Rhine or its neighboring canals for the im-

port of ore.

The smelting industry is carried on in about 15 separate works, all on the plain between the Rhine in the west and Dortmund in the east. At all of them the steel is rolled into sheets, bars, and girders. Steel-using industries, especially those making castings, boilers, tubes, and wire, lie not only in the neighborhood of the steel plants but also scattered throughout the Ruhr area.

• Metal-Fabricating, Chemical, and Textile Industries

South of the area of large towns and heavy industries, in the hills where the ancient craft of smelting was carried on, there are many metallurgical industries which call for refinement and skill rather than for large quantities of metal and fuel: the manufacture of screws, nuts, springs, and locks, of high-quality alloy steels, of cutting and machine tools. Here industry is carried on in small workshops, and handwork and skill

A characteristic industrial landscape in the Ruhr. The view shows iron and steel mills and congested barge traffic along the Rhine in the vicinity of Duisburg. (Dr. Paul Wolff and Tritschler.)

count for more than mass production. The towns of Remscheid [103,000] and Solingen [148,000] are centers of this branch of the metal industry.

In terms of war potential, the northern plain, with its huge factories and large cities, produces armor plate, guns, and heavy castings; the hilly area to the south, the motors, machines, precision instruments, and fuses.

Although the coal-mining and steel industries dominate the manufactures of the Ruhr, chemicals and textiles are also of some importance. Chemicals are made in several of the larger cities, notably Duisburg [427,000], Leverkusen [65,000], and Düsseldorf. The textile manufactures are now concentrated in just two areas: the Wupper Valley, in which lies the great cloth-making city of Wuppertal [400,000 with suburbs], and the cities west of the Rhine of München-Gladbach [125,000], Rheydt [79,000], and Krefeld-Uerdingen [172,000].

The Ruhr thus has a varied industrial development, but the coal and steel industries stand supreme. The area accounted for five-sixths of German coal production before 1939, and more than two-thirds of German steel.

Following World War II, a considerable number of industrial plants in the Ruhr (as well as elsewhere in Germany) were dismantled and shipped to various Allied nations as reparations. In 1949 the Ruhr was placed under an international control authority representing the United States, Britain, France, the Netherlands, Belgium, and Luxembourg. Restrictions were placed on Ruhr production of steel and other strategic commodities. Behind these measures was the idea of preventing the Ruhr from again becoming an industrial base for German aggression. However, it eventually became apparent that continued dismantling of Ruhr plants and continued restrictions on Ruhr production, especially of steel, would greatly hinder the economic recovery, not merely of Germany, but of all Western Europe. Under these circum-

stances the Allied powers gradually modified their stand regarding the Ruhr, and by 1953 Ruhr production of most commodities had returned to prewar levels.

▶ Industrial Districts Outside the Ruhr

The industrial district which ranks second in importance to the Ruhr is found in Saxony, immediately to the northwest of Czechoslovakia. The production of this district is very diversified, although somewhat lacking in the heavier types of industry. The district is particularly noted for types of goods requiring an extremely high degree of skill in manufacture—cameras and other optical equipment, electronic equipment, high-grade chinaware, and so on. Textiles, manufactured from imported cotton and local and imported wool, represent the leading branch of industry in employment and value of production. The main industrialized area of Saxony is shaped like a triangle. At the northwestern apex is the city of Halle (278,000), in the center of an important potash, salt, and lignite-mining and chemical-manufacturing region. Near by is the largest city of Saxony, the diversified industrial center of Leipzig (608,000), especially noted for its printing and publishing industry before the war. At the southeastern corner of the triangle is another diversified industrial city, Dresden (510,000), on the Elbe River. Westward from Dresden a line of small to medium-sized manufacturing towns and cities extends along the northern foothills of the Ore Mountains, through the grimy textile center of Karl-Marx-Stadt, formerly Chemnitz (300,000), to a smaller textile city, Plauen (85,000), at the southwestern corner of the triangle. The Saxon Triangle lies entirely within East Germany. With its extremely varied range of production and highly skilled labor force, this industrialized area represents one of the richest prizes to fall within the orbit of the Soviet Union as a result of World War II.

No brief résumé can do justice to the

great variety and complexity of industrial production in Germany. The range of products extends from the basic lines of metals, textiles, and chemicals, through electrical, optical, leather, wood, paper, tobacco, processed food, and divers other goods to such specialty items as chinaware, toys, and musical instruments. Manufacturing is by no means confined to the Ruhr and the Saxon Triangle, but is spread through a multitude of other cities and towns outside these major industrial foci. Berlin was the most important single manufacturing city before World War II, with Hamburg probably ranking second.

Special mention should also be made of the important group of industrial cities located along the upper Rhine and its tributaries, the Main and Neckar—Frankfurt-on-the-Main, Mainz, Mannheim, Stuttgart, and many smaller places. The latter cities as a group are extremely diversified in types of production, but have been especially prominent in the manufacture of chemicals. Prior to World War II the city of Frankfurt-on-the-Main was the headquarters of the giant I. G. Farben chemical cartel. After the war this organization was partially broken up by the occupying powers, along with many of the other monopolistic combines which formerly played so large a role in German industry.

▶ The Scientific Agriculture of Germany

The fact that Germany is predominantly a manufacturing nation should not be allowed to obscure its agricultural productivity. Prewar estimates of German agricultural self-sufficiency ranged from 70 percent to 90 percent. This high output from soils which are, in the main, only moderately fertile is a tribute to German enterprise and skill. The art of soil improvement through careful use of natural and artificial fertilizers, crop rotation, and other scientific land-management practices has been developed to a high degree, and the average crop yields secured by German farmers are among the highest in the world. Only the much smaller, intensively cultivated neighboring countries of Belgium, the Netherlands, and Denmark definitely surpass Germany in all-around per-acre yields. The highly developed chemical industry of Germany has aided the farmer by providing large quantities of chemical fertilizers. Prewar Germany was exceeded only by the Netherlands, Belgium, and New Zealand in total consumption of commercial plant food per acre of arable land. Despite all efforts at self-sufficiency, however, Germany must import sizable quantities of foodstuffs, fibers, and other agricultural products. In 1951 such items represented approximately 60 percent by value of all imports entering the German Federal Republic.

Rye, oats, and potatoes are the staple crops of the North German Plain except along the southern margin in the zone of fertile loess soils, where wheat and sugar beets predominate. The depressions in the southern upland country grow rye, wheat, oats, and barley in fairly equal proportions; potatoes, also, are important, though somewhat less so than on the northern plain. In the far southwest orchards and vineyards are major specialties in the sheltered valleys of the upper Rhine and the lower Main and Neckar.

Livestock production is an important branch of agriculture in all parts of Germany. Major emphasis is placed on the growing of cattle and hogs: Germany raises more hogs than any other European country (excluding the Soviet Union), and is exceeded in number of cattle only by France. Sheep are of minor importance. In the cooler, more infertile, and poorly drained portions of the North German Plain, large sections are given over principally to the grazing of livestock, and the same is true of the rougher areas in the southern uplands. Dairying is especially prominent in two areas: (1) the German Alps and Alpine Foreland, south of the

Danube, and (2) the reclaimed coastal marshes bordering the North Sea. It should be noted, however, that cattle in Germany primarily consist of dairy varieties. There is no well-developed beef animal, and thus, although certain districts may specialize in fattening steers for slaughter, there is not the sharp difference between the beef and dairy industries that one finds in the United States. Some hogs, cattle, and, of course, poultry, are present on nearly all German farms. These livestock provide cash products which are readily salable in near-by urban markets; supply quantities of manure for enriching the soil; consume kitchen wastes and crop residues such as the tops and pulp left over from sugar beet processing; and generally fit well in the intensive, careful agriculture of such a densely populated, urbanized country as Germany.

▶ Transportation Facilities

Proper functioning of the complex German economy requires a large-scale and continuous interchange of goods between various parts of the country and also between Germany and foreign lands. This interchange is made possible by an elaborate system of oversea and internal transportation facilities. The principal seaports are Hamburg and Bremen, located well upstream on the estuaries of the Elbe and Weser, respectively. Although freight vessels make the journey upriver to these ports, fast passenger liners ordinarily call at the outports of Cuxhaven, at the mouth of the Elbe, and Bremerhaven, at the mouth of the Weser. The great Dutch seaport of Rotterdam on the lower Rhine handles large tonnages of German trade and in a functional sense may be counted as one of the major German ports. In the harbors of Rotterdam and Hamburg a major specialty is the direct transfer of goods between ocean ships and river or canal barges. The Rhine River, navigable for barges from the Swiss port of Basel to the

sea, is the largest German carrier of barge traffic, and the city of Duisburg-Ruhrort, located on the Rhine at the western end of the Ruhr industrial district, is one of the most important river ports in the world. Outstanding among the other inland waterways of Germany are (1) the Elbe River, navigable for barge traffic from Czechoslovakia to the North Sea, (2) the Mittelland Canal System connecting the Rhine and the Ruhr district with the Weser, Elbe, and, via Berlin, with the Oder, (3) the Dortmund-Ems Canal connecting the Ruhr with the North Sea via the Ems River and the port of Emden (40,000), and (4) the North Sea–Baltic Canal or Kiel Canal, a ship canal which crosses the base of the Danish peninsula and thus eliminates the sea journey around Denmark for vessels plying between the Baltic and the German North Sea ports.

Fast inland transportation is provided by an effective system of railways and superhighways (*autobahns*) focusing on the larger cities, especially Berlin. An important postwar development has been the emergence of the truck as a major freight carrier. As in the United States, many trucking fleets are owned by manufacturing companies, while others serve as public carriers. Unfortunately, however, most German roads were not built to accommodate heavy truck traffic, and the *autobahn* system, which is capable of bearing heavy loads, converges on Berlin and hence cannot be used to full capacity because of the existence of the Iron Curtain.

Large-scale transfer of passengers and freight by air is still in an immature stage of development. Perhaps the most significant contribution of air transportation at present is the quick and sure access it provides to West Berlin. A spectacular demonstration of the latter was the famous Berlin Airlift of 1948–1949 in which the Western occupying powers, through ferrying necessary supplies to West Berlin by air over a period of more than a year, succeeded in overcoming a Russian blockade of surface transportation into the city.

▶ Economic Dissection: The Example of Hamburg

As a consequence of defeat in World War II, Germany underwent not only a political, but also a severe economic dissection. The country lost control of important coal-mining and steel-milling districts in Upper Silesia and the Saarland, as well as agricultural lands east of the Oder-Neisse line which normally had produced a considerable surplus of foodstuffs in prewar times. Probably the most damaging aspect of the postwar situation, however, was the disruption of normal trade relationships between East and West Germany. Some of the effects of this disruption are illustrated in the following concrete example.

During the late 1930's the port of Hamburg was one of the leading seaports of Europe and of the world. The war brought great destruction to the city and particularly to the harbor. When peace came the over-all capacity of the port had been reduced to about one fifth of its prewar status. By 1954 an energetic program of rebuilding had restored most of the port's capacity, but the trade of the port was still considerably below its prewar level. Failure of Hamburg to regain its prewar trade was largely due to the political boundary between East and West Germany, which interposed a trade barrier between the port and a major part of its prewar hinterland. In 1954 Hamburg's total commerce with the Russian-controlled areas east of the Iron Curtain stood at less than one third of its prewar level. Although Hamburg was still the leading German seaport in 1954, its situation contrasted with that of its principal German competitor, Bremen, which had more than regained its prewar volume of commerce.

The postwar severance of the German Democratic Republic has required extensive readjustments not only in Hamburg, but in many other centers of industry and trade in both republics. Each of the two Germanies needs the trade of the other in order to function most effectively. There appears to be little evidence, however, that the political and economic cleavage represented by the Russian-imposed Iron Curtain will be fundamentally altered within the foreseeable future.

Absorption of Political and Ethnic Expellees

German recovery from World War II has also been hindered by the necessity of caring for a great number of expellees and other displaced persons. By 1950 the German Federal Republic had accepted nearly 8 million and the German Democratic Republic nearly 4½ million newcomers, most of them either political or ethnic expellees from Communist-held areas. The political expellees were former occupants of German national territory transferred to Polish or Russian administration following the war. The ethnic expellees were people of German descent who lived in countries outside of Germany before the war, but were alleged to have had strong pro-German leanings. The latter group came mainly from Czechoslovakia, Poland, the former Free City of Danzig (now Gdansk), Hungary, Rumania, and Yugoslavia. Of the approximately 70 million people now comprising the two republics, nearly 18 percent is made up of the two categories of expellees. Further complexity has been added by the voluntary migration of some 1½ million persons from the German Democratic Republic and Berlin to the German Federal Republic.

The influx of these homeless people into a defeated nation created considerable difficulties. Those immigrants who had been rural dwellers tended to fit more comfortably into the new arrangement than did the newcomers with a wholly urban background, for difficult as country life was in postwar Germany, it was less strenuous than life in the stilled and partially destroyed cities. In the German Federal Republic, and presumably in the German Democratic Republic, most of the new-comers, regardless of background, were initially located in temporary shelters away from the cities. It was feared that absorption of these millions of people with their differing skills into the economy of a war-shattered country considerably reduced in area and resources would prove an insuperable task. Yet the fact is that in the German Federal Republic, at least, the task had been largely accomplished by 1954.

Problems and Prospects of German Rebirth

For over three years following defeat, Germany was in ruins. Much of her machinery had been carried off as reparations. Her merchant fleet was gone. She had practically no credit. Industrial production stood at less than one tenth of the prewar level. Approximately one third of all housing had been bombed out; in the major cities the proportion was nearly twice as high. Unemployment, inflation, and hunger existed everywhere.

Beginning in 1949, however, the western zones began rebuilding at a frenzied pace. This rebuilding was stimulated by more than $4 billion worth of economic aid from outside countries, chiefly from the Marshall Plan of the United States. Success of the German Federal Republic in finding jobs for the great majority of its displaced persons was an indication of the drive toward complete economic recovery. In September 1953 the total unemployment in the Federal Republic was reported as only 968,000, and over-all industrial production was half again as high as in 1936.

Meanwhile East Germany has been drawn ever more fully into the Russian economic orbit. Reported shortages of coal, steel, and many consumer items in 1953 indicated that the collectivized economy of this Communist-held area was lagging behind the free economy of the German Federal Republic in recovery from the war. Not the least among the difficulties of the German Democratic Republic was a continued exaction of reparations by the Soviet Union.

Prewar Germany was the economic cornerstone of continental Europe. The country secured more than half of its imports from and sent more than half of its exports to other nations of Western Europe. An additional 15 percent of its export and import trade was with countries now east of the Iron Curtain. The complex interlocking of Germany's economy with the economies of its neighbors, and particularly the need of these neighbors for German coal and steel, made the country an indispensable balance wheel in the European economic system. Today West Germany has succeeded to the latter function with respect to the nations of continental Europe outside of the Iron Curtain. But the economic rebirth of this segment of Germany, larger in population and stronger industrially than any continental nation west of Russia, has roused old fears of German domination in the minds of neighboring peoples. Whether the new German Federal Republic can overcome these fears, win the confidence of its neighbors, and become a peaceful and fully accepted partner in the economic development and defense of a free Europe, will be a matter of the utmost importance as the struggle between the Communist and non-Communist portions of mankind continues to unfold.

The Benelux Countries

The three small countries of Belgium, the Netherlands, and Luxembourg have been closely associated with each other throughout their long histories. During some periods they have been included in a single political unit, although they have been politically separated during the greater part of the past four centuries. Since World War II they have been attempting to strengthen their mutual relations and to weld themselves into an economic union, while maintaining their respective political sovereignties. The new economic union has been designated Benelux, from the first syllable of each country's name, and the three nations are now often referred to collectively as "the Benelux Countries."

An older name often applied to the three is "the Low Countries." In its strictest sense, however, this term is properly applied only to the two larger countries, Belgium and the Netherlands, and will be so used in this chapter; while "Benelux" will be reserved for all three countries.

Lands of Low Relief

"Low Countries" is very descriptive of Belgium and the Netherlands, since approximately the northern two thirds of the former and practically all of the latter consists of a very low plain facing the North Sea. This plain is the narrowest section of

Manufacturing is highly developed in the densely populated Benelux nations. Pictured above is an extensive cement works in the environs of Mons, Belgium. (*Sabena Belgian Airlines.*)

the great plain of northern Europe which extends from France into the Soviet Union. In the Low Countries the plain seldom reaches as much as 300 feet above sea level. Large sections near the coast, especially in the Netherlands, are actually below sea level. They are protected from flooding only by a coastal belt of sand dunes, by man-made dikes, and by constant artificial drainage.

The only land in the Low Countries with even a moderate elevation lies mainly in Belgium, south of the line formed by the Sambre and Meuse Rivers. Here the Ardennes plateau rises in some places above 2000 feet, although its surface is more commonly around 1200 feet above

sea level. Much of the Ardennes is an upland of little relief, though in places intrenched rivers produce a more rugged terrain. The term "Ardennes," as used in this chapter, includes the lower northern foreland or Condroz, located between the Ardennes proper and the Sambre-Meuse Valley. The edges of the Ardennes overlap Belgium's frontiers, extending without a break into the Rhine Uplands of the German Federal Republic on the east, and into France on the west. To the south the Ardennes includes the northern half of the tiny country of Luxembourg. Southern Luxembourg and a small adjoining tip of Belgium have a lower, rolling terrain similar to that of neighboring French Lorraine.

Populations and Standards of Living

High population densities are an outstanding characteristic of the Benelux nations, and especially of the Netherlands

and Belgium. In fact, no sovereign nation in the entire world can match either of the latter two countries in over-all population

Delivering kerosene in a Netherlands village where all transportation is by boat. (Standard Oil Company [N. J.].)

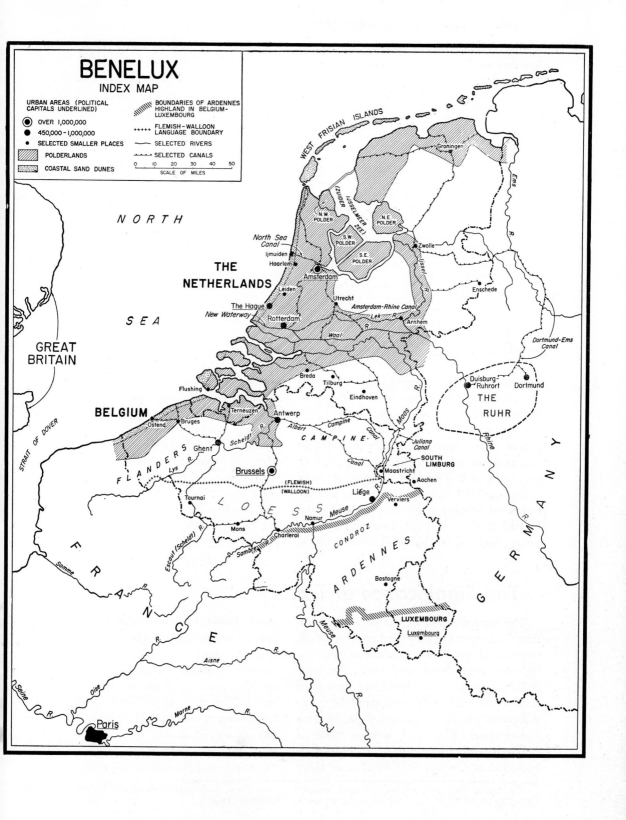

BENELUX
INDEX MAP

URBAN AREAS (POLITICAL
CAPITALS UNDERLINED)

◉ OVER 1,000,000

● 450,000–1,000,000

• SELECTED SMALLER PLACES

▨ POLDERLANDS

COASTAL SAND DUNES

▨ BOUNDARIES OF ARDENNES
HIGHLAND IN BELGIUM–
LUXEMBOURG

+++++ FLEMISH–WALLOON
LANGUAGE BOUNDARY

SELECTED RIVERS

SELECTED CANALS

0 10 20 30 40 50

SCALE OF MILES

NORTH

SEA

GREAT
BRITAIN

STRAIT OF DOVER

WEST FRISIAN ISLANDS

Ems R.

Groningen

THE
NETHERLANDS

North Sea
Canal

Ijmuiden

Haarlem

Leiden

Amsterdam

Utrecht

N.W.
POLDER

S.W.
POLDER

N.E.
POLDER

S.E.
POLDER

(ZUIDER
ZEE)

(IJSSELMEER)

Zwolle

Ijssel R.

Enschede

The Hague

New Waterway

Rotterdam

Amsterdam-Rhine Canal

Lek R.

Arnhem

Waal R.

Dortmund-Ems
Canal

Breda

Tilburg

Eindhoven

Maas R.

Rhine R.

Duisburg-
Ruhrort

Dortmund

THE
RUHR

Flushing

BELGIUM

Ostend

Bruges

Terneuzen

Antwerp

Scheldt R.

Albert

Campine

Canal

CAMPINE

Juliana
Canal

SOUTH
LIMBURG

Maastricht

Aachen

GERMANY

FLANDERS

Ghent

Lys R.

Escaut (Scheldt) R.

Brussels

(FLEMISH)
(WALLOON)

LOESS

Liége

Verviers

Tournai

Mons

Charleroi

Sambre R.

Namur

Meuse

CONDROZ

ARDENNES

Bastogne

LUXEMBOURG

Luxembourg

FRANCE

Somme R.

Escaut (Scheldt) R.

Meuse R.

Aisne R.

Oise R.

Seine R.

Marne R.

Paris

density. The density of population in the Benelux area as a whole is about equal to that of the most densely populated American state, Rhode Island. New York, which has the largest population of any state, is about twice as large in area as Benelux, but has only four fifths as many people. Areas, populations, and population densities of the Benelux countries are given in Table 5.

In many countries of the world an un-

TABLE 5

BENELUX: AREA AND POPULATION DATA

COUNTRY	AREA (THOUSAND SQUARE MILES)	POPULATION (MILLIONS: 1953 ESTIMATES)	DENSITY (PER SQUARE MILE: TO NEAREST WHOLE NUMBER)
Netherlands	12.9 [a]	10.45	812
Belgium	11.8	8.76	744
Luxembourg	1.0	0.30	304
Total	25.7	19.51	761

[a] Excluding inland waterways and sheets of water larger than 185 acres.

usually high density of population is associated with a low standard of living. In the Benelux nations, however, the reverse is true. By effective utilization of such opportunities and resources as their small and crowded national territories afford, the peoples of these countries are able to maintain standards of living which are equaled or surpassed by few nations. According to an estimate of the comparative per capita incomes of seventy countries made by the United Nations in 1949, Belgium, Luxembourg, and the Netherlands ranked tenth, eleventh, and twelfth from the top, respectively.[1] The four highest-ranking countries in the list were, in order, the United States, Canada, New Zealand, and Australia. Five countries of northwestern Europe—the United Kingdom, Switzerland, Sweden, Denmark, and Norway—completed the list of nations outranking Benelux in per capita income. While income level is not exactly equivalent to standard of living, the relationship is sufficiently close to indicate the high position of the Benelux nations among the world's countries.

The Significance of Trade

The economic life of the Benelux countries is characterized by an intensive development of three interrelated activities—industry, agriculture, and trade. An especially distinctive and significant feature of their economies is an unusually high development of, and dependence on, international trade. The total foreign trade of Belgium and Luxembourg combined is exceeded in Europe only by that of three much larger countries, the United Kingdom, France, and Germany. (Since 1922 Belgium and Luxembourg have maintained a customs union, and trade figures for the two countries are reported as a unit.) The *per capita* trade of Belgium-Luxembourg exceeds that of any other European nation except Iceland. The somewhat smaller trade of the Netherlands is exceeded on a per capita basis only by that

---

[1] "National and Per Capita Incomes, Seventy Countries—1949." *Statistical Papers*, Series E, No. 1. New York: Statistical Office of the United Nations, October, 1950.

of Belgium-Luxembourg, Switzerland, Sweden, and Norway.

Several factors help to explain the unusual development of foreign commerce in the Benelux countries:

1. Trade is essential to such small countries, if they are to make maximum use of a limited variety of internal resources. Such resources as Luxembourg's iron ore or Belgium's coal must either be left in the ground or exported for comparatively small returns unless complementary materials needed for manufacturing can be imported.

2. The need of these countries to trade is matched by their ability to trade. Specializing in activities which offer the greatest possibilities for effective use of limited resources, the Benelux nations are able to export large surpluses of such items as processed metals, certain types of machinery, and, in the case of the Netherlands, dairy products.

3. The position of the Benelux countries is highly favorable for trade. These countries lie in the heart of the most highly developed part of Europe. Their nearest neighbors, Germany, France, and the United Kingdom, are among the world's foremost producing, consuming, and trading nations. The resulting commercial opportunities are reflected in the fact that between 40 and 50 percent of Benelux foreign trade is accounted for by trade among the Benelux countries themselves or with their three larger neighbors. A second significant aspect of position lies in the location of the Netherlands and Belgium at or near the mouth of the Rhine. This river is the greatest inland waterway of Europe, and one of the greatest in the world. Location where the Rhine meets the sea permits the Low Countries to handle in transit much of the foreign trade of Switzerland, eastern France, and, especially, West Germany with its Ruhr industrial district.

4. The trade of the Low Countries has profited somewhat from the fact that both the Netherlands and Belgium have held large colonial empires in the tropics. The Belgian Congo and the former Netherlands East Indies (now the independent republic of Indonesia) have offered assured markets for goods and capital, and have allowed the home countries to act as European entrepôts for certain tropical agricultural products and nonferrous minerals. Indonesian independence has jeopardized the entrepôt function in the Netherlands, although much of the former trade still endures. Belgium, however, has retained full control to date over the government and trade of the Congo. At present between 5 and 10 percent of the Low Countries' foreign trade is with their current or former colonies.

Importance of the Dutch and Belgian Ports

Exploitation of their commercial opportunities by the Low Countries is reflected in the presence of three of the world's major port cities within a distance of about 80 miles: Rotterdam and Amsterdam in the Netherlands, and Antwerp in Belgium. During the twentieth century Rotterdam has normally ranked second only to New York among the world's seaports on the basis of total tonnage of goods handled. By the same criterion Antwerp has ordinarily been exceeded only by Rotterdam, London, and Hamburg among European ports; since World War II the slow recovery of Hamburg has enabled Antwerp to surpass this German port and rank second only to Rotterdam on the continent. The larger city of Amsterdam is a considerably less important port than Rotterdam or Antwerp, though its trade is large, nonetheless. The commercial activities of the three major ports are supplemented by those of numerous smaller ports in the Low Countries, particularly Ghent in Belgium.

▶ Amsterdam—The "Colonial" Port of the Netherlands

Amsterdam (850,000; including suburbs, 1,125,000) is the largest city and the constitutional capital of the Netherlands, although the government is actually located at The Hague (579,000). As a port, Amsterdam handles mainly the trade of the Netherlands itself, plus a considerable entrepôt traffic in tropical products. The latter specialty stems from the fact that Amsterdam was the main port of the Netherlands during the centuries when the country's colonial empire was being acquired and organized, before the rapid rise of Rotterdam in the latter nineteenth century. Although the East Indian empire has been lost, Amsterdam has retained business connections and specialized marketing facilities built up during the colonial period, and so it has been able to keep a considerable amount of its "colonial" trade. In addition, the profits accumulated during several centuries of the East Indian trade have been used to finance industrial development in Amsterdam, and, by supplying capital for the large foreign investments of the Netherlands, have helped to make Amsterdam a center of international finance. Although the Eastern trade no longer appears to be a really major element in the economy of the Netherlands, it is still far from negligible, and has been of great importance in the historical development of the country, and particularly of Amsterdam.

In modern times Amsterdam has experienced considerable difficulties as a port. The original approach from the sea by way of the Zuider Zee eventually proved too shallow for modern shipping. This problem was solved in 1876 with the opening of the North Sea Canal, through which ships now enter the harbor. More recently, location away from the mouth of the Rhine has proved a disadvantage, and the city has been attempting to attract a larger share of Rhine traffic by providing better canal connections with the river.

▶ Rotterdam—The Major Port of the Rhine

Rotterdam (690,000; including suburbs, 875,000) is better situated with respect to Rhine shipping than either Amsterdam or Antwerp, being located directly on one of the navigable distributaries of the river rather than to one side. Accordingly, Rotterdam controls and profits from the major portion of the river's transit trade, receiving goods by sea and dispatching them upstream by barge, and receiving goods downstream by barge and dispatching them by sea. Two developments have been mainly responsible for the city's rapid rise in the last century. First was the opening in 1872 of the New Waterway, an artificial channel to the sea far superior to the shallow and treacherous natural mouths of the Rhine, and superior also to the sea connections of either Amsterdam or Antwerp. Second, and more fundamental, has been the increasing industrialization of areas near the Rhine, particularly the Ruhr district, for which Rotterdam has become the main sea outlet. The need of the inland industrial districts for imports of ores, cereals, and similar bulky commodities, coupled with their exports of such heavy goods as coal, steel, and chemicals, accounts for the huge tonnage of Rotterdam's trade.

▶ The Scheldt Port of Antwerp

Antwerp (about 800,000 with suburbs), located about 50 miles up the Scheldt River, is primarily a port for Belgium itself, but also handles an important share of the Rhine transit trade. Belgium's coast is straight and its rivers shallow, so that the deep estuary of the Scheldt gives Antwerp the best harbor in the country, even though it must be reached through the Netherlands. The city has become a major focus in Belgium's dense railway net, and has river and canal connections to Ghent, Brussels, and Liége. Transit trade is facilitated by Antwerp's position in relation to the major inland industrial areas of northwestern continental Europe. It is slightly closer than either Rotterdam or Amsterdam to these areas, and it has somewhat shorter and more direct rail connections. Thus Antwerp ordinarily handles a large share of the transit trade in goods of a type which can move more profitably by the relatively expensive but faster rail lines than by the cheaper but slower barge.

Competition between Antwerp and the Dutch ports has provided a fertile field for controversy between the Low Countries in the past. Throughout the seventeenth and eighteenth centuries the Dutch were able to keep the lower Scheldt, which runs through their territory, closed to traffic, and thus to throttle Antwerp almost completely. Later disputes have arisen over the maintenance of the river's shipping channel, over Belgium's desire for a canal through Dutch territory to connect Antwerp directly with the Rhine, and over Belgium's payment of special subsidies to attract Rhine barges through the southwestern part of the Netherlands to Antwerp in preference to the more convenient Rotterdam. The Benelux Economic Union now being developed will have the task of resolving the problems arising from the strenuous competition between the Belgian and Dutch ports, particularly between Antwerp and Rotterdam.

Manufacturing in the Benelux Countries

Despite the basic importance of international trade, it is manufacturing which forms the greatest source of employment in each of the Benelux countries. Belgium and Luxembourg, better endowed with mineral resources, are somewhat more industrialized than the Netherlands and have a far greater development of the heavier types of industry. Belgium, best endowed with coal, is the most important manufacturing nation of the three.

▶ Heavy Industry in the Sambre-Meuse District

One of Europe's major coal fields crosses Belgium in a narrow east-west belt about a hundred miles long. It follows roughly the valleys of the Sambre and Meuse Rivers, and extends into France on the west and Germany on the east. Charleroi (445,-000), Namur (215,000), and Liége (575,000; populations for all three cities include suburbs) and smaller industrial cities strung along this Sambre-Meuse field account for most of Belgium's metallurgical and other heavy industrial production. The iron and steel industry is the most important, and its production is sufficient to place Belgium fourth among the steel-producing nations of Europe. The industry imports its ores, mainly from Luxembourg, France, and Sweden, and sells a great part of its production outside of the relatively small home market. Liége, the largest manufacturing center on the coal field, has metallurgical industries dating back to handicraft days, and was the first city in continental Europe to develop modern, large-scale iron and steel manufacture following the Industrial Revolution.

Small deposits of iron ore and zinc in the Ardennes originally furnished raw material for the Sambre-Meuse metallurgical industries. Although the zinc, like the iron ore, has long been exhausted, it started Belgian industry toward what has now become a remarkable specialty in nonferrous smelting. Belgium produces nearly 10 percent of the world's smelter zinc, a production exceeded only by that of the United States and Canada. In addition, the little country has become Europe's third greatest smelter of tin (after the United Kingdom and the Netherlands) and lead (after Germany and Yugoslavia). The nonferrous ores and concentrates for the smelting industry are now entirely imported, and the bulk of the production is exported to other European nations in one form or another. Belgium thus acts as a processing middleman between the overseas ore producers and the European industrial consumers of these metals. Certain other specialties have also developed in the Sambre-Meuse district, notably the production of cement, glass, and nitrogenous chemicals. These products, which require much coal in manufacture, are principally made from local raw materials.

▶ The Light, Diversified Industries of Brussels

Throughout Belgium even the smaller towns are generally characterized by some industrial development. Away from the coal fields there is a tendency to specialize in lighter types of industry having smaller power requirements than the industries located near to coal. In these industries labor is often of great importance as a factor in the total cost of production. The Belgian capital, Brussels, is the outstanding center of such industries. Like most European political capitals, it is the largest city in the country, with a current population, including suburbs, of about 1,300,000, and is primarily a product of political and cultural centralization. The labor force, transport facilities, and local market it provides, however, have led to the development of a great variety of light industries, including textiles and clothing, skilled metal work, printing, food-processing, and luxury crafts.

▶ The Belgian Textile Industry

As in most countries, textile manufacturing is the leading branch of Belgium's lighter industries. As far back as the twelfth century, Flanders (roughly the part of Belgium north of the Scheldt and west of Ant-

werp) was a center of commercial cloth production, importing raw wool (mainly from England) and selling woolen cloth in various parts of Europe. The same area is now the center of Belgium's cotton, linen, and jute industries. It still imports its raw materials and exports a large part of the finished product. Flanders readily adapted its long textile tradition to machine production during the early nineteenth century simply by concentrating the former cottage workers into factory cities. The greatest of these cities today is the ancient commercial center of the industry, Ghent, which has a population of about 450,000 including suburbs.

Flanders lost its leadership in Belgium's woolen industry to Verviers (40,000), in the edge of the Ardennes, by the eighteenth century at the latest. The pure and soft water flowing from the Ardennes gave this place a considerable advantage in washing the wool preparatory to spinning. Its value can still be seen in the fact that Verviers not only produces a major share of Belgium's woolen goods, but also specializes in cleaning raw wool for distant mills, both in Belgium and in neighboring countries.

▶ Manufacturing in Luxembourg

Luxembourg's simple industrial structure presents a picture of dependence on foreign trade proportionately equal to, or greater than, that of Belgium. About 40 percent of the country's entire working population is employed in the iron and steel industry, which is carried on in several small centers near the southern border, where the Lorraine iron ore deposits of France overlap into Luxembourg. Annual production of both pig iron and steel ranges upward from 2 million tons. The tiny country ranks sixth to eighth among the steel producers of Europe, and not lower than twelfth in the world. The very small home market both necessitates and permits export of most of the production. In return, Luxembourg buys fuel (mainly coal from Germany), alloy metals, and many other products.

▶ Industries of the Netherlands

The Netherlands differs from Belgium and Luxembourg in the small part which domestic mineral resources have played in the rise of its industries. It resembles Belgium-Luxembourg, however, in the dependence of its industries on international trade. Basic factors in the rise of Dutch industrial production have been (1) the ability of Dutch industries to import both fuel and raw materials cheaply and (2) the availability of an abundant, skilled, and relatively low-priced labor force. Generally speaking, in their location the industries of the Netherlands are transportation and labor oriented rather than materials or market oriented.

Amsterdam and Rotterdam are the main seats of industry as well as of commerce. Both ports maintain important shipbuilding and associated engineering industries. Although the Netherlands has never dominated the seas since a brief period of glory in the seventeenth century, a strong maritime tradition has survived, and a disproportionately large merchant marine is an important factor in the Dutch economy. The ports are also the locale for a variety of industries which process overseas materials, particularly tropical products such as sugar and oilseeds, for sale in European markets. Three major specialties of this type have developed. One is the manufacture of oleomargarine, of which the Netherlands is Europe's third producer, after the United Kingdom and Germany. A second specialty is oil refining. A huge concentration of refineries, especially at Rotterdam, is in good part an expression of the Netherlands' important financial and managerial interest in the world-wide operations of the Royal Dutch Shell Company. Among Europe's oil-refining nations, the Netherlands is again third, after Britain and France. The third specialty is the smelting of tin. Indonesian tin, channeled into Europe through the Netherlands, has placed the country second only to Britain among European nations in tin smelting. This industry is centered at Arnhem (155,000 with suburbs) on the Rhine rather than at one of the major ports.

Away from the ports, and especially in some of the poorer agricultural districts, surplus labor and good transportation have led to the development of numerous small industrial cities. Textiles, light machinery, and consumer goods of various kinds are their major products. The industries of these cities rely heavily on imported raw materials, and export a large part of the finished product. The only really important manufacturing industry which is based wholly on domestic raw materials is the widespread food-processing industry, which prepares for the domestic market and export the butter, cheese, meat, and other products of the Netherlands' specialized agriculture.

The Intensive Agriculture of Benelux

Through manufacturing and trade the Benelux nations are able to support considerably larger populations than their agriculture can feed under present conditions. Like Great Britain and Germany, these nations import large quantities of food, together with feed for livestock and fertilizers to help increase their domestic agricultural production. Imported food ordinarily supplies more than a third of the total food requirements in the Benelux countries, and it is the most costly item on the import bill. Domestic production is particularly deficient in the case of food grains. Only limited areas in the Benelux countries are really well suited to the production of grains, particularly wheat, the grain consumed in the largest quantities for human food. Imported wheat has proved able to undersell the domestic product on the Benelux market, and thus farmers in the Benelux nations have usually concentrated their main efforts on farm commodities other than wheat.

The extremely high density of population makes domestic food production insufficient despite the fact that crop yields in the Low Countries are among the highest in the world. Wheat, for example, ordinarily gives an average yield of more than 40 and sometimes more than 60 bushels per acre in these countries, as compared with a world average of about 15 bushels per acre. However, such yields are only obtained through large expenditures of both labor and capital. So intensive is the labor expended on the cultivation of each acre that agriculture often resembles gardening. This type of farming is made both possible and necessary by the density of rural population and the small size of most farms. More than half of all Dutch farms and nine tenths of all Belgian farms are smaller than 12½ acres. Most Belgian farms are actually closer to 2 acres. Along with labor, capital is applied to the soil abundantly, mainly in the form of fertilizer. The Netherlands uses more fertilizer per acre than any other country in the world, and Belgium is not far behind.

A close adaptation of agriculture to climatic and soil conditions helps the Low Countries to obtain the maximum output from their restricted acreages of farm land. Since climatic conditions tend to be relatively uniform over both countries, differences in type of agriculture are mainly related to differences in type of land. Although in detail the picture is intricate, three main types of land, each with its associated types of agriculture, may be identified. These are the *polder lands,* the *loess lands,* and the *infertile lands.*

▶ Dairy Farming in the Polder Lands

Polder lands are those which have been surrounded by dikes and artificially drained. The process of turning former swamps, lakes, and shallow seas into agricultural land has been going on for over seven centuries. An individual polder, of which there are a great many of various sizes, is an area enclosed within dikes and kept dry by constant pumping into the drainage canals which surround it. Almost 40 percent of the Netherlands now consists of an intricate patchwork of polders and canals, while Belgium has a narrow strip of such lands behind its coastal sand dunes. The polder lands of the Netherlands extend for about 180 miles between the Belgian and German borders, in a belt which is seldom more than 40 miles wide and usually much less. The belt is roughly parallel to the seacoast, and is separated from the sea by dunes, swamps, or dikes.

The polders are the best lands in the Netherlands, and their production is the heart of Dutch agriculture. The reclaimed soil is very rich, water supply is subject to considerable control, and the canals form a complete transport network. The drier polders are often used for crop farming, and produce huge harvests. Most polders, however, are kept in grass, and dairy farming is the main type of agriculture. It thrives so well that large quantities of dairy products are exported, mainly to near-by industrial areas in Germany, Belgium, and the United Kingdom. Pork production is ordinarily a part of dairy farming, since the necessary feed for the hogs can largely be supplied by skim milk left over from butter making. The production of vegetables, fruits, and horticultural specialties such as the famous Dutch flower bulbs, is also of considerable importance in the polder zone. Dairying and other specialized types of agriculture supply about a fourth of the total exports of the Netherlands, and compensate, in

The intricate canal network of the Dutch polders. Windmills, such as those in this photo, have largely been replaced by motor-driven pumps. (*Netherlands Information Service.*)

value at least, for the necessary food imports.

▶ The Fertile Loess Lands

A second section of outstanding fertility and agricultural production is found in Belgium. In central Belgium a gently rolling topography was mantled in glacial times by a blanket of loess, a fine dust picked up by the wind from glacial debris. This material has formed soils of exceptional fertility in Belgium, as in many other places. These soils are found in a belt across the country between the Sambre-Meuse Valley on the south and a line just beyond Brussels on the north.

Three characteristics distinguish the agriculture of the loess belt. One is an emphasis on wheat, which has been able to survive foreign competition on these good lands. Another is the production of sugar beets, a crop requiring an exceptionally fertile soil.

Third is the production of fodder crops, which give very high yields and permit the loess area to specialize in the production of beef cattle, often brought in for fattening from poorer areas. This combination of food, feed, and livestock production supports the largest and most prosperous farms in Belgium.

▶ The Infertile Lands

The remaining lands of the Low Countries, and most of Luxembourg as well, can be described as relatively infertile, though small areas sometimes contradict this generalization. Sandy soils are dominant in northern Belgium and practically all of the Netherlands outside of the polder areas, though the sands are often interspersed with peat bogs and patches of clay, both of which can be made into good soil if properly managed. The soil of the sandy areas is generally lacking in humus, lime, and

A cattle market in an open street of the old Flemish city of Bruges. This view reflects the importance of livestock in the intensive, prosperous agriculture of the Low Countries. (*Belgian Information Center.*)

plant nutrients. That of the Ardennes is no better.

The agriculture of these areas is generally centered about livestock production, and crops are grown primarily for feed. The most common crops are rye, potatoes, oats, turnips, and hay. All are well adapted to the climate, and all except hay suffer relatively little, or actually grow better, in light and infertile soils. Rye and potatoes are used in these areas for human food as well as stock feed. Potatoes and turnips give especially good returns per acre, provided the necessary labor is available for harvesting. In addition, these root crops fit well with rye in that they give a crop during the summer on the same land that produced rye during the winter and spring. Livestock grown may be either beef cattle or dairy cattle, often both. Besides providing a cash income, they supply an important part of the large quantities of fertilizer necessary in farming such lands.

Although the density of population and intensity of agricultural production on the poorer lands are generally less than on the polders or the loess, they are often surprisingly great. In one sandy area, Flanders, the average production per acre is almost as large as on the naturally better lands, and the density of population is even greater. Here intensive agriculture and systematic improvement of the land have a continuous history dating back at least to the eleventh century. The precocious urban, commercial, and industrial development of Flanders stimulated Flemish agriculture during these early times. A garden type of agriculture has developed, especially centered on livestock, dairy, and vegetable production, but making some use of almost every crop that can be grown in the Low Countries and using soils almost completely transformed by centuries of improvement. Few of the world's farming areas are more skillfully handled.

Major Problems of the Benelux Nations

The Benelux countries share the general problems of the modern world. Like many other countries, they are concerned with achieving and maintaining international peace and cooperation, national security, and internal unity, freedom, and economic well-being. However, due to peculiarities of position, resources, population, and economic development, the Benelux countries are faced with certain types of problems which present themselves in distinctive form or with particular urgency.

▶ The Belgian Problem of National Unity

Belgium has had the most difficulty among the Benelux nations in securing and maintaining internal unity and cooperation. Division of the population into two major language groups has been at the root of the difficulty. If one draws an east-west line across Belgium just south of Brussels, it will approximate a line of sharp linguistic division. To the north Flemish, a slight variant of Dutch, is the dominant language except in Brussels. To the south live the French-speaking Belgians known as Walloons. Rivalries and antagonisms have sometimes arisen between the two groups. The Flemish people, until recently the minority group, have occasionally shown separatist tendencies. Differential birth rates have now given the Flemish group a majority, however, and Walloon uneasiness has appeared. There is always a latent danger that political issues will be fought primarily along language lines. How explosive such a situation can be was shown in 1950 when violent disturbances threatened over the question of the return of an exiled king. In the face of this language division constant care must be exercised to maintain national unity. Flemish clericalism and Walloon anticlericalism intensify this difficulty.

▶ Problems of National Security

At present, however, all three of the Benelux nations find the problems of national security and economic welfare more pressing than others. The two types of problems are closely related due to the heavy costs involved in war and in peacetime provision of armaments against possible attack.

The position of the Benelux countries between Germany, France, and the United Kingdom, and their inability to defend themselves against these more powerful neighbors, tends to involve them in every general European war, usually as a battleground. The low plains of Belgium offer a short and easy route between Germany and Paris, and even the Ardennes is no longer very effective as a military barrier, as was demonstrated by the German offensive through this upland area in the spring of 1940. Both world wars of the twentieth century have added to Belgium's long history as an international battlefield.

The Netherlands offers a valuable base for operations from the continent against England and, conversely, is an approach to the industrial heart of Germany. Flooding the polders is no longer the effective defence against modern armies that it has been in times past. Thus, although the Netherlands escaped invasion in World War I, the country was conquered by the Germans early in World War II after five days of savage fighting in May 1940, and it was again a battlefield as the German tide was rolled back by the Allies in the latter part of the war. Few nations endured comparable destruction.

Luxembourg, also, suffered German invasion and occupation from May 1940 until liberation by the Allies in September 1944. In December 1944 and early January 1945 about a third of Luxembourg was laid waste in the Battle of the Ardennes, which represented the last major offensive effort by Germany on the western front.

▶ Trade Problems

The resulting concern of the Benelux countries for international peace is paralleled by a concern with international trade which is proportional to their dependence on it. Since 1945 particular difficulties in the latter regard have resulted from the loss of the rich East Indian empire by the Netherlands, the postwar restriction of trade with Eastern Europe, the attempts of the United Kingdom and France to reduce the size of their imports, and the relatively depressed state of the German Ruhr. These and other factors have made it necessary for the Benelux nations to trade more with the United States, and the finding of ways to export to that relatively self-sufficient country has presented a major problem.

Since the Benelux countries can do little by themselves to solve problems which are international in scope, it is understandable that they have become ardent supporters of international projects to achieve peace through collective security, to bring an end to Europe's centuries of internal warfare by uniting its countries, and to facilitate freer trade. At present the three countries are members of the United Nations, the North Atlantic Treaty Organization, the European Coal and Steel Community formed under the Schuman Plan, and various other international bodies. Among themselves, they are giving the world an outstanding example of international cooperation, by making steady progress toward the realization of the Benelux Economic Union. The objective they are approaching is the eradication of all trade barriers among the three nations and the welding of their separate economies into a single larger, more powerful, and more efficient economic unit. However, full economic union had not yet been achieved at the time of writing.

▶ Population Problems

Internally, the main problem of both Belgium and the Netherlands seems to be the expansion of agriculture and industry, already intensively developed, to support still increasing populations. The situation is particularly acute in the Netherlands, whose abnormally high rate of natural increase, higher than that of any other European nation except Poland, has added about 4 million people to the population of an already crowded country in the last four decades. In such a small, densely populated country as the Netherlands, such an increase may be disastrous if long continued.

▶ Reclamation of New Land for Agriculture

Land reclamation has been one response to increasing populations in both countries. Cultivation of the infertile lands has been greatly expanded in recent times, and the process continues. In Belgium such effort has centered in the Ardennes and, especially, in the Campine, the sandy area south and east of Antwerp. In the Netherlands special attention has been directed toward bringing into productivity some of the vast peat bogs which are interspersed with the sandy areas of the eastern part of the country, and also toward an extension of dairy farming into the poorer lands.

The most important and celebrated reclamation work currently going on in the Netherlands, however, is the formation of new polders from the former Zuider Zee. A massive 18-mile-long dike was completed across the entrance of the Zuider Zee in the early 1930's, and a sizable area of sea bottom has now been reclaimed. At present, two of the four large polders planned are under cultivation, and work is proceeding on the other two, while the remainder of the Zuider Zee has become a fresh water lake, the Ijsselmeer. The completed project will add about 7 percent, all excellent farm land, to the land area of the Netherlands.

▶ Coal as a Factor in Industrial Expansion

Agricultural expansion alone cannot maintain the present high standard of living in the Low Countries. The governments of both the Netherlands and Belgium regard increased industrialization as essential. One of the most critical factors in further industrialization will be the provision of an adequate supply of power, which in the Low Countries essentially means coal. Belgium's Sambre-Meuse field was the first major coal field on the continent to be intensively developed. Thin, broken, and inclined seams, often of relatively poor quality, must now be mined at great depths. Consequently, this field has now become extremely difficult and costly to exploit, and total production has declined by about a third from the peak reached as far back as 1913. Belgium has now become a slight importer of both coal and coke.

Fortunately, an adequate solution seems possible to the serious problem this situation presents to Belgian industry. The existence of a second Belgian field, in the Campine, was discovered in 1898, and development was begun in 1917. The location of the coal some 1600 feet below the surface explains the late discovery and development. However, thick seams, large reserves, and high quality have resulted in relatively efficient production, and much of Belgium's industrial future seems tied to

the further development of the Campine field, which already accounts for about a third of the country's total output of coal. A certain amount of heavy industry has already located in the Campine in preference to the Sambre-Meuse district.

The Netherlands feels the need for industrial expansion even more strongly than Belgium. Until a few years ago the lack of any adequate source of power within the boundaries of the country was considered a major obstacle to its industrial development. However, the same coal field which underlies the Belgian Campine extends across the southernmost part of the Netherlands, known as South Limburg, and on to the vicinity of Aachen, Germany. Since World War I the Dutch have gradually developed here what is perhaps the most efficient mining industry in Europe, and the Netherlands can now supply the major part of its coal requirements. The production, though still relatively small, is increasing, and augurs well for future industrial development.

Thus the problems of the Benelux countries are being vigorously attacked, as has usually been the case throughout their histories. An astonishing record of past accomplishment in these little countries suggests that insofar as solutions to their present difficulties can be found within their own boundaries, such solutions will be found and applied. Problems wider in scope, however, can only be solved through world developments over which the Benelux nations can exercise, at best, only a modest influence.

Switzerland and Austria

The two small countries of Switzerland and Austria, located in the heart of Europe, have often been contrasted and otherwise compared. Despite certain environmental and cultural similarities, these neighbors have been remarkably different in their historical development. One of the two countries, Switzerland, represents perhaps the world's foremost example of the economic and political success of a small nation, whereas the other, Austria, at least so far, is in many respects an outstanding example of the economic and political failure of a small nation. The likenesses and differences of the two countries will form a major theme in the present chapter.

Physical Similarities of Switzerland and Austria

With respect to physical environment Switzerland and Austria have much in common. Over half of each country is occupied by the high and rugged Alps Mountains. North of the Alps both countries include part of the rolling morainal foreland of the mountains. The Swiss section of the Alpine Foreland is often called the Swiss Plateau. It lies mostly between 1500 and 3000 feet in elevation and extends between Lake Geneva, on the French border, to the southwest, and Lake Constance, on the German border, to the northeast. The Austrian section of the foreland is slightly lower in

A tiny village in the Swiss Alps. Note the characteristic church tower, jagged skyline, and forested slope at right behind the small inn. (*Standard Oil Company* [N. J.].)

elevation and extends from the Alps to the Danube River between Salzburg on the west and Vienna on the east. The Swiss and Austrian sections are separated from each other by a third portion of the foreland which lies in southern Germany. North of the foreland both Switzerland and Austria include uplands which are much lower in elevation and smaller in areal extent than the Alps. These uplands differ somewhat in character. The Jura, on the border between Switzerland and France, consists of parallel ridges, while the Austrian uplands, on the border with Czechoslovakia, represent the irregular, eroded southern edge of the extremely old Bohemian massif. North of the Jura in Switzerland the area around Basel opens onto the Upper Rhine Plain of Germany and France, while in eastern Austria the Vienna Basin and a strip of lowland to the south (Burgenland) adjoin the Little Hungarian Plain on the east and the Moravian Lowland of Czechoslovakia on the north. The Alps extend from Switzerland southward into Italy and southwestward into France, and from Austria southward into Italy and Yugoslavia.

Relative Superiority of Austrian Natural Resources

The physical similarities of Switzerland and Austria are not paralleled by an equal endowment of natural resources. The resources of Austria are, on the whole, superior to those of Switzerland, and in addition Austria is favored by a lower density of population. Some of these advantages of Austria appear in Table 6.

TABLE 6

SWITZERLAND AND AUSTRIA: AREA, POPULATION, AND LAND USE [a]

ITEM	AUSTRIA	SWITZERLAND	SWITZERLAND AS APPROX. % OF AUSTRIA
Area (thousand square miles)	32.4	15.9	50%
Population (millions: 1953 estimates)	6.97	4.86	70%
Approximate population density (per square mile)	215	305	142%
Cultivated land (including fallow and orchards): 000 acres	701 (21%)	174 (10%)	25%
Permanent meadows and pastures (000 acres)	950 (29%)	715 (43%)	75%
Forests and woodlands (000 acres)	1210 (37%)	409 (24%)	34%
Other land use: mostly waste (000 acres)	432 (13%)	373 (22%)	86%

[a] Land use data from FAO, *Yearbook of Food and Agricultural Statistics*, 1952. Data are for 1951.

The more favorable situation of Austria with respect to land under cultivation is due primarily to the higher proportion of relatively level terrain in Austria, although it reflects also to some degree the greater specialization in dairy farming in Switzerland, which leads the Swiss to keep a larger percentage of potentially cultivable land in pasture. At all events, Switzerland is much more dependent than Austria on food imports. The greater proportion of forest land in Austria primarily reflects the fact that the Austrian Alps are in general lower and less rugged than the Swiss Alps, and hence more suitable for forestry. Austria has important exports of forest products, whereas Switzerland is a considerable importer.

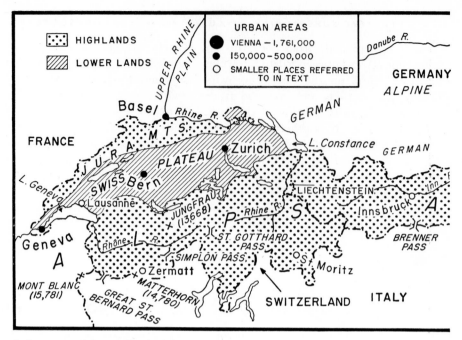

Index map of Switzerland and Austria.

In addition, Austria has considerable advantages with regard to mineral and power resources. Switzerland is almost devoid of mineral resources, while Austria's mineral production is varied and valuable, although exhibiting on the whole more variety than quantity. Oil from the Zistersdorf field north and east of Vienna is produced in export quantities and places Austria second only to Rumania among European oil producers outside of the Soviet Union. Iron ore, produced mainly north of Graz, is more than sufficient for Austria's needs. There are scattered deposits of lignite, coal, bauxite, and salt, as well as other minerals. Both Switzerland and Austria have large hydroelectric resources relative to their areas, but Austria's potential is greater.

The Superior Swiss Standard of Living

The advantages of Austria with respect to natural resources have been overweighed by other factors in the historical development of the two countries so that the economic situation of Austria is today more adverse than that of Switzerland and the Austrian standard of living is much lower. Switzerland, in fact, is generally regarded as having one of the world's soundest and most successful economies, while Austria has been saved from complete economic collapse and actual starvation several times since World War I only by the extension of large amounts of foreign aid. The Swiss standard of living is certainly one of the highest in Europe and may well be the highest, while Austria's is closer to that of the underdeveloped countries of eastern and southern Europe. Austria's per capita cash income is only one fourth that of Switzerland. These contrasts between the two countries can be attributed primarily to a long period of peace enjoyed by Switzerland during which time its citizens have been able to develop an economy finely adjusted to their country's potentialities and opportunities and an economy supported by a stable and democratic government, while the economy of Austria has been badly disoriented, warped, and hindered by a series of military and political calamities.

Role of Switzerland as a Neutral Buffer State

Except for some minor internal disturbances in the nineteenth century, Switzerland has been at peace inside stable boundaries since 1815. The basic factors underlying this long period of peace seem to have been (1) Switzerland's position as a buffer between larger powers, especially a buffer across much of whose terrain military movement would not be easy, (2) the relatively small value of Swiss economic production to an aggressive state, (3) the country's value as an intermediary between belligerents, and (4) Switzerland's own policy of strict and heavily armed neutrality. The difficulties which a great power might encounter in conquering Switzerland are often popularly exaggerated, since the Swiss

Plateau, the heart of the country, lies open to Germany and France, and the Alps have frequently proved no impossible military barrier to strong forces in the past. On the other hand, resistance in the mountains might well be hard to thoroughly extinguish. In World War II Switzerland was able to hold a club over the head of Germany by mining the tunnels through which Swiss rail lines avoid the crests of the Alpine passes. Destruction of these tunnels would have been very costly to Germany, as well as to its military partner, Italy, since the Swiss railways were depended on to carry much traffic between them. The Swiss served the belligerents in many ways, such as the forwarding of prisoners' mail.

The Productive Swiss Economy

The efficient and highly successful Swiss economy finds its greatest development in three lines of enterprise: (1) the production of highly finished, specialized manufactures for export, (2) dairy farming, and (3) the world's most renowned tourist industry.

► Industrial and Urban Development in Switzerland

In terms of employment and income Switzerland is primarily an industrial country, despite the fame of its picturesque resorts and Alpine dairy farms. Swiss industry is based on the only important resources available—hydroelectric power and the skill of Swiss workers. Most raw materials as well as supplementary fuels are imported. The industry of the country is specialized along lines that minimize Switzerland's lack of bulky raw materials, while making full use of the country's excellent power resources and traditions of workmanship dating back to handicraft days before the Industrial Revolution. The major products are (1) metal goods, including machinery (much of it designed to order) and, of course, the famous Swiss watches, and (2) textiles, generally of very high quality and including silks and embroideries in addition to more ordinary materials. In recent years chemical products and aluminum have been gaining in importance. In 1952 the foregoing lines of goods accounted for 71 percent of all Swiss exports by value (watches, clocks and parts, 23 percent; machinery, 21 percent; textiles, 14 percent; chemicals and related products, 13 percent).

Reliance on hydroelectricity as the major source of power has facilitated the development of many small industrial centers throughout the country. The majority of these are located on the Swiss Plateau, but some are found in the valleys of the Jura and Alps. The largest Swiss city, Zurich, has only around 400,000 people (425,000 including suburbs). Only four other cities have populations of more than 100,000: Basel (186,000, or 305,000 including suburbs in France and Germany), Bern, the capital (149,000; with suburbs, 192,000), Geneva (150,000; with suburbs, 172,000), and Lausanne (108,000; with suburbs, 126,-000). Four of the five cities form virtually a straight line along the center of the Swiss Plateau, from Zurich on the northeast to Geneva on the southwest. Basel, however, lies beyond the Jura at the point where the Rhine River turns northward between Germany and France. This city, located at the head of important navigation on the Rhine, handles most of Switzerland's river-borne commerce. In addition, it is the largest railway center in the country.

▶ Swiss Agriculture

An estimated 45 percent of Switzerland's food requirements must ordinarily be imported. The salability of Swiss exports has made such food imports possible and has enabled Swiss agriculture to become adjusted to lands which on the whole are better suited to pasture and hay than to cultivated crops. The result has been a high degree of specialization on dairy farming. The dairy industry is centered on the rolling to hilly lands of the central plateau, although mountain pastures in the Alps are extensively used. The latter is an especially well-known aspect of Swiss agriculture. Dairy cattle and goats, accompanied by herdsmen or the entire farm family, are driven in the spring to pastures near the snow-line, where they are kept throughout the summer. This seasonal migration of farm people and their livestock between the valley floors and high mountain pastures is known as *transhumance* and is practiced in many mountainous regions of the world. The high pastures of Switzerland, known as "alps," have given their name to the Alps Mountains. In recent times there has been an increasing tendency among Swiss farmers to pasture only the young cattle on the high meadows and to keep the main dairy herds at lower levels the year round. Switzerland has a limited export of cheeses, condensed milk, and milk chocolate, but some dairy products, especially butter, are imported in small amounts. Recently the government has been encouraging greater self-sufficiency in foodstuffs, particularly wheat, in order to place the country less at the mercy of belligerents in time of war.

▶ The Highly Developed Tourist Industry

The total cost of Swiss imports is not ordinarily covered by exports of goods, but

Farms and wooded hills on the rolling Swiss Plateau near Lake Geneva. (*Standard Oil Company* [*N. J.*].)

the deficit is more than made good by various "invisible" exports, of which services to tourists are the most important. Few countries have so much to offer the tourist, and probably no country has developed and organized the tourist trade so completely and successfully. Special training programs are made available to personnel in the tourist industry, and high standards are enforced. Alpine resorts such as Zermatt, Davos, and St. Moritz have become world famous, as has the name of a pioneer in the trade, Ritz. Switzerland, more than any other, is a country which exports its scenery. Other important sources of revenue from "invisible" exports include the return from foreign investments and charges for international banking and insurance services, all of which Switzerland, as a relatively wealthy country and long-standing neutral, is in a good position to supply.

The National Unity of Switzerland

In their successful pursuit of economic goals, the Swiss have been aided by an effective national unity expressed in a stable, democratic, and competent government. The unity of the Swiss is the more remarkable in that it embraces a population divided in both language and religion. At present about 73 percent of the Swiss speak German as a native tongue, about 21 percent speak French, about 5 percent Italian, and about 1 percent Romansch, the latter an almost extinct descendant of Latin which has been preserved in the mountains of southeastern Switzerland. German, French, and Italian are dominant, respectively, in the sections of Switzerland adjoining Germany, France, and Italy. A religious division also exists, since approximately 58 percent of the Swiss are listed as Protestants and about 41 percent as Roman Catholics.

The internal political organization of Switzerland expresses and makes allowance for the ethnic diversity of the population. Originally the country was a loose alliance of small sovereign units known as cantons. When a stronger central authority became desirable in the nineteenth century, not only were the customary civil rights of a democracy guaranteed, but governmental autonomy was retained by the cantons except for limited functions specifically assigned to the central government. Although the functions allotted the central government have tended to increase with the passing of time, each of the local units (now 25 in number, including 22 cantons of which 3 are divided into half-cantons) has preserved a large measure of authority. Local autonomy is supplemented by the extremely democratic nature of the central government. In no country are the initiative and the referendum more widely used. Through these devices most important legislation is submitted directly to the people for their decision. Thus guarantees of fundamental rights, local autonomy, and close governmental responsiveness to the will of the people have been successfully used to foster national unity despite the potential handicaps of ethnic diversity and local particularism.

The central government, in turn, has pushed the country's economic development vigorously. Two outstanding accomplishments have been the construction and operation of the railroads and the development of the hydroelectric power system. Despite the difficult terrain the Swiss government has succeeded in building a rail network whose density on a country-wide basis is exceeded only by the railway systems of Belgium and Great Britain. It carries not only Switzerland's own traffic, but a volume of international transit traffic sufficiently large to be an important source of revenue. The highly developed hydroelectric power system, utilizing the many torrential streams of the mountains, places Switzerland second only to Norway in Europe in the amount of hydroelectricity available per capita, and possibly third to Norway and Canada in the world. In total developed capacity Switzerland ranks fifth in Europe, behind France, Italy, Norway, and Sweden. Despite a doubling of power output since 1930 the hydroelectric system is still being expanded in order to relieve some of the continuing need for supplementary imports of fuel. Only about one fifth of Switzerland's estimated potential capacity is yet in use.

Thus internal unity and effective government have contributed greatly to Switzerland's economic success. On the other hand, economic success has undoubtedly reinforced the internal unity and political stability of the country. And a century and a half of peace has provided highly favorable conditions for both political and economic adjustment. Few modern nations have been so fortunate.

Political and Economic Problems of Austria

In contrast to Switzerland's happy circumstances, Austria has been the victim during the twentieth century of a series of military and political disasters which have required large and difficult readjustments of its economic life. These difficulties have been occasioned by the two World Wars and the political and economic arrangements following them. Austria emerged in its present form as a defeated remnant of the Austro-Hungarian Empire when that empire disintegrated in 1918 under the stress of war and internal difficulties. Austria's population is essentially German in language and cultural background, and there is evidence that a majority wished to unite with Germany following World War I. This was forbidden by the victors, and Austria became an independent national state. Torn by internal strife and with an economy seriously disoriented by the loss of its empire, the country limped through the interwar period until absorbed by Nazi Germany, now against the will of a majority, in 1938. In 1945 it was reconstituted a separate state, but as in the case of Germany, was divided into four occupation zones administered respectively by the United States, the United Kingdom, France, and the Soviet Union. Vienna, like Berlin, was placed under joint occupation by the four powers. The situation of Austria is different from that of Germany, however, in that the Soviet zone of Austria has not been declared a separate state and detached from the rest of the country. Vienna has continued to function as the capital for the entire country. The Soviet zone has, however, been subjected to extensive removal of machinery and other equipment as reparations, and one of its most important natural resources, the oil of the Zistersdorf field, has been mainly appropriated for Soviet use.

As the core area of an empire of 50 million people, Austria developed a diversified industrial economy during the years prior to 1914. Iron and steel were manufactured in a number of small centers, of which Graz was the most important. Production of a variety of secondary metal goods was centered largely in Vienna. Textiles were manufactured in the Alps and at Vienna. Wood industries made use of the Alpine forests. These industries were closely tied to the existence of the empire as an extraordinarily self-contained economic unit. Austrian iron ore was smelted mainly with coal drawn from Bohemia and Moravia, now in Czechoslovakia. The Aus-

trian textile industry specialized to a considerable extent on spinning, leaving much of the weaving to be done in Bohemia. In general, Austrian industry was not outstandingly efficient, but it had the benefit of a protected market in the agricultural parts of the empire to the east—areas now included in Hungary, Rumania, Czechoslovakia, Yugoslavia, Poland, and the Soviet Union. In turn, Austria drew foodstuffs and some industrial raw materials from these areas, while Austrian agriculture was relatively neglected.

When the empire disintegrated at the end of World War I, the areas which had formed Austria's protected markets were incorporated in the independent states referred to in the preceding paragraph (excepting the Soviet Union). These states, motivated by a desire to develop industries of their own, began to erect tariff barriers. Other industrialized nations began to compete with Austria in their markets. The resultant decrease in Austria's ability to export to its former markets made it more difficult for the country to secure the imports of food and raw materials which its unbalanced economy required. Such difficulties have been further increased since World War II by the absorption of East Central Europe into the Communist sphere. Reorientation of Austrian industries toward other markets, now found principally in various countries of free Europe, has not been easy. There is competition with industries already established in those markets. Often these industries enjoy the advantage of superior natural resources and/or tariff protection. Consequently, Austrian exports of goods have not been sufficient to pay for the necessary imports of food, coal, and other materials. Therefore, lacking the extensive "invisible" exports of Switzerland, the country has run a consistent deficit in international trade since 1918.

Needed readjustments to this situation have been rendered difficult by certain internal conditions and problems. One of these is the financial drain of a notoriously oversized bureaucracy, originally developed to meet the needs of a great empire and now far too large for the small Austrian state. Another inheritance from the empire is the rigidly noncompetitive structure of Austrian industry. Firms and cartels enjoying a high degree of monopoly control over their respective sectors of the internal market and having great influence in Austrian politics have not always been amenable to changes which would be in the best interests of the country and the people. In addition, Austria was subjected to especially violent class and party disputes

during the period between World Wars I and II. Economic crisis deepened class antagonisms, and feelings were further embittered by disagreements over the role of the church in a country 90 percent Roman Catholic. In 1934 the anticlerical socialists who controlled Vienna were suppressed in open civil war by a clerically oriented authoritarian government drawing its main support from the peasants and the upper classes. Pro-German and anti-German sentiments and parties also divided the country and resulted in further violence. Such internal divisions contributed materially to the ease with which Austria was absorbed by Germany in 1938.

Austrian Efforts Toward Economic Readjustment

Despite the difficulties described in the preceding paragraphs, the economy of Austria has been far from static since 1918, and a notable amount of progress toward readjustment to the new conditions has been made. The economic life of the country has been directed toward a greater exploitation of, reliance on, and adaptation to Austria's domestic resources, and, conversely, toward a decreased reliance on imports and the industries dependent on imports. The introduction and growth of new industries together with the persistence of old ones has resulted in a very diversified industrial structure.

▶ Adaptation to Domestic Resources

The movement toward a more intensive exploitation of and adaptation to the resources found within the country is evident in an increased development of domestic power resources, wood industries, chemical and aluminum industries, dairy farming, and the tourist industry. Certain resemblances to Swiss economic development, reflecting environmental similarities, are obvious.

1. Installed hydroelectric capacity in-

creased about sixfold between 1918 and 1947. Hydroelectric development is still proceeding rapidly, and this type of power now supplies about three quarters of the mechanical energy used in Austrian factories. However, the total installed capacity is still only a little more than half that of Switzerland. The production of both coal and lignite has approximately doubled since 1913, but coal production has now dropped back from peaks reached in 1936 and 1943. Nearly all of the coke and high-grade coal needed in the iron and steel industry must be imported, principally from West Germany and Poland.

2. Austrian forests are an especially great asset in view of a general shortage of wood in most of the European countries with whom Austria trades. Large and consistent increases in the production and export of a variety of wood products have been obtained. Production of wood pulp alone has quintupled since 1913. Forest products, notably lumber, wood pulp, and paper, now form one of the main categories of Austrian exports, accounting in 1952 for 30 percent of all exports by value.

3. Austria's chemical and aluminum in-

dustries, based on hydroelectric power, extensive salt deposits (mainly near Salzburg), and small bauxite deposits, were largely developed by Nazi Germany as a means of furthering the German war effort. They have proved well adapted to Austrian conditions, however, and have been increasing in importance since World War II.

4. An increased development of dairy farming since World War I has represented an attempt to make more intensive use of the relatively large area which is best adapted to pasture. Austria managed to achieve a modest export of dairy products before World War II, but the economic dislocations associated with that conflict dealt a severe blow to dairy farming, as to all Austrian agriculture. Not until the early 1950's did dairy production again reach prewar levels, while the output of most other farm commodities remained below the prewar mark.

5. The proceeds of the Austrian tourist industry do not yet compensate for the country's deficit in foreign trade. However, substantial progress was made during the interwar period and has been even more rapid since 1945. Since the war Austria has been able to offer serious competition to Switzerland by catering to the straitened financial circumstances of many European vacationists. To some extent the country has become the "poor man's Switzerland." The drawing-power of Alpine scenery only slightly less imposing than that of Switzerland has been supplemented by a number of carefully fostered cultural attractions, such as the world famous music festivals at Salzburg.

▶ Results of Decreased Reliance on Imports

The movement toward a smaller reliance on imported materials, together with Austria's inability to pay for such imports, has been reflected in agricultural developments and in trends in the textile and iron and steel industries.

The spire of St. Stephen's Cathedral can be seen from all corners of Vienna. Here it dominates Graben, the fashionable shopping center in the heart of the city. (*Austrian State Tourist Department.*)

1. Austria's difficulties in foreign trade have not only stimulated an intensified use of pasture lands for dairy production, but have also led to an attempt to achieve the greatest possible self-sufficiency in other foods. Hence grains, representing by far the

largest category of imported foods, have occupied the dominant position in the country's crop production. Wheat leads in production, although rye and oats occupy slightly larger acreages, and barley and corn are important. The variety of grain crops reflects the surprising diversity of soil and local climatic conditions in this small but varied country. Two root crops, potatoes and sugar beets, have risen sharply in acreage and production since 1918. Overall crop yields per acre have been steadily increased through more intensive management, although comparison with yields in the North Sea countries reveals substantial room for further improvement. Nevertheless, imported foodstuffs still represent one fourth and grains one tenth of all Austrian imports by value. In view of the limited amount of arable land in the country and the relative poverty of much of the soil, a higher degree of self-sufficiency promises to be increasingly difficult to obtain.

2. Depending almost entirely on imported raw materials, the Austrian textile industry has failed to make gains commensurate with those of industries depending more on domestic materials. In the early 1950's, for example, the value of cotton and woolen yarns produced was lower than in the late 1920's and late 1930's.

3. The Austrian iron and steel industry, largely dependent on imported coke and coal, never regained its pre-World War I production until the period of Nazi domination. However, the Nazis, for reasons of military preparedness rather than purely economic considerations, more than doubled the capacity of the industry. The new plants, bolstered by American aid, have enabled postwar Austrian production of iron and steel to reach new peacetime highs, although many of the plants have been able to operate at only a small percent of capacity. Iron and steel manufactures, including machinery and transportation equipment, currently account for about a fourth of all exports by value. However, the total Austrian production of steel, amounting to 1,166,000 tons in 1952, is only a little more than a third as great as the production of Luxembourg or the Saar, and less than one seventieth of the average annual production of the United States since World War II. Although the industry is able to supply most of its needs for iron ore from deposits in the eastern Alps, the finding of markets for the finished product and the financing of adequate imports of coal and coke are problems that render the future of Austrian iron and steel production somewhat problematical.

The Role of Vienna

A significant aspect of Austrian readjustment since World War I has been the somewhat lessened importance of the famous Austrian capital of Vienna. Although Vienna is still by far the largest city and most important industrial center of Austria, there has been a pronounced tendency for population and industry to shift away from the capital and toward the smaller cities and mountain districts. Thus Vienna, which had about 2,000,000 people in 1910, had only 1,761,000 in 1951, while the smaller cities of Graz (226,000), Linz (185,000),

Salzburg (100,000), Innsbruck (95,000), and Klagenfurt (63,000) have all experienced rapid growth. Since 1930 the combined growth of these cities has been about 300,-000, more than balancing the population loss suffered by Vienna. The shift reflects the damage in Vienna's situation from the capital of an empire to that of a small country. It also reflects the increased importance of forests and water power in the Austrian economy, as well as the dispersal of Nazi war industries into less vulnerable locations away from the capital.

Vienna's importance, however, has now persisted since Roman times, and is based on more than purely Austrian circumstances. The city is located at the crossing of two of the European continent's major natural routes: the Danube Valley route through the highlands separating Germany from the Hungarian Plain and southeastern Europe; and the route from Silesia and the North European Plain to the head of the Adriatic Sea. The latter route follows the lowland passageway of Moravia to the north, and makes use of the passes of the eastern Alps, especially the Semmering Pass, to the south. These routes have been important corridors of movement throughout European history. Whenever political conditions have permitted, Vienna has been a major focus of transportation and trade, and doubtless would be able to regain much of its old importance were restrictions imposed by the Iron Curtain to be relaxed. But the city's position has also made it a major strategic objective in time of war—a fact that is partly responsible for its role as an occupied area and the capital of an occupied country since World War II.

Countries of Northern Europe

The five countries of Denmark, Norway, Sweden, Finland, and Iceland may be defined as the countries of Northern Europe. This regional grouping accords with a geographic concept which is well established in the countries themselves. The peoples of these lands recognize their close relationships with each other and habitually group themselves and their countries geographically under the regional term *Norden,* or "The North."

A more common term used in referring to some or all of these countries is Scandinavia or the Scandinavian countries. But this regional name is somewhat ambiguous, being used sometimes to refer only to the two countries which occupy the Scandinavian Peninsula, Norway and Sweden; more often to include these countries plus Denmark; and sometimes is extended to include these three plus Finland, Iceland, and even Greenland. Sometimes when Finland is included in the group the term Fennoscandia, or Fennoscandian countries, is used, thus taking account of the comparatively greater difference of the Finns in ancestry, historical relationships, and language as compared with the other nations. These differences, however, are overshadowed by many similarities.

Agricultural settlement on the tiny plain at the head of a Norwegian fjord. (*Norwegian Information Services.*)

Characteristics of Northern Europe as a Region

"The North" is a good descriptive term for these lands. No other highly developed countries have their principal populated areas so near the pole. Located in the general latitude of Alaska, and occupying a geographical position in Eurasia analogous to that of Alaska in North America, the countries of Northern Europe represent the northernmost seat of advanced culture in the world. The 182,000 people of Alaska inhabiting a slightly larger total area can hardly compare in numbers or in economic and cultural achievements with the 19 million people of Northern Europe. The Soviet Union has several cities and areas of importance in these northern latitudes, but its economy and population are based for the most part on land units farther south.

▶ Climate Effects of the Atlantic Ocean

West winds from the Atlantic, warmed here in winter by the North Atlantic Drift, moderate the climatic effects of northern location considerably. Temperatures average above freezing and harbors are ordinarily ice-free in winter over most of Denmark and along the coast of Norway. But away from the direct influence of the west winds, winter temperatures average below freezing and are particularly severe at elevated, interior, and northern locations. In summer the ocean tends to be a cooling rather than a warming influence, and most of Northern Europe has July temperatures averaging no higher than the fifties or low sixties. Highlands have temperatures sufficiently low that a number of glaciers exist, both on the Scandinavian Peninsula and in Iceland. Despite the over-all moderation of the climate of Northern Europe as compared with what might be expected from the latitude, the populations of the various countries tend to cluster in the southern sections, and all of the countries except Denmark have considerable areas of sparsely populated terrain where the problems of development are largely those of overcoming a northern environment.

▶ Historical and Cultural Unity of Northern Europe

Close historical interconnections and cultural similarities are more important factors in the regional unity of Northern Europe than partial similarity of environmental problems, however. Historically, each of the countries of Northern Europe has been more closely related to others of the group than to any outside power. Finland was ruled by Sweden from the twelfth century until 1809. Denmark and Norway had a common sovereign from the fourteenth century until 1814, as did Sweden and Norway from 1814 to 1905. The southern part of Sweden (*Skane*) only passed from Danish to Swedish control in the seventeenth century. Iceland was a possession of Denmark from the fourteenth century until 1918; in the latter year it secured independence, but remained under the Danish sovereign until 1944. At times, warlike relations have prevailed among various countries in the group. For the past century and a half, however, internal relations in Northern Europe have been peaceful, and the feelings of relationship among these countries have been expressed in close international cooperation.

Cultural similarities among the countries of Northern Europe are many. Similarities of language, religion, and form of government are probably the most important in fostering regional unity. The languages of Denmark, Norway, and Sweden are descended from the same ancient tongue and are mutually intelligible, though not identical. Icelandic, though a branch of the same root, is more difficult for the other peoples only because it has evolved less and become less modernized. Only Finnish,

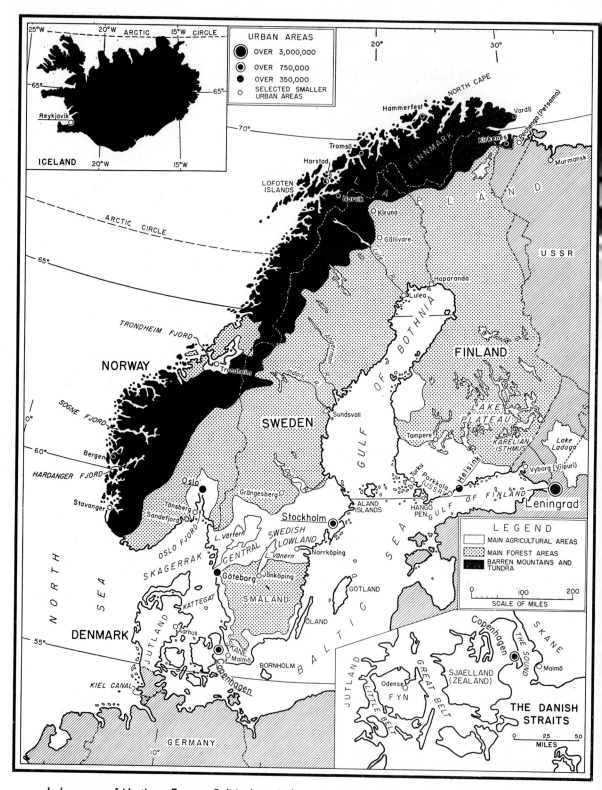

Index map of Northern Europe. Political capitals are underlined. Short dashes indicate pre-1939 Russo-Finnish boundary.

which belongs to a different language family, is entirely distinct from the other languages of Northern Europe. Even in Finland, however, about 10 percent of the population is of Swedish descent and speaks Swedish as a native tongue. Swedish is recognized as a second official language in Finland.

Among these countries there are no exceptions to the cultural unity embodied in a common religion. The Evangelical Lutheran Church is the dominant religious organization in each country, with over 95 percent of the respective populations adhering to it. It is a state church, supported by taxes levied by the respective governments, and is probably the most all-embracing organization outside of the state.

The countries of Northern Europe also exhibit basic similarities with respect to law and political institutions. These countries have very old traditions of individual rights, broad political participation, limited governmental powers, and democratic control. Thus old foundations have been available for building modern democracies, and the countries of Northern Europe are recognized as outstanding strongholds of democratic institutions. Iceland claims to have the world's oldest legislature, founded in 930 A.D. Today Iceland is a republic, as is Finland, while the other three states are constitutional monarchies. In all these countries real power rests with an elected parliament. In the twentieth century the countries of Northern Europe have consciously and actively worked to increase their similarities respecting legal codes and political institutions by coordinating their laws wherever feasible.

One other similarity not yet mentioned is the small size of these countries, especially in population. Comparative figures on area, population, and population density for the five countries are given in Table 7.

TABLE 7
NORTHERN EUROPE: AREA AND POPULATION DATA

COUNTRY	LAND AREA (THOUSAND SQUARE MILES)	POPULATION (MILLIONS: 1952–53 ESTIMATES)	DENSITY (PER SQUARE MILE: TO NEAREST WHOLE NUMBER)
Denmark	16.3	4.33	265
Norway	119.2	3.34	28
Sweden	158.5	7.15	45
Finland	117.9	4.13	35
Iceland	39.7	0.15	4
Totals	451.7 [a]	19.10	42

[a] Discrepancy due to rounding of figures.

▶ Disadvantages of an "In-Between" Position

Small populations and limited resources have forced the countries of Northern Europe to give up imperial ambitions during recent times, though their armies and fleets were the scourge of much of Europe in times past. A policy of neutrality plus a relatively isolated position in one corner of Europe allowed them a long period of peace between the Napoleonic Wars and World War II. In the twentieth century, however, the increasing strategic importance of North Atlantic air and sea routes has jeopardized their safety. In the present world situation, these countries occupy an "in-between" position. They lie on the most direct routes between the United

States and the western coreland of the Soviet Union. The coast of Norway, which
adjoins the Soviet Union in the far north,
offers some of the world's best and most
strategically located naval harbors in the
famous fjords. This coast is especially suitable as a base for submarine operations
against North Atlantic shipping and was
so used by the German Navy in World
War II. Denmark, Norway's neighbor to
the south, controls the outlet from the
Baltic Sea, on which some of the main
Russian seaports and naval bases are located. Finland lies between the Soviet Union and the Scandinavian Peninsula, and
Sweden, the largest and most powerful
country of Northern Europe, lies in the
midst of these various positions. The
changed significance of their position has
presented the countries of Northern Europe with a common problem of national
security, evidenced by the fact that only
Sweden escaped involvement in World
War II. It has also focused on them an
increased degree of world attention and
concern.

▶ Social and Cultural Achievements

Small size and resource limitations have
made it necessary for each of the countries
of Northern Europe to build a highly specialized economy in attempting to attain a
high standard of living. Success in such
endeavors has been so marked that these
countries are probably known as much for
high living standards as for any other characteristic. In general, they rank below only
the United Kingdom and Switzerland
among the countries of Europe in this

respect, although Finland falls somewhat
short of the other countries of the group.
Their high standards of health, education,
security for the individual, and creative
achievement are evidenced by impressive
health statistics, long life expectancy, almost nonexistent illiteracy, disproportionately great achievements in art and science,
and the reputation, particularly in Sweden,
of having "abolished poverty."

In their attack on economic problems the
countries of Northern Europe have employed a moderate socialism, consciously
seeking a "Middle Way" between uncon-
trolled capitalism and communism. They
have attempted to put a floor under the
living standard of every member of the
community, while closely limiting the accumulation of wealth. Great emphasis on
conservation of resources, the exercise and
general acceptance of economic control and
initiative by the state, and often the development of resources cooperatively by the
state and private enterprise are prominent
features of economic life in these countries.
At the same time private business and
ownership are fostered by the state in many
lines of activity, as is trade unionism.

Parallel with the development of this
"Middle Way," the countries of Northern Europe have experienced the world's
greatest development of the private cooperative type of economic enterprise, reaching into almost every phase of production,
distribution, and consumption. Cooperatives are particularly widespread and important in two countries of the group, Finland and Denmark. They are present, however, in all five countries.

Denmark

Denmark has the somewhat paradoxical
distinction of possessing the largest city in
Northern Europe, and of being at the same
time the most dependent on agriculture of
any country in the region. The Danish

capital of Copenhagen has a population of
1,200,000 in its metropolitan area, out of a
national population of some 4.3 million.
Denmark has a much greater density of
population than the other countries of

Northern Europe, a fact accounted for by the presence of Copenhagen, the greater productivity of Danish agriculture, and the lack of any sparsely populated zone of frontier settlement.

▶ Copenhagen and the Danish Straits

Copenhagen lies on the island of Sjaelland (Zealand) at the extreme eastern margin of Denmark. Sweden lies only 12 miles away across The Sound, the main passage between the Baltic and the wide Kattegat Strait leading to the North Sea. Copenhagen grew beside a natural harbor well placed to control all traffic through The Sound, which is the most direct and most used channel for traffic in and out of the Baltic. For many years before the seventeenth century Denmark controlled adjacent southern Sweden, as well as the less favored alternative channels to The Sound —the Great Belt and Little Belt. Toll was levied on all shipping passing to and from the Baltic. Although the days of levying toll are now long past, Copenhagen still benefits from its strategic location. The city does a large transit and entrepôt business in North Sea–Baltic trade, and has encouraged this business by setting up a free zone in its harbor, where goods destined for redistribution may be landed without paying customs duties. Increasing trade has led to the development of industry, and the city is the principal industrial center of Denmark as well as its chief port and capital. Shipbuilding and food processing are the most important branches of industry. The latter industry prepares products of Denmark's specialized agriculture for export and processes the many foods that Denmark must import.

▶ Agriculture

Denmark stands out sharply from the other countries of Northern Europe in the nature of its land and the place of agriculture in its economy. The topography of the country results principally from glacial deposition. The western part of the peninsula of Jutland consists mainly of sandy outwash plains and coastal dunes. Eastern Jutland and the Danish islands exhibit a rolling topography of ground and terminal moraine. The highest hill in the country is less than 600 feet in elevation. Although the sandy areas of the west are not very fertile in their natural condition, they have mostly been reclaimed and are cultivated, while the clay soils of the moraine areas, with greater natural fertility, support a very intensive and productive agriculture.

[EDITORIAL COMMENT. *Outwash plains* are formed of glacial materials deposited by melt water flowing from an ice sheet. Sheets of material deposited directly by the ice sheet are known as *ground moraine*. A ridgelike accumulation of such materials at the edge of an ice sheet is a *terminal moraine*.]

Consequently, most of Denmark is available for farming, and about three quarters of the entire country is normally cultivated, the largest proportion of any European country. It is fortunate that so much of Denmark is arable because the country is practically without resources except for soil, climate, and its strategic position for trade. Danish agriculture is so efficient that only about a fourth of the working population is actively employed on the land. Agriculture, however, is absolutely basic to the country's whole economy. Many additional workers are engaged in processing and marketing agricultural products, and many others in supplying the needs of the farms. Well over 60 percent of Denmark's exports ordinarily come from her farms.

Few countries or areas which depend so heavily on agriculture are as materially successful as Denmark has been during the first half of the twentieth century. Danish agriculture is based on a highly specialized and very consciously and carefully fostered development of dairy farming, which began to be emphasized when the competition of cheap grain from overseas brought ruin to the previous Danish system of grain farming in the latter part of the nineteenth century. The following factors help to explain the outstanding success of dairy farming in Denmark:

1. The land and climate of the country are well suited to fodder crops. Potatoes and other root crops, together with barley and oats, are the crops which are most emphasized. These crops generally take precedence over hay, since they yield a larger quantity of nutrients per acre. Hay tends to be relatively more important in the less fertile west than elsewhere in the country. Despite the emphasis on fodder crops, however, the total production of feedstuffs is inadequate, and Denmark is a major importer of livestock feeds. As such, the country has been likened to a large agricultural "factory" which imports raw materials and exports the finished products.

2. Near-by markets, primarily in Great Britain and Germany, have generally been adequate to accommodate the bulk of Danish export production. Nearly three fifths of all Danish exports in 1952 were taken by three countries: United Kingdom, 38 percent; German Federal Republic, 14 percent; and Sweden, 5 percent. The same three countries also provided more than half of all Danish imports: United King-

dom, 27 percent; German Federal Republic, 16 percent; and Sweden, 9 percent.

3. The Danish government has ranged itself actively and intelligently behind the development of a prosperous agriculture. Probably the most important government measures have been: (a) encouragement of family farming, in contrast to the large estates which formerly dominated the countryside, by the provision of liberal and low-cost credit for farmers desirous of purchasing land, including loans covering up to nine tenths of the total purchase price; (b) financial aid to agricultural education and research; and (c) financial encouragement of reclamation projects carried out by private societies, especially in the sandy west. Denmark has become a land of small to medium-sized farms, more than half being less than 25 acres in size. Over 90 percent of all farms are owned by their operators, and most of them are very efficiently and scientifically handled.

4. Cooperative societies have played a major role in the development of agricultural prosperity. Practically all Danish farmers are members of farm cooperatives. Cooperative dairies and other food-processing plants prepare the products of the farms for sale, cooperative export societies conduct a large share of the marketing in

Cans of milk arriving at the processing plant of a dairy cooperative in Denmark. (*Danish Information Office.*)

foreign countries, and still other cooperatives supply many of the farmers' needs. Thus the individual farmer derives the benefit from large-scale marketing and buying, and the profits of a middleman are largely eliminated. Through his membership in the cooperative the farmer has become to some extent his own middleman. A further important function largely performed by the cooperatives is rigid quality control and grading of farm products. Danish agricultural products enjoy an enviable reputation for dependable quality—which is an important factor in insuring a steady market.

5. Probably underlying much of the success of Danish agriculture, and especially the success of the cooperative movement, is a very high level of education. The traditional school system, noted for high standards, is supplemented by various forms of adult education. An emphasis on the continuing education of adults is characteristic not only of Denmark, but of all the countries of Northern Europe.

Thus Danish agriculture has become noted for its efficiency, rationality, and prosperity. Milk production is combined with supplementary activities, particularly the raising of hogs, fed partly on skim milk, and the raising of poultry. Butter, bacon, and eggs are Denmark's main contributions to the European economy.

In certain respects the Danish economy is very fragile. If the few export markets which customarily absorb the major share of Danish production were closed, the country would find itself in a critical situation. British austerity and German depression and disorganization following World War II retarded Danish recovery seriously. The country is currently trying to become somewhat more self-sufficient, at least in bread grains. But a pronounced lessening in specialization probably would mean a lessening in prosperity.

Norway

Norway stretches for well over a thousand miles along the west side and around the north end of the Scandinavian Peninsula. The peninsula, as well as Finland, occupies part of the Fennoscandian Shield, a block of very ancient and hard rocks, especially gneiss and granite, similar geologically to the Canadian or Laurentian Shield of North America. This block has been tilted up along the western side of the peninsula and eroded, particularly by the continental glaciation which centered in Scandinavia. Thus Norway is an extremely rugged land, mainly mountains and steep-sided valleys. Most areas have little or no soil to cover the rock surface, scraped bare by glaciation. About three quarters of the country must be classified as waste land, only about 3 percent as arable or pasture land, and the remainder as forest land.

Not only agriculture, but also transportation is hindered by the nature of the terrain. Glaciers deepened the valleys of streams flowing from the mountains into the sea, and when the ice melted, the sea invaded the valley floors. Thus were created the famous fjords—long, narrow, and deep extensions of the sea into the land, usually edged by steep valley walls. Some run 100 miles or more inland. The difficulties of building highways and railroads parallel to such a coast are obvious. Coastal steamers and planes, often seaplanes, must bear a major transport burden, while the quickest land route from south to north is via the Swedish railroads. The fjords provide some of the finest harbors in the world, but most of them have practically no hinterland. Much of the Norwegian population is scattered in relatively small and isolated settlements on narrow ribbons of lowland along the various fjords. The basic economic activity of such settlements is ordinarily a combination of livestock farming and fishing.

▶ Northern Norway

Over northern Norway, as well as adjacent parts of Sweden and Finland, wander the Lapps, a relatively primitive people who live mainly by reindeer herding. The Norwegian coast as far south as Trondheim is occupied mainly by small and scattered fishing villages. Places sufficiently large and varied to be classed as commercial towns are few in number, and none exceeds 12,000 people in size. Especially noteworthy among the latter are Tromsö, Narvik, Hammerfest, and Harstad, each an important fishing port as well as the commercial center for a considerable area. One of these places has an additional activity which gives it much international importance. This is the port of Narvik, which is the Atlantic outlet, ice-free the year round, for the tremendous iron exports of northern Sweden. The importance of Narvik was brought to the attention of the world in 1940, when Germany conquered Norway and the British fought a bitter though unsuccessful campaign to keep possession of the port.

▶ The Southwest Coast

From Trondheim south the intensity and scale of settlement along the coast is somewhat greater. The major communities are Trondheim (60,000), which benefits from an unusually large area of agricultural lowland roundabout as well as from gaps in the highlands giving access to Sweden and Oslo; Bergen (116,000), the most important center for the Norwegian fishing industry and the commercial metropolis of western Norway; and Stavanger (52,000), another large fishing and commercial center.

The southwestern coastal area has a number of advantages over the coast farther north. Agricultural conditions are slightly more favorable, some areas of forest occur, and the location is better for utilization of the hydroelectric power

which is one of Norway's primary resources. Norway already uses more electricity per capita than any other nation in the world, and only an estimated one fifth of the potential hydropower has been developed. Along the southwest coast a considerable electrochemical and electrometallurgical industry has come into being. The raw materials are imported for the most part and products exported. Among the more important products are carbide, aluminum, zinc, and ferroalloys.

▶ The Southeastern Core Region

More than half of the population of Norway lives in the southeast, which centers on the capital, Oslo. This is the core region of modern Norway. Here, where valleys are wider and the land is less rugged, are found the most extensive agricultural lands and the largest forests in the country. Streams coming down from the mountains to the west and north furnish power for sawmilling, pulp and paper production, metallurgy, the electrochemical industry, and industries which process imported materials, such as woolen and cotton yarns, for Norwegian consumption. Near the mouth of Oslo Fjord the towns of Tönsberg and Sandefjord are the home ports of the world's largest whaling fleet, which now operates mainly in Antarctic waters. Oslo, which lies at the head of the fjord where several valleys converge, is now a city of 440,000 people, or slightly more than 500,000 with suburbs. It is the principal seaport and industrial, commercial, and cultural center of Norway as well as its capital.

▶ Resources and National Economy

Norway's basic natural resources are land, water power, fish, and forests. Although a variety of metalliferous ores are present, they are mostly of such low metallic content that they cannot be worked economically under present conditions. Some iron, from near Kirkenes in the far northeast, and some copper are mined.

The 3 percent of Norway which is usable

for agriculture is employed mainly to produce fodder crops, such as hay and oats, and also potatoes, used to feed both animals and humans. A large share of the land on Norwegian farms is kept in pasture. The country is nearly self-sufficient in animal products. Despite the meager amounts of arable land, agriculture plays a critical role in Norway's economy. From the standpoint of employment it is the nation's second most important occupation. Many Norwegians combine farming with part-time fishing or forestry. Norway ranks with the United Kingdom as one of the two most important fishing nations in Europe. In 1951 the total Norwegian catch was exceeded by only four nations—Japan, China, the Soviet Union, and the United States and Alaska. The forests of Norway, mainly composed of coniferous trees, are much less extensive than those of Sweden or Finland. Nevertheless, wood, pulp, and paper account for a quarter of all Norwegian exports.

Manufacturing employs a larger number of adult workers than any other occupation. It is based mainly on domestic resources of hydroelectric power, forests, and fish. Electrically processed ores and chemicals, pulp and paper, some lumber and other timber products, and fish in various forms make up the great bulk of Norway's exports. Wood and fish products outrank other classes of exports in value. Industries besides those listed serve mainly the domestic market. However, the latter industries account for about 80 percent of the total employment in manufacturing.

International earnings from the products of export industries are supplemented by those of the world's third largest merchant marine. Norway's merchant fleet is exceeded in size only by the merchant shipping of the United States and the United Kingdom, and it is by far the largest in the world on a per capita basis. It is a tangible expression of the country's intimate relation with the sea and long and distinguished sea-faring traditions dating back at least to the Vikings.

Sweden

Sweden is the largest in area and population and the most diversified of the countries of Northern Europe. In the northwest it shares the mountains of the Scandinavian Peninsula with Norway; in the south it has rolling, fertile farm lands like those of Denmark; in the central area of the great lakes another relatively extensive area of good farm land occurs. To the north, between the mountains and the shores of the Baltic Sea and Gulf of Bothnia, Sweden consists mainly of ice-scoured, crystalline, forested uplands similar to those which constitute the greater part of Finland. A smaller area of the latter type occurs south of Lake Vättern.

▶ Agriculture

Agriculture normally supplies about 90 percent of Sweden's food requirements. In addition, it provides a small export of dairy products, eggs, and meat. Sweden has other important sources of exports; consequently, the agriculture of the country has not had to be as specialized as that of Denmark. A major emphasis on fodder crops and livestock, representing a good adaptation to the soil and climate, has been accompanied in recent years by expanded production of bread grains for the home market. About 9 percent of the total area of the country is cultivated, most of this land being found in the two most favorable areas, *Skane,* and the central lowland or lakes district. Skane is a regional name for the southernmost tip of Sweden, an area with a surface largely morainal, like that of the adjoining Danish islands. It has always been the most productive agricultural area in Sweden, with soils of above average fertility and the country's mildest climate. Skane is the most densely populated part of Sweden, having about 10 percent of the national population on about 2 percent of the total area. The main urban center of the region, Malmö, is the third largest city of Sweden, with a present population of about 200,000. It lies slightly to the southeast of Copenhagen on the opposite shore of The Sound.

The Central Swedish Lowland, extending across the full width of Sweden between the important port cities of Stockholm and Göteborg, ranks second to Skane in agricultural importance. However, agriculture in the Central Lowland is now subordinate to manufacturing in terms of employment and value of product. The average elevation of this part of Sweden is several hundred feet lower than in the crystalline uplands to the north and south, and a considerable amount of glacial and marine deposition has provided the basis for fairly fertile soils. Patches of farm land are scattered through a forested terrain with many lakes. Farming in this area is built around dairying and associated fodder crops, leaving most of Sweden's substantial wheat production for the better soils and milder climate of Skane.

Some farming is found in other parts of Sweden, but it is severely restricted by bare rock surfaces, thin and infertile soils, and, in the north, by a harsher climate. In these areas agricultural settlement is scattered and farming is often combined with seasonal work in other occupations, especially logging.

▶ The Forest Industries

Practically the whole of Sweden is naturally forested, with spruce and other conifers predominating north of the Central Swedish Lowland and mixed conifers and broadleaved deciduous hardwoods in the southern part of the country. In the extreme north the forest cover becomes sparser and the trees stunted.

As a group, the wood products industries based on these forests are the most important in Sweden from the standpoint of employment, value of product, and value of exports. This group of industries includes sawmilling, pulp milling, paper-making, the manufacture of wood chemicals and synthetic fabrics, and the production of fabricated articles such as plywood, window and door frames, furniture, and prefabricated houses. Pulpwood, paper, and lumber account for most of the value of production. While logging and wood industries are characteristic of most of Sweden, the main concentration is found in areas to the north of the Central Lowland. In these areas other economic opportunities are less abundant, large quantities of good timber are available, and logs can be transported with relative ease in winter by sled, or floated to mill in summer on the numerous rivers. Most of the sawmills and pulp mills are located in industrial villages which dot the coast of the Gulf of Bothnia at the mouths of the rivers. From these mills huge quantities of wood products are exported to other countries by ship during the summer months when the Gulf of Bothnia is free of ice. Power for the milling operations is supplied by numerous hydroelectric stations, and much electricity is transmitted by high tension systems to the central and southern parts of the country where growing demands cannot be met by streams which are now almost completely developed for power.

▶ The Mineral Industries and Manufacturing

It is the mineral wealth of Sweden and associated high development of the metallurgical and mechanical industries which most distinguish the Swedish economy from that of the other individual countries of Northern Europe. Sweden is abundantly supplied with high-grade iron ore and mines some copper, zinc, and manganese as well. However, the utility of these minerals

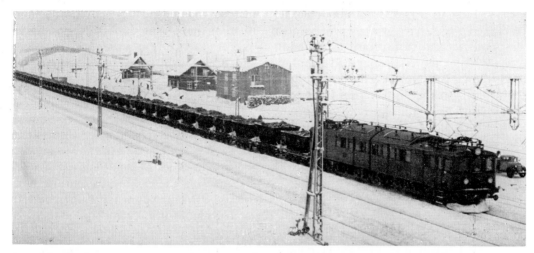

A trainload of iron ore en route from the Kiruna mines of northern Sweden to the ice-free Norwegian shipping port of Narvik. Note the electrified railway. (*Swedish State Railways.*)

is somewhat lessened by a shortage of coal, a deficiency which Sweden shares with the other countries of the region. A few hundred thousand tons of low-grade coal are produced each year from mines in Skane, but this production is far from sufficient for the country's needs.

The largest and best known iron fields are located in the far north beyond the Arctic Circle. Here at Kiruna and Gällivare entire mountains of ore are being mined with power shovels and dumped into railway cars for export. The iron ore of northern Sweden has a high content of phosphorus impurities but is also very rich in metallic iron. It finds a ready market in the steel-milling districts of Germany, the United Kingdom, Poland, Czechoslovakia, and Belgium. An electrified rail line connects the ore fields with the port of Lulea (25,000) on the Gulf of Bothnia, through which ore shipments move from May until the first of December, and with the ice-free Norwegian port of Narvik, which ships ore the year round. Total yearly shipments through Narvik are normally more than twice as large as shipments through Lulea.

Sweden itself is an important steel producer, but more in terms of quality than quantity. Domestic steel production is mainly based on extremely high-grade deposits of nonphosphoric iron ore located in the edge of the uplands to the north of the Central Lowland. The principal mining center is Grängesberg. The ore is customarily smelted with charcoal, and the steel is made in electric furnaces. This process is not adapted to really large-scale production, but the quality of the product is so high that 'Swedish steel" has become practically a synonym for fine steel.

The Swedish steel industry's emphasis on skill and quality carries over into the finishing and fabricating industries which use the steel. Among Swedish specialties which have acquired a world-wide reputation are such items as cutlery, tools and machine tools, surgical instruments, antiaircraft artillery, ball bearings, home appliances, business machines, and electrical equipment. Emphasis on skill in design and execution is also basic to the success of some Swedish industries outside the metal goods field. The most noted of these is the glass industry of Smaland, the infertile and rather sparsely populated crystalline plateau south of the Central Lowland.

Swedish manufacturing is principally carried on in numerous small industrial centers in the Central Lowland. These places, ranging in size from about 80,000 to mere villages, have grown up in an area favorably located with regard to minerals, forests, water power, labor, food supplies, and trading possibilities. The Central Lowland has been the historic core of Sweden and has long maintained an important agricultural development and a relatively dense population. At opposite ends of the lowland are Sweden's two major ports and major cities, Stockholm, on the Baltic Sea, and Göteborg, on the Kattegat.

► Stockholm and Göteborg

Stockholm, with a population of 766,000 (about 1,000,000 with suburbs) is the second largest city in Northern Europe. The location of the capital reflects the role of the Central Lowland as the early core of the Swedish state and the early orientation of that state toward the Baltic and trans-Baltic lands. Stockholm is the principal administrative, financial, and cultural center of the country and shares in many of the manufacturing activities typical of the Central Lowland.

In the past century as Sweden has come to do more and more trading via the North Sea, Stockholm has been displaced by Göteborg as the chief port of the country. Besides its advantage of position, the latter city has a harbor which is ice-free the year round, whereas icebreakers are needed to keep open the harbor of Stockholm in midwinter. Göteborg has a population of 363,-000, or 415,000 including suburbs. The city combines the handling of nearly half of Sweden's foreign trade by volume with nu-merous manufacturing activities, among them an important shipbuilding industry.

► The Swedish Policy of Neutrality and Preparedness

In the Middle Ages and early modern times Sweden was a powerful and imperialistic country. Finland was conquered in the twelfth century, and in the seventeenth century the Baltic became almost a Swedish lake. During the eighteenth century, however, the rising power of Russia and to some extent of Prussia put an end to Swedish imperialism, aside from a brief campaign in 1814 through which Sweden won control of Norway from Denmark. Since 1814 Sweden has never been engaged in a war, and it has become known as one of Europe's most successful neutrals. A century and a half of peace has undoubtedly been partially responsible for the country's success in attaining a high level of economic welfare and a reputation for social advancement. At present, however, Sweden is carrying a heavy burden of armaments. As the strongest military power in Northern Europe and one of the strongest in all of Europe, Sweden represents an important obstacle to possible Soviet domination of the Baltic area. Although the country escaped involvement in World War II, successful neutrality in another general war seems less likely. The dangers inherent in the international situation have led the Swedish government to build up strong armed forces while maintaining, at least formally, the nation's traditional policy of neutrality.

Finland

Taken before the eighth century by the Finns from the Lapps, Finland was conquered and Christianized by the Swedes in the twelfth century. In 1809 it was ceded by Sweden to Russia, and was controlled by the latter nation until 1917. Under both the Swedes and the Russians the status of Finland was that of a semiautonomous grand duchy, and its people developed their own culture and feelings of nationality to such an extent that the opportunity for independence provided by the collapse of Czarist Russia toward the end of World War I was eagerly seized.

▶ Importance of Livestock and Forestry in the Economy

Most of Finland is a sparsely populated, glaciated, subarctic wilderness of coniferous forest, crystalline rock, and thousands upon thousands of lakes. Finland is primarily an agricultural country, and the majority of the population is concentrated in relatively fertile and warmer lowland districts scattered through the southern half of the country. Hay and oats are the main crops of an agriculture which is predominantly directed toward livestock production, especially dairying. Wheat, rye, and potatoes are important supplementary crops whose growing has been fostered by the Finnish government in an attempt to achieve more self-sufficiency in foodstuffs. Despite such efforts, however, substantial food imports are required, amounting to around a fifth of all imports by value. Wheat, sugar, coffee, vegetable fats and oils, and fruits and nuts are the major food items on the import list.

To pay for food and many other imports, the nation depends primarily on exports of forest products. About three quarters of the country is forested, mainly in conifers mixed with birch, and ordinarily 80 percent or more of the total exports consist of lumber, wood pulp, and other timber products of a type largely duplicating the forest exports of Sweden. Forest production is especially concentrated in the south central part of the country, often referred to as the Lake Plateau. A poor and rocky soil discourages agriculture here, but the timber is of good quality and a multitude of lakes, connected by streams in interlocking systems, provide ready transportation for the logs.

Immense quantities of logs are floated to sawmills and pulp mills along Scandinavian rivers. The river shown in the photo is in Finland. (*Finnish National Travel Office.*)

▶ Problems of a Buffer State

For centuries Finland has occupied the position of a buffer between Russia and Scandinavia. Seldom has its position been more difficult than today, when an unsuccessful outcome of two recent wars with the Soviet Union has made Finland almost a prisoner of the latter country. In 1939, shortly after the outbreak of World War II, Finland refused to accede to Russian demands for the cession of certain strategic frontier areas, and despite a valiant resistance, was overwhelmed by the Soviet Union in the "Winter War" of 1939–1940. Then, in an attempt to regain what had been lost, Finland fought with Germany against the Soviet Union from 1941 to 1944, and again went down to defeat as German power waned. The peace settlement following the war left Finland still in existence as an independent country, although shorn of considerable areas in the east and north which were annexed by the USSR. In the southeast the Karelian Isthmus between the Gulf of Finland and Lake Ladoga passed into Russian control, and with it went the city of Viipuri, now Vyborg (40,000), which had been Finland's main timber port. Further territory was lost along the central part of the eastern frontier, and in the north the area surrounding the small seaport of Petsamo, now Pechenga, was ceded, thus cutting Finland off from access to the Arctic Ocean and giving the Soviet Union rich nickel mines and smelting facilities, as well as a land frontier with Norway. Perhaps the most damaging cession from the standpoint of political and military security, however, was the requirement that Finland lease the small Porkkala peninsula to the Soviet Union for use as a naval base. This permits large Soviet forces to be stationed within easy artillery range of Helsinki, the Finnish capital.

Following the war the economy of Finland was heavily burdened by (1) the necessity for rebuilding the northern third of the country, which was devastated by retreating German soldiers after Finland surrendered to Russia, (2) the necessity for resettling a tenth of the total population of the country after they fled as refugees from the areas ceded to Russia, (3) the loss of the ceded areas themselves, some portions of which were of disproportionate importance in the prewar economy of the country, and (4) the necessity for making large reparations payments to the Soviet Union. In spite of these various difficulties, however, the hard-working and thrifty Finns have made a rapid recovery from the war period. In the course of this recovery the economy of the country has been drastically changed in some respects. One of the most striking changes has been the rise of metalworking to a position as the most important branch of industry, at least as judged by employment. This was made necessary by the fact that the Soviet Union required a large part of the reparations to be paid in metal goods. Several small steel plants and other metalworking establishments were built to meet this demand. Since Finland is deficient in high-grade metallic ores and also in coal, the future of at least some of these establishments, now that the reparations have been paid, is problematical.

▶ The Major Cities

The most important industrial center of the country, as well as the capital, largest city, main seaport, and principal commercial and cultural center, is Helsinki (385,-000; including suburbs, 433,000), located about in the center of the southern coast. This city has diversified food-processing, shipbuilding, mechanical, chemical, and other industries. Two smaller industrial centers are Finland's second and third cities in population, the port of Turku at the southwestern corner of the country, and the inland city of Tampere farther north. Each has slightly more than 100,000 people, and each is especially important for textile production. The industries of all these cities depend heavily on hydroelectricity, the main source of power in Finland, as in all the other countries of Northern Europe except Denmark.

Few countries today occupy a more precarious strategic position than Finland. The Finns struggle to get along as best they can with their powerful neighbor to the east, meanwhile striving to maintain democratic institutions and hoping that nothing causes the Soviet Union to move militarily toward Scandinavia or to regard Finnish independence as a threat.

Iceland

Iceland is a fairly large, mountainous island in the Atlantic Ocean just south of the Arctic Circle. Its rugged surface shows the effects of intense glaciation and vulcanism. Some upland glaciers and many active volcanoes and hot springs remain. The vegetation consists mostly of tundra, with considerable grass in some coastal areas and valleys. Trees are few, being discouraged by summer temperatures averaging in the low fifties or below as well as by the prevalence of strong winds. The cool summers are also a great handicap to agriculture. Mineral resources are almost nonexistent.

Despite the deficiencies of its environment, however, Iceland has been continuously inhabited at least since the ninth century, and is now the home of a progressive and democratic republic of about 150,000 people. Practically all of the population lives in coastal settlements, with the largest concentration in the vicinity of the capital, Reykjavik, which itself has about 60,000 people. Due to the proximity of the relatively warm North Atlantic Drift, the coasts of Iceland, and especially the southern coast where Reykjavik is located, have winter temperatures which are unusually mild for the latitude. Reykjavik has an average January temperature of 30°F., only 3° lower than the January average for New York City.

Agriculture and fishing are the main occupations of Iceland. Agriculture is centered around the raising of cattle and sheep. Farm land is used for hay and pasture, potatoes, and hardy vegetables. Although some agricultural products are exported, the real backbone of the economy is fishing. Fish products supply about 90 percent of all exports by value, and thus pay for the many kinds of goods which must be imported. Manufacturing is confined mainly to food processing. It has been encouraged somewhat in recent years by the development of a small part of the island's considerable potential of hydroelectric power.

For centuries before 1918 Iceland was a colony of Denmark. In the latter year it became an independent country under the same king as Denmark, and in 1944 declared itself a republic. It has attracted much notice since the beginning of World War II because of its strategic position along major sea and air routes across the North Atlantic. The island was used by British and American forces as an air and sea base during the war. As a member of the North Atlantic Treaty Organization, Iceland at present is host to a small American military contingent which maintains base facilities at the important Keflavik international airport, 20 miles from Reykjavik.

Greenland, The Faeroes, and Svalbard

Two of the countries of Northern Europe, Denmark and Norway, possess outlying islands of some significance. Denmark holds Greenland, the world's largest island, off the coast of North America, and the Faeroe Islands between Norway and Iceland. Both of these areas are now considered integral parts of Denmark, and their peoples have equal political rights with other Danish citizens. Although the area of Greenland, approximately 840,000 square miles, is more than a fourth that of the United States, about 85 percent is covered by an ice cap, and the population, mainly distributed along the west coast, amounts to only about 25,000 persons. The latter figure does not include American forces stationed at the large air base maintained at Thule, in extreme northwest Greenland, under the auspices of the North Atlantic Treaty Organization, to which Denmark belongs. Aside from several hundred non-native Danes, and a small number of pure Eskimos in the remote northwest, the population of the island is of mixed Eskimo and Scandinavian descent. The principal means of livelihood are fishing, hunting, trapping, a limited amount of sheep grazing, and the mining of cryolite, a mineral used in the aluminum industry and found in large commercial quantities only in Greenland. The deposits of the latter are located in the far southwest.

The Faeroes are a group of treeless islands where 32,000 people of Norwegian descent make a living by fishing and grazing sheep. They enjoy considerable autonomy under the Danish government.

Norway controls the island group known as Svalbard, located in the Arctic Ocean and commonly called Spitsbergen after the most important of the included islands. Although largely covered by ice, the main island of West Spitsbergen contains the only substantial deposits of high-grade coal which are known to exist in Northern Europe. Mining operations are carried on by Norwegian and Soviet Russian companies, with the coal being shipped to Norway and the Soviet port of Murmansk. About 1500 Norwegians and 2300 Russians are employed in the mines. Norway also holds the volcanic island of Jan Mayen in the Arctic, plus two small islands in the far South Atlantic, and claims a share of the Antarctic Continent.

Countries of Southern Europe

On the south the continent of Europe is separated from Africa by the Mediterranean Sea, into which three large peninsulas extend. To the west, south of the Pyrenees Mountains, is the Iberian Peninsula, unequally divided between two countries, Spain and Portugal. In the center, south of the Alps, is the Italian Peninsula and its southern offshoot, the island of Sicily. To the east, between the Adriatic and Black Seas, is the Balkan Peninsula, from which the Greek subpeninsula extends still farther south between the Ionian and Aegean Seas. The countries which occupy the two western peninsulas and the Greek sub-peninsula—Portugal, Spain, Italy, and Greece—may be conveniently grouped as the countries of Southern Europe. Three of the four countries include islands in the Mediterranean, the largest of which are Sicily and Sardinia, held by Italy; Crete, held by Greece; and the Balearic Islands, held by Spain. These islands are governed as integral parts of their respective countries. Some Mediterranean islands are held by countries outside this group, the most notable being Corsica, administered as a department of France, and Malta and Cyprus, which are possessions of the United Kingdom. Gibraltar, also, though not an

Ruined temples and a Roman road at Paestum bespeak the antiquity of civilization in Southern Europe and the ancient power of Rome. (*Italian State Tourist Office.*)

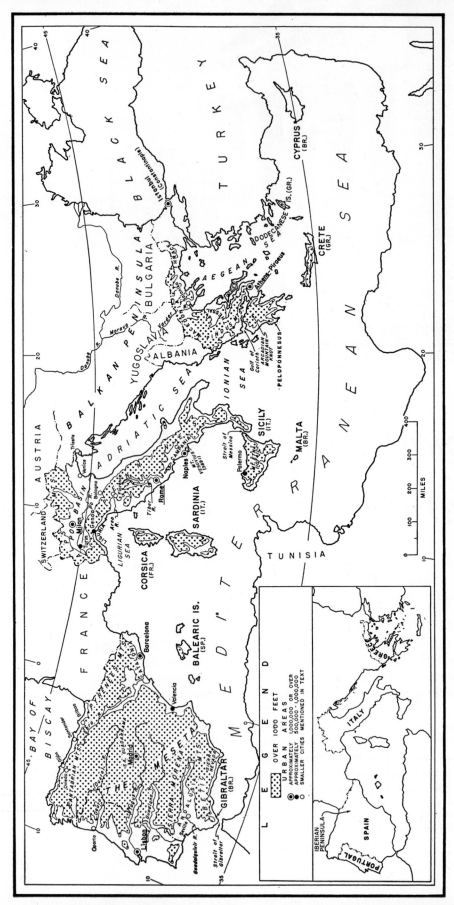

Index map of Southern Europe. Political capitals are underlined.

island, is an important British possession in Southern Europe.

The countries of Southern Europe exhibit many natural and cultural similarities as a group. Most of their natural characteristics, however, while tending to differentiate them from other parts of Europe, are shared with lands of northern Africa and southwestern Asia which front on the Mediterranean. Throughout the Mediterranean area the broad pattern of natural features tends to be much the same, despite differences in detail from place to place. There also tends to be a broad similarity in agricultural practices. However, the countries of Southern Europe are distinguished as a group from their Mediterranean neighbors by important cultural differences, including differences in language and religion. Most of the African and Asian lands fronting on the Mediterranean are predominantly Mohammedan in religion, whereas Roman Catholicism is the prevailing religious faith in Spain, Portugal, and Italy, and the Orthodox Eastern Church is dominant in Greece. The Spanish, Portuguese, Italian, and Greek languages are quite distinct from Arabic, the principal language in most of the non-European Mediterranean countries. Moreover, the countries of Southern Europe have shared in the development of Western or Occidental culture, whereas most of the African and Asian countries of the Mediterranean realm have principally been influenced by Moslem-Arab form of culture.

The areas, populations, and population densities of the four countries of Southern Europe are given in Table 8.

TABLE 8

SOUTHERN EUROPE: AREA AND POPULATION DATA

COUNTRY	AREA (THOUSAND SQUARE MILES)	POPULATION (MILLIONS: 1953 ESTIMATES)	DENSITY (PER SQUARE MILE: TO NEAREST WHOLE NUMBER)
Italy	116.2	47.0	405
Spain [a]	194.9	28.5	146
Portugal [a]	35.4	8.6	243
Greece	51.2	7.8 (1952)	152
Totals	397.7	91.9	231

[a] Figures for Spain include Balearic and Canary Islands. Figures for Portugal include Azores and Madeira Islands. The island groups named are governed as integral parts of Spain and Portugal, respectively.

The Distinctive Mediterranean Climate

Probably the most distinctive natural characteristic of Southern Europe is its climate, which typically combines mild, rainy winters with hot, dry summers. The Mediterranean area has given its name to this particular combination of climatic qualities. In systems of climatic classification a "mediterranean" type of climate is customarily recognized, although the designation "dry-summer subtropical," also in common use, is perhaps more descriptive. Other areas having this type of climate occur in southern California, central Chile, southwestern South Africa, and southern Australia.

Generally speaking, the countries of

Southern Europe experience temperatures averaging 40° to 50°F. in the coldest month and 70° to 80°F. in the warmest month. The total precipitation received during a year varies considerably from place to place, in response to differences in elevation and exposure to rain-bearing winds. The general average is between 15 and 35 inches per year, with most places falling in the lower half of this range. What does not vary appreciably in most areas is the characteristic seasonal regime of precipitation, with its relatively moist winters and dry summers.

In Southern Europe the characteristics associated with the mediterranean climate become increasingly pronounced toward the south. The northern extremities of both Spain and Italy have atypical climatic characteristics. Northern Spain has a marine climate like that of northwestern Europe, cooler and wetter in summer than the typically mediterranean areas, while northern Italy is distinguished by cold month temperatures in the lowlands averaging just above freezing, and a relatively wet summer. Much of the high interior plateau of Spain, the Meseta, cut off from rain-bearing winds by fringing mountains, has somewhat less precipitation and colder winters than is typical of the mediterranean climate, although the seasonal regime of precipitation is characteristically mediterranean. Table 9 illustrates some of the climatic characteristics of Southern Europe.

TABLE 9

CLIMATIC DATA FOR SELECTED SOUTHERN EUROPEAN STATIONS

CLIMATIC TYPE OR AREA AND STATION	JANUARY AVERAGE TEMPERATURE (DEGREES F.)	JULY AVERAGE TEMPERATURE (DEGREES F.)	AVERAGE ANNUAL PRECIPITATION (INCHES)	AVERAGE PRECIPITATION JUNE–AUGUST (INCHES)
Typically Mediterranean				
Athens	47°	80°	15.6″	1.3″
Rome	45°	76°	32.6″	3.2″
Palermo	50°	76°	25.3″	1.2″
Valencia	50°	75°	19.1″	1.6″
Seville	50°	82°	19.5″	0.6″
Lisbon	51°	70°	27.1″	1.1″
Spanish Meseta				
Madrid	41°	78°	16.5″	2.1″
Po Basin				
Turin	33°	73°	35.5″	9.3″
Northern Spain (Marine West Coast Climate)				
Oviedo	44°	64°	36.8″	6.3″

Mediterranean Agriculture

In the areas of mediterranean climate frosts are rare, the summers are hot and sunny, and thus the temperature regime is, in general, excellent for agriculture. But total precipitation is generally low, and a summer drought must be faced each year. Thus water is a critical factor, and its availability or nonavailability greatly influences the types of agriculture which are feasible in various parts of Southern Europe. With

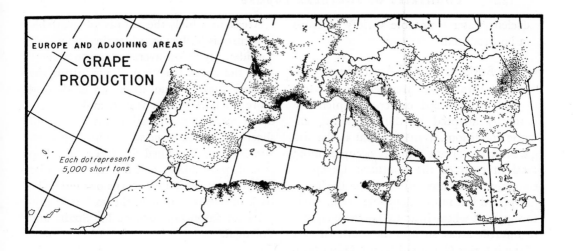

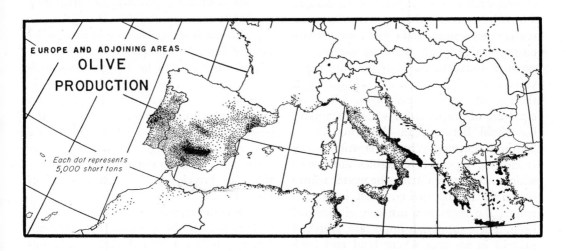

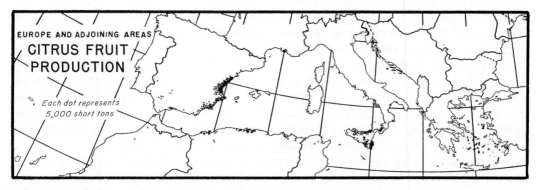

Distribution of grape, olive, and citrus production in Europe and adjoining areas. Note the concentration of these crops in areas bordering the Mediterranean Sea. Short dashes indicate prewar boundaries. (Modified from maps by the Office of Foreign Agricultural Relations based on prewar data.)

sufficient water a notable variety of crops can be produced.

▶ The Basic Pattern of Agriculture

Agriculture in the Mediterranean Basin is principally based on crops which are naturally adapted to the prevailing climatic conditions. Winter wheat is the single most important crop. It occupies more land in each of the Southern European countries than any other crop. Barley, a less prized but more adaptable grain, tends to supplant wheat in some particularly dry or infertile areas, such as the southern part of the interior plateau of Spain. Other typical crops are olives, grapes, and vegetables. The olive tree and the grapevine have extensive root systems and certain other adaptations which allow them to survive the summer droughts, and they yield for many years. Olive oil is the main source of fat in the typical Mediterranean diet. The principal use of grapes is for wine, a standard household beverage in the countries of Southern Europe. Where irrigation water is lacking, types of vegetables are grown which will mature during the wetter winter season or in the spring. Most important among the vegetables are several kinds of bean. These supply an important source of protein in an area where land and feedstuffs are not plentiful enough for meat animals to be fattened in large numbers and where parched summer pastures further inhibit the development of an adequate meat supply. Extensive areas which are too rough for cultivation are used for grazing, but sheep and goats, which can survive on a sparser pasturage than cattle, are the favored animals. In many places grazing depends on a system of transhumance utilizing lowland pastures during the wetter winter and mountain pastures during the summer. In some areas a non-food crop supplements the basic Mediterranean products. This is particularly true in Greece, where tobacco is an important crop on many farms.

Areas in which the supply of available moisture is either considerably above or considerably below average tend to diverge from the normal pattern of agriculture described above. The drier areas depend more on barley than wheat, and the very driest areas depend mainly on grazing of sheep and goats. Some wet and rough areas which have remained in forest are also grazed, particularly oak forests where pigs can feed on the fallen acorns or mast. The bark of one type of oak, the cork oak, supplies an important export for Spain and Portugal.

▶ The Intensive Agriculture of Irrigated Areas

Mediterranean agriculture comes to its peak of intensity and productivity in areas where the land can be irrigated. In such areas relatively abundant and dependable supplies of moisture allow full exploitation of the subtropical temperatures; and the growing of a variety of fruits and vegetables, often with a large proportion destined for export, tends to supplement and sometimes to largely displace other types of production.

Although irrigation on a small scale is widespread in the countries of Southern Europe, a few irrigated areas stand out from the rest in size and importance. They are usually outstanding also for high population densities. Among these major areas of irrigation farming are northern Portugal; the Mediterranean and southwestern coasts of Spain, together with adjoining districts of Portugal; the northern coast of Sicily; the Italian coastal areas near the city of Naples; and the narrow Italian coastal plain fronting on the Ligurian Sea around the city of Genoa.

In northern Portugal irrigation is used mainly to intensify a type of agriculture which does not differ radically from the normal Mediterranean type. The major differences are that irrigated corn replaces wheat as the major grain crop and some cattle-raising is possible on irrigated meadows. Grapes and sheep are the other agricultural mainstays.

In the coastal regions of Spain that front the Mediterranean Sea, irrigation has made possible the development of extensive orchards. Oranges are the most important product, and Spain, though not the greatest producer, is the world's largest exporter of this fruit. The United States exceeds Spain about three or four to one as a producer of oranges, but Spain is the larger exporter, normally supplying around a third to half of all world exports. The pre-eminent orange-growing district of Spain, around the city of Valencia, has given its name to a type of orange. Small acreages of irrigated rice in the coastal areas provide an important element in Spanish cookery. Vegetable gardening and in some places even tropical fruits like dates and bananas also supplement the more ordinary wheat, vines, and olives.

As an agricultural area, northern Sicily is mainly differentiated from ordinary Mediterranean areas by its concentration of irrigated citrus groves. Lemons are particularly important. Sicily is the largest producer of lemons in Europe and is second only to the United States in the world.

The district around Naples, known as Campania, and the Ligurian Coast in the vicinity of Genoa are probably the most highly developed and densely populated agricultural areas of Southern Europe. Vegetables and temperate fruits, especially peaches, supplement the olive and the vine in Liguria, while to vegetables, olives, and grapes Campania adds citrus fruits, tobacco, and hemp.

▶ Agriculture in the Regions of Summer Rain

The northern parts of the countries of Southern Europe, which do not have truly mediterranean climates, exhibit corresponding differences in agriculture. In northern Spain wheat becomes subordinate to corn and rye, and the summer rainfall allows a greater development of cattle raising than is usual in Southern Europe. Northern Italy, the basin of the Po River, is of outstanding importance in Italian agriculture. There is considerable summer rainfall on the level plain of the Po, and the surrounding mountains provide superior water supplies for irrigation. On the Po Plain, corn, grown both in irrigated and unirrigated fields, and irrigated rice become important cereal crops along with wheat. Vineyards are supplemented by orchards of peaches and other temperate fruits. In addition, the Po Plain is the center of Italian production for such industrial crops as sugar beets and hemp, and for cattle, nourished on fodder crops and irrigated meadows. Crop yields and the general welfare of the peasants stand at considerably higher levels than in the more typically Mediterranean areas to the south. The parts of northern Greece known as Macedonia and Thrace are distinguished agriculturally by a strong tendency to substitute cotton for grapes and olives to supplement the common grains and tobacco, which are the agricultural mainstays.

Relief and Population Distribution

In terrain and population distribution as well as in climate and agriculture the countries of Southern Europe present various points of similarity. Rugged terrain is predominant in all four countries, and lowland plains occupy a relatively small part of the total land area. Individual plains tend to be small and to face the sea. They are separated from each other by the sea and by mountainous territory.

Population distribution corresponds in a general way with topography, with the lowland plains being densely populated and the mountainous areas much less so, although a number of comparatively rough areas attain surprisingly high densities. Thus on the whole the picture of population distribution is one of relatively isolated areas of dense population facing the sea and separated from one another by large areas of comparatively low population density.

In the Iberian Peninsula the greater part of the land consists of a plateau, the Meseta, with a surface lying at a general elevation of between 2000 and 3000 feet. The plateau surface is interrupted at intervals by deep river valleys and ranges of mountains rising above the general level. Population density on the level reaches of the plateau is restricted, mainly by lack of rainfall, to figures ranging generally between 25 and 100 per square mile. For the most part the edges of the plateau are steep and rugged. The Pyrenees and Cantabrian Mountains border it on the north, and the Betic Mountains, culminating in the Sierra Nevada, on the southeast. Most of the population of Spain and Portugal is distributed peripherally on the discontinuous coastal lowlands which ring the peninsula. In the part of southern Spain known as Andalusia, the depression followed by the Guadalquivir River extends the coastal plain inland for more than 100 miles. In southern and central Portugal, also, the coastal plains are broader than in other parts of Iberia.

In Italy the Alps and the Apennines are the principal mountain ranges. Northern Italy includes the greater part of the southern slopes of the Alps. The Apennines form the backbone of the peninsula, extending from their junction with the southwestern end of the Alps to the toe of the Italian boot, and appearing again across the Strait of Messina in Sicily. The Apennines vary considerably in height and appearance from place to place. East of Rome the mountains reach more than 9000 feet elevation. In Sicily, Mount Etna, a volcanic cone, reaches 10,741 feet. This is the highest elevation in the entire mountain chain. Other cones tower above the general summit level in various places. Near Naples, Mount Vesuvius, which rises to 4000 feet, is one of the world's most famous volcanoes. West of the Apennines, most of the land between Florence on the north and Naples on the south is occupied by a tangled mass of lower hills and mountains, often of volcanic origin. Both Sicily and Sardinia, the two largest Italian islands, are predominantly mountainous or hilly.

Parts of the Italian highlands have population densities of more than 200 per square mile. Yet even these areas are sparsely populated as compared with most Italian lowlands. The largest lowland, the Po Plain, contains about two fifths of the entire Italian population, with densities that are often over 500 and sometimes over 1000 per square mile. Other lowland areas with extremely high population densities are the narrow Ligurian Coast centering on Genoa, the plain of the Arno River as far inland as Florence, the Campania around Naples, much of the eastern coastal plain of the peninsula, and the northern and eastern coastal areas of Sicily.

In Greece most of the peninsula north of the Gulf of Corinth is occupied by the Pindus Range and the ranges which branch from it. Extensions of these ranges form islands in the Ionian and Aegean Seas. Greece south of the Gulf of Corinth, commonly known as the Peloponnesus, is composed mainly of the Arcadian mountain knot. Along the coasts of Greece many small lowlands face the sea between mountain spurs and contain the majority of the people. Probably the best known of these lowlands, though far from the largest, is the Attic Plain, still dominated as in ancient times by Athens and its seaport, the Piraeus. Larger lowlands are found in Thessaly and to the north in Macedonia and Thrace.

Historical Contrasts in Wealth and Power

In each of the countries of Southern Europe present conditions of poverty and national weakness offer a striking contrast to a past period of wealth and power. In Greece this period of past glory is the most remote, centering in the fifth and fourth centuries B.C., when Greek city-states were spreading the seeds of Western civilization through the Mediterranean area. To some degree there was a rebirth of Greek power and influence in the Middle Ages, when Constantinople was the capital of a Byzantine Empire which was largely Greek in population and control.

Italy's main period of former eminence was, of course, the centuries when the Roman Empire embraced the whole Mediterranean Basin and lands beyond, and Rome was considered the capital of the civilized world. During the later Middle Ages, some centuries after the final collapse of the Roman Empire in the fifth century A.D., many of the Italian cities became independent centers of trade, wealth, and power. Venice became the center of a maritime empire within the Mediterranean area, as did Genoa to a lesser extent. Such inland cities as Milan, Bologna, and Florence also prospered and grew powerful on the basis of their trade with Europe north of the Alps. The growth of a hostile Turkish Empire astride routes to the East, the unification of powerful states such as France and Spain, and the discovery of sea routes to the East which bypassed the Mediterranean were factors contributing to the end of this second period of Italian pre-eminence. Following its appearance in the nineteenth century, the modern unified state of Italy made an attempt to emulate ancient Rome. A colonial empire was gradually acquired which included Libya, the Dodecanese Islands, Eritrea, Italian Somaliland, and Ethiopia. All of these colonial territories were lost as a result of World War II except Italian Somaliland, which was placed under Italian administration as a United Nations Trust Territory pending independence after a transition period lasting until 1960. Italy has been the only nation of Southern Europe to attempt the role of a Great Power during modern times. The futility and unreality of this attempt became manifest with the country's military collapse during the Second World War.

The main period of Spanish power and influence began in the Middle Ages when Spain stood as the bulwark of Christian Europe against Mohammedan civilization and in a struggle lasting for centuries eventually expelled the Moors from Europe. It was in the same year that this expulsion was finally accomplished, 1492, that Christopher Columbus, an Italian navigator in the pay of the Spanish court, crossed the Atlantic and discovered the lands that were eventually to be called the Americas. For a century thereafter Spain stood at a peak of power and prestige never attained before or since. It was the greatest power not only in Europe, but in the entire world, and built one of the largest empires ever known, in areas as diverse and widely separated as Italy, the Netherlands, North and South America, Africa, and the Philippine Islands. This empire shrank in size with the gradual decline in the relative power of Spain, until all that now remains is some comparatively unimportant territories on the mainland of Africa, together with islands off the African coast such as Fernando Po and the Canaries.

Portugal, also, played a part in expelling the Moors from Iberia, and took the lead in the fifteenth century in seeking a sea route around Africa to the Orient. The first Portuguese expedition to succeed in the voyage, headed by Vasco da Gama, returned from India in 1499. For the better part of a century thereafter Portugal dominated European trade with the East, and built an empire there and across the Atlantic in Brazil. However, there was a rapid decline in Portuguese fortunes as the small homeland was conquered and held by Spain between 1580 and 1640, and as other powers offered increasingly successful commercial and colonial competition. Although stripped of many of its early holdings, Portugal has been left in possession of a considerable colonial empire in Africa and Asia, as well as the nearer Azores and Madeira Islands. The latter are administered with the home country.

Today the nations of Southern Europe have fallen far behind those of northwestern Europe in wealth and power. Greece is probably the most poverty-stricken country in Europe. The other countries of Southern Europe are somewhat better off, but nevertheless stand far below such countries as the United Kingdom, Sweden, or Belgium in per capita income and general level of living. In all of the Southern European countries widespread poverty has caused considerable social unrest. This unrest has been aggravated by the fact that these countries exhibit great internal contrasts in wealth, both as between regions and between social classes.

Industry and Its Problems

Many of the difficulties of the countries of Southern Europe in modern times have been closely related to retarded industrial development. All of these countries have remained essentially agricultural, although there are important differences among them in the extent of industrialization. Italy has attained a far greater total development of industry than any of the other three countries and also a greater relative degree of industrialization. Spain ranks second to Italy in these respects, judged by employment in manufacturing. The essential point is that in none of the countries of Southern Europe has manufacturing become the main basis of the national economy or developed to such an extent that it has helped much in modifying conditions of poverty associated with too great a dependence on insufficient agricultural resources.

▶ Shortage of Industrial Resources

With the exception of Spain, the countries of Southern Europe are severely handicapped in industrial development by a lack of natural resources. The most serious deficiency is in sources of power. Both Italy and Portugal mine small quantities of coal and Greece mines small amounts of lignite. But deposits and production are inadequate in all three countries, and each is a considerable importer of coal. Indeed Italy, the largest and most industrialized of the three countries, is one of the world's principal coal importers. The situation with regard to petroleum is even less satisfactory. Aside from a few minor deposits and a small production in Italy, all Southern Europe seems even more devoid of oil than of coal.

Most of the other important industrial materials are either absent or insufficient in quantity. Small quantities of iron ore are mined in Greece and Italy, but in neither case are the reserves or production of much importance. The dry climate plus centuries of deforestation have made supplies of wood inadequate. Many "forested" areas are covered only with scrub, a vegetation so typical as to have a special name, *maquis* in French and *macchia* in Italian. True forests are quite restricted in area and are especially characteristic of areas not typically mediterranean in climate, such as northwestern Spain and Alpine Italy. The textile industry, developed to some extent in all four countries, depends mainly on imported raw materials despite the growing of small amounts of cotton and considerable wool production from the large areas devoted to sheep grazing.

The mineral resources which are present might be of much greater use were it not for the lack of some of the critical materials already mentioned. Small deposits of a great many metals and other minerals do exist, and some are even abundant enough to make the Southern European countries important world suppliers. Outstanding among these is mercury; Italy and Spain together normally account for one half to three fourths of the total world production of this mineral. Other important minerals which are present and are mined in considerable quantities include lead, zinc, sulfur, and bauxite in Italy, and sulfur (pyrites) and tungsten in Portugal. In addition, a large proportion of certain lesser known minerals which are nevertheless important in modern industry, such as beryl and barite, come from Southern Europe, especially from Italy and Spain. But such materials offer practically no industrial advantage to the possessing country when that country is lacking in such fundamental resources as coal, iron ore, and wood.

▶ The More Favorable Position of Spain

Spain presents a somewhat different picture with regard to industrial resources than the other Southern European countries, largely because it possesses appreciable deposits of both coal and iron ore. These deposits are located in the Canta-

brian Mountains, both coal and iron ore being found in the vicinity of Oviedo and Gijón and iron ore near Bilbao and Santander. In addition, Spain has important deposits and a considerable production of lead and zinc, wolframite (the ore of the important alloy metal, tungsten), potash, mercury, pyrites for sulfur, and a number of other minerals. Yet Spain, much better endowed with mineral resources than many highly industrialized and relatively prosperous nations, has never developed an important metallurgical or metal-fabricating industry. Nine tenths of the iron ore mined in Spain is exported, and a comparable situation prevails with respect to most of the other mineral resources. Many of the mines are owned and operated by foreign companies which draw the profits from the operations out of Spain as well as the materials mined.

A scene in the Mediterranean Basin. This villager on the island of Cyprus has collected a load of pine and cedar branches for household fuel Securing an adequate supply of fuel is a constant problem in the deforested lands surrounding the Mediterranean. The widely spaced trees on the rocky hillside have extensive root systems and other special adaptations enabling them to survive the dry Mediterranean summers. (*U. S. Department of Agriculture.*)

In the centuries since the period of Spanish world power in the sixteenth century, the social and economic order in Spain has tended to stagnate. During these centuries an ironclad conservatism on the part of the ruling classes has on the whole succeeded in fastening on Spain an almost feudal system of society which other European nations in varying degree shed long ago in favor of a capitalism which sanctioned profits and development. The failure of Spain to develop economically and socially from a feudal condition contrasting a wealthy and privileged aristocracy with a poverty-ridden and repressed populace led to a series of bloody revolutions in the twentieth century and finally to the savage civil war of 1936 to 1939. In this war the Fascist victory stabilized a Spanish society of privilege and repression. Other European nations, especially in the south and east, have also been marked by the maintenance of feudal conditions in modern times, coupled with a failure to take full advantage of their resources in developing modern economies. Spain is an outstanding example of this situation.

▶ Transportation Difficulties

Besides lack of resources, other hindrances to industrial development in Southern Europe have been the poverty of home markets in the various countries and, except in the case of Italy, the lack of a modern, efficient transportation system. Inability of consumers, especially peasants, to buy adequate quantities of industrial consumer goods and thereby support needed industrial development is part of a vicious circle which is common to many primarily rural and underdeveloped or overpopulated countries. Industry needs prosperous consumers to buy its products, but for the rural consumer to be prosperous one of the things most needed is for industry to develop sufficiently to draw the excess of people out of an overpopulated countryside. Modern industry also requires efficient transportation for large quantities of bulky materials. The railway and highway systems of the Southern European countries, excepting Italy, are inadequate to meet this need. The mountainous nature of much of the terrain is a considerable block to rail and road building, and the lack of coal and other fuels tends to hinder transportation just as it does manufacturing. A peripheral distribution of population in the various countries helps to alleviate the situation somewhat by allowing extensive use of coastal steamers to handle trade between the various populated sections, but cannot completely compensate for retarded and expensive land transportation.

Among the Southern European nations only Italy has a reasonably good system of highway and rail transport. The Italians have been renowned road builders since Roman times. Many modern highways follow Roman roads laid out two thousand years ago. The Italian railway system is extensively electrified, especially in the north. It benefits from the continuing importance of old routes through the Alpine passes as major connecting links between the Mediterranean Basin and Europe north of the Alps. Other factors which have helped to make possible the development of a modern rail network have been the availability of electric power from extensive hydroelectric developments in the Alps and northern Apennines, and an adequate freight traffic provided by the industrialized sections of northern Italy.

▶ Industrial Importance of the Po Basin

Lack of coal and many other important materials has forced industry in Southern Europe to depend mainly on two resources: hydroelectric power and cheap labor recruited from a poverty-stricken rural population. In the areas of strictly mediterranean climate the development of hydroelectricity has been hindered by the seasonality of the rainfall. During the summer most of the streams in such areas dry up to a trickle (in some cases completely), or become intermittent stagnant pools along a stream bed which may hold a torrent in the winter. This condition creates a major handicap which can be overcome only by construction of large and expensive reservoirs to equalize the flow of water between seasons, or by provision of coal-powered steam generating plants to maintain the flow of electricity in summer. Construction of adequate reservoirs in the Mediterranean area would in some cases require the flooding of densely populated valleys in places already short of farm land. Such difficulties plus a lack of capital for the execution of large projects have severely retarded hydroelectric development in many parts of Southern Europe.

Much better possibilities for the generation of hydroelectric power are found in the northern areas which are not typically mediterranean in climate. The most favorable situation and the greatest development are found in northern Italy. Around the edges of the Po Plain, the Alps and, to a lesser degree, the Apennines, offer many excellent sites for hydroelectric installations. The possibilities offered by these mountain areas have been exploited so well that Italy now ranks with France as one of Europe's two largest hydroelectric producers, and the Po Basin has become not only the most important industrialized area in Southern Europe, but one of the major industrial regions of all Europe. Two of Italy's four largest cities, Milan (1,293,000; with suburbs about 1,500,-000) and Turin (720,000) are the main centers of this industrial area, while many lesser centers share in the production, as does the port of Genoa (683,000), which dominates the overseas trade of the area. Textile manufacture is the leading form of industry in the Po Basin, the materials processed including cotton, artificial fibers, wool, and silk, as well as some lesser fibers. A small steel industry centers at Genoa and relies on imported raw materials. The rela-

tive scarcity and expensiveness of steel, together with an abundant supply of skilled but cheap labor have encouraged the metal-fabricating industries of the Po Basin to specialize in complex and expensive products. Typical products are sewing machines, ball bearings, automobiles (particularly luxury and custom-built models), and motor scooters, the most important means of family transport in postwar Italy.

Heavy dependence on imported raw materials as well as uncertain foreign markets and an approaching saturation point in hydroelectric development would seem to place definite limits on further industrial expansion in the Po Basin. Although this part of Italy is in general much more prosperous than most parts of Southern Europe, the wages paid to workers have been comparatively low. Even so, the area has generally suffered from chronic unemployment in recent years. An important factor which would seem a barrier to further industrialization through exploitation of labor is the strength of the Communist Party in this area. The Italian Communist Party is the largest in free Europe, and its main centers of influence are in the northern industrial cities, although it has made some progress among the impoverished peasants of southern Italy.

▶ Industry in Northeastern Spain

The second most important seat of industry in Southern Europe is found in the northeastern corner of Spain. The city of Barcelona (1,280,000; including suburbs about 1,500,000), second largest in Spain, forms, together with its environs, the major Spanish industrial district. In certain respects this district is quite similar to the Po Basin industrial area. Hydroelectric power is available in quantity, mainly from the Pyrenees; industrial labor is plentiful, sufficiently skilled, and cheap; textiles form the main branch of industry; and industrial raw materials are largely imported. Unlike the Po Basin, however, the Barcelona area is not an important exporter of manufactured goods. Its products supply primarily the internal market of Spain and the Spanish colonial territories.

In both Spain and Italy there is a certain hostility to be observed between the industrialized and the rural sections. In Catalonia, the industrialized province of Spain in which Barcelona is located, this hostility has been reinforced by a jealous local patriotism and a distinct feeling of separateness from the rest of Spain. The Catalan language, spoken in the province, is distinct from Castilian Spanish, the major tongue of Spain. Other cultural, economic, and historical differences have helped to foster resentment against too close a control by the central government in Madrid, and repeated demands for a greater degree of local autonomy have occurred in the past. Since 1939, however, such aspirations have been rigidly suppressed by the Fascist dictatorship, as have similar aspirations which exist with varying degrees of strength in certain other Spanish provinces.

Urban Centers Outside the Major Industrialized Areas

The Po Basin and Catalonia represent the only really important industrialized areas in Southern Europe. The general lack of industrial development is indicated by the character of large cities found outside these two areas. Most of these cities are either political capitals or ports serving especially productive agricultural areas, or both. They are, of course, not without industries appropriate to a port or to any large city, particularly one forming a reservoir of cheap labor, but their industrial functions are on the whole subordinate to government and trade.

The largest city of Greece is the capital, Athens, which has about a million people in the city itself and nearly 1.5 million in the metropolitan area, which includes the port of Piraeus and other suburbs. The other political capitals of Southern Europe are also the largest cities of their respective countries. Lisbon, the main seaport of Portugal, has around 800,000 people in the city and about a million including suburbs. The population of Rome is about 1,750,000 and of Madrid about 1,600,000. The latter two capitals have in common a central location. Rome lies about halfway down the west coast of the Italian Peninsula, in a position to some extent intermediate between contrasting northern and southern sections of the country. Rome profits in various ways from the fact that it is an important religious capital (the center of Roman Catholicism), as well as a political capital. Madrid was purposely chosen as the capital of Spain in the sixteenth century because of its location near the mathematical center of the peninsula, approximately equidistant from the various peripheral areas of dense population. Located in a poor countryside, it has little economic excuse for existence, but its position as the capital has made it the center of the Spanish rail and road networks and thus has given it certain business advantages.

Most of the remaining large cities in Southern Europe are seaports. Salonika, in the north of Greece, is the second city of that country, although its population is only a little more than 215,000. It is the sea outlet for an important route through the mountains of southern Yugoslavia formed by the combined valleys of the Morava and Vardar Rivers. Naples (about 1,000,000 in the city; including suburbs, about 1,250,000) is the port for the Campania district and much of southern Italy, and is the third largest Italian city. Palermo (500,000) is the major port of Sicily. The largest inland city of Italy, apart from Rome and the industrial cities on the Po Plain, is Florence, at the head of the Arno Plain and at the southern end of an important route through the Apennines. It has 390,000 people and is a famous cultural as well as an industrial center. In Spain, the third city, after Madrid and Barcelona, is Valencia (500,000), the port for the main citrus producing and exporting district. In Portugal, the only large city aside from Lisbon is Oporto, or Porto (285,000), the principal port for the northern part of the country.

Agricultural Problems of Southern Europe

Retarded development of industry has thrown upon agriculture the burden of supporting the great majority of the people in Southern Europe. While agriculture has developed sufficiently to produce a surplus for export of certain specialties, such as Greek tobacco and raisins, Italian fruits and vegetables, Spanish oranges and olives, and Portuguese cork and wines, it has not supplied adequate quantities of cereals and animal products or a good living for most of the people engaged in agricultural occupations. An indication of the unsatisfactory agricultural situation lies in the fact that all of the Southern European countries must import large quantities of grain to supplement their home production. This is true despite the heavy emphasis on production of grain cereals in the agriculture of this region.

The populations of the Southern European countries have increased rapidly in modern times, as have the populations of most other countries in the world. In Southern Europe, however, the increase continues to be comparatively rapid, while a number of the more highly industrialized and prosperous countries have experienced a decline in their rates of population growth during recent decades. Rapid growth of population in Southern Europe, coupled with retarded industrial development, has required the absorption of an increasing number of people into agriculture. The result has been an excessive subdivision of land, hence a decrease in the average amount of land available for the support of each farm family.

Farms which are too small might in themselves supply an adequate reason for rural poverty. This difficulty, however, has been augmented in Southern Europe by relatively low crop yields, at least by European standards. For example, Spain is the most favored of the Southern European countries in the average amount of land available to each person or family engaged in agriculture. Yet the Spanish farmer, on the average, gets only about a third as much grain from each acre as does his neighbor in France, and less than a third as much as the Belgian, Danish, or English farmer.

▶ Reasons for Low Agricultural Productivity

Many different factors underlie the generally low productivity of Southern European farms. Pressure of population on the available land has led to the farming of some rather infertile land, especially rugged areas where the growing of cultivated crops soon leads to soil erosion with consequent damage not only to the hillside farms, but also to farms in the valley below. The perennial lack of rainfall in summer, and sometimes in winter, is a hindrance. Some irrigated areas produce good yields, but only limited amounts of land have been or can be irrigated. In many areas a lack of adequate markets near at hand, or a lack of transportation giving access to distant markets, has prevented farmers from specializing in types of production giving promise of higher returns and has obliged them to operate on a semi-subsistence basis. Farmers in Southern Europe are ordinarily too poor to afford sufficient amounts of fertilizer or satisfactory farm implements to make their fields productive. Few have access to adequate technical information on modern methods of farming. Thus many of the difficulties of farmers in this region can be traced ultimately to a lack of capital which might be used to improve their water supply, land, tools, or knowledge. Poverty results in lack of capital, and lack of capital leads to poverty. Thus the farmer in Southern Europe is caught in a vicious circle. The difficulty of accumulating a little capital, of getting ahead a little, is increased by the variability in the rainfall from year to year. Very often the earnings from sale of products in a year of adequate rain will be absorbed in the losses of a succeeding year of drought.

► Problems of Landownership

In some areas of Southern Europe rural poverty is partly the result of a system of landownership under which most of the land is held in large estates and the actual farmers are tenants or, occasionally, day laborers. Tenants on these estates are required to yield a considerable share of their meager produce to the landowner as rental for the land. Large estates are particularly characteristic of southern Italy and southern Spain. Estates in southern Italy may run to 30,000 acres, tenanted by as many or more people. Portions of such estates are often devoted to grazing or some type of commercial crop which is profitable to the landowner but is bitterly resented by the tenants, who would prefer to use the land for the production of food. Since World

War II a number of peasant riots have occurred, resulting from the efforts of landowners to eject tenants from portions of large estates which they have simply occupied and begun to use without permission. Such happenings are a clear indication of intense land hunger among the peasants. The Italian government has indicated that it considers land reform in southern Italy to be of pressing importance for political stability in that area. However, actual progress has been slow because the government has also felt that it needed the support of the landowners. In Spain substantial reforms were instituted during a brief period of republican government in the early 1930's, but most of these were rescinded by the Fascist regime which succeeded to power as a result of the civil war of 1936 to 1939.

► Rural Poverty—An Example from Macedonia

However, land tenure is not really the fundamental agricultural problem of Southern Europe. This is clearly shown by the conditions of poverty which generally prevail even in those areas where the peasants customarily own their land. Some idea of the situation and problems of the individual Southern European farmer, in this instance one almost certainly better off than the average, can be gained from the following brief selection: [1]

A farmer in Macedonia who had the reputation of being one of the most progressive in his village said when interviewed that he had not bought fertilizer for his fields, even though he knew very well that it would improve the harvest, simply because he could not afford the risk. In a good year, he calculated, fertilizer would pay off, for the increased yield meant more grain to sell and enough money to pay back the cost of the fertilizer. In a bad year,

---

[1] Frank Smothers, William Hardy McNeill, and Elizabeth Darbishire McNeill, *Report on the Greeks.* New York: The Twentieth Century Fund, Inc., 1948. Pp. 85–87. Used by permission of The Twentieth Century Fund, Inc.

however, fertilizer would not make his fields produce enough grain for him to feed his family and at the same time pay the fertilizer debt. Consequently, rather than risk indebtedness, and be forced to sell some part of his small capital—half a dozen sheep, a pig, a donkey and a mule—he preferred to do without the fertilizer, even though he knew that in the long run his fields would be impoverished and the task of feeding his family would become all the harder.

This man was both intelligent and hard-working. He had just returned to his little two-room house after cultivating his vines with a spade all day in the fields. He was dressed in carefully patched trousers and a tattered shirt, and on his feet he wore homemade moccasins. He owned about 15 acres of land, of which 5 were devoted to vines and fruit trees and the rest produced wheat and beans in alternate years. Each morning the village shepherd came and collected his six sheep and drove them out to the hill slope behind the village where they were pastured with the others from the community; in the evening they were returned to a fold made out of brushwood, where the farmer milked them. His donkey and mule were needed for plowing, and served the year round as beasts of burden. They were fed on straw from the wheat through the winter, and picked up what they could along the paths and field margins of the village in summer. In all this, he was quite average.

He had four children, three sons and a daughter, between eleven and eighteen years of age. The problem which worried him most was not the hardship of day-to-day existence, real though it was, but rather the question of his children's future. With 15 acres to divide among four chil-dren, less than 4 acres could be given to each; and even though each child married someone who had an equivalent amount of land, there would be only 8 or 10 acres to support each of the new families. Life on his farm of 15 acres was a desperate struggle already; with less land, his children would face an impossible situation.

In this particular case, the peasant hoped to keep his farm intact for the eldest son. He was preparing to send his second son to the high school in Katerini, a town near by, where he could learn to be a clerk and with luck find a job. But the problem of supporting the boy away from home was serious, for he would have to buy both food and lodging. The farmer expected to sell his pig, although it was not full grown, in order to get the cash he needed to keep his son at school until the harvest, when, with a good season, he hoped to have a surplus of grain to sell for the same purpose. Looking ahead, he wondered how he would be able to manage when his eldest son was called up to serve in the army and his help on the farm would no longer be available. For the boy of eleven he had made no plans. The girl, he expected, would marry in the village.

Life for this peasant family was a grim and laborious business, a constant struggle to escape from sinking into still deeper poverty. With luck, good harvests and enormous hard work the farmer could hope to pass his farm down unimpaired to his eldest son, and open a way to a tolerable living for his other children. But he realized all too well that illness, bad weather or accident could bring the whole structure of his plans and effort down in ruins and impose an apparently irremediable poverty on his children.

The Strategic Position of Southern Europe

The poverty and political impotence of the Southern European countries in modern times have not made them politically unimportant. Rather, they have retained a considerable political significance deriving largely from a strategic position. The international political orientation of these countries has been a matter of grave concern to various outside nations, which have often vied with each other for power and influence in Southern Europe.

▶ Greece—A Pawn Between Land and Sea Power

The international importance of Greece stems largely from the fact that the Greek peninsula lies between the Aegean and Adriatic Seas and thus commands the routes of access to the Mediterranean from the Balkan Peninsula and Black Sea. In addition, the important route of sea trade running through the Mediterranean and Red Seas can be effectively threatened from Greece. The strategic implications of its position has made Greece to some extent a pawn between land power and sea power in past times. Since its liberation from Turkey in the first half of the nineteenth century, Greece has customarily been under the influence and protection of Britain. As a major sea power vitally dependent on the Mediterranean–Red Sea route, the latter nation has naturally been anxious to keep strong land powers away from Mediterranean shores. Following World War II, Greece became the scene of a civil war between Communist and anti-Communist forces, and it seemed for a time that the country might be added to the list of Russian satellite nations. However, this threat was averted by assistance furnished the anti-Communist elements by the United States, taking over this responsibility from a weakened Britain. The position of Greece made such action feasible, since the country was easily accessible from the sea.

▶ The Italian Causeway to North Africa

Italy's position makes it a natural sea outlet for parts of Central Europe, a potential threat to the security of the British-dominated sea route through the Mediterranean, and a land bridge extending most of the way across the Mediterranean toward northern Africa. In World War II Italian participation on the side of Germany forced Britain to largely abandon the strategic Mediterranean–Red Sea route and to rely on the old pre-Suez route around Africa for traffic with areas surrounding the Indian Ocean. Separated from Africa only by the narrow stretch of water between Sicily and Tunisia, the Italian causeway also permitted German and Italian land forces to wage their African campaigns in relative security from Allied sea power.

The population of Italy, third largest in Europe (excepting the Soviet Union), adds to the international importance deriving from the country's position. In consequence, several outside powers have attempted in recent years to control or gain an alliance with Italy. During the latter stages of World War II the country was the scene of a desperate and destructive struggle between Allied and German armies. Since the end of the war the struggle for Italian allegiance has been primarily a contest between the Soviet Union on the one hand and the Western bloc of nations headed by the United States on the other. This contest has been mainly fought in the arena of Italian internal politics, with American support being given the anti-Communist Italian political parties, and Russian influence being asserted through the powerful Italian Communist Party.

▶ The Spanish Base for Air Power

In Spain the civil war of 1936–1939 reflected the general tendency of internal political struggles in Southern Europe to be directly influenced by the action of outside powers. In this war the Fascist or Insurgent faction eventually triumphed with the aid of an entire army provided by the then Fascist Italy and an air force and other special units largely provided by Germany. The losing Republican or Loyalist side profited somewhat from aid by the Soviet Union, at that time a major antagonist of Germany and Italy on the European stage. In addition, a considerable number of volunteers from several nations fought in the Loyalist armies. The Insurgent victory was regarded as a considerable defeat for Britain and France, neither of which had intervened directly in the war, since it placed a hostile Spain on the flank of important British sea routes and left France almost surrounded by Fascist countries. As it turned out, the new Spanish government refrained from entering World War II, though it maintained a generally hostile attitude toward the Allied nations.

At present Spain's principal significance in international affairs seems closely tied to its position behind the Pyrenees and well removed from Russian-held territory, thus appearing to offer a relatively protected location for American air bases in Europe. An agreement for the establishment of such bases was signed between Spain and the United States in the late summer of 1953. Thus strategic considerations have brought about an accord between the two nations, despite strained official attitudes which have generally prevailed since the Fascist victory in the Spanish Civil War.

▶ The Smaller Strategic Significance of Portugal

Portugal seems to have had a lesser degree of political and strategic significance during recent times than the other three nations of Southern Europe, and it has been less involved in international conflicts. The proximity of the country to Atlantic sea routes passing near its coast has made it an object of British attention and support during most of its modern history, and the lack of any strong power in a position to challenge British influence has given Portugal a relatively peaceful existence.

Thus a common factor in the strategic geography of the Southern European nations lies in their relation to the great sea route through the Mediterranean, or, in the case of Portugal, a position on the approaches to this route. The strategic importance of their position as viewed by outside powers has been manifest by a long history of outside interference in Southern European affairs. Britain, the leading sea power throughout most of modern history, has been especially active in this area. Concrete evidence of British interest and concern lies in the fact that Britain has retained political control over the colonies of Gibraltar, Malta, and Cyprus—small but critical areas along the Mediterranean route.

Countries of East Central Europe

The Soviet Union is bordered on the west by a belt of small nations extending the full width of the European peninsula from the Arctic Ocean to the Mediterranean Sea. In this book the part of the belt lying south of the Baltic Sea and north of Greece is referred to as East Central Europe. Seven different political units are included: Poland, Czechoslovakia, Hungary, Rumania, Bulgaria, Albania, and Yugoslavia. With an area of approximately 451,000 square miles, East Central Europe is a little smaller than the combined areas of Texas, California, and Maine. However, the population total is more impressive, amounting to some 90 million people or well over half the population of the United States. The largest countries in area and population are Poland, Yugoslavia, and Rumania; Czechoslovakia is intermediate in size; and Hungary, Bulgaria, and Albania are smaller. The areas, populations, and population densities of the various countries are given in Table 10.

In the period between 1945 and 1948, all of these countries except Yugoslavia fell under the control of the Soviet Union. Under Soviet direction Communist forms of political, economic, and social organization were instituted, and each country

The Danube River at the Iron Gate. Boats are assisted upstream against the swift current by a railway on the bank. (*Yugoslav Information Center.*)

TABLE 10

EAST CENTRAL EUROPE: AREA AND POPULATION DATA

COUNTRY	AREA (THOUSAND SQUARE MILES)	POPULATION (MILLIONS)	DENSITY (PER SQUARE MILE: TO NEAREST WHOLE NUMBER)
Poland	120.4	26.20 (1953 Est.)	218
Czechoslovakia	49.4	12.34 (1950 Census)	250
Hungary	35.9	9.46 (1952 Est.)	263
Rumania	91.7	16.30 (1952 Est.)	178
Bulgaria	42.8	7.39 (1952 Est.)	173
Albania	10.6	1.25 (1952 Est.)	117
Totals, Soviet Satellites	350.7	72.94	208
Yugoslavia	99.3	17.00 (1954 Est.)	171
Totals, East Central Europe	450.0	89.94	200

was brought firmly within the economic and strategic orbit of the USSR. Although this program fell short of official annexation, the Soviet Union, working through local Communist governments, and using force or the threat of force where necessary, imposed a close supervision over the national life in each of the subject countries. Thus was created a cordon of Communist satellite nations in the border zone between the Soviet Union and the industrialized non-Communist countries of Western Europe. Yugoslavia was numbered with the satellites at first, but succeeded in breaking away from Soviet control in 1948. However, even in Yugoslavia a Communist form of government and society was retained after the break with the USSR. Although not discussed with East Central Europe in this chapter, the Soviet zones of occupation in Austria and East Germany became for practical purposes a part of the satellite area during the postwar period. The necessity for protecting lines of communication between the USSR and the occupation zones provided a convenient excuse for Soviet garrisons to be maintained in the intervening satellite countries.

Political Instability in the "Shatter Belt"

East Central Europe is often spoken of as "The Shatter Belt," a term referring to the fragmented and unstable pattern of nationalities and political units in this region. This pattern has evolved from a complicated history of migrations, conquests, and reconquests involving many different peoples. A succession of empires have arisen and dissolved, sometimes created by peoples within the region, but more often imposed from without. The new Soviet empire in East Central Europe is only the latest episode in a long history of control by outside powers. Over the centuries as the various indigenous peoples have fought and quarreled with each other and with intruders from outside, the political pattern has remained in a state of flux. Constant shifting of boundaries and reorganization of political units have evidenced the political instability which has come to be recognized as an outstanding characteristic of this region.

The majority of the governments which have held power in the countries of East Central Europe during recent centuries

BALTIC SEA

(GERMANY)

POMERANIA

Berlin

SAXONY INDUSTRIAL CONCENTRATION

SAXON GATE

H
L
C D
P
Ore Mts.
Jachymov

Prague

BOHEMIA
Pilsen

Bohemian Forest

MORAVIAN GATE

Gdynia
Kaliningrad (Königsberg)
Gdansk (Danzig)
Szczecin (Stettin)

Bydgoszcz

Poznan (Posen)

Warta R.
Oder R.
Neisse R.
Elbe R.

SILESIA

Wroclaw (Breslau)
Czestochowa

Sudeten Mts.

UPPER SILESIA INDUSTRIAL CONCENTRATION

B
G C
O

Cracow
Nowa Huta

MASURIA

Narew R.
Bug R.
Vistula R.

Bialystok
Warsaw
Brest (Brest-Litovsk)
Lodz
Lublin

(USSR)

50° N

GALICIA

50° N

Lvov

(U.S.S.R.)

MORAVIA

Brno

Vienna

(AUSTRIA)

Alps Mts.

(ITALY)

Tatra Mts.

SLOVAKIA

Carpathian

Kosice
Ozd
Miskolc

Little Hungarian Plain

Bratislava
Gyor

Bakony Forest

Great Hungarian Plain

Budapest
Debrecen
Dunapentele
Szeged

Lake Balaton

RUTHENIA

Tisa R.

Mts.

BUKOVINA

MOLDAVIA

BESSARABIA

Dniester R.
Prut R.

Jassy

TRANSYLVANIA

Cluj

Bihor Mts.

Transylvanian Alps

SLOVENIA

Ljubljana

Trieste

ISTRIAN PEN.

Zagreb

Rijeka (Fiume)

CROATIA

ADRIATIC SEA

Dinaric Alps

DALMATIAN COAST

Split

Drava R.

Subotica
Timisoara

Sava R.

Danube R.

BANAT

Belgrade

Resita

IRON GATE

Ploesti

WALLACHIA

Bucharest

Galati
Braila

45° N

45° N

Mouths Of The Danube

Constanta

30° E

BOSNIA

Sarajevo

HERCEGOVINA

MONTENEGRO

S E R B I A

Morava R.

Danube

DOBRUJA

Stalin (Varna)

BLACK SEA

Sofia

Balkan Mts.

Burgas

Plovdiv
Maritsa R.

Skoplje

Vardar R.

Rhodope Mts.

Bosporus

Istanbul (Constantinople)

SEA OF MARMARA

Tirana

MACEDONIA

Dardanelles

40° N

(TURKEY)

Salonika

(GREECE)

AEGEAN SEA

IONIAN SEA

40° N

LEGEND:

MOUNTAINOUS AREAS
MAJOR INDUSTRIAL CONCENTRATIONS

URBAN AREAS BY APPROXIMATE POPULATION CATEGORIES

⬤ OVER 3,000,000
◉ 1,000,000 - 2,000,000
● 500,000 - 1,000,000
• 250,000 - 500,000
○ SELECTED SMALLER PLACES

0 50 100 150 200
SCALE OF MILES

Inset map:

LITHUANIA, LATVIA, ESTONIA (NOT SHOWN) ABSORBED BY USSR
FREE CITY OF DANZIG, TO POLAND

GERMANY

Danzig

LITHUANIAN SSR

EAST PRUSSIA

LATVIAN SSR

TO USSR FROM GERMANY

TO POLAND FROM GERMANY

POLAND

USSR

FROM POLAND

FROM CZECHO-SLOVAKIA

CZECHOSLOVAKIA

AUSTRIA

HUNGARY

FROM RUMANIA

Trieste

RUMANIA

TO YUGOSLAVIA FROM ITALY

ITALY

YUGOSLAVIA

TO BULGARIA FROM RUMANIA

BULGARIA

GREECE

50°N

MAIN TERRITORIAL CHANGES SINCE 1938

have been notoriously inefficient, corrupt, and operated in the interests of a privileged few. Various forms of authoritarian or semi-authoritarian rule have prevailed, so that democratic institutions have had little chance to become firmly rooted. An exception is found in Bohemia, the industrialized western province of Czechoslovakia, where traditions of democracy date back for several centuries. The capture and repression of this enlightened and progressive province, first by German Nazism in the late 1930's and then by Russian Communism in the late 1940's, has been one of the most tragic features of the twentieth century political history of East Central Europe.

► Origins of the Present Political Pattern

Several of the present countries in East Central Europe did not exist as separate political entities prior to World War I. From the eighteenth century onward this region was divided among four large empires: the Turkish, Austro-Hungarian, German, and Russian. The present pattern of countries resulted from the disintegration of these empires in the nineteenth and early twentieth centuries. This process was hastened by World War I, in which Germany, Austria-Hungary, and Turkey were on the losing side. Russia, though on the side of the victors, withdrew from the war following the Bolshevik Revolution of 1917, and was not represented at the Paris Peace Conference of 1919. At the latter conference the political map of East Central Europe was rearranged in order to satisfy the aspirations of the various national groups which had been included in the old empires. It was hoped that this process of

self-determination would remove the potential causes of another great war. Such hopes, of course, were to prove futile, since the European phase of World War II, like World War I, commenced in East Central Europe.

As a result of the Paris Peace Conference of 1919, Poland, which had been partitioned among Russia, Prussia, and Austria in the eighteenth century, was reconstituted as an independent country. Czechoslovakia, the homeland of two closely related Slavic peoples, the Czechs and Slovaks, was carved out of the Austro-Hungarian Empire as an entirely new country. Hungary, greatly reduced in size, was severed from Austria. The Kingdom of Serbia, which had won independence from Turkey in the nineteenth century, was joined with several districts taken from Austria-Hungary to form the new Kingdom of the Serbs, Croats, and Slovenes, later known as Yugoslavia. Rumania, which had been independent of Turkish control since the mid-nineteenth century, was enlarged by territories taken from Austria-Hungary, Russia, and Bulgaria. Independence from Turkey had been achieved by Bulgaria in the second half of the nineteenth century and by Albania immediately before the outbreak of World War I. Both of the latter countries were confirmed as sovereign nations by the Paris Peace Conference.

► Boundary Problems

The territorial settlement in East Central Europe resulting from the Paris Peace Conference left unsolved a number of important boundary questions. Such questions arose because several of the respective national states in this region, as constituted

---

Index map of East Central Europe. The "mountainous areas" are rather broadly generalized to bring out the major outlines of the topography. The Bakony Forest, separating the Great Hungarian and Little Hungarian Plains, and the narrow highland spur extending eastward from Slovenia in northern Yugoslavia are hilly rather than truly mountainous, and the same is true of certain other areas shown in the same pattern. Political capitals are underlined.

by the Paris Conference, included sizable boundary districts claimed by one or more neighboring countries on historical or ethnic grounds. At various times in past centuries a number of the different nationalities in East Central Europe, especially the Poles, Serbs, Hungarians, and Bulgarians, had ruled over extensive territories outside of their national limits as established following World War I. Thus historical possession could be used by the respective national states as a basis for claiming territory presently included within the political boundaries of other countries. More important, however, were claims based on ethnic considerations. Due to a complicated intermixture of nationalities in frontier zones, as well as to complex economic and strategic factors, the delimitation of precise political boundaries following the war frequently resulted in the inclusion of large ethnic minorities within each national state. Such groups, customarily localized in frontier areas, furnished a basis for territorial claims by adjacent states regarding themselves as mother nations for the respective minorities involved.

Between World Wars I and II the many boundary questions provided a fruitful source of bickering and dissention among the nations of East Central Europe. Space will not permit a discussion of each individual dispute. A few of the more important disputed areas may be summarized as follows:

1. Transylvania, Bessarabia, and the southern Dobruja, acquired by Rumania from Hungary, Russia, and Bulgaria, respectively, but continuing to be claimed by the latter countries.

2. Macedonia, divided between Yugoslavia and Greece, with portions of Yugoslav Macedonia being claimed by Bulgaria and Albania, and Greek Macedonia being claimed by Bulgaria and Yugoslavia.

3. The Banat, divided between Yugoslavia and Rumania, with the Rumanian Banat being claimed by Hungary and the Yugoslav Banat being claimed by Hungary and Rumania.

4. Various border areas separating Yugoslavia from Italy and claimed by both nations.

5. Silesia, divided among Germany, Poland, and Czechoslovakia, and subject to a complicated series of claims by these nations.

6. Portions of the Sudeten Mountains and Ore Mountains (Erzgebirge) incorporated in Czechoslovakia but claimed by Germany.

7. The part of Poland known as the "Polish Corridor" and the Free City of Danzig, separating East Prussia from the remainder of Germany, and claimed by Germany.

▶ Boundary Changes and Population Transfers Since 1939

As a result of World War II, several shifts of territory have occurred involving some of the disputed areas listed above. Rumania has been forced to cede Bessarabia and the northern portion of adjoining Bukovina to the Soviet Union, and the southern Dobruja has been returned to Bulgaria. The Soviet Union has annexed a wide strip of territory in eastern Poland amounting to some 46 percent of the prewar area of the latter country. However, Poland has been partially compensated for the loss by being permitted to annex Pomerania, Silesia, the prewar "Free City" of Danzig, and the southern half of East Prussia from Germany. Thus the prewar Polish Corridor no longer exists, since the northern half of former East Prussia has now been absorbed by the Soviet Union. Ruthenia, or Transcarpathian Ukraine, a mountainous, rather backward area at the extreme eastern end of prewar Czechoslovakia, has been ceded by the latter country to the Soviet Union. A number of boundary changes benefiting Yugoslavia occurred along the Yugoslav-Italian frontier. In 1947 the important seaport of Trieste (300,000), near the head of the Adriatic Sea, was included, together with adjoining areas, in the Free Territory of Trieste, under United Nations supervision. This enclave existed as a sore spot between Italy and Yugoslavia until September 1954, at which time the two countries signed an agreement including the port of Trieste under Italian administration but made it a free port. Most of the remaining area comprising the Free Territory was transferred to Yugoslav sovereignty.

In addition to boundary adjustments, East Central Europe has witnessed extensive transfers of population since the beginning of World War II. Such transfers, involving millions of Germans, Poles, Hungarians, Italians, and other nationalities, have notably simplified the pattern of eth-

nic groups. Nearly a third of the prewar population of Poland and Czechoslovakia was composed of minority groups, but today these countries have become nearly homogeneous. Both countries have transferred the bulk of their German minorities to Germany, the Soviet Union has absorbed most of the Ukrainian and White Russian minorities of Poland and the Ruthenian minority of Czechoslovakia, and Czechoslovakia has transferred part of its Hungarian minority to Hungary. The East Central European countries with the largest remaining minority groups are Yugoslavia (mostly Hungarians, Rumanians, Albanians, Bulgarians, and Turks) and Rumania (mostly Hungarians). Even in the latter countries, however, minority groups represent a smaller proportion of the population than before World War II.

Dominance of Slavic Peoples

The postwar expulsion of more than 12 million Germans from East Central Europe has intensified the predominantly Slavic character of this region. Slavic peoples form the overwhelming majority of the population in every country except Hungary and Albania. The Slavs are thought to have originally developed as a distinct ethnic group in forested lands between the Vistula and Dnieper Rivers. In the early Middle Ages groups of Slavs began migrating into various parts of East Central Europe, as well as eastward into Russia. The Elbe River seems to have marked the limit of Slavic penetration toward the west. Especially after 1100, an intermittent warfare was carried on between the Slavs pushing westward and Germans pushing toward the east. Austria and Prussia originated in the Middle Ages as military "march states" on the German-Slav frontier. Persistent colonization by Germans in East Central Europe over a period of centuries resulted in the

large German minorities found in nearly every country of this region prior to World War II.

▶ The Major Slavic Groups

Today the Slavs are often grouped into three large divisions: the East Slavs, including the Russians, Ukrainians, Belorussians (White Russians), and Ruthenians; the West Slavs, including the Poles, Czechs, and Slovaks; and the South Slavs, including the Serbs, Croats, and Slovenes. The Bulgarians and Macedonians are frequently included with the South Slavs, although each of the latter peoples has been considerably affected by cultural influences other than Slavic. One remaining group, the Rumanians, came under the influence of the later Roman Empire, and the Rumanian language is often classed with the Romance languages derived from Latin. However, in most respects the Rumanians have become Slavicized, especially in the rural areas, and for practical purposes may be counted as a Slavic people.

Although the various Slavic groups speak related languages, they differ among themselves in other respects. For example, although Serbo-Croat, the major language of Yugoslavia, is essentially a single language, the Serbs, like the Bulgarians and most of the East Slavs, employ a Cyrillic alphabet in writing, while the Croats use a Latin alphabet, as do the Slovenes and the West Slavs. Roman Catholicism has been the dominant religious faith among the West Slavs, Croats, and Slovenes, while the East Slavs, Rumanians, Bulgarians, Serbs, and Macedonians have mainly been adherents of the Orthodox Eastern Church.

• *Non-Slavic Peoples.* The principal non-Slavic population groups in East Central Europe, excluding the Rumanians, are the Hungarians and the Albanians. The Hungarians, also known as Magyars, are the descendants of Asiatic nomads who settled in the plains of Hungary in the ninth century. They are related to the Finns, and speak an Asiatic language which is entirely distinct from the Slavic languages. The majority of Hungarians who profess any religious faith are Roman Catholics, the remainder being principally Calvinists or Lutherans.

The Albanians speak an ancient Thraco-Illyrian language which is not related to the other languages of East Central Europe except in a very distant sense. Excluding Turkey, Albania is the only European country in which Moslems (Mohammedans) form a majority of the population. Disregarding possible changes brought about under Communist rule, the population is estimated as being 66 percent Moslem, 23 percent Greek Orthodox, and 11 percent Roman Catholic. Another country of East Central Europe, Yugoslavia, has a Moslem minority estimated at 12.5 percent of the population, and a third country, Bulgaria, is estimated to be 11.5 percent Moslem. The Mohammedan groups in these countries reflect the long period of Turkish rule in the Balkan Peninsula from the sixteenth century until the twentieth.

The peoples of East Central Europe have had a troubled history of contention and warfare among themselves. Even the Slavic groups have fought each other repeatedly. Since World War II, however, an involuntary peace has descended on this region, enforced by the strong hand of the Soviet Union. Whether the new Soviet-instituted political order in East Central Europe can effectively extinguish the ancient quarrels of the various national groups will be a question of much interest and importance.

Major Physical Divisions of East Central Europe

The cultural and political complexity of East Central Europe is matched by the physical diversity of this region. Mountains, hill lands, plains, and plateaus form a pattern which is extremely complicated when viewed in detail. Considered in broad outline, however, a certain order can be discerned in the arrangement of surface features. The latter tend to group themselves into four major physical belts or zones, which may be listed as (1) the north-ern plain, (2) the central mountain zone, (3) the Danubian plains, and (4) the south-ern mountain zone.

▶ The Northern Plain

Most of Poland lies in the northern plain, between the Carpathian and Sudeten Mountains on the south and the Baltic Sea on the north. This plain is a segment of the great North European Plain, which extends without a break into Germany on the west and the Soviet Union on the east. The central and northern reaches of the Polish plain are rather sandy and infertile, with much swampy and marshy land and many lakes, especially in the eastern Masurian Lakes district. The level expanses of plain are broken at intervals by terminal moraines, the low, regular hills created by the continental ice sheets which covered this area during the Great Ice Age. At the south the plain gradually rises to low, rolling uplands. Here a thick cover of loess has formed the most fertile soils of Poland.

The major rivers of Poland, the Vistula and the Oder, rise in the Carpathian Mountains and wind across the northern plain to the Baltic Sea. Each is navigable by barges for most of its length. The principal seaports of Poland are located at or near the mouths of these rivers. Gdansk, formerly Danzig (195,000), and Gdynia (120,000) handle the largest tonnages of cargo. Danzig, located near the western edge of the Vistula delta, was created a Free City in 1919 because of its predominantly German population. Poland was given a privileged position in using the port, but nevertheless decided to build Gdynia a short distance to the northwest as an all-Polish port. At present the two ports are about equal in tonnage handled. The Baltic coast west of Gdynia is exceptionally regular and hence lacking in natural harbors. The third seaport of Poland, Szczecin, formerly Stettin, is located on the wide estuary of the Oder River about 50 miles inland. Formerly an all-German river except for the headwaters, the Oder is now controlled by Poland for the greater part of its length. The lower river is shared with Germany for a considerable distance, although the portion from just above Szczecin to the Baltic Sea is entirely within Polish territory. Szczecin, with a prewar population of 375,000, was severely damaged by aerial bombing during World War II. Its postwar recovery was slow, and the popu-

lation was estimated at only 200,000 in 1950. Szczecin has declined considerably as a port since prewar days, and is now definitely secondary to Gdansk and Gdynia. The port was transferred from Germany to Poland in 1945, at which time its name was changed from Stettin.

▶ The Central Mountain Zone

The central mountain zone is formed by the Carpathian Mountains and lower ranges rimming the western part of Czechoslovakia. The plow-shaped Carpathians swing in a 1000-mile arc from Slovakia and southern Poland to south central Rumania. Geologically, these mountains are a continuation of the Alps. They are lower than the Alps, however; are cut by a greater number of easy passes; and have fewer snow-capped peaks. Elevations of 8000 feet are reached only in the High Tatra of Slovakia and Poland, and in the Transylvanian Alps of Rumania. The latter two mountain areas are the most rugged and scenic parts of the Carpathian system. Only the High Tatra has permanent snow fields. Stalin Peak (8737 feet) in the Tatra is the highest summit of the Carpathians.

West of the Carpathians, lower mountains enclose the rolling basin of Bohemia, the industrialized core of Czechoslovakia. On the north the Sudeten Mountains and Ore Mountains (Erzgebirge) separate Czechoslovakia from Poland and Germany. Between these ranges at the Saxon Gate the valley of the Elbe River provides a lowland connection leading from the Bohemian Basin to the highly developed industrial region of Saxony in southern Germany. To the southwest the Bohemian Forest occupies the frontier zone between Czechoslovakia and Germany and Austria. Lower highlands border Bohemia on the southeast. The mountainous rim of Bohemia has a general elevation of only 2000 to 5000 feet. The floor of the Bohemian Basin lies generally at 1500 feet or less.

Between the mountain-rimmed upland basin of Bohemia and the high Carpathians of Slovakia, a convenient and historic passageway is provided by the lowland corridor of Moravia. Through this corridor run major routes of transportation connecting Vienna and the Danube Valley with the plains of Poland. To the north, near the Polish frontier, the corridor narrows to a width of about 10 miles at the Moravian Gate between the Sudeten Mountains and the Carpathians. Beyond the Gate on the upper reaches of the Oder River stands the intensively developed coal-mining and industrial region of Upper Silesia.

▶ The Danubian Plains

Two major lowlands, rimmed by mountains and drained by the Danube River and its tributaries, comprise the Danubian plains. The larger of the two is the Great Hungarian Plain, which occupies two-thirds of Hungary and smaller adjoining portions of Rumania, Yugoslavia, and the Soviet Union. The Great Hungarian Plain is very level for the most part, and contains much poorly drained land along its sluggish rivers. To the northwest a rolling outlier, the Little Hungarian Plain, extends into the margins of Czechoslovakia and Austria. The second major lowland drained by the Danube is comprised of the plains of Wallachia and Moldavia, constituting the core region of modern Rumania. These plains of the lower Danube are less extensive than the Great Hungarian Plain, but are better drained.

The Danubian plains represent the most fertile and productive large farming region in East Central Europe. Wide expanses of level land with deep, rich grassland soils, an average growing season of 190 days or more, and a summer maximum of rainfall provide good natural conditions for the growing of wheat and corn. Before World War II this region regularly exported a surplus of grain to other parts of Europe.

The Danube River, which supplies a navigable water connection between these lowlands and the outside world, is the longest river in Eurasia west of the Volga. It rises in the Black Forest of southwestern Germany and follows a winding course of some 1750 miles to the Black Sea, which it enters through three delta channels. The Danube is customarily divided into three principal sections: Upper, Middle, and Lower. The Upper Danube, above Vienna, is principally fed by tributaries from the Alps. This section of the river is swift and difficult to navigate, although river vessels of 1000 tons or more make use of it as far upstream as Regensburg, Germany, and smaller craft as far as Ulm. Below Vienna the Middle Danube flows leisurely across the Little Hungarian and Great Hungarian Plains past the Czechoslovak river port of Bratislava and the Hungarian and Yugoslav capital cities of Budapest and Belgrade. Three major tributaries enter the river between Budapest and Belgrade: the Tisza from the Carpathians, and the Drava and Sava from the Alps. In the border zone between Yugoslavia and Rumania the Danube follows a series of gorges through a belt of mountains some 80 miles wide where the Carpathians reach southward to merge with the Balkan Mountains. At the eastern end of the gorges is the famous Iron Gate, a sharply constricted narrows through which the river flows with such great swiftness that vessels moving upstream must be assisted by locomotives on the bank. Beyond the Iron Gate the Lower Danube marks the boundary between the level plains of southern Rumania and the low plateau of northern Bulgaria. The river enters the Black Sea through a low, marshy delta with many lakes and swamps. The inland river ports of Braila (95,000) and Galati (80,000) in Rumania are accessible to seagoing vessels, and vie in commercial importance with Constanta (80,-000), the principal Rumanian port on the Black Sea itself. No river in the world touches so many different countries as the

Barren karst highlands in western Yugoslavia tower above Cetinje, the capital of Montenegro. (*Yugoslav Information Center.*)

Danube—eight in all, including Germany, Austria, Czechoslovakia, Hungary, Yugoslavia, Rumania, Bulgaria, and the USSR.

▶ The Southern Mountain Zone

The southern mountain zone occupies most of the Balkan Peninsula. Bulgaria, Yugoslavia, and Albania, the East Central European countries within this zone, are predominantly mountainous.

In Bulgaria the principal ranges are the Balkan Mountains in the center of the country and the Rhodope Mountains in the south. These are rugged mountains extending east and west, and attaining heights of 9000 feet in a few places. Stalin Peak (9597 feet) in the western Rhodope is the highest summit in East Central Europe. Between the Rhodope and the Balkan Mountains is the productive valley of the Maritsa River, which together with the adjoining Sofia Basin constitutes the agricultural and industrial core of Bulgaria.

North of the Balkan Range a wheat-growing loess plateau slopes to the Danube.

In central and southern Yugoslavia a tangled mass of mountains constitutes a major barrier to travel. Through this difficult region a historic lowland passage connecting the Danube Valley at Belgrade with the Greek port of Salonika on the Aegean Sea follows the trough of the Morava and Vardar Rivers. An important east-west route linking the Morava-Vardar Trough with the Maritsa Valley leads through the high basin in which stands Sofia, the capital of Bulgaria.

Along the rugged and picturesque Dalmatian Coast of southwestern Yugoslavia, mountains rise steeply from the Adriatic Sea, and deep, canyonlike inlets supply a multitude of protected harbors. However, a wide expanse of difficult mountain country traversed by few rail lines or highways separates this coast from the Danubian core of Yugoslavia in the northeast, and the seaports of Dalmatia have only a limited commercial utility. In fact, the entire Adriatic coast of Yugoslavia has only three seaports of much consequence, these being Split (50,000) in Dalmatia, the former Italian port of Fiume (now Rijeka, 70,000), located farther north, and the major Italian seaport of Trieste (300,000).

Western Yugoslavia is continuously mountainous from the Italian and Austrian Alps in the extreme north to the mountains of Albania in the south. The principal ranges trend parallel to the Adriatic Coast and impose a succession of rocky heights crossed by only a few significant passes. The general range of elevations is 4000 to 6000 feet, but scattered summits reach 8000 to 9400 feet. Some of the most picturesque scenery is found in the heavily wooded Dinaric Alps, bordering the Dalmatian Coast. Much of the mountainous region of western Yugoslavia is characterized by karst or sinkhole topography caused by the solvent action of underground waters in limestone bedrock. The dry, inhospitable karst plateaus are among the most desolate and sparsely settled parts of Europe.

Nearly all of Albania is composed of rugged mountains, the principal exception being a narrow, swampy coastal lowland. Perhaps best of all the Balkan countries Albania exemplifies Gottmann's statement that "The Balkan highlands have lived as a tissue of isolated cells, preserving archaic forms of life and resisting to the best of their abilities the multitude of influences and external interferences that have swirled across the peninsula throughout history."[1]

The Climatic Pattern

The climates of East Central Europe are transitional between the marine climate of northwestern Europe, the extreme continental climate of Russia, and the dry-summer subtropical or mediterranean climate of Southern Europe. Nearly everywhere the winters are colder than in the British Isles, France, or the Low Countries, although not so cold as in Russia. The average January temperature is 29°F. at Poznan, 26° at Warsaw, 30° at Prague, 32° at Budapest, 31° at Belgrade, 27° at Bucharest, and 28° at Sofia. Only in protected valleys and coastal lowlands of the extreme south do midwinter average temperatures rise significantly above freezing. An example is provided by the small seaport and resort city of Dubrovnik, on the Dalmatian Coast of Yugoslavia, which has a January average temperature of 48°. Summer temperatures are higher than in northwestern Europe, the average for July being 66° at Poznan and Warsaw, 67° at Prague, 70° at Budapest, 71° at Belgrade, 72° at Bucharest, 69° at Sofia, and 79° at Dubrovnik.

In most parts of East Central Europe the average annual rainfall is between 20 and 30 inches. The heaviest precipitation occurs in Yugoslavia along the Adriatic coast: Dubrovnik receives 60 inches a year, and some of the higher areas in the coastal mountains receive 180 inches or more—the heaviest rainfall in Europe. Most areas in East Central Europe have a summer maximum of rainfall except for the extreme south of Yugoslavia, the Dalmatian Coast, Albania, and extreme southern Bulgaria. The latter areas have the dry summers characteristic of the Mediterranean region. Only a tenth of the annual rainfall at Dubrovnik falls in the months of June, July, and August.

[1] Jean Gottmann, *A Geography of Europe,* rev. ed. New York: Holt, 1954. P. 561. Used by permission of the author and the publisher.

In the Danubian plains hot summers decrease the efficiency of the summer rain, and recurrent droughts make agriculture somewhat more hazardous than in the more dependable climate of northwestern Europe. Nevertheless, in most years the available moisture is sufficient for a good harvest. The humid continental long-summer climate of the Danubian plains is comparable in many respects to the climate of the American Corn Belt, although Corn Belt summers are hotter and the average rainfall is greater. The plains of Poland have a humid continental short-summer climate comparable to the climate of the American Great Lakes region.

Rural Life in East Central Europe

In this region the vagaries of climate are a matter of more direct importance to the masses of the people than in the industrialized lands bordering the North Sea. Aside from western Czechoslovakia, southwestern Poland, and a scattering of large urban centers in other areas, East Central Europe is predominantly rural and agricultural rather than urban and industrial. In the 1930's peasant farmers represented about 34 percent of the population in Czechoslovakia, 55 percent in Hungary, 63 percent in Poland, 75 percent in Yugoslavia, 78 percent in Rumania, 80 percent in Bulgaria, and 91 percent in Albania.

▶ Agriculture in an Underdeveloped Region

As an agricultural region, East Central Europe presents a great contrast to the North Sea lands. This region has borne many of the characteristic marks of an underdeveloped area: a high degree of illiteracy and ignorance among the rural people, poorly developed transportation facilities, a lack of capital except at exorbitant rates of interest, and antiquated and inefficient farming methods with resultant low yields. Sowing and harvesting of grain by hand has been the common practice; horses, oxen, and cows rather than tractors have been the main source of farm motive power. As a result of rural overpopulation, relatively low crop yields, poor transportation, and a lack of urban markets, the bulk of farm production has been utilized at home so that agriculture has shown a strong tendency to be of a subsistence rather than a commercial character. Prior to World War I much of the best land was held in large estates worked by hired laborers or tenants, and rural life in many areas had an almost feudal cast. Such estates were especially common in Hungary, Rumania, Poland, and Slovakia. Following World War I programs of land redistribution undertaken by the various governments in East Central Europe succeeded in breaking up many of the old estates and also in consolidating some of the scattered strip holdings of the peasants into more compact and efficient farm units. However, the purposes of such programs had by no means been fully accomplished at the outbreak of World War II. Since 1945 the remaining large private holdings have been liquidated by the new Communist governments and a program of collectivized agriculture on the Russian model has been instituted. Information on the extent and success of this program was still very fragmentary at the time of writing.

In general, poverty and backwardness in East Central Europe increase toward the south and east. Undoubtedly the poorest and most backward country of all is Albania, the country which has the smallest proportion of arable land and the one which remained longest under Turkish rule. Albania is the most rural country in Europe. Tirana, its capital and largest city, has an estimated population of only 65,000.

▶ *The Pattern of Crops and Livestock*

The principal crop-growing areas of East Central Europe are the extensive plains and low plateaus of Poland, Hungary, Rumania, northern Yugoslavia, and northern Bulgaria; the uplands and valleys of western Czechoslovakia; and the Maritsa Valley of Bulgaria.

On the sandy plains of central and northern Poland rye and potatoes are the major crops, although wheat and sugar beets are important in the loess zone of southern Poland. More rye and potatoes are grown in Poland than in all the other countries of East Central Europe combined.

In the Danubian plains corn and wheat are the main crops. The long, hot, rainy

Harvesting sugar beets by machine on a collective farm in Bohemia. The large harvester in the background is a Soviet Russian model. (*Eastfoto*)

summers make these plains one of the few areas in Europe suitable for growing corn on a large scale. Rumania, Hungary, and Yugoslavia ordinarily produce more than half of Europe's corn. Wheat is an important crop in all of the East Central European countries, being more extensively grown through the area as a whole than any other grain. Rye, oats, barley, potatoes, and sugar beets are major crops in Poland and Czechoslovakia, but are of minor importance in the other countries. The raising of cattle, hogs, horses, and associated fodder crops is a prominent feature of agriculture in all these countries; sheep are most important in Yugoslavia, Bulgaria, Rumania, and Albania. Throughout East Central Europe stock raising is the principal form of agriculture in the highlands. Transhumance, the seasonal movement of farm animals between the valleys and mountain pastures, is widely practiced.

The agriculture of East Central Europe reaches a climax of efficiency and productivity in western Czechoslovakia, the area which maintains the best balance between agriculture and industry. Here in Bohemia and Moravia diversified farming is practiced which is more similar to the agriculture of the North Sea countries than is true of other areas in East Central Europe.

▶ *Subtropical Agriculture in Bulgaria and Yugoslavia*

A relatively small but very distinctive agricultural region is found in the Maritsa Valley of Bulgaria, where subtropical temperatures coupled with summer rain permit the growing of tobacco, grapes, cotton, rice, and many varieties of fruits and vegetables. However, wheat occupies a larger acreage than any other crop. The Maritsa Valley is famous for its rose gardens, exporting attar of roses to the world's perfume industry.

Another distinctive area of subtropical farming is the Dalmatian Coast of Yugoslavia and adjoining districts of Albania, where citrus and olive groves and vineyards portray the characteristic agriculture of the zone of mediterranean or dry-summer subtropical climate.

Urban Development

The predominantly rural and agricultural character of East Central Europe is reflected in the small number of large cities. Only three metropolitan cities can boast a million inhabitants or more: Budapest (1,600,000), Bucharest (1,400,000), and Prague (1,000,000). These cities are the political capitals and main cultural, industrial, transportation, and trading centers of their respective countries. Each is several times larger than any other city in its country. Budapest is twelve times as large as Szeged (133,000), and Bucharest is twelve times the size of Cluj (120,000). Prague, in a more industrialized country, is less than four times the size of the second city, the woolen-milling center of Brno (275,000). Of the four remaining cities in East Central Europe having populations of 450,000 or more, three are national capitals: Warsaw (900,000), Sofia (500,000), and Belgrade (470,000). Lodz, the "Polish Manchester," is a major textile center with a population of more than 650,000. Only three other cities in East Central Europe, all important industrial centers, reach populations of approximately 350,000. These are Cracow and Wroclaw (Breslau), in southwestern Poland, and Zagreb, the progressive, Westernized capital of Croatia in northwestern Yugoslavia. An immense amount of damage was sustained by some of the larger cities in East Central Europe during World War II. Probably the greatest destruction was experienced in Warsaw, which was left largely in ruins following the war.

Most of the smaller cities in East Central Europe are primarily agricultural market centers and have only a local importance. In only two areas do important clusters of industrial cities occur which are in any way comparable to the great urban constellations found in the larger manufacturing districts of northwestern Europe. The largest such cluster is found in southwestern Poland and adjoining areas of Czechoslovakia, on or near the major coal field of Upper Silesia. A second, less concentrated cluster occurs in Bohemia; it includes Prague, Pilsen, and smaller cities.

Industry, Transportation, and Trade

The industrialized areas of Upper Silesia and western Czechoslovakia have provided a highly important base for an extensive program of planned industrial development which has been undertaken in East Central Europe under Communist auspices since World War II. Under close supervision by the Soviet Union, measures have been taken to increase industrial output in each of the satellite countries and to foster an integrated development of industry for the satellite area as a whole. In Yugoslavia, not a part of the satellite bloc, industrial development has proceeded on a separate basis. As in the Soviet Union itself, Communist planning has stressed heavy industry (particularly the manufacture of iron and steel, heavy chemicals, and machinery) as being a necessary prerequisite for over-all industrial progress. An important feature of the program has been the construction of large new steel plants in a number of separated localities: in Poland at Nowa Huta (a suburb of Cracow) and Czestochowa; in Czechoslovakia near Ostrava in Czech Silesia, and near Kosice in Slovakia; in Hungary at Dunapentele on the Danube River below Budapest; and in East Germany at Fürstenberg on the Oder River approximately 50 miles southeast of Berlin near the junction of the Oder and Neisse.

▶ Upper Silesia—the "Second Ruhr"

However, despite the construction of new steelworks in other areas, the most important center of heavy industry in East Central Europe will doubtless continue to be the industrial concentration of Upper Silesia, sometimes referred to as "The Second Ruhr." As the latter title would indicate, the major industrial resource of Upper Silesia is a huge reserve of coal, much of it excellent for coking. At present most of the mining is done in thick seams at depths of less than 1000 feet; therefore, extraction of the coal is relatively simple and inexpensive. The total estimated reserve rivals that of the Ruhr in size. Prior to 1945 the coal field was divided among Germany, Poland, and Czechoslovakia. With the cession of Germany's eastern provinces, however, control over the German part of the field has passed to Poland. The latter is now the fifth coal-producing nation of the world, being surpassed only by the United States, Germany, the Soviet Union, and the United Kingdom. Production in Upper Silesia is considerably in excess of Polish needs; consequently, Poland is a major exporter of coal, being in fact the world's largest exporter for a number of years following World War II. In addition to coal, Upper Silesia contains some of the largest deposits of lead and zinc in Europe, a few small oil deposits, and a limited amount of iron ore. Some copper is available from the near-by Sudeten Mountains.

Heavy metallurgy is the main industrial specialty. This area contains the largest concentration of iron and steel plants on the European continent between the German Ruhr and the Ukrainian Industrial Region of the USSR. The 1951 production of 2.8 million tons of crude steel was double the prewar level. On the Polish side of the border, a number of medium-sized industrial cities cluster around Katowice

Extensive postwar rebuilding has been necessary in several of the larger cities of East Central Europe. The view shows a group of new apartment buildings in the Hungarian capital of Budapest. (*Eastfoto.*)

(170,000), renamed Stalinogrod in 1953. The latter is connected by a direct rail line with the coal-shipping port of Gdynia. Ostrava (180,000) is the leading industrial center on the Czech side.

► Industrial Development in Bohemia

Czechoslovakia is the most industrialized and generally advanced of the East Central European countries. Although Czech Silesia is an important center of coal mining and steel milling, the principal focus of industry in the country is found in the Bohemian Basin. Here Pilsen (120,000) with its Skoda works, is a famous center of steel-making and armaments production, but the capital, Prague, has a much larger over-all industrial development. "Prague (Praha) has a population of over one million. It is a great historical center of administration and learning, with many monuments and beautiful residential sections. . . . Until 1850 the city had less than 100,-000 inhabitants, mostly foreigners, particularly Germans. The railroads and modern industry, using the coal of the Kladno field, made it a large city—300,000 people in 1878, 400,000 in 1910, 921,000 in 1947. The industrial function, spread among the suburbs, is varied: iron and steel finishing industries and engineering make the core of it; anything that can be made out of steel is produced here, railroad rolling stock, automobiles, electrical machinery and machine tools playing a great part. Textile and leather industries are well represented as are chemical manufacturing and, of course, glassware." [2] Dozens of smaller industrial cities in the Bohemian Basin manufacture an extremely wide variety of metalwares, cotton and linen textiles, glassware and crystal, ceramics, and wood products.

► Mineral Resources of East Central Europe

Although East Central Europe has not been outstanding in the past as a producer of minerals, sufficient resources undoubtedly exist to support a greatly increased development of industry. Within the satellite area the available minerals include immense deposits of coal in the Upper Silesian field, important petroleum deposits in Rumania in the vicinity of Ploesti, and some of the world's largest deposits of bauxite in Hungary. Huge reserves of rock salt in Poland and potash and salt in East Germany provide the basis for chemical manufacturing. Throughout the mountain zones are many small to medium deposits of metals: lead, zinc, copper, iron, and others. Yugoslavia, outside of the satellite orbit, is the largest producer and exporter of metals among the East Central European countries. In the Ore Mountains of East Germany and Czechoslovakia uranium-bearing ores are worked in closely guarded mines. The Soviet Union is thought to rely heavily on this area for the uranium needed in the manufacture of atomic bombs. Possibly the most critical mineral deficiency of East Central Europe is an inadequate supply of iron ore. Small local deposits cannot meet the needs of the iron and steel industry. As a result, large imports of ore are required, principally from Sweden and the Soviet Union.

In addition to minerals, industry in East Central Europe can draw upon substantial forest resources. Nearly a third of the entire region is wooded, and every country except Hungary has sizable reserves of timber. Conifers predominate at the higher elevations, although beech, oak, and other deciduous hardwoods make up a considerable part of the forest growth on the lower lands.

► Transportation Problems

One of the main hindrances to industrialization in East Central Europe is an inadequate system of rail and water trans-

---

[2] Gottmann, *op. cit.* P. 436. Used by permission of the author and the publisher.

portation. As in the Soviet Union itself, Communist planning to the present has emphasized modernization of existing facilities rather than development of new rail lines and water routes. Construction is proceeding on a number of new canals, but reliable information as to progress is very scanty. Among the canal projects are a Danube–Black Sea Canal linking the Danube River above Braila with the coast of the Black Sea north of Constanta, an Oder-Danube Canal through the Moravian Corridor, and a series of canals linking the Dnieper, Vistula, and Oder.

▶ **Orientation of Trade toward the USSR**

Prior to World War II Germany occupied a predominant position in the trade of East Central Europe. German coal and manufactures were sent to the countries of this region in return for surplus agricultural products and industrial raw materials. Since 1945, however, the trade of the satellite area has been increasingly oriented toward the USSR. The indications are that the Soviet Union manipulates this trade largely in its own interest, draining off such products as it chooses from the satellite area without too much regard for local needs within the satellite countries, and shipping such products in return as it can easily spare. Meanwhile Yugoslavia pursues an independent course, trading mainly with the United States, West Germany, Great Britain, Italy, and other countries outside the Russian Iron Curtain. However, in 1954 a trade agreement was signed between the governments of Yugoslavia and the Soviet Union.

Significance of the New Industrial Revolution

Today under Soviet direction the satellite area is being transformed in a manner comparable to the earlier transformation of Russia itself. The significance of this change is summarized in the following selection by a specialist on East Central Europe, Jan Wszelaki: [3]

An industrial revolution is taking shape in Europe behind the Iron Curtain. The western boundary of peasant Europe is retreating eastward beyond the Vistula, the Carpathians and the Danube, and when a few more years have passed, the majority of the population in Poland, Hungary, Slovakia and Rumanian Transylvania will no longer live by agricultural occupations. This half-enforced and half-spontaneous industrialization of the mid-European area is a major event in European history. The Communist system may endure or perish, but what has already been done can hardly be undone: Middle Europe will not return to its pastoral era. . . .

Since 1948 the area has been molded into a well-knit Russian dependency, and its industrial potential is much more substantial than is generally assumed in the West. The 90,000,000 satellite population [including East Germany] produces as many basic industrial goods per capita as the 200,000,000 or more inhabitants of Soviet Russia. Roughly speaking, the captive European countries produce one-half as much hard fuel and electric power, about one-third as much steel, and more than one-fifth as much oil as Russia. If the satellite long-range plans are realized, their share of the production of the Soviet empire will become even larger. . . .

All satellites are to produce almost every kind of industrial goods, but each will have to stress certain types of production. Thus Czechoslovakia is intended to become the principal steelmaker, and to supply heavy machinery for the entire area. Czechoslovakia will also manufacture precision tools, though Eastern Germany's long tradition of specialization in electrical, optical and elec-

---

[3] Jan Wszelaki, "The Rise of Industrial Middle Europe," *Foreign Affairs*, v. 30 (1951), pp. 123–133.

Used by permission of *Foreign Affairs*.

tronic equipment gives that region first place in this field. . . . Eastern Germany will also be called upon for making heavy machinery, shipbuilding, and the production of synthetic oil and rubber. Hungary is slated to produce aluminum, rolling stock, and much machinery. Poland, which provides coal and coke for the entire area, will become the principal producer of chemicals, as well as a large manufacturer of medium machinery. Rumania is to concentrate on the output of oil and natural gas, and to develop new industries, based on electric power, serving mechanized agriculture. Bulgaria's industrial role is inconsequential for the time being. . . .

Will these plans be fulfilled? Can satellite industry be developed as planned without foreign capital (or, for that matter, any capital) and without plant equipment from the West? Can the satellite countries develop enough technicians and skilled workmen to construct and operate so large and diversified an industrial plant? Can their manpower stand the ever-increasing pressure, the long hours, the inadequate wages, the lack of freedom and incentives? We should not assume that the answers to these questions must be in the negative. Some people made the mistake of supposing that Hitler could never make the German people work and produce for him. A generation ago Russia was a backward rural country and today she is the second industrial power of the world. Given time, what could be done in Russia could undoubtedly be done in the captive countries, whose manpower is perhaps more intelligent, and where, as in Eastern Germany, there is already a great deal of industrial experience. . . .

It would be erroneous, and perhaps even dangerous, for the West to underrate the powerful appeal of industrial creation for the new generation of intellectuals in the captive part of Europe. Many of these young people sincerely believe that, at the cost of immense efforts and privations, they are laying foundations for the future prosperity of their countries. They hope that one day the Iron Curtain will be lifted, that the Russians will go (or be sent) where they belong, and that they themselves will then deal with the local Communist rulers. When that day of liberation comes, the belated industrial revolution of backward peasant Europe will have been accomplished: the mines, plants, and factories will remain as the heritage of strong and free nations.

PART 3
The Soviet Union

Introduction to the Soviet Union

The Union of Soviet Socialist Republics [1] emerged from World War II as a major center of world power. Such a development would have been difficult to foresee before the war. In the prewar period there was a pronounced tendency in the outside world to undervalue the political, economic, and military strength of the USSR. Russia was defeated by the Central Powers in World War I, after suffering possibly a greater toll of military casualties than any other participant. Between 1917 and 1921 the country experienced a destructive period of revolution, foreign intervention, and civil war. The October Revolution of 1917 and success of the Red Army in the subsequent civil war gave control of the government to the radical Bolshevik fac-

[1] Union of Soviet Socialist Republics, frequently shortened to USSR or Soviet Union, is the present official name of the Russian state. The USSR is the successor to the Russian Empire of tsarist (czarist) times. It came into existence following the overthrow of the last of the Romanov tsars in 1917. Pre-Revolutionary Russia is often spoken of as Old Russia, Tsarist Russia, or Imperial Russia. Post-Revolutionary Russia is often referred to as Soviet Russia. The name Russia is used loosely to refer to the country either before or after the Revolution. The part of the country west of the Ural Mountains and north of the Caucasus Mountains is often referred to as European Russia. The part east of the Urals and north of Soviet Middle Asia is called Siberia.

The main street of a collective farm village in the Moscow region. (*Sovfoto.*)

tion of the Communist Party. During the 1920's and 1930's a series of major internal crises occurred as the Communist leaders attempted to fasten a program of Marxian socialism on an exhausted and partly unwilling country, and in the meantime carried on a struggle for power among themselves.

Emergence of the USSR as a Major World Power

When Germany attacked the Soviet Union in June 1941, it was freely predicted in outside countries that the USSR would prove too weak and disunited to withstand the German assault for more than a few weeks or months. The Russians, however, showed an unexpected ability to resist. After suffering tremendous casualties and losses of territory in the early part of the war, their forces eventually rallied. Late in 1942 the German invasion was checked in a decisive battle at Stalingrad, on the Volga River. Thereafter the Germans were gradually pushed back, and by early 1945 Russian armies were besieging Germany itself. The end of the war found the Russians in possession of the eastern third of Germany, which became a postwar Russian zone of occupation.

Russian success in World War II was undoubtedly due in part to economic and military assistance furnished by outside nations, especially the United States, United Kingdom, and Canada. These Allies sent large shipments of munitions and other supplies to Russia, and their military campaigns in North Africa, Italy, and northwestern Europe diverted sizable German forces from the Russian front. Mismanagement of the Russian campaigns by the German dictator, Adolf Hitler, may also have worked in favor of Russia. Nevertheless, the failure of Germany to conquer Russia was a clear indication that the strength of the USSR had been badly underrated. The end of World War II found the Soviet Union established as a world power ranking second in importance only to the United States.

▶ Soviet Territorial Gains

Following the war the actions of the Soviet Union created a state of profound uneasiness among the non-Communist nations of the world. Beginning in 1939 the Soviet government had considerably enlarged the national territory of the USSR by successive annexations of areas taken from neighboring countries. Most of these annexations took place in the western frontier zone of the Soviet Union between the Black Sea and the Arctic Ocean. The three independent Baltic republics of Lithuania, Latvia, and Estonia were completely absorbed in 1940. Other European nations losing territory to the USSR included Poland, Finland, Rumania, Czechoslovakia, and Germany. The greater part of the annexed lands had been Russian-held territory prior to World War I, but some areas were acquired for the first time. In the Far East the Soviet Union took the southern half of Sakhalin Island and the entire island chain of the Kuriles from Japan. Both of these island areas had been ceded to Japan by Tsarist Russia. In addition, the small semi-independent Asian country of Tannu Tuva was absorbed. All of the foregoing annexations were complete by the end of 1945. They added to the national domain of the USSR a total area of approximately 287,000 square miles (20,000 square miles larger than Texas), with an estimated population of 25 millions.

After 1945 the political influence of the Soviet Union was extended still further through its dominance over the European satellite nations of Poland, Czechoslovakia,

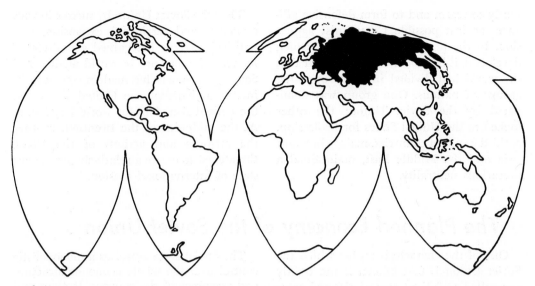

World location of the Soviet Union. (*Boggs Equal Area Projection, copyright A. J. Nystrom and Co.*)

Rumania, Hungary, Bulgaria, Albania, and East Germany, as well as the Soviet-occupied zone of Austria. In the Far East Communist governments took power in North Korea, in China, and in northern Indochina (North Vietnam). By 1954 about a third of the world's people were under Communist control, and the Soviet Union had become the center of a political system much greater in extent than the empire of the tsars.

Meanwhile, industrial progress in the Soviet Union kept pace with political expansion. Large sections of the western USSR, including the productive Ukraine, had been overrun by Germany. These areas, which included some of the most important industrial and mining districts in the USSR, had suffered an enormous amount of physical damage. By 1950, however, the worst of the destruction had been repaired. Meanwhile production expanded in the industrialized areas which had not been invaded. In 1950 the over-all industrial output of the USSR showed an estimated 45 percent increase over the highest prewar levels.[2]

► The "Cold War"

Although the United States and Britain had rapidly demobilized after World War II, the USSR was slow to follow suit. Large military forces continued to be maintained, and the production of armaments was kept at a high level. Since the 1920's Soviet industrial expansion had emphasized the heavier types of industry, for example, iron and steel production and the manufacture of heavy machinery. This emphasis was continued following World War II. Such industries furnished a necessary basis for peacetime industrial progress, but they could also be converted readily to war purposes.

Meanwhile, agitation by local Communist groups was carried on in many countries outside of the Soviet orbit. Actual fighting between Communist and anti-Communist forces broke out in Greece, Indochina, Korea, and a number of other countries. The foregoing series of events gradually created a state of alarm in the non-Communist world. Many nations outside the Soviet "Iron Curtain" began reluc-

[2] "The Kremlin's Plan V." *Fortune* (February, 1953), p. 115.

tantly to rearm and to form defensive alliances against possible Communist aggression. In the period of "Cold War" which developed, it became increasingly clear that the world had divided into two opposing groups of nations. One group was dominated by the Soviet Union; the other looked to the United States for leadership. A third group of countries, mainly in South Asia and the Middle East, maintained a precarious neutrality.

Thus the Soviet Union by success in war, economic and territorial expansion, and political intrigue has gained a position of immense importance in world affairs. The Soviet government has made no secret of its intent to challenge the United States and the United Kingdom for world leadership. At the midpoint of the twentieth century the attitude and actions of the USSR threatened to create a relatively permanent state of international tension.

The Planned Economy of the Soviet Union

One of the characteristics for which the Soviet Union is best known is the tightly controlled, socialized type of planned economy which the Communist Party has developed in the country and which is now being introduced in the satellite nations and China. Since 1928 the economy of the USSR has been operated under a series of Five-Year Plans touching every major sector of economic life. These plans prescribe in great detail the goals of production for the entire nation. They specify the types and quantities of minerals, manufactured goods, and farm commodities to be produced, the factories, rail lines, highways, canals, and dams to be built or improved, the locations of new residential areas to house industrial workers, and so on. To a considerable degree the Soviet economy may be regarded as a single gigantic enterprise directed from Moscow. This all-embracing and rigidly controlled system of state socialism is possible because (1) the Soviet dictatorship gives the Communist planners the necessary political power to carry their plans into effect, and (2) most of the means of production are owned and operated, or at least controlled, by the state. The economic system of the USSR has been succinctly described as follows: [3]

The Soviet state exercises a monopolistic control over the whole economic structure and resources of the country. It owns and operates large-scale industry, mines, power plants, railways, shipping, and other means of communication. It engages in farming on its own account through the institution of state farms, and it largely controls peasant agriculture through the organization of collective farming. It has an exclusive monopoly of banking, foreign trade, and exchange operations. It controls the domestic channels of distribution in its capacity as a manufacturer, farmer, merchant, shipper, and banker. Moreover, by administrative measures it can suppress such private competition as still exists.

All these branches of economic life are subject to the system of economic planning by the state; they are within the orbit of "planned economy" as it is understood and practiced in the Soviet Union.

It is true that the private market, however diminished or limited in scope, has never become entirely extinct, at any rate so far as petty trade is concerned. Although the Soviet policy toward private enterprise has generally been unmistakably restrictive, it has occasionally relaxed in the direction of greater liberality, at least in the realm of trade. But whatever its concessions to private enterprise, the Soviet state has maintained, unaltered, its dominance

---

[3] Lazar Volin, *A Survey of Soviet Russian Agriculture*. U. S. Department of Agriculture Monograph No. 5. P. 10.

Kolkhoz - collective farm

in the economic sphere. From the fields of large-scale industry and foreign trade, over which the Soviet state early asserted a monopoly, it extended its dominance to domestic trade and finally to agriculture—that branch of economic life that had been the citadel of economic individualism in the Soviet Union. Since the early 1930's collectivization of agriculture has been an achieved fact.

The economic system described above was initiated by stages following the Bolshevik Revolution of 1917. Essentially the aim of the revolutionary leaders was twofold. They meant to abolish the old aristocratic and capitalist institutions of Tsarist Russia and to develop a strong socialist state able to stand on an equal footing with the major industrial nations of the West. Space will not permit an examination of the ideology which lay behind this program, or the numerous contradictions between Communist theory and practice which have marked the history of Soviet Russia. Discussions of these matters fill many volumes, and authorities are not in agreement on vital points. Much of the truth is hidden behind an official wall of silence or misrepresentation. Enough is known, however, to sketch in the main outlines of what has occurred in the USSR since the Revolution.

For the first decade the Communist leaders were mainly occupied in consolidating their hold on the country and in putting a limited part of their program into effect. Large-scale industry, banking, and foreign trade were nationalized, but a certain amount of private trading, together with private ownership of small industries and agricultural land, was permitted under the "New Economic Policy" announced in 1921. This compromise policy was the result of a near breakdown in the newly instituted Communist economy during the difficult period of civil war and foreign in-tervention following the Revolution. However, it was intended only as a temporary expedient.

▶ *The Five-Year Plans*

In 1928 the first of the Five-Year Plans was announced, and succeeding Plans have covered the period up to the present. Two of the most prominent features of the First Five-Year Plan were (1) the collectivization of agriculture and (2) a rapid expansion of large-scale industry.

• *Collectivization of Agriculture.*[4] Between 1929 and 1933 about two thirds of all peasant households in the Soviet Union were collectivized. By 1940 this figure had risen to 97 percent. Today the number of independent peasant cultivators is insignificant. Collectivization was fiercely resisted by the land-hungry peasants, and the most drastic measures, including wholesale deportations and executions, were necessary to put the government decrees into effect. Millions of livestock were slaughtered by the peasants, and crops were burned to avoid turning them over to the new collectives. Today three main types of farm unit exist. The most familiar of these is the collective farm or *kolkhoz.* These vary widely in average size from region to region. In 1938 the average collective farm for the USSR as a whole included 78 farm households and 3700 acres of land, of which 1196 acres were planted in crops. Since 1938 there has been a definite trend toward consolidation of collectives into still larger units, as a consequence of the tendency in Soviet planning to make farming as much of a factory-type enterprise as possible. On a collective farm the members of each farm household spend the greater part of their time in work for the collective. Payment for such labor is made partly in cash and partly in farm products. The collective is obligated to deliver to the government specified quantities

---

[4] The discussion under this heading is based principally on Volin, *op. cit.,* pp. 10–80.

of farm commodities at prices set by the government. Such prices are ordinarily much lower than prices prevailing on the free market or in government retail stores. After the required sales to the government have been made and other obligations of the collective have been met, any remaining surplus of farm products is divided among the members of the collective. Each household is allowed to keep a garden plot and to own a few head of livestock, and surplus produce from these sources as well as any surplus distributed by the collective may be sold on the free market in a nearby town or city.

Disastrous early experiences in putting tractors and agricultural machinery into the hands of ignorant peasants on the collective farms, as well as the desire to utilize each piece of machinery to the maximum advantage in terms of time, led to the institution of a second type of farm unit—the machine-tractor station (MTS). With limited exceptions, the collectives themselves no longer own tractors or large machines, such equipment being made available to them on a custom basis by the machine-tractor stations. Tractor drivers and other employees of the MTS are paid wages or salaries. In addition to supplying power-driven equipment, the machine-tractor stations render technical assistance to the collectives and exercise important supervisory functions. They vary widely in size and scale of operations. In 1937 an average machine-tractor station serviced 33 collective farms with a total sown area of 45,000 acres.

A third basic type of farm unit is the large factory-type state farm or *sovkhoz*. These units are maintained by the government as experimental and demonstration farms and also function as reclamation projects preparing new agricultural land for occupancy by *kolkhozi* (collectives). They are worked by laborers paid in cash wages. The *sovkhoz*, backed by the fiscal power of the state, has played an especially significant role in marginal zones where uncertainties of climate render ordinary farming hazardous.

As originally conceived, the system of collectivized agriculture was supposed to result in the following major advantages:

1. The old system of farming small, noncontiguous strips would be replaced by larger fields suited to mechanized farming.

2. Increased mechanization would release surplus farm labor for employment in factories and mines, thus facilitating industrialization and bringing into existence the large urban working class looked to as the principal support for the Communist system.

3. Mechanization, improved methods of farming, and reclamation of new land under state supervision would result in greater over-all production.

4. Increased production, plus easier collection of surpluses from a greatly reduced number of farm units, would result in larger and more dependable food supplies for the growing urban populations.

5. Liquidation of individual peasant farming would remove the most important capitalist element still remaining in the USSR.

In general, the results of collectivization do not appear to have justified the original hopes of the Soviet planners, especially the hope of increased production. Much evidence points to the fact that the government has found it difficult to rouse enthusiasm for the system among the peasants. Modest increases in crop production have occurred, but the numbers of livestock have been slow to recover from the disastrous slaughter accompanying collectivization in the early 1930's, as well as widespread losses in the war zones during World War II. Even in 1953 the over-all numbers of livestock had not regained the level of 1928.

• *Industrial Emphases under the Five-Year Plans.* The most important objective of the First Five-Year Plan was a large increase in industrial production, with emphasis on the production of heavy machinery and other capital goods, increased exploitation of minerals, and improvement of the existing transportation facilities. On the whole, this phase of Soviet planning has experienced far more success than the planned expansion of agriculture. Since 1928, and especially since 1945, the Soviet Union, which had been largely an agricultural country prior to World War I, has industrialized at an exceedingly rapid rate. Masses of illiterate peasants have been converted into factory workers, great new industrial centers have been created and old ones enlarged, and over-all industrial production has greatly increased. Nevertheless, in the mid-1950's production of most lines of goods was still far below the production of the United States. Even in the case of steel, a commodity which has had a top priority in Soviet planning, the estimated Soviet production in 1953 was only about a third as great as American production. In light consumer items the gap is much wider. Such items as watches and clocks, radios, television sets, household appliances, and good ready-made clothing are in very short supply in the USSR. This deficiency is mainly the result of a deliberate governmental policy which has favored the production of heavy machinery and other capital equipment at the expense of highly finished consumer goods. It also reflects the relatively undeveloped state of advanced technology in the Soviet Union. All the available evidence in the early 1950's indicated that the country was still seriously lacking in the highly trained technical and managerial personnel and the plant facilities required to mass produce intricate consumer items in really large quantities.

Size, Boundaries, and Resources of the Soviet Homeland

We may now proceed to consider some of the pertinent physical and locational characteristics and the territorial evolution of this immense country of 210 million people which has witnessed such revolutionary developments since 1917, and whose future poses so much uncertainty for mankind.

▶ Size

The territorial base from which Soviet ambitions proceed is the largest country in area on the globe. It is, in fact, a country which ranks with the continents in size. With a total area of approximately 8.6 million square miles, Soviet Russia is larger than either the North American mainland or South America. It is more than twice as large as China, Canada, or Brazil, nearly three times as large as continental United States or Australia, 40 times as large as France, and 171 times as large as England. It is two thirds as large as the entire British Commonwealth. One out of every seven square miles of the earth's land surface is Soviet territory (one out of every six if the ice caps of Antarctica and Greenland are excluded).

Even more impressive, perhaps, than its area, is the tremendous east-west extent of the Soviet Union. The westernmost point of the country, near Kaliningrad (formerly Königsberg) on the Baltic Sea, is separated from Cape Dezhnev (East Cape) on Bering Strait by approximately 170° of longitude, representing a distance of nearly halfway around the world. In terms of sun time this means a difference of approximately 11 hours between the easternmost and westernmost points of the USSR. When it is 6:00 A.M. by sun time at Kaliningrad, it is already 9:00 A.M. in the Ural Mountains and is approaching 1:30 in the afternoon at

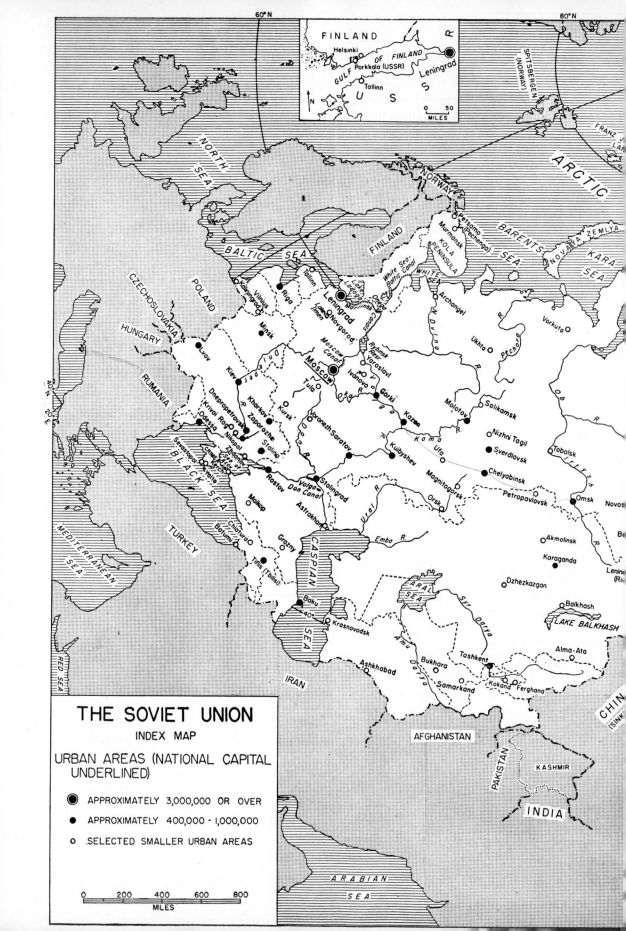

THE SOVIET UNION

INDEX MAP

URBAN AREAS (NATIONAL CAPITAL
UNDERLINED)

◉ APPROXIMATELY 3,000,000 OR OVER

● APPROXIMATELY 400,000 - 1,000,000

○ SELECTED SMALLER URBAN AREAS

0   200   400   600   800
MILES

95° E

170° W

80° N

60° N

170° W

Bering Strait

ARCTIC OCEAN

WRANGEL ISLAND

CAPE DEZHNEV (EAST CAPE)

BERING SEA

PACIFIC OCEAN

NEW SIBERIAN ISLANDS

EAST SIBERIAN SEA

LAPTEV SEA

SEVERNAYA ZEMLYA (NORTH LAND)

CAPE CHELYUSKIN

○ Ice Breaker
TAIMYR PENINSULA

Nordvik

KSON

Verkhoyansk ○

Olmekon ○

Kolyma R.

Magadan ○

Okhotsk ○

KAMCHATKA

Petropavlovsk ○

○ Norilsk

○ Igarka

Lena R.

Yakutsk ○

Aldan R.

Aldan ○

SEA OF OKHOTSK

Nikolaevsk ○

SAKHALIN

KURILE ISLANDS

Yeniseisk ○

Yenisei R.

Upper Tunguska (*Angara*) R.

LAKE BAIKAL

Shilka R.

Komsomolsk ○

Bureya R.

Amur R.

Khabarovsk ○

Ussuri R.

Sovetskaya Gavan (Soviet Haven) ○

JAPAN

Tomsk ○

○ Kemerovo

Krasnoyarsk ○

Cheremkhovo ○

Katun R.

Stalinsk ○

Tashtagol ○

Bey-Kem R.

Irkutsk ○

Ulan-Ude ○

Petrovsk ○

Onon R.

Argun R.

Chita ○

60° N

Voroshilov ○
Vladivostok ○

SEA OF JAPAN

JAPAN

TANNU TUVA

MONGOLIAN   PEOPLE'S   REPUBLIC

CHINA (MANCHURIA)

KOREA

CONSTITUENT UNION REPUBLICS

LITHUANIAN SSR (Vilnius)

LATVIAN SSR (Riga)

KARELO-FINNISH SSR (Petrozavodsk)

ESTONIAN SSR (Tallinn)

RUSSIAN SFSR

RUSSIAN SFSR

BELORUSSIAN (WHITE RUSSIAN) SSR (Minsk)

(Moscow) ◎

(Kiev) UKRAINIAN SSR

MOLDAVIAN SSR (Kishinev)

RUSSIAN SOVIET FEDERATED SOCIALIST REPUBLIC

GEORGIAN SSR (Tiflis [Tbilisi])

KAZAKH SSR

(Alma-Ata)

ARMENIAN SSR (Yerevan)

UZBEK SSR

AZERBAIJAN SSR (Baku)

TURKMEN SSR

KIRGHIZ SSR (Frunze)

(Ashkhabad)

(Tashkent)

TADZHIK SSR (Stalinabad)

CONSTITUENT UNION REPUBLICS

(POLITICAL CAPITALS ARE IN PARENTHESES)

95°

Vladivostok. At Cape Dezhnev it is shortly after 5:00 P.M. The time difference between Kaliningrad and Cape Dezhnev is more than twice the difference between New York and London (5 hours) and is nearly four times the difference between New York and San Francisco (3 hours).

[EDITORIAL COMMENT. The concepts of longitude and time are closely related. The meridians of longitude are imaginary straight lines connecting the poles. Every meridian runs due north and south. The meridians converge at the poles and are widest apart at the equator. Longitude is an angular measurement of distance east or west of a base meridian. The meridian which is customarily used as a base, or starting point, runs through the Royal Astronomical Observatory in Greenwich, England. It is known as the meridian of Greenwich, or prime meridian. Longitude, like latitude, is measured in degrees, minutes, and seconds. Every point on a given meridian has the same longitude. The prime meridian has a longitude of 0°. Places east of the prime meridan are in east longitude; places west of it are in west longitude. The meridian of 180°, exactly halfway around the world from the prime meridian, is the dividing line between places east and west of Greenwich. The longitude of Kaliningrad is correctly stated as 20°31′ East of Greenwich, or simply as 20°31′E. The longitude of Cape Dezhnev is 170°W. At the equator, 1° of longitude is equivalent to 69.15 statute miles. Since the circumference of the earth decreases toward the poles, however, a degree of longitude at 60°N., the latitude of Leningrad, is equivalent to only 34.6 miles.

The earth, rotating on its axis, turns completely around once every 24 hours. Thus it turns through 15° of longitude every hour (360° divided by 24) or 1° every four minutes. Since the earth turns toward the east, the day breaks and the sun comes into view on the Pacific side of the USSR while places farther west are still in darkness. It is noon at a place when the earth's turning has brought the meridian of that place directly under the sun, that is, when the sun has climbed highest above the horizon for that day. Noon occurs simultaneously at all points along a given meridian. When it is noon at Vladivostok by sun time, the earth must still turn for approximately 7½ hours before the meridian of Kaliningrad will come under the sun and it will be noon at that place. In other words, the apparent solar time (sun time) at Kaliningrad is about 4:30 A.M. when the time at Vladivostok is 12 noon.

Development of modern means of transportation has made it desirable to establish standard time zones so that the same time prevails over a considerable extent of longitude. Watches of travelers are set forward or back one hour when crossing the boundary of such a zone. The United States has four standard time zones (Eastern, Central, Mountain, Pacific). The Soviet Union has eleven such zones.]

The east-west length of the Soviet Union is much greater than its north-south width, but even the latter is impressive. The maximum latitudinal extent, exclusive of islands in the Arctic Ocean, is about 42°, which is short by only 5° of the combined extent of the United States and the Canadian mainland. Cape Chelyuskin (77°41′N.) in the Soviet Arctic is about 6° farther north than any point on the mainland of Canada, while the town of Kushka (35°38′N.) in Soviet Middle Asia is in the general latitude of Memphis, Tennessee, and Oklahoma City, Oklahoma, and is only 1° farther north than Los Angeles, California.

▶ **Sea Frontiers**

The land and water boundaries of the USSR have a total length of about 37,500 miles.[5] More than two thirds of this dis-

---

[5] N. T. Mirov, *Geography of Russia*. New York: Wiley; London: Chapman and Hall, 1951. P. 3.

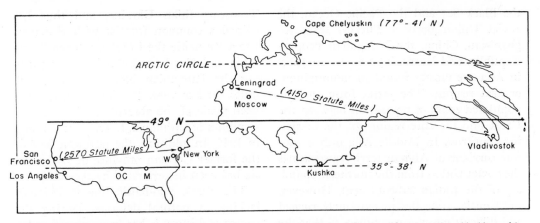

The Soviet Union compared in latitude and area with the United States. Key to cities: M, Memphis; OC, Oklahoma City; W, Washington, D. C.

tance is coastline, giving the Soviet Union a longer sea frontage than any other country. To only a limited degree, however, does the USSR have unrestricted access to the world ocean. Despite its great length of coast, it is essentially a landlocked country. Most of the main ports are located on enclosed or semi-enclosed seas having entrances controlled by another country. The entrances to the Baltic and Black Seas are controlled by Denmark and Turkey, respectively, and the entrances to the semi-enclosed Sea of Japan can be controlled or threatened by Japan. Acquisition of the Kurile Islands from Japan has given unrestricted access to the Sea of Okhotsk, but that body of water borders remote and sparsely populated regions, is frozen for a considerable period in winter, and is used relatively little by shipping.

Most of the Arctic Ocean ports are small, and except in the extreme west are completely icebound for more than half of the year. Nearly all of the major Soviet ports are hampered to some degree by winter freezing, although most ports on the Black Sea, Baltic Sea, and Sea of Japan can be kept open all winter by the use of icebreakers. However, Leningrad, the foremost seaport of the USSR, is frozen in for a few weeks in midwinter. Only in the far northwest does a stretch of ice-free coast

bordering the Barents Sea give unrestricted access to the open ocean. A tongue of water from the North Atlantic Drift warms this coast in winter and prevents the formation of ice in the harbor of Murmansk, the principal port. The latter city is connected with Leningrad and Moscow by rail. However, its value as a port is lessened by remoteness from the main centers of population and industry in the USSR. Murmansk is located on a narrow gulf resembling a Norwegian fjord. Other fjordlike indentations to the west offer protected anchorages for shipping. However, the shores of these inlets are lower and not so steep as the shores of true fjords. The indented Murman coast is exceptional among Soviet coastlines, which are ordinarily rather low and regular, often marshy, and generally lacking in good natural harbors.

Thus the apparent advantages of a long sea frontier to the USSR are largely nullified by the nature of the bordering waters and the coasts.

▶ Land Frontiers

The Soviet Union has a common land frontier with no less than twelve other countries in Europe and Asia. No other nation of the world borders so many different countries.

Along the 8000-mile boundary between

the Black Sea and the Pacific Ocean, the Soviet Union borders Turkey, Iran, Afghanistan, China, the Mongolian People's Republic, and Korea. The Soviet frontiers in Asia are mostly found in mountainous or arid regions. The latter form sparsely populated zones of separation between the USSR and the core regions of the bordering countries. In Middle Asia only a narrow corridor of Afghan territory separates the Soviet Union from the northern boundary of the Indian subcontinent. However, the frontier zone lies in extremely rugged and difficult mountain country, so that the narrow political separation as seen on a map does not express the true reality of military and economic separation. In the Far East the Soviet island of Sakhalin is separated by a 25-mile-wide strait from the northernmost main island of Japan, and even narrower straits separate Japan from the Russian-held Kurile Islands. If India, Pakistan, and Japan are included, the Soviet Union in Asia is a near neighbor of about half the human race.

The Soviet frontiers on the west are very different from the frontiers in Asia. This is especially true of the 900-mile-long boundary zone between the Black Sea and the Baltic Sea. Here the USSR abuts on Rumania, Hungary, Czechoslovakia, and Poland. The boundary line passes mostly through well-populated lowlands that have long been disputed territory between the Russian state and its western neighbors. The fluctuating boundaries in this area have contrasted with Soviet boundaries in Asia, which have changed relatively little during the twentieth century. Since 1939 the USSR has made important gains of territory along the Black Sea–Baltic frontier. The boundary has been pushed westward 100 to 200 miles in Poland, although not so far west as the boundary of Russian-held territory in Poland prior to World War I. From Czechoslovakia the Soviet Union has acquired a section of the Carpathian Mountains known as Ruthenia or Transcarpathian Ukraine, and thus has gained a common frontier with Hungary. From Rumania the USSR has taken Bessarabia and Northern Bukovina, thus pushing the Rumanian boundary 50 to 125 miles farther west. Previous mention has been made of the absorption of the Baltic republics of Lithuania, Latvia, and Estonia in 1940. In addition, the northern half of the former German province of East Prussia has been incorporated by the USSR.

The Black Sea–Baltic line is seriously lacking in natural defenses. During the course of history it has been crossed many times by invading armies, including the French under Napoleon in 1812 and more recently the German armies in 1941. The recent frontier changes have shortened the boundary and have given the Soviet Union additional defense in depth. Other strategic advantages which have accrued to the USSR are (1) a better frontage on the Gulf of Finland and a new frontage on the Baltic Sea proper, (2) possession of a number of strategic junction points on major rail lines leading westward, including the important rail hub of Lvov (400,000), acquired from Poland, (3) control over important passes leading to the plains of Hungary through former Czechoslovak territory in the low central Carpathians, and (4) a frontage on the northernmost of the three main distributaries of the Danube River.

The USSR has also made important strategic gains along the 900-mile frontier between the Gulf of Finland and the Barents Sea. Rectification of the boundary with Finland has given the Soviet Union possession of the Karelian Isthmus between Lake Ladoga and the Gulf of Finland. By this means the defensibility of the important city of Leningrad has been increased. Prior to 1940 the city lay only about 12 or 15 miles from the nearest points on the Finnish border. Conversely, Soviet acquisition of the Karelian Isthmus and establishment of a Soviet military base on the Porkkala Peninsula, leased from Finland, have lessened the ability of the Finns to defend themselves against a military move by the USSR. A further cession of Finnish territory to the USSR in the far north has given the latter nation a common frontier with Norway and important nickel mines and smelting facilities in the Pechenga (Petsamo) district.[6]

► Natural Resources

Soviet economic and military strength rests in considerable measure on an outstanding collection of natural resources. Within the vast confines of the USSR, nature has assembled a rich and varied complement of minerals and water resources, together with enormous areas of forest and grazing land, some of the world's most fertile soils, and sizable resources of fur, fish, and game. Although much of the country *is* handicapped by excessive cold, low rainfall, poor drainage, acid soils, or rugged terrain, the over-all resource base of the Soviet Union is undoubtedly superior to that possessed by any other nation with the exception of the United States. Space will not permit a detailed comparison of Soviet and American resources, and the available data on Soviet resources are not sufficient for such a comparison to be made with any great accuracy. In general, the mineral, water, grassland, and faunal resources of the USSR seem comparable in size and quality to the corresponding American resources; Soviet forest resources, while larger in volume of timber, lack the great variety of American forests (for example, the USSR has no forest area comparable to the giant Douglas fir or redwood forests of our Pacific Coast); and the agricultural soils of the USSR, while larger in total area and broadly comparable in over-all natural fertility, are inferior to American soils in general productivity, partly because of the more favorable American climate.

• The Superior Mineral Position of the USSR.[7]

The resource position of the Soviet Union is particularly strong with regard to minerals. The USSR is well supplied for the foreseeable future with deposits of coal, lignite, and petroleum among the mineral fuels; iron, magnesium, titanium, antimony, platinum, and the ferroalloys manganese, vanadium, and chromium among the metals; phosphate, potash, common salt, and sulfur among the major chemical raw materials; and asbestos, bromine, graphite, mica, fluorspar, china clay, fire clay, and mercury among other minerals. Somewhat less adequate are Soviet reserves of the basic nonferrous metals copper and aluminum and the important ferroalloy nickel. The Soviet electrical, aircraft, and armaments industries have been handicapped by periodic shortages in the production of these latter metals during recent years. Nevertheless, the USSR is known to have sizable reserves and is an important world producer of all three metals. The domestic reserves of aluminum are supplemented by the import of high-grade bauxite from satellite Hungary. Definite deficiencies exist in the case of lead, zinc, and tin among the basic nonferrous metals; cobalt, molybdenum, and tungsten among the ferroalloys; and natural gas and probably uranium among the power minerals. However, the USSR has small to medium-sized deposits of even these minerals, and the deficiencies can be at least partly overcome by imports from other nations of the Communist bloc: tungsten, molybdenum, zinc, and lead from North Korea; tungsten, tin, zinc, and lead from China; zinc and lead from Poland; and uranium from East Germany and Czechoslovakia.

---

[6] The foregoing discussion of Soviet frontier changes is mainly based on W. Gordon East, "The New Frontiers of the Soviet Union." *Foreign Affairs,* v. 29 (1951), pp. 591–607.

[7] The discussion under this heading is principally based on Demitri B. Shimkin, *Minerals: A Key to Soviet Power.* Cambridge, Mass.: Harvard University Press, 1953. *Passim.*

The USSR is known to be a major producer of gold, but data on Soviet gold reserves are very meager. No reserves of diamonds are known to exist.

The coal and lignite reserves of the Soviet Union are exceedingly widespread, but the known reserves of most other minerals are concentrated in a relatively few areas. The outstanding mineralized areas, together with the minerals for which each area is particularly noteworthy, are as follows:

1. The Ukraine (coal, iron, manganese, common salt).
2. The Ural Mountains (iron, ferroalloys, copper, aluminum, titanium, asbestos, petroleum).
3. The Caucasus-Caspian region (petroleum, manganese, lead, zinc).
4. The Kazakh Upland of Soviet Middle Asia (coal, copper).
5. The Altai Mountains (lead, zinc).
6. The Kuznets Basin of south central Siberia (coal).
7. The Kola Peninsula, adjoining Finland and Norway (phosphate, nickel, copper, iron).

On the whole, the mineral position of the USSR appears extremely strong, and seems likely to be improved by future discoveries of minerals in the varied geological formations with which the country is endowed. Large sections, especially in Soviet Asia, have been imperfectly prospected, if at all.

Development of minerals has ranked high on the list of priorities in Soviet planning. Since the middle 1920's the output of minerals has increased at a spectacular rate. The total value of minerals produced was probably 8 or 9 times as great in 1950 as in 1926. Even this increase, however, has not been sufficient to meet the demands of expanding industry. In 1926 the USSR was a net exporter of minerals; in 1950 it had become a net importer. During World War II the mineral situation became desperate when the important mineral-producing areas of the Ukraine, Central Russia, and the North Caucasus were overrun by Germany. This problem was met by large-scale imports from other Allied nations, plus expansion of mining in the Urals and Soviet Asia. Primarily as a result of the war, the center of gravity in the mining industry has definitely shifted toward the east. This development is in line with a pronounced eastward shift in the centers of population and manufacturing. In 1950 nearly half of the total estimated production of minerals by value came from the regions east of the Volga River and Caspian Sea, as compared with less than a fifth in 1926.

In spite of the tremendous increases since 1926, the USSR still ranks well below the United States as a producer of minerals. The estimated Soviet output of minerals in 1950 was only a fourth as great as the estimated value of American production.

The Severe Climate of the USSR

Despite its immense area and resources, large and growing population, and increasing industrial production, the Soviet Union suffers from a number of important disadvantages which considerably lessen its effectiveness as a political, economic, and military power. Among these might be mentioned (1) the difficulty of providing adequate transportation and communication facilities in a country of such vast distances and containing so much marshy, arid, densely forested, and mountainous terrain, (2) the additional burden on transportation and the problems of defense caused by the peripheral location of many important centers of population, mining, agriculture, and industry, and (3) the technological difficulties due to the late start of the USSR as an industrial nation. Not the least among Soviet disadvantages is (4) the severe climate.

▶ General Nature of the Climate

Most parts of the Soviet Union have a continental climate characterized by long, extremely cold winters, warm to hot summers, and low to moderate precipitation. The temperature averages 32°F. or below for 1 month in the year at Tashkent in Soviet Middle Asia, 3 months at Odessa on the Black Sea and Astrakhan on the lower Volga, 4 months at Kiev on the middle Dnieper River, 5 months at Moscow and Leningrad, 6 months at Archangel on the White Sea and Novosibirsk on the upper Ob River in south central Siberia, 7 months at Yakutsk on the middle Lena River in eastern Siberia, 8 months at Nordvik on the Arctic coast west of the Lena delta, and 10 months at Ice Breaker on the Taimyr Peninsula. There is an abrupt transition between winter and summer.

Winter is scarcely over before April. The rivers are set free in an impressive breakup of the ice, which is generally accompanied by terrible floods. The snow melts, and highways, which shortly before were streets of towns like Tomsk, are turned into indescribably evil-smelling sloughs and streams of brown mud. . . . Then comes a spring which would be delightful but for the too frequent returns of cold weather and which is anyhow extremely short. Summer follows abruptly, is very pronounced, generally as hot as in France, and sometimes scorching; but on the whole is not very pleasant owing to its whirling clouds of dust, its thunder- and hailstorms, and its myriads of mosquitoes. . . . However, the season does not last long. By August the north and east may have night frosts and slight falls of snow, and the trees begin to shed their leaves. These are the first signs of an autumn

which is as short as the spring. At the end of September bits of ice begin to drift down some of the rivers, and a few weeks later winter is back again, frigid and silent.[8]

The severe winters of the USSR are the result of a northerly continental location, coupled with mountain barriers on the south and east. Four fifths of the total area is farther north than any point in the United States. The Soviet Union lies principally in the higher middle latitudes of the Northern Hemisphere where the land masses of the world reach their greatest extent relative to the bordering oceans. In these latitudes the climatic influence of the land is paramount over the influence of the sea in continental interiors, and the most extreme continental climates of the world prevail. The effects of continental location are heightened in the Soviet Union by the presence of the Arctic Ocean on the north, which is frozen for most of the year and thus in a sense forms an extension of the land. Continuous chains of mountains and high plateaus occupying the southern and eastern margins of the country act as a screen against moderating influences from the Indian and Pacific Oceans. In addition, most of the USSR is a zone of high atmospheric pressure in winter, with resultant outflowing winds. Westerly winds from the Atlantic serve to moderate the winter temperatures somewhat, but their effects become steadily weaker toward the east. Thus Leningrad (60°N., 30°E.) has an average January temperature of 18°F., whereas Yakutsk (62°N., 130°E.) has a January average of −46° and Verkhoyansk (68°N., 133°E.) a January average of −58°. The region of Verkhoyansk in *Oimekon* northeastern Siberia is often referred to as *−110°* the "cold pole" of the earth. Lower temperatures have been recorded here than anywhere else on the earth's surface, including the polar regions. Verkhoyansk has

[8] Georges Jorré, *The Soviet Union.* New York, London, and Toronto: Longmans, Green and Co., 1950. P. 21. Used by permission of the publisher.

experienced an official temperature reading of −94°F., the lowest official surface temperature ever reported.

Aside from the vicinity of the "cold pole," most parts of the USSR experience winter temperatures which do not differ greatly from the temperatures of places located at comparable latitudes and altitudes in the interior of North America. Indeed, many places in the west and south of the Soviet Union are actually warmer in midwinter than comparable interior places in North America. Kiev (50°N.) is 24° warmer in January on the average than Winnipeg, Odessa (46°N.) is 12° warmer than Montreal, and Tashkent (41°N.) is 8° warmer than Omaha. Moscow has the same average temperature in January as Minneapolis, although located 11° farther north. Leningrad, located a thousand miles north of Minneapolis, is 4° warmer in January than the latter city.

Nevertheless, the Soviet Union as a whole is definitely handicapped by the winter climate. Huge areas are permanently frozen at a depth of a few feet. The average frost-free season of 150 days or less in most parts of the country except the extreme south and west is too short for a wide range of crops to mature.

Most places are relatively warm during the brief summer, and the southern steppes and deserts are hot. Even the "cold pole" has July temperatures averaging in the high fifties or low sixties. A factor partially offsetting the brevity of the summer is the length of summer days. Leningrad has 19 hours of daylight on June 22, and Moscow has 17½ hours. Throughout the summer long hours of sunlight facilitate the growth of plants and thus compensate somewhat for the shortness of the growing season.

From an agricultural standpoint, lack of moisture is probably an even greater handicap to the Soviet Union than low temperatures. The annual precipitation is less than 20 inches nearly everywhere except in the extreme west, along the eastern coast of the Black Sea and the Pacific littoral north of Vladivostok, and in some of the higher mountain areas. North of the Arctic Circle and in the southern desert zone, the average precipitation is less than 10 inches. Since most of the precipitation is derived from the Atlantic Ocean, the total amount decreases with some regularity from west to east. The average is 19 to 25 inches at Moscow, Riga, Leningrad, and Kiev, 15 to 17 inches at Kazan and Sverdlovsk, 12 inches at Omsk and Krasnoyarsk, and 5 to 7 inches at Verkhoyansk and Yakutsk. Precipitation also decreases toward the south, being 10 to 20 inches in the fertile black-earth belt, and 5 to 10 inches or even less in the dry steppes and deserts bordering the black-earth belt on the south. The general pattern of precipitation is described in the following selection: [9]

The precipitation in the northern part of the country, accompanied by the low temperature and the consequent slight evaporation, is normally sufficient for the crops that are grown there. In fact, that region, with its abundant marshy lands and numerous lakes, suffers more often from an excess than from a deficiency of moisture. The reverse, however, is true in the south and east, where light rainfall is accompanied by high summer temperature and moisture is the limiting factor in crop production.

Not only is the annual precipitation light in most of the southern and eastern agricultural regions of the Soviet Union, but it is irregular from year to year and its seasonal distribution is often unfavorable to the growth of crops, particularly of the early spring cereals such as wheat. The maximum rainfall occurs in the summer months everywhere in the Soviet Union except in the southernmost regions (Crimea, Central Asia, and Transcaucasia), where it occurs in the winter and late autumn. In the north, August is the rainiest month; in the central regions, July; and in the south,

---

[9] Volin, *op. cit.*, pp. 7–9. One word has been italicized in editing.

June. The July and August rains, however, are too late to be utilized by the small grains and sometimes even cause damage by interfering with the harvest. Though the June rains in the south and southeast are more beneficial, they often come in the form of heavy showers that tend to run off the surface of the soil without increasing its moisture supply and, what is even more serious, often are so delayed that a more or less prolonged dry spell is likely to occur in May and June. These months are the critical period in the growth of the crops, for it is then that the moisture in the soil, accumulated during the autumn and winter months, is quickly depleted both by the growing plants and by the increased evaporation that accompanies the quickly rising temperatures. . . .

When, as often happens in the southeast, a dry spring is preceded by a dry autumn and a winter with little or no snow, the situation becomes even more serious, for the winter crops are adversely affected and the supply of soil moisture in the spring is diminished. If, in addition, the scorching dry winds, the so-called *sukhovei,* which play havoc with the crops, also begin their destructive work, then the stage is all set for one of those catastrophic droughts that often mean famine conditions for the peasants, the destruction of their livestock, . . . and a general deterioration and retrogression in the Russian countryside. . . .

It can be generalized therefore that the crucial disadvantage of the continental Russian climate is the reverse relation between the territorial distribution of heat and moisture, both of which are essential for plant life. As the amount of heat increases, from north to south and west to east, moisture tends to diminish and the maximum of heat is accompanied by a minimum of moisture.

▶ Types of Climate

In the USSR five main east-west climatic belts—tundra, subarctic, humid continen-

tal, steppe, and desert—are customarily recognized in classifications of climate. These belts, each with its associated vegetation and soils, succeed each other from north to south in the order named.

• *Tundra Climate.* The zone of *tundra climate* occupies a continuous strip, 50 to several hundred miles in width, along the Arctic coast from the Norwegian frontier to Bering Strait. Tundra is both a climatic and a vegetational term. Climatically, it signifies a region which has at least 1 month averaging above 32°F. but which has no month averaging 50° or higher. In most areas of tundra 2 to 4 months average above freezing. Generally speaking, the climatic conditions of the tundra are too severe for trees to grow, except in occasional protected localities and toward the southern margins, where trees are found along the streams. The typical vegetation of this treeless region consists of mosses, lichens, sedges, and scrubby brushes.

The tundra consists largely of desolate, wind-swept wastes with many sedge bogs (especially in western Siberia) and numerous lakes, all of which turn into solid ice most of the year. It is a frozen land the soil of which never thaws save on the surface, when, for a brief period in summer during which daylight is almost continuous, innumerable large, brightly-colored flowers lighten the dull grey of the mosses and lichens. The short summers are damp and cold. The dark, icy arctic winter grips the land for 8 to 9 months, and in June ice still lies under the mossy clumps. Snow lies all the year round in the deeper hollows of the tundra and forms ribs along the sides of low hills during the summer.[10]

Some of the islands in the Arctic Ocean, including northern Novaya Zemlya, have temperatures averaging below freezing or

[10] M. Y. Nuttonson, *Agricultural Climatology of Siberia, Natural Belts, and Agro-Climatic Analogues in North America.* Washington, D. C.: American Institute of Crop Ecology, 1950. Pp. 11–12. Used by permission of the American Institute of Crop Ecology. The description applies particularly to the Si-

berian tundra. It applies only partially to the strip of tundra along the Murman coast, where permafrost (permanently frozen subsoil) is almost entirely lacking and the climate is in general less rigorous than in the areas of tundra which lie east of the White Sea.

A lumbering operation in the taiga. The photo was taken in the Karelo-Finnish Soviet Socialist Republic, which adjoins Finland. (*Sovfoto.*)

only slightly above freezing even during the warmest month of the year. Here the land is covered with glaciers and an ice-cap climate similar to that of interior Greenland or Antarctica prevails.

• *Subarctic Climate.* At the south the tundra climate gradually merges with the zone of *subarctic climate.* In this climate zone from 1 to 4 months average above 50°F. Thus the subarctic climate differs from the tundra climate in having a warmer summer. Winters, however, are extremely long and cold, most places averaging below freezing

for 5 to 7 months. The "cold pole" of northeastern Siberia lies within the subarctic climate zone. This climate type occupies a wedge-shaped area extending the full length of the USSR from the Finnish border to the Pacific Ocean. It is narrowest at the west, and broadens eastward to the neighborhood of Lake Baikal, where it occupies the full width of the country except for a narrow strip of tundra at the north.

The zone of subarctic climate is essentially coextensive with the *taiga,* or northern coniferous forest. The taiga of the Soviet Union is the largest continuous area of forest land on earth. A similar belt of forest covers much of Canada. The prevailing tree species are spruce, fir, larch, and pine. These coniferous softwood trees, while excellent for pulpwood and firewood, are frequently too small, twisted, or knotty to make good lumber. Nevertheless, vast reserves of timber suitable for lumber exist in parts of the taiga, and this part of the Soviet Union is one of the major areas of lumbering in the world. Intermixed with the conifers of the taiga are stands of certain broad-leaved species such as birch and aspen. These deciduous trees are of little commercial utility. They are ordinarily second growth, replacing stands of conifers removed by fires or cutting.

Some agricultural settlement occurs in the taiga, especially toward the south. However, the farming is definitely of a marginal character. Agriculture in this forested region is handicapped by the short summers, the occasional summer frosts, the marshy or swampy character of much of the land, and the prevalence of poor soils. The dominant soils of the taiga are the *podzols*. This term, derived from Russian words translated as "ashes underneath," refers to a group of soils which characteristically have a grayish, bleached appearance when plowed, are lacking in organic matter (humus), and are very low in natural fertility. The acidity of these soils is unfavorable for most crops and also for bacteria, earthworms, and other soil-improving organisms.

The boundary between the taiga and the tundra is not a sharp line, although it appears so when generalized on small-scale maps. A transitional area of "wooded tundra" (small forest stands alternating with tundra) marks the contact between the tundra and taiga in most places.

• *Humid Continental Climate.* South of the subarctic zone a triangular area of *humid continental climate* extends eastward from the western border of the USSR to the vicinity of Novosibirsk. At the west the triangle is more than 600 miles wide, but the Siberian portion averages only 100 to 200 miles in width. Roughly half the total population of the USSR is found within this climate zone. The humid continental climate of the USSR differs from the subarctic climate in having longer summers, milder winters, and more precipitation. However, these are only differences of degree. Even within the humid continental zone most places have an average frost-free period of 150 days or less, except at the extreme west (Leningrad, 160 days; Kiev, 172 days). Winters are long and cold, with average cold-month temperatures ranging from −3°F. (Novosibirsk) to 24°F. (Riga). The absolute minimum of record is −35° at Leningrad, −44° at Moscow, and −54° at Novosibirsk. The average annual precipitation is relatively low, being only 18 to 25 inches at most places. However, the low rate of evaporation increases the effectiveness of the precipitation, so that the available moisture is generally adequate for the staple crops of this climate zone. The Soviet Union has the short-summer subtype of humid continental climate. A comparable climate is found in the Great Lakes region and the northern Great Plains of the United States and Canada. In this climate zone of the USSR mixed or deciduous forest supplants the evergreen taiga forest. Oak, ash, maple, elm, and other deciduous species alternate with coniferous trees in the vegetation cover. At the south is found the "wooded steppe," a transitional zone between the deciduous forest and the open steppe grassland.

Both climate and soil are more favorable for agriculture in the area of humid continental climate than in the subarctic zone. Soils developed under a cover of deciduous or mixed forest are normally more fertile by nature than the podzol soils of the taiga, although less fertile than grassland soils. The forest soils in the area of humid continental climate are of major importance in Soviet agriculture, supporting a varied development of crop and livestock farming. Among the climatic regions of the USSR, only the steppe region vies with the humid continental area in over-all farm production.

• *Steppe Climate.* The grassy plains of Russia south of the forest zone are known as the *steppe,* or steppes. This term refers both to a type of climate and to the characteristic form of vegetation associated with it. On climatic maps the zone of steppe climate in the USSR is shown as an east-west band of varying width extending from the Rumanian border to the Altai Mountains in Soviet Asia. As compared with the humid continental short-summer type of climate, the steppe climate is characterized by warmer summers, a somewhat longer frost-free season, and less precipitation. The average annual precipitation is 10 to 20 inches, an amount barely sufficient for field agriculture without irrigation. Recurring periods of drought add to the hazards of farming in the steppe zone. Nevertheless, this part of the Soviet Union is a major area of crop and livestock production. The handicap of low and variable rainfall is partially offset by the fertility of the soils in the famous *black-earth belt.* This expanse of deep, black, exceedingly fertile soils extends for about 3000 miles in an east-west direction and 300 to 600 miles from north to south. It contains an estimated two thirds to three fourths of the land in the Soviet Union which is suitable for cultivation. The characteristic soils of the black-earth belt are the *chernozems*— a term meaning "black earth" in Russian. Chernozem soils are exceptionally thick, productive, and durable, being in fact among the best soils to be found anywhere. A similar belt of soils occurs in the eastern Great Plains of North America. The great fertility of the chernozems is largely due **to** an abundance of organic matter or *humus* in the topsoil and to the presence of sufficient lime to neutralize excessive acidity. Both characteristics are associated with the fact that these soils have developed under a cover of steppe grasses rather than forest. The accumulated remains of grasses in a steppe climate provide a more satisfactory supply of humus than the leaves and twigs of a forest. Strictly speaking, the term humus refers to organic remains, both plant and animal, which have decayed and become mixed with the soil. Humus is rich in the nutrient materials needed by growing plants, and in addition helps to make still other nutrients available from the mineral constituents of the soil. In all soils some of the plant nutrients in the topsoil are constantly being removed and carried to a lower level by the action of water percolating downward through the soil. This process, known as *leaching,* proceeds more rapidly in the moist, cool climate of the humid continental and subarctic zones than in the warmer, drier climate of the steppe. Not only does the greater abundance of moisture in the former areas result in faster removal of plant nutrients, but the process is facilitated by the solvent action of weak acids formed during the slow decay and fermentation of organic remains in the upper layers of the soil. In steppe soils the organic matter decays faster and has less tendency to ferment and produce acid solutions. In addition, acidity is constantly being neutralized by lime, which is much more plentiful in these grassland soils than in soils developed under a vegetation cover of forest. The steppe zone includes extensive areas of *chestnut soils* in the areas of lighter rainfall south of the chernozems. The chestnut soils are lighter in color than the chernozems and lack the superb fertility of the latter soils. Nevertheless, the chestnut soils are among the better soils of the world. In North America a belt of chestnut soils occurs to the west of the chernozems in the Great Plains.

Within the zone of steppe climate a considerable range of natural vegetation types is found, varying from tall grass and scattered forest stands in the "wooded steppe," where moisture is more abundant, to a sparse cover of low grasses and shrubs in the drier areas. The most characteristic form of natural vegetation is short grass, forming a carpet which is continuous, or nearly so. The treeless steppe grasslands, stretching monotonously over a vast area between the forest zone and the southern mountains and deserts, were tenanted from an early time by tribes of pastoral nomads with their flocks and herds. Today, however, much of the steppe is cultivated, with wheat as the main crop.

Some confusion is occasioned by the fact that the wooded steppe and a portion of the black-earth belt extend into the zone of humid continental climate as customarily defined on climatic maps. However, the treeless part of the steppe is largely outside of the humid continental zone, as is the larger part of the black-earth belt.

• **Desert Climate.** To the east and immediate north of the Caspian Sea, the steppe zone trends gradually into an extensive area of desert. In the desert zone rainfall is even more scanty and erratic than in the steppe. Widely spaced shrubs and occasional tufts of grass afford only the sparsest pasturage for livestock. Agriculture is precluded by lack of moisture, except for scattered oases watered by wells or springs, or by streams originating in the high mountains which border this desert region on the south. The desert zone of the Soviet Union includes two extensive areas of sandy desert. Such deserts, with their monotony of dunes and wind-rippled sand, are a type made familiar by the motion pictures, but are much less common on a world basis than deserts floored by gravel, rock fragments, or the bare bedrock.

• *Subtropical, Monsoon, and Highland Climates.* A number of relatively small but distinctive climatic areas remain to be mentioned. The south coast of the Crimean Peninsula, sheltered by the Yaila Mountains, has the mild temperatures and summer rainfall minimum associated with the *mediterranean* or *dry-summer subtropical* climate. This picturesque area, with its orchards, vineyards, and resorts, of which Yalta (40,000) is the most famous, is sometimes referred to as the "Russian Riviera." A subtropical climate also prevails in the coastal lowlands and valleys south of the high Caucasus Mountains. Mild winters and warm to hot summers are characteristic throughout the lowlands of Transcaucasia. However, the rainfall is very unevenly distributed. The lowlands bordering the Black Sea in western Transcaucasia receive the heaviest rainfall of the USSR (50 to 100 inches) and are classed as *humid subtropical* in climate, while the lowlands of eastern Transcaucasia, bordering the Caspian Sea, receive so little precipitation in most places as to be classed as steppe.

The coastal regions of the Soviet Far East, from Vladivostok northward to the mouth of the Amur River, have a humid continental climate characterized by a distinct *monsoon* tendency. As in near-by parts of Korea, China, and Japan, most of the annual rainfall results from moist onshore winds of the summer monsoon. In contrast, the dry outflowing winds of the winter monsoon produce little precipitation. The average annual precipitation is 20 to 30 inches, of which three fourths or more falls from April through September.

The mountains of the USSR are characterized by climates varying according to altitude. However, the range of the climates involved is smaller than in mountains located closer to the equator.

Climatic data for selected Soviet stations are given in Table 11.

TABLE 11

CLIMATIC DATA FOR SELECTED SOVIET STATIONS

STATION	LATITUDE AND LONGITUDE TO NEAREST WHOLE DEGREE	ELEVA-TION ABOVE SEA LEVEL (FEET)	TYPE OF CLIMATE	AVERAGE TEMPERATURE (DEGREES F. TO NEAREST WHOLE DEGREE)			AVERAGE LENGTH OF FROST-FREE SEASON (DAYS)	AVERAGE ANNUAL PRECIPI-TATION TO NEAREST INCH
				AN-NUAL	JANU-ARY	JULY		
Archangel	65°N., 87°E.	50	Subarctic	32°	8°	59°	120	17″
Igarka	67°N., 87°E.	115	Subarctic	17°	−20°	59°	No Data	16″
Nordvik	74°N., 111°E.	102	Tundra	7°	−21°	41°	No Data	5″
Verkhoyansk	68°N., 133°E.	400	Subarctic	3°	−58°	60°	65	5″
Leningrad	60°N., 30°E.	30	Humid Continental	39°	18°	63°	160	19″
Moscow	56°N., 38°E.	480	Humid Continental	40°	14°	66°	130	21″
Sverdlovsk	57°N., 61°E.	925	Humid Continental	33°	3°	63°	No Data	17″
Novosibirsk	55°N., 83°E.	436	Humid Continental	31°	−3°	66°	122	15″
Irkutsk	52°N., 104°E.	1532	Subarctic	30°	−6°	63°	95	15″
Vladivostok	43°N., 132°E.	95	Humid Continental	40°	7°	69° (August)	152	24″
Odessa	46°N., 31°E.	210	Steppe	50°	26°	73°	208	16″
Yalta	45°N., 34°E.	135	Mediterranean	56°	39°	75°	245	20″
Batumi	42°N., 42°E.	20	Humid Subtropical	58°	43°	73°	308	93″
Baku	40°N., 50°E.	0	Steppe	57°	38°	77°	296	10″
Akmolinsk	51°N., 71°E.	1148	Steppe	35°	0°	70°	No Data	11″
Tashkent	41°N., 69°E.	1568	Steppe	56°	30°	80°	206	15″
Krasnovodsk	40°N., 53°E.	−56	Desert	61°	37°	84°	No Data	5″

Territorial Evolution of Modern Russia

Territorial and economic expansion, so much in evidence during recent decades, is not a new theme in Russian history. The gigantic Russian state has reached its present limits through a long process of colonization, conquest, territorial annexation, and associated economic development extending back for more than a thousand years.

The modern phase of this process began toward the end of the European Middle Ages. In the second half of the fifteenth century Ivan III, the ruler of Muscovy, a small feudal state with its capital at Moscow, began to expand his holdings rapidly by military conquest or the threat of conquest. To the north the rival principality of Novgorod was annexed and a domain

thus secured which extended to the Arctic Ocean and eastward to the Ural Mountains. Ivan IV, the Terrible or Dread, added large new territories by conquering the Tatar (Tartar) principalities of Kazan and Astrakhan in 1552 and 1554, respectively, thus giving the Russian state control over the entire course of the Volga River. Upon ascending the throne in 1547 Ivan was crowned as tsar (czar or Caesar), being the first Russian ruler to assume this title. Later tsars pushed the frontiers of Russia westward toward Poland and the Baltic Sea and southward toward the Black Sea. Peter the Great (reigned 1689–1725) gained a secure foothold on the Baltic Sea by defeating the Swedes under Charles XII, and Catherine the Great (reigned 1762–1796)

ostrogs - block houses

secured a frontage on the Black Sea at the expense of Turkey.

Meanwhile the conquest of Siberia had proceeded rapidly. This vast, thinly populated wilderness between the Urals and the Pacific Ocean was already being penetrated by traders and Cossack military pioneers at the end of Ivan the Dread's reign. In 1639 a Cossack expedition reached the Pacific. Russian expansion toward the east did not stop at Bering Strait, but continued down the west coast of North America as far as northern California, where a Russian trading post existed between 1812 and 1841. In 1867, however, Alaska was sold to the United States and Russia withdrew from North America.

▶ Role of the Rivers in Russian Expansion

Early Russian expansion in Eurasia followed the river lines. The Moscow region lies in a low upland from which a number of large rivers radiate like spokes of a wheel. The longest rivers lead southward: the Volga to the land-locked Caspian Sea, the Dnieper to the Black Sea, and the Don to the Sea of Azov, which is connected with the Black Sea through a narrow strait. Shorter rivers lead north and northwest to the Arctic Ocean and the Baltic Sea. These river systems are accessible to each other by easy portages. In the early history of Russia the rivers formed natural passageways for trade, conquest, and colonization. The technique of expansion followed by the tsars was to dominate the river lines by *ostrogs* (blockhouses) built at portages and other strategic places. From these strong points political control could gradually be extended over the hinterland.

▶ Expansion in Siberia

The rivers were especially valuable aids to expansion in the enormous reaches of Siberia. The latter region, larger by two thirds than the United States, is drained by some of the greatest rivers on earth: the Ob, Yenisei, Lena, and Kolyma, flowing to the Arctic Ocean, and the Amur, flowing to the Pacific. By following these rivers and their lateral tributaries the Russians advanced from the Urals to the Pacific in less than a century. The latter movement has been summarized as follows by a specialist on Russian expansion, Robert J. Kerner: [11]

The earliest background of the eastward movement across the Urals is to be found in the fur-trading enterprise of Novgorod. Daring merchants and trappers from Novgorod exploited the lower reaches of the Ob from about the fourteenth century by portaging from the tributaries of the Pechora. They and the Muscovites, who carried out expeditions in 1465, 1483, and 1499, raided the inhabitants beyond the Urals for the purpose of obtaining tributes of furs, of which there was a diminishing supply in European Russia. The Russian raids were often followed by counterraids of Siberian natives, which endangered the security of the Ural frontier. It was the latter which especially concerned Tsar Ivan the Dread. He received news that the Volga pirate Yermak, who was wanted for offenses against the laws of tsardom, had, in the employ of the Novgorodian family of the Stroganovs, raided beyond the Urals. The tsar, in fact, ordered the Stroganovs to bring him back for trial. He feared the Ural frontier would be overrun by the tribesmen of the Tatar khan, Kuchum. Yermak's success in capturing Sibir, the capital of Siberia, caused the tsar to change his intentions in regard to Yermak; instead of beheading him he gave Yermak his blessing and a real coat of armor. Incidentally, it was this heavy accoutrement that caused Yermak to lose his life by drowning.

Moscow took over in 1538 and ended the practice of raids. It initiated a planned domination of rivers and portages through

[11] Robert J. Kerner, "The Russian Eastward Movement: Some Observations on Its Historical Significance." *Pacific Historical Review*, v. 17 (1948), pp. 136–137. Spellings of some proper names have been slightly modified. Used by permission of the author and the *Pacific Historical Review*.

the building of blockhouses, called *ostrogs* in Russian. This was in line with centuries of Russian tradition in Europe. The original motive for the advance into Siberia was the acquisition of furs. Moscow sought to add to it the search for gold and silver. The conquest of the Tatar khanate gave security to the Ural frontier and created a base for further expansion. Thus from its origins to the present day, Russian rule in Asia was planned and regimented from Moscow.

The first Russians in Siberia were fur merchants and trappers, government officials, Cossacks, and Orthodox priests. The advance was rapid, once the khanate had been subdued. Within a decade and a half after Yermak's death the basin of the Ob had become a Russian possession with the ostrog of Tobolsk on the Irtysh, founded in 1587, as the key, but with ostrogs guarding the route to it from Russia and others built on the lower reaches of the Ob and the upper reaches of its tributaries. The pattern set in the Ob basin was followed, in the years 1607–1625, in that of the Yenisei, directly to the east with its center at Yeniseisk (1618). The basin of the Lena was occupied between 1630 and 1648, with its center at Yakutsk, an ostrog founded in 1632. The Russians reached the Pacific in 1639. Their occupation of the Lake Baikal and Amur region, with its center at Irkutsk (1652) followed in the 'fifties and 'sixties. Forced out of the Amur River region by the Chinese under the Manchu emperor Kang-hsi by the negotiations which resulted in the Treaty of Nerchinsk (1689), the Russians lost the base of an adequate supply of grain and vegetables. This was to make their hold on eastern Siberia precarious for nearly two centuries. Even more than that, they lost easy access to the Pacific, which they did not regain until 1858–1860.

Large areas in the Caucasus region and in Turkestan (the arid or semi-arid area east of the Caspian Sea) were not secured by Russia until the nineteenth century. These regions, and Siberia as well, were administered as colonial areas by the tsars.

▶ The Role of Topography

Most of the important rivers of Russia wind slowly for hundreds or thousands of miles across vast expanses of plain. Early expansion was facilitated not only by the long, continuous highways provided by the rivers themselves, but also by the easy overland connections between river systems. Only in the extreme south and east of Russia are the river basins separated by ranges of high mountains. Elsewhere the divides are ordinarily found in areas of low hills, or even in level plains where the gradients between headstreams are so gentle as to be scarcely perceptible.

Plains and low hills occupy nearly all of Russia from the Yenisei River to the western borders of the country. The only mountains which rise in the midst of this vast lowland are the Urals, a low range located about midway between the western frontier of Russia and the Yenisei. The Urals trend due north and south, but do not occupy the full width of the lowland. A wide gap between the southern end of the mountains and the Caspian Sea permits uninterruped east-west movement. Actually the Urals themselves do not constitute a serious barrier to transportation, the main range being less than 100 miles wide in most places and cut by river valleys offering easy passageways through the mountains. Today the main rail lines connecting Moscow with Siberia pass directly through the Urals. In general form and elevation these mountains bear many resemblances to the Appalachian Mountains of the United States. Like the Appalachians, they are old, worn-down mountains with rounded contours. The average elevation is less than 2000 feet, and the highest summit, located toward the northern end of the range, is only 6183 feet above sea level. The central Urals are especially low, being little more than high hills. Rail lines connecting Moscow with the important Ural city of Sverdlovsk cross this part of the range over a di-

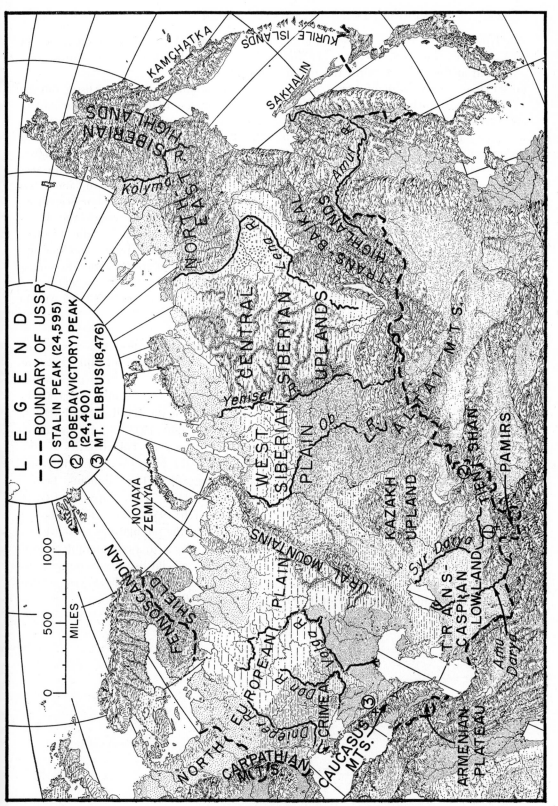

LEGEND
- - - BOUNDARY OF USSR
① STALIN PEAK (24,595)
② POBEDA (VICTORY) PEAK (24,400)
③ MT. ELBRUS (18,476)

MILES
0   500   1000

KAMCHATKA

KURILE ISLANDS

SAKHALIN

SIBERIAN HIGHLANDS

NORTHEAST

Kolyma R.

Amur R.

TRANS-BAIKAL HIGHLANDS

CENTRAL SIBERIAN UPLANDS

Lena R.

WEST SIBERIAN PLAIN

Yenisei R.

Ob R.

ALTAI MTS.

KAZAKH UPLAND

TIEN SHAN

PAMIRS

NOVAYA ZEMLYA

FENNOSCANDIAN SHIELD

URAL MOUNTAINS

NORTH EUROPEAN PLAIN

Volga R.

Dnieper R.

CRIMEA

Don R.

CARPATHIAN MTS.

CAUCASUS MTS.

Syr Darya

TRANS-CASPIAN LOWLAND

Amu Darya

ARMENIAN PLATEAU

Major landforms of the Soviet Union. (Base map is a portion of A. K. Lobeck's Physiographic Diagram of Asia, copyright, The Geographical Press, a division of C. S. Hammond & Company, Maplewood, N. J.)

vide lying at only 1350 feet above sea level. The southern and central Urals are forested, but at the extreme north the mountains extend into the zone of Arctic tundra.

The Russian lowlands west of the Urals are mostly undulating or rolling rather than flat. To the east, however, between the mountains and the Yenisei River, the great lowland of western Siberia is one of the most level areas on earth. Much of the latter area is covered by immense swamps and marshes through which the Ob River and its tributaries slowly wend their way. This waterlogged country is a major barrier to land transportation and is extremely uninviting to settlement. Large sections are almost devoid of people. In the spring tremendous floods occur when the breakup of ice in the upper basin of the Ob releases great quantities of water while the river channels farther north are still frozen. Such floods are characteristic of all the major rivers flowing into the Arctic Ocean but are especially severe along the Ob because of the huge stretches of level land which enable the waters to spread out over thousands of square miles.

The area between the Yenisei and Lena Rivers is occupied by hilly uplands lying at a general elevation of 1000 to 1500 feet. Occasional summits reach 3000 feet. East of the Lena River and Lake Baikal the landscape is dominated by mountains. Extreme northeastern Siberia is especially wild and difficult mountain country, with a few peaks reaching elevations of 10,000 feet or more. This bleak region is one of the least inhabited and least known areas on earth.

High mountains border Russia on the south from the Black Sea to Lake Baikal, and lower mountains from Lake Baikal to the Pacific. Elevations of 15,000 feet or higher are reached in the Caucasus Mountains between the Black and Caspian Seas and in the Pamir, Tien Shan, and Altai Mountains east of the Caspian Sea. From the foot of the latter ranges and lower ranges between the Pamirs and Caspian Sea, arid or semi-arid plains and low uplands extend northward and gradually merge with the West Siberian Plain and the broad plains and low hills lying west of the Urals.

[EDITORIAL COMMENT: Populations of Soviet cities given in Chapters 12 and 13 are recent estimates taken from two principal sources. (1) For cities under 400,000 the main source was the Rand McNally *World Guide* (copyright 1953 by the Columbia University Press). (2) For all cities of 400,-000 or over, the source was Theodore Shabad, "Geographic Developments Behind the Iron Curtain," *The Professional Geographer* (March, 1955), p. 14. It must be emphasized that the populations cited are estimates and subject to a considerable margin of error. No official list of city populations has been published by the Soviet government since 1939.]

Population and Major Territorial Divisions of the USSR

13

In 1954 the Soviet Union had an estimated population of somewhat more than 210 million, a figure exceeded only by China and India among the world's countries. The last official census returns in 1939 showed a population of 170.5 million. Absorption of the Baltic republics and other areas along the western frontier increased this figure to an estimated 193 million in 1940. Earlier censuses had recorded a total of 129 million in 1897 and 147 million in 1926. Thus in spite of enormous losses from war, revolution, famine, and disease, the population of Russia has increased by about two thirds since the beginning of the century. The estimated rate of increase in 1950, virtually all due to excess of births over deaths, was 3.5 million per year, or 1.75 percent. Continuance of the same rate would give the Soviet Union a population of around 300 million by 1975.

A postwar view of the central thoroughfare in Kiev, the capital of the Ukrainian SSR. The buildings along this street were severely damaged in World War II. (*Sovfoto.*)

Recent Population Movements

Two striking movements of population have occurred in recent decades. One of these has been a shift in the center of population toward the east, as a consequence of large-scale emigration into the Volga region, the Urals, and Siberia. The other has been a movement of population into the cities, resulting in spectacular increases in urbanization. An American geographer, Chauncy D. Harris, has written as follows concerning urbanization in the period 1926–1939: [1]

The rapid growth of cities in the Soviet Union between the 1926 and 1939 censuses is unequaled either in the earlier history of Russia or in the urban development of other countries. The numerical increase in urban population in the Soviet Union in this 12-year period exceeded the total numerical increase in all the previous centuries of Russian history. During this time the urban population more than doubled (112.5 per cent increase), in contrast with the rural population, which decreased slightly. Of the urban increase of 29.6 million, 5.4 million came from the natural increase within the urban areas themselves and 24.2 million from rural areas. The proportion of the total population living in cities increased from 17.9 per cent to 32.8 per cent. A comparable increase in degree of urbanization required about 31 years in the United States (1856–1887) and probably about a century in most European countries, though exact comparisons are difficult because of the incompleteness of early statistics. . . .

In absolute as well as in percentage increases the growth of Soviet cities in the intercensal period from 1926 to 1939 is unparalleled. In this period 38 cities increased in population at the rate of 100,000 per decade. The increase in population in Moscow was 2,108,000 persons, approximately equivalent to 1,740,000 in a decade. This is considerably greater than the American record, held by New York City, which increased 1,329,000 in the period 1900 to 1910. The numerical increase in Leningrad was at about the same rate as that of New York City at its peak of rapid growth, yet in percentage figures Leningrad was below the average of Soviet cities. . . .

Urbanization has been part of the industrialization that has been planned and executed by the government in a series of 5-year plans. The long-delayed impact of the Industrial Revolution has struck in the Soviet Union with a suddenness unknown in Western Europe or the United States.

The Slavic Majority

Slavic peoples represent the dominant population element in the USSR, both in numbers and political and economic power. The major Slavic groups are the Great Russians, often referred to simply as Russians, the Ukrainians or Little Russians, and the Belorussians or White Russians. The Great Russians constitute about half, the Ukrainians nearly a fifth, and the Belorussians about a twentieth of the total population of the USSR.

▶ Early Scandinavian and Byzantine Influences

The Slavs have inhabited Russia since the early centuries of the Christian era.

---

[1] Chauncy D. Harris, "The Cities of the Soviet Union." *Geographical Review*, v. 35 (1945), pp. 107–112. Used by permission of the author and the American Geographical Society of New York. Three footnotes are omitted.

During the Middle Ages Slavic tribes living in the forested regions of western Russia came under the control of Viking adventurers from Scandinavia. In the ninth century these newcomers, known as Varangians or Russ-men, opened a trade route from the Baltic to the Black Sea by way of the Dnieper River. Two cities on this route, Kiev on the Dnieper and Novgorod on Lake Ilmen, rose to prominence as centers of trade and political power. The ruling houses of these cities came to control much of present-day Russia west of the Urals.

The southern terminus of the Viking trade route across western Russia was the great city of Constantinople, located on the straits connecting the Black Sea with the Mediterranean. Constantinople was the capital of the Eastern Roman or Byzantine Empire, which endured for nearly a thousand years after the fall of Rome itself in 476 A.D. As a result of trading contacts, the Russians adopted many features of the Byzantine civilization, including the Cyrillic alphabet and the Orthodox Eastern Church. After Constantinople fell to the Ottoman Turks, a Mohammedan people, in the fifteenth century, the Russian tsars carried on the traditions of the Eastern Empire. They came to regard Moscow as a "Third Rome," and the Russian Orthodox Church was made the official church of the Russian Empire.

The Orthodox Christian religion was a powerful influence in the life of Old Russia. Since the Communist Revolution of 1917, however, religious worship has been actively discouraged by the state, though not actually forbidden. Authorities differ regarding the effect of the government's attitude on fundamental beliefs among the people.

▶ The Tatar Invasion

Another cultural influence reached the Russians from the heart of Asia. Since the earliest known times the steppe grasslands of southern Russia had been the haunt of nomadic horsemen of Asiatic origin. During the later days of the Roman Empire and in the Middle Ages these grassy plains, stretching far into Asia, provided a passageway for inroads into Europe by the Vandals, Huns, Bulgars, and other Asiatic peoples. In the thirteenth century appeared the Tatars (Tartars). These Mongolian horsemen owed allegiance to the great conqueror Genghis Khan, who ruled an empire reaching from China to the Dnieper River. Following the death of Genghis in 1227, his successors pushed as far west as Hungary and Poland, subjugating all of Russia except the northern principality of Novgorod. The Tatars in the Russian area called themselves the Golden Horde and established important political centers at Astrakhan and Kazan, on the Volga River. The Russian princes paid tribute to them, and in return they were allowed considerable latitude in matters of local government. Even the princes of Novgorod paid the tribute in order to avoid trouble. When the Tatar power declined in the fifteenth century, the rulers of the Moscow principality were able to begin the process of territorial expansion previously described, which resulted in the formation of present-day Russia.

▶ West European Influences

Thus four different cultures—Slavic, Scandinavian, Byzantine, and Tatar—furnished significant elements in the civilization of Old Russia. Under Peter the Great important elements of West European culture were added. Western manners were introduced into the Russian court, industry was stimulated to develop along Western lines, and the capital was moved in 1713 from Moscow to the new city of St. Petersburg (now Leningrad) on the Gulf of Finland, thus affording a closer contact with Western Europe. Further cultural importations from the latter area have continued up to the present. Many of the basic doctrines of Russian Communism were developed by West European thinkers, and the modern industrial techniques which the

Communist Party has introduced on a large scale in the USSR were originally a West European development.

Minority Groups and the Political Structure

About a fourth of the present population of the Soviet Union is composed of non-Slavic peoples. More than 100 separate nationalities can be distinguished, most of which are small in numbers. However, seventeen different nationalities, including the three principal Slavic groups, number a million people or more, and twelve additional nationalities number 250,000 or more. Soviet policy has encouraged the different national minorities to retain their own languages and other elements of their traditional cultures. This procedure has helped to allay discontent, and in addition

retention of native languages by minority groups has facilitated mass education, regarded by the Communist Party as a necessity for the success of the Communist system. However, a definite tendency toward Russification of minority areas has been apparent in recent years, evidenced by compulsory teaching of the Russian language in schools, as well as by officially sanctioned infiltration of Russian settlers into such areas. During World War II a number of nationalities in the Caucasus, Volga, and Crimean regions were dispersed and official recognition of their separate identity

TABLE 12
UNION REPUBLICS: AREA AND POPULATION DATA

REPUBLIC	AREA (THOUSAND SQUARE MILES)	ESTIMATED POPULATION, 1950 (MILLIONS) [a]
Russian SFSR	6533.6	116.4
Ukrainian SSR	222.6	40.8
Belorussian SSR	80.2	9.3
Moldavian SSR	13.1	2.7
Lithuanian SSR	25.2	3.0
Latvian SSR	24.9	2.1
Estonian SSR	17.4	1.2
Karelo-Finnish SSR	68.9	0.6
Azerbaijan SSR	33.1	3.3
Georgian SSR	29.4	3.6
Armenian SSR	11.5	1.5
Kazakh SSR	1063.2	6.6
Uzbek SSR	156.6	6.0
Kirghiz SSR	76.7	1.5
Tadzhik SSR	54.8	1.5
Turkmen SSR	187.2	1.2
Totals	8598.4	201.3

[a] To the total population figure of 201,300,000 as shown in the table should be added 2,100,000 for persons serving in the armed forces and not counted in the figures for individual republics, thus giving a grand total for the USSR of 203,400,000 persons. Sources of data: Area, official Soviet figures; population, Theodore Shabad, *Geography of the USSR* (New York: Columbia University Press, 1951), p. xv.

was withdrawn because of alleged collaboration with the invading German forces.

The multinational composition of the Soviet Union is directly reflected in the political structure. From the standpoint of political control the USSR is, of course, a highly centralized Communist dictatorship. From the standpoint of administrative organization, however, it is a federation of sixteen Union Republics, each organized primarily around a particular national group. The largest and most important is the Russian Soviet Federated Socialist Republic, or RSFSR, the homeland of the Great Russians. It includes nearly four fifths of the area and over half the total population of the Soviet Union. The Great Russian ethnic group constitutes about three fourths of its population. The fifteen smaller republics are located around the margins of the RSFSR. They fall into three distinct groups: a Middle Asian group of five republics separating the RSFSR from Iran, Afghanistan, and China; a Transcaucasian group of three republics bordering Turkey and Iran; and a Western group of seven republics bordering the European satellites and also Finland and Norway. Area and population figures for the sixteen republics are given in Table 12.

Peoples not considered sufficiently numerous or advanced to form Union Republics are organized into Autonomous Soviet Socialist Republics, Autonomous Oblasts (Regions), or lesser autonomous units. Each autonomous unit is politically subordinated to a Union Republic. The majority are under the jurisdiction of the Russian Soviet Federated Socialist Republic. In the course of time, autonomous units may be promoted to full status as Union Republics. A number of such promotions have occurred since the formation of the USSR.

The Slavic Coreland

Most of the Slavic population of the Soviet Union is found within an irregular triangle extending from the Black and Baltic Seas to the neighborhood of Novosibirsk and Stalinsk in Siberia. This part of the USSR is customarily referred to as the

Major regional divisions of the Soviet Union as considered in the present chapter.

Slavic Coreland, Fertile Triangle, or Agricultural Triangle. It is the core region of the country in every sense, containing about three fourths of the total population, all of the principal industrial concentrations, most of the major mining areas, 22 of the 26 cities having populations of 400,000 or more, and by far the greater part of the total sown acreage. The coreland is about two thirds as large as the United States in area and has approximately the same population. It is really the "Russia that matters," despite the fact that it occupies only a fourth of the total area of the USSR. Lowlands predominate within the coreland, the only mountains being the Urals, a small segment of the Carpathians, and a minor range in the south of the Crimean Peninsula. The original vegetation was mixed coniferous and deciduous forest in the northern part of the coreland and steppe grassland in the south. Moscow and Leningrad, with estimated populations of 5.25 million and 3.15 million, respectively, are by far the largest cities. Moscow, the capital of Russia before 1713 and again since 1917, is today the most important manufacturing city and the principal rail hub. Leningrad, the capital from 1713 to 1917, is the second industrial city and the leading seaport. Most of the other major cities within the coreland are found in the principal industrialized regions, or in other words, in the vicinity of Moscow, in the Ukraine, in the Urals, along the Volga River, or in the vicinity of the Kuznets coal basin in Siberia.

▶ The Ukraine

The Great Russians are the largest ethnic group in the coreland, followed by the Ukrainians. Most of the latter are found in the Ukrainian Soviet Socialist Republic. Although closely related to the Great Russians in language and culture, the Ukrainians are a distinct national group. The

name Ukraine means "borderland." In this area the Russian tsars fought for centuries against nomadic steppe peoples and also against Poles, Lithuanians, and Turks before the Ukraine was finally brought under control in the eighteenth century. The principal agents of tsarist expansion were the Cossacks, a class of semi-nomadic military retainers forming a sort of early foreign legion. The Cossacks subjugated the Ukraine by advancing down the Dnieper and Don Rivers, planting forts at strategic points and establishing agricultural settlements.

Today the Ukraine is one of the most densely-populated and productive areas in all of Russia. Its significance has been described as follows by a specialist on the USSR, Theodore Shabad: [2]

The economy of the Ukrainian SSR combines a rich agricultural development with a powerful mining and metallurgical industry, based in particular on the coal of the Donets Basin and the iron ore of Krivoi Rog. As a result of the industrialization of the USSR, the Ukraine became not only a basic grain-exporting region of the USSR, as well as an area of intensive agriculture and agricultural industry, but also the major coal and metallurgical base and heavy-machine construction center of the USSR. The Ukraine has more than one fifth of the total sown acreage of the USSR and produces one quarter of the grain, two thirds of the sugar, three fifths of the coal and pig iron, one half of the salt, and about one fifth of the machines and chemicals.

The Ukraine lies partly in the forest zone and partly in the steppe. Near the border between these vegetation realms is the historic city of Kiev (900,000), the capital of the Ukrainian SSR and a major industrial and transportation center.

▶ Lesser Republics of the Coreland

The Ukrainian SSR is separately repre-

---

[2] Theodore Shabad, *Geography of the USSR.* New York: Columbia University Press, 1951. P. 441.   Used by permission of the publisher.

sented in the General Assembly of the United Nations. The same is true of the adjoining Belorussian (White Russian) Republic. By virtue of this arrangement the Soviet Union commands three separate votes in the General Assembly, as compared with one vote for the United States. The Belorussian SSR is much smaller in area and population than the Ukrainian SSR, and is far less productive. The political capital and main industrial center is Minsk (420,000), located on the direct rail line from Moscow to Warsaw and Berlin. This republic suffers from a lack of mineral resources, a retarded industrial development, poor soils, and general economic backwardness. The climate is too cool and damp for the best wheat production, and the favored crops are rye, oats, hay, and potatoes. Hogs and dairy cattle are the principal livestock.

Somewhat similar to the Belorussian SSR in general characteristics, though on a slightly higher economic plane, are the Lithuanian, Latvian, and Estonian SSR's, bordering the Baltic Sea. These small republics were part of the Russian Empire before World War I, but successfully asserted their independence following the Russian Revolution. In 1940, however, they were reabsorbed by the USSR as Union Republics. The Latvians and Lithuanians have some Slavic affinities, but are not considered to be true Slavs. The Estonians, related to the Finns, are distinctly non-Slavic. Like the Belorussian SSR, the three Baltic republics are predominantly agricultural. Dairy farms alternate with patches of mixed forest in a hilly, glaciated landscape. Lumbering is an important activity in all three republics. Mineral resources are generally lacking, although Estonia has extensive deposits of oil-bearing shale. The principal industries are concentrated in a few medium-sized cities, of which the largest is the important seaport of Riga (530,000), the capital of the Latvian SSR.

Adjoining the Lithuanian SSR on the southwest is former German East Prussia, the northern half of which is now a part of the Russian Soviet Federated Socialist Republic. In environment and economic activities this small area is essentially a continuation of the Baltic republics.

Also included within the coreland at the extreme west is the small Moldavian SSR, largely constituted of territory acquired from Rumania in 1940. The Moldavians, a people with many Slavic characteristics, speak a dialect of the Rumanian language. Mainly a fertile black-earth steppe upland, the Moldavian SSR is largely agricultural, its industries being essentially confined to food processing. Corn, wheat, and other grains occupy about three fourths of the total crop acreage. Dairy cattle and hogs are the principal livestock in the north of the republic, but sheep and goats predominate in the drier south. An important specialty is the growing of vegetables and fruits, especially grapes. This republic is one of the major grape-growing and wine-producing areas of the USSR, its natural environment for vineyards being somewhat similar to that of the famous French district of Champagne.

▶ Industrial Development in the Coreland

Although pre-Revolutionary Russia was basically an agricultural country, a slow development of modern industry, partially financed by foreign capital, took place before World War I. At the time of the Revolution industrial development in the country was mainly confined to three areas: the region around Moscow, the Leningrad area, and the Ukraine. Under the Soviets these areas have continued to represent major concentrations of industry. In addition, industry has been greatly expanded in a fourth area, the Urals, and an entirely new industrial concentration has been created in the Kuznets Basin. All five industrialized areas are within the coreland.

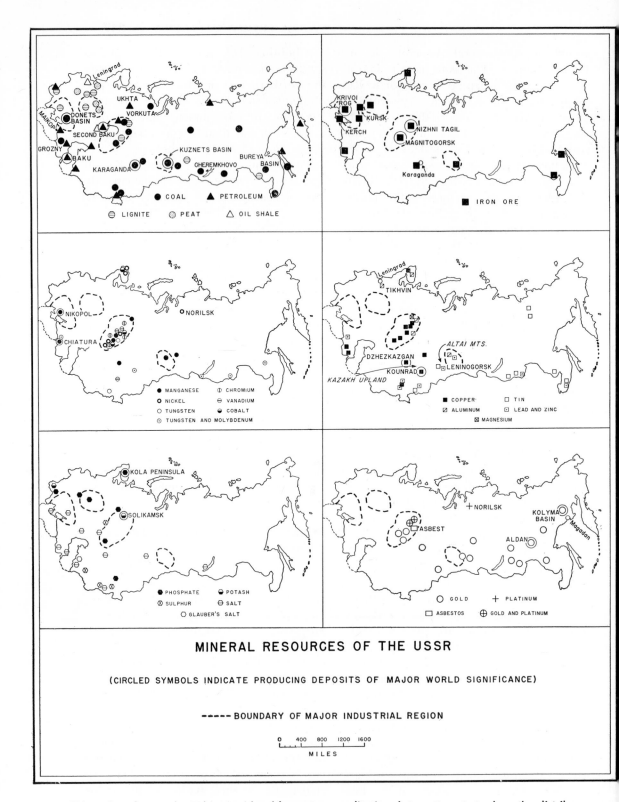

MINERAL RESOURCES OF THE USSR

(CIRCLED SYMBOLS INDICATE PRODUCING DEPOSITS OF MAJOR WORLD SIGNIFICANCE)

----- BOUNDARY OF MAJOR INDUSTRIAL REGION

0 400 800 1200 1600

MILES

This series of maps, based in considerable part on qualitative data, attempts to show the distribution of the major known deposits of minerals in the USSR.

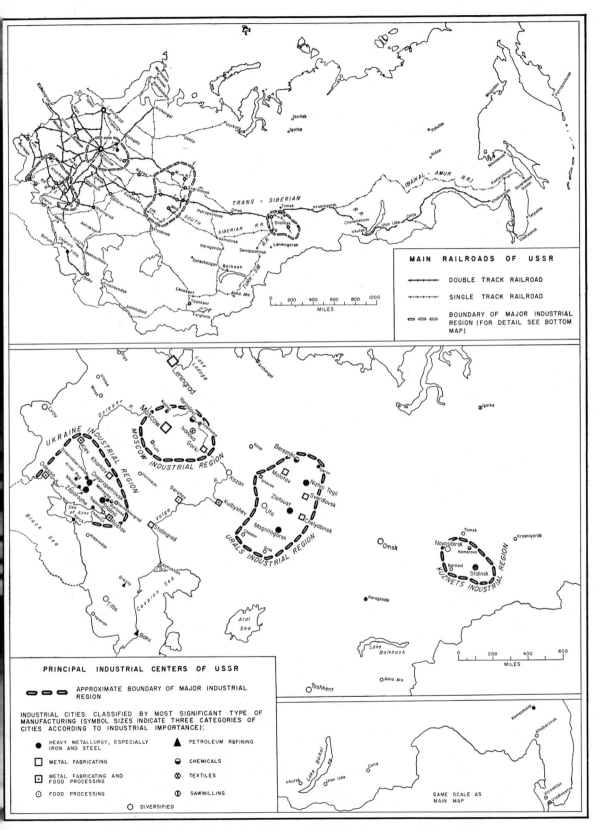

MAIN RAILROADS OF USSR

+++++ DOUBLE TRACK RAILROAD

+++++ SINGLE TRACK RAILROAD

– – – BOUNDARY OF MAJOR INDUSTRIAL REGION (FOR DETAIL SEE BOTTOM MAP)

PRINCIPAL INDUSTRIAL CENTERS OF USSR

◯◯◯ APPROXIMATE BOUNDARY OF MAJOR INDUSTRIAL REGION

INDUSTRIAL CITIES CLASSIFIED BY MOST SIGNIFICANT TYPE OF MANUFACTURING (SYMBOL SIZES INDICATE THREE CATEGORIES OF CITIES ACCORDING TO INDUSTRIAL IMPORTANCE):

● HEAVY METALLURGY, ESPECIALLY IRON AND STEEL

▲ PETROLEUM REFINING

☐ METAL FABRICATING

⊖ CHEMICALS

⊡ METAL FABRICATING AND FOOD PROCESSING

⊗ TEXTILES

⊙ FOOD PROCESSING

⊕ SAWMILLING

◯ DIVERSIFIED

SAME SCALE AS MAIN MAP

The classification of industrial cities is based partly on qualitative data.

• *Industry in the Moscow Region.* The industrialized area surrounding Moscow is often referred to as the Central Industrial Region, Old Industrial Region, or Moscow-Tula-Gorki Region. These names indicate important characteristics of the region. It is centrally located, not only in a geographical, but also in a functional sense. Moscow is the center of the Soviet rail and air nets, and is connected by river and canal transportation with the Baltic, White, Black, and Caspian Seas. It is an old region in the sense of being the first major center of modern large-scale industry to be developed in pre-Revolutionary Russia. From Moscow the region extends southward to the iron-mining and metallurgical center of Tula (250,000) and eastward to the great automobile center of Gorki (900,000)—the "Soviet Detroit." To the north the region includes the major textile center of Ivanovo (325,000)—the "Soviet Manchester"—and Yaroslavl (325,000), important in synthetic rubber manufacture. Textile milling, largely on the basis of imported American cotton and Russian flax, was the earliest form of large-scale manufacturing to be developed. It gradually replaced the earlier handicraft industries during the nineteenth century. Although the Moscow region is still the largest center of textile production in the USSR, a great variety of other light and heavy manufactures have been developed. The metal-fabricating industries, emphasizing types of construction requiring a relatively high degree of skill and precision in manufacture, are the most important in value of product. This industrial region produces at least a fifth of the total industrial output of the USSR by value and contains about a tenth of the total population of the country.

The industrial pre-eminence of the Moscow region has been achieved in spite of a notable lack of natural resources within the region. The minerals of greatest consequence are large deposits of lignite south of Moscow and peat deposits north of the city—both used mainly in steam-generating plants to produce electricity. Iron deposits of only local importance near Tula and phosphate deposits southeast of Moscow complete the list of major industrial minerals present in any quantity. However, the excellent transportation facilities of the capital, partly a product of political centralization, have provided the means for a constant inflow of foods, fibers, metals, fuels, timber, and other necessary materials, and a return outflow of finished products to all parts of the USSR. A direct trunk rail line brings high-grade coal to the region from the rich fields of the Donets Basin in the Ukraine. Additional supplies of good coal are brought from fields near the Arctic Circle in the basin of the Pechora River.

• *Industrial Development in the Leningrad Area.* Leningrad does not form the center of an industrial region comparable in area and population to the Moscow Region, the Ukraine, or the Urals. Nevertheless, the city and its immediate environs produce an estimated one tenth of the total Soviet industrial output by value. Leningrad is even more handicapped than Moscow from the standpoint of mineral resources. Local deposits of peat and deposits of oil shale and lignite at a somewhat greater distance are supplemented by hydroelectricity from several generating stations to the north and east of the city. High-grade coal and petroleum must be brought from hundreds of miles away, as must all of the metals except aluminum, produced east of Leningrad at Volkhov from bauxite deposits near Tikhvin. Nevertheless, the metal-fabricating industries are by far the most important branch of manufacturing. The distinctive role of the Leningrad area in the development of Soviet industry has been briefly described as follows by Theodore Shabad: [3]

[3] Shabad, *op. cit.*, p. 150. Used by permission of the Columbia University Press.

As one of the oldest machine-building centers of the USSR, the city of Leningrad played a vital role in the industrialization of the country during the first Five-Year Plans. Its well-equipped plants and skilled labor supply served to develop and to introduce into other industrial areas of the Union the manufacture of machinery never before produced in the USSR, including such items as tractors, steam turbines, rolling mills, textile, tobacco- and food-processing machines, counting and printing machines, fishing trawlers, motorcycles, photographic, telephone, and radio apparatus. Leningrad is still the only producer in the USSR of such specialized products as large hydroelectric turbine installations, special machine tools, and others. Similar pioneering work was done by the Leningrad chemical industry, which was the first to develop the methods of production of synthetic rubber from potato alcohol. Among the other important industries centered at Leningrad are textile mills, producing linen, cotton, and knitted goods, clothing mills, food-processing and printing plants.

• *The Ukrainian Industrial Region.* For more than a quarter-century, Soviet planning has consistently emphasized the heavier types of industry. Today, heavy metallurgy, together with associated coal and iron mining and chemical manufacturing, is mainly concentrated in three regions: the Ukraine, the Urals, and the Kuznets Basin. In 1950 these regions produced an estimated 86 percent of the total Soviet output of steel (Ukraine 40 percent, Urals 35 percent, Kuznets Basin 11 percent).

Heavy industry in the Ukraine is based essentially on major deposits of four indispensable industrial minerals: coal, iron, manganese, and salt. The coal is found in the Donets Basin coal field of the eastern Ukraine, often referred to as the Donbas Field. Mining began in this area under the tsars, and as late as 1913 the Donbas produced nearly nine tenths of all coal mined in Russia. By 1950, however, its share had fallen to 35 percent of the total, due to

development of coal fields in other areas. However, the Donbas still produces around twice as much coal as any other field, and its *absolute* production has increased by about 250 percent since 1913. The Donbas produces a variety of bituminous and anthracite coals, including much high-grade coking coal. The total reserves appear sufficient for many decades to come at present rates of production.

About 300 miles to the west of the Donbas, at Krivoi Rog, is the major iron field of the Union. Iron has been mined here since tsarist days, and the Krivoi Rog field has been the leading Russian producer for many decades. The ore is high-grade hematite, with an average iron content of 58 to 65 percent. The Krivoi Rog field, which has by far the largest known reserves of high-grade ore in the USSR, ranks in general world importance with the great ore fields of Lorraine in France and Kiruna in northern Sweden.

Manganese, the most important of the ferroalloys, is mined at Nikopol, about 60 miles southeast of Krivoi Rog. The Soviet Union is the largest world producer of manganese and has the largest known reserves of this valuable alloy metal. More than nine tenths of all Soviet manganese reserves are concentrated either in the vicinity of Nikopol or at Chiatura in Transcaucasia.

The principal concentration of iron and steel plants in the Ukraine is located on the coal field, in the general vicinity of the important coal-mining and heavy industrial center of Stalino (600,000). Iron ore and manganese are brought by rail from Krivoi Rog and Nikopol. This area is also a major center of chemical manufacturing, based principally on blast furnace wastes and huge deposits of common salt.

A secondary concentration of iron- and steelworks is found in the vicinity of the great bend of the Dnieper River about 250 miles below Kiev. Here at Dnepropetrovsk (500,000), Zaporozhe (400,000), and smaller places, a variety of electrometallurgical and electrochemical manufacturing activities are carried on, including the making of special steels in electric furnaces. Manufacturing in this district is based principally on Donbas coal and coke, Krivoi Rog iron, manganese from Nikopol, and hydroelectric power from the Dnieper Dam at Zaporozhe.

South of the Donbas at Kerch (120,000), on the Crimean Peninsula, immense deposits of low-grade, high-phosphorus iron ore are found. The ore is utilized locally for manufacturing iron and steel, and is shipped by water across the Sea of Azov to iron and steel plants at Zhdanov, formerly Mariupol (225,000). Coal and manganese for these operations are brought from the producing fields to the north.

Surrounding the inner core of mining and heavy metallurgical districts in the Ukraine is an outer ring of large industrial cities which carry on metal-fabricating and various other types of manufacturing. These cities include the Ukrainian capital of Kiev (900,000) on the Dnieper, the great machine-building and railway center of Kharkov (850,000), about 250 miles east of Kiev, and the major seaports and diversified industrial centers of Rostov (600,000) on the lower Don River and Odessa (600,-000) on the Black Sea.

• *Industrial Development in the Urals.* The Ural Mountains contain an extraordinarily varied collection of economic minerals. Although deficient in coking coal, this highly mineralized area has valuable deposits of iron, copper, nickel, chromium, manganese, tungsten, zinc, lead, bauxite, platinum, gold, asbestos, magnesium, potash, industrial salt, and various other minerals. Much low-grade coal and lignite and some anthracite occur, though relatively little of the available coal is suitable for coking. Petroleum is produced in the large new fields of "the Second Baku" in the western foothills of the mountains.

The Soviet regime has placed great emphasis on the development of the Urals as an industrial region well removed from the exposed western frontier of the Union. This emphasis was amply repaid in World War II, when the Ukraine was overrun by German armies and the Urals became the principal arsenal of the USSR. The major industrial activities of the region are as follows:

1. Heavy metallurgy, including the manufacture of iron and steel and the smelting of nonferrous ores.

2. The manufacture of heavy chemicals, especially concentrated in the Solikamsk-Berezniki area, where some of the world's largest deposits of potassium and magnesium salts are found.

3. The manufacture of machinery and other metal-fabricating activities, carried on in the important industrial and transportation centers of Sverdlovsk (750,000), Chelyabinsk (600,000), Molotov (450,000), Ufa (225,000), and dozens of smaller places.

Old pre-Soviet metallurgical and machine-building plants in the Urals have been modernized and expanded, and a number of immense new plants have been constructed. Probably the most famous and spectacular development has been the creation of an entirely new iron and steel center at Magnitogorsk in the southern Urals. This place, located near a large reserve of exceptionally high-grade iron ore, was not even a village prior to 1931. In that year construction of a huge steel plant was begun and a city was built to house the workers. Today Magnitogorsk is one of the three or four largest centers of iron and steel production in the USSR and has a population estimated at 225,000. It is one of several new cities created in various parts of the USSR under the Soviet regime. Coking coal for the blast furnaces at Magnitogorsk was secured at first by rail from the Kuznets Basin, 1200 miles to the east in Siberia. Steel milling was developed in the latter area to utilize iron ore transported from the Urals on the return trip. Thus was created the famous Urals-Kuzbas *combinat*—a spectacular example of the integrated industrial development favored by Soviet planners. Today each end of the original *combinat* has largely become independent of the other. A newly developed coal field at Karaganda in Soviet Middle Asia provides coking coal for the Urals, and iron deposits are being exploited south of the Kuznets Basin to supply the iron and steel mills of the latter area.

A second major center of iron and steel milling, also based on extremely high-grade local ores, has been developed at Nizhni Tagil (250,000), about 300 miles north of Magnitogorsk. Zlatoust (125,000), about 120 miles north of Magnitogorsk, is an important metallurgical center specializing in the manufacture of special alloy steels.

Sverdlovsk, located on the eastern flank of the mountains, is the largest city of the Urals and the pre-eminent economic, cultural, and transportation center of the region. Direct trunk rail lines connect the city with Moscow and Leningrad. The second most important rail center is Chelyabinsk, about 120 miles south of Sverdlovsk. Chelyabinsk also has direct rail connections with Moscow. In western Siberia between the Urals and the large industrial and trading center of Omsk (600,000), rail lines from Sverdlovsk and Chelyabinsk join to form the Trans-Siberian Railroad, the main artery of traffic linking the Soviet Far East with the coreland.

• *The New Kuznets Industrial Region.* The newest of the major industrial regions of the USSR has the most strategic location for purposes of defense. The Kuznets area is located about midway between the eastern and western borders of the country, and thus has the protection of tremendous distances in both directions. To the north, additional defense in depth is provided by nearly the full width of Siberia, plus the icy barrier of the Arctic Ocean. To the

south, the greatest mass of high mountains and plateaus on the globe separates the Kuznets area from the Indian Ocean.

The principal localizing factor for industry in the Kuznets region is an enormous deposit of high-grade coal, much of it suitable for coking. Seams up to 50 feet in thickness lie close to the surface and are consequently very easy and inexpensive to mine. The total coal reserves are estimated at some 400 to 450 billion tons, about four or five times the size of the reserves in the Donbas Field. The coal field of the Kuznets Basin is possibly the richest in the world, with the exception of the Appalachian Field of the United States.

The manufacture of iron and steel is the pre-eminent industrial activity of the Kuznets region. Iron ore is secured partly from deposits to the south of the coal field and partly from the Urals. The major steel center is Stalinsk (275,000), which rivals the great Ural centers of Magnitogorsk and Nizhni Tagil in importance. The iron and steel industry at Stalinsk began to be developed in 1932, concurrent with the development of Magnitogorsk. North of Stalinsk coke is made, and important chemical manufacturing is carried on at Kemerovo (200,000). The largest urban center of the Kuznets region, however, is Novosibirsk, a diversified industrial, trading, and transportation center located on the Ob River at the junction of the Trans-Siberian and Turkestan-Siberian (Turk-Sib) Railroads. Sometimes called the "Chicago of Siberia," Novosibirsk has developed rapidly from a town of a few thousand in 1900 to an estimated 750,000 at the present time.

• *Other Industrial Centers of the Coreland.* Various industrial cities outside of the five major industrial concentrations are scattered through the coreland. Perhaps the most notable of these are a group of cities spaced at fairly regular intervals along the Volga River between Gorki and the Caspian Sea. They include Kazan (550,000), the major center of the Soviet fur-processing industry; the diversified metal-fabricating, food-processing, and oil-refining centers of Kuibyshev (750,000), Saratov (600,000), and Stalingrad (450,000); and Astrakhan (325,000), a food-processing center and the headquarters for the important fishing industry of the Caspian Sea.

▶ *Agriculture in the Coreland*

Nearly all of the important crops of the middle latitudes are grown in the Soviet Union. The grain crops lead in acreage and production, wheat and rye being the principal bread grains and oats and barley the major feed grains. Millet, corn, buckwheat, and rice occupy smaller though substantial acreages. Potatoes and sugar beets are the most important root crops; flax, cotton, and hemp the main fiber crops; and sunflowers the major source of vegetable oil. Substantial quantities of tobacco, citrus fruits, hardy fruits, and various other crops are grown. Cattle, sheep, hogs, and horses are the major types of livestock. In 1938 grain crops accounted for three fourths of the total crop acreage. However, Soviet policy has been to lessen the grain acreage in favor of other crops as much as possible.

The Fertile Triangle is the agricultural core of the Union. It is by far the leading area of production for all of the major crops except cotton and subtropical fruits and for all the major types of livestock. Within the Fertile Triangle two major crop zones have long been recognized: a black-soil zone in the southern steppes, and a nonblack-soil zone roughly corresponding to the region of mixed forest. Although some of the same crops and types of livestock are raised in each, the differences tend to outweigh the similarities, and these zones are essentially complementary rather than competitive.

• *The Black-Soil Zone.* The black-soil zone includes not only the chernozem soils proper, but also associated areas of chestnut and other grassland soils. These are excellent wheat soils, and this crop zone is one of the major wheat-growing areas of the world. Wheat, shipped through Odessa, Rostov, and other Black Sea ports, is the leading export crop of the USSR. However, the exports today are far smaller than before World War I, when Russia was the largest wheat exporter of the world. Wheat is ideally suited to the large-scale, mechanized agriculture stressed in Soviet planning. Both spring wheat and winter wheat are grown, with spring wheat accounting for about 60 percent of the total acreage for the Soviet Union as a whole in 1938. The Ukraine is the principal area of winter wheat, while spring wheat predominates in the harsher climate of the Volga region and Siberia. The black-soil zone is also the principal producing area for sugar beets and sunflowers.

• *The Nonblack-Soil Zone.* In the nonblack-soil zone, with its cooler and more humid climate and poorer soils, rye replaces wheat as the major grain crop. This is also the major producing region for potatoes and for flax and hemp grown for fiber, although flax and hemp grown for seed are also important in the black-soil zone.

The nonblack-soil zone has traditionally been the leading dairy region of the USSR. However, most cattle in the Soviet Union are multipurpose animals grown for both milk and meat, as well as for draft purposes.

The Outlying Regions

The majority of the non-Slavic population of the USSR is found outside the coreland. Four major outlying regions can be distinguished: the Caucasus Region, Soviet

Dairy farming in the nonblack-soil zone of the coreland. This view was taken on a collective farm in the Minsk Region. (*Sovfoto.*)

Middle Asia, the Soviet Far East, and the Northern Lands.

▶ The Caucasus Region

The Caucasus region occupies the mountainous southern borderland of the USSR between the Black and Caspian Seas. It includes the rugged Caucasus Mountains, a fringe of foothills and level steppes north of the mountains, and the area to the south known as Transcaucasia.

The Greater Caucasus Range forms practically a solid wall from the Black Sea to the Caspian. It is similar in age and general character to the Alps, but is considerably higher: Mt. Elbrus, the highest summit, stands at 18,476 feet, as compared with 15,-782 feet for Mt. Blanc, the highest peak of the Alps. Railroads to Transcaucasia follow narrow coastal lowlands at either end of the range. However, three strategic military highways cross the central part of the mountains. In the south of Transcaucasia is the Armenian Plateau, a mountainous highland reaching 8300 feet. Between the Greater Caucasus Range and the Armenian Plateau are subtropical valleys and coastal plains where the majority of the people in Transcaucasia are found.

The population of the Caucasus region totals about 6 million in the North Caucasus and 8 million or more in Transcaucasia. Russians and Ukrainians predominate in the North Caucasus, but non-Slavic groups form a large majority in Transcaucasia, as well as on the northern slopes of the Caucasus Mountains. The Caucasian isthmus between the Black and Caspian Seas has been an important north-south passageway for thousands of years, and the present population is composed of many different peoples who have migrated into this region at different times. At least 25 or 30 nationalities can be distinguished, most of which are

Rugged, snow-capped heights in the Georgian Caucasus. (*Sovfoto.*)

small in numbers and largely confined to mountain areas that have served as places of refuge in past times. Besides Russians and Ukrainians, mostly found north of the Greater Caucasus, the nationalities of greatest importance are the Georgians, Armenians, and Azerbaijanians, each represented by a separate Union Republic.

Subtropical crops and minerals are the main contributions of the Caucasus region to the economy of the USSR. Transcaucasia, sheltered by the high wall of the Caucasus Mountains, is the Florida of the Soviet Union and in some respects its California as well, although the south coast of the Crimea, with its mediterranean-type climate, fruit orchards, vineyards, and resorts, would contest for the latter title. The lowlands bordering the Black Sea, with the heaviest rainfall and warmest winters of the USSR, produce such specialty crops as oranges, lemons, grapefruit, tangerines, tea, tobacco, tung oil, almonds, camphor, silk, and wine. This area, the most densely pop-

ulated part of Transcaucasia, is located in the Georgian SSR. The Caspian lowlands of eastern Transcaucasia, located in the Azerbaijan SSR, have colder winters and less rain; here irrigated cotton, grown in rotation with alfalfa, is the main crop except in the narrow coastal lowlands at the extreme south where warmer temperatures and greater precipitation permit the culture of rice, tea, citrus, and other subtropical specialty crops. Temperate fruits and nuts, including apples, pears, apricots, peaches, plums, chestnuts, and walnuts, are grown in many parts of Transcaucasia, and viticulture and sericulture are widely practiced, not only in the lowlands but also on the warmer slopes of the mountains. Livestock, principally sheep and cattle, are grazed on mountain pastures during the summer months and wintered in the lowlands. The dry steppes of eastern Transcaucasia are especially prominent as a winter grazing ground.

Petroleum is the most important mineral

resource of the Caucasus region. The main field is located on the shore of the Caspian Sea at Baku (890,000), and lesser fields occur north of the mountains in the vicinity of Grozny (175,000) and Maikop (70,000). Baku, the largest city of Transcaucasia and capital of the Azerbaijan SSR, has been the leading center of petroleum production and refining since the beginning of the Russian oil industry in the 1870's. The Baku field is connected by pipeline with the oil-refining and shipping port of Batumi (70,000) on the Black Sea. Pipelines also connect the fields north of the mountains with the industrialized areas of the eastern Ukraine. Much of the oil produced in the Caucasus region moves northward by tanker on the Caspian Sea and Volga River.

In addition to petroleum, this region has some fair-sized deposits of coal and is an important producer of metals. At Chiatura in the Georgian SSR is one of the largest known deposits of manganese. Other metals include zinc and lead, mined on the northern slopes of the Greater Caucasus, copper in Armenia, and iron in Azerbaijan. The Caucasus region is estimated to have reserves of hydroelectric power equal to the reserves of the remainder of the Soviet Union west of the Ural Mountains.

Besides Baku, only one city of the Caucasus region reaches a population of half a million or more. This is the diversified industrial center of Tiflis or Tbilisi (580,000), the capital of the Georgian SSR.

The Caucasus region vies with the Crimea as a center of resort development. The principal resorts are found along the Black Sea coast and in the mountains of the Georgian SSR.

▶ Soviet Middle Asia

East of the Caspian Sea and south of the black-earth belt is a vast expanse of deserts, dry grasslands, and high, snow-capped mountains occupying an area nearly half the size of the United States. Like Transcaucasia, this outlying part of the USSR is mainly peopled by non-Slavic nationalities. The most numerous of the latter are four Turco-Tatar peoples, the Uzbeks, Kazakhs, Kirghiz, and Turkmen, and a people of Iranian descent, the Tadzhiks. As reported in the 1939 census, their respective numbers totaled 4.8 million Uzbeks, 3.1 million Kazakhs, 1.2 million Tadzhiks, .9 million Kirghiz, and .8 million Turkmen. Each of the five peoples has its own Union Republic. By far the largest republic in area is the Kazakh SSR, or Kazakhstan, which totals slightly more than a million square miles and is over twice as large as the remaining four republics combined.

The entire area occupied by the five republics is often referred to by its traditional name of Russian Turkestan. It is also known as Soviet Central Asia, although a certain amount of confusion attends the latter term, due to the fact that some writers reserve it for the four smaller republics, excluding Kazakhstan. In the present chapter the name Soviet Middle Asia will be employed when the five republics are referred to as a group.

Mohammedanism is the traditional religious faith among the non-Slavic peoples of this region. The region itself is predominantly composed of plains and low uplands except for the Tadzhik and Kirghiz SSR's which are extremely mountainous. In the latter republics are found the highest summits of the USSR: Stalin Peak, 24,595 feet, in the Pamirs (Tadzhik SSR), and Pobeda (Victory) Peak, 24,400 feet, in the Tien Shan (Kirghiz SSR). Soviet Middle Asia is remote from the world ocean, and is almost entirely a region of interior drainage. Only the waters of the Irtysh, a tributary of the Ob, reach the open sea; all of the other streams either drain to completely enclosed lakes and seas or gradually dry up and disappear in the arid wastes of the Middle Asian deserts.

The majority of the people in Soviet Middle Asia live in irrigated valleys at the base of the southern mountains. Here the soils are generally fertile, the growing season is long, and rivers issuing from the mountains provide large supplies of water for irrigation. The largest of the latter streams are the Amu Darya (Oxus) and the Syr Darya, both of which empty into the Aral Sea. Both rivers are fed by the melting of glaciers and snow fields in the high mountains, and thus carry their maximum flow during the summer months when the water is most needed. The irrigated area of Soviet Middle Asia has been substantially increased both in size and productivity under the Soviets, and large new schemes of water control for irrigation and associated hydroelectric development are reported.

Population densities in the more productive areas of irrigated farming reach 1000 to 1500 per square mile—the highest rural densities in the USSR. Most of the larger irrigated districts are found in the Uzbek

SSR, the most populous of the five republics in the region. Especially important are the fertile Ferghana (Fergana) Valley, watered by the Syr Darya, and the oases surrounding the cities of Tashkent (615,000), Samarkand (150,000), and Bukhara (60,-000). The latter cities are historic trading centers on ancient caravan routes connecting southwestern Asia and the Mediterranean basin with the Far East. Today Tashkent, the capital of the Uzbek SSR, is the largest city and principal center of diversified industry in Soviet Middle Asia. Textile production, based on Middle Asian cotton and wool, and food-processing industries have been supplemented since the beginning of World War II by expanded metal-fabricating industries and a certain amount of heavy metallurgy.

The major crop of the Middle Asian oases is cotton, and this area ranks first by a wide margin among the cotton-producing regions of the USSR. Other irrigated crops

Soviet-made mechanical cotton-pickers in operation on irrigated land in the Uzbek SSR near Tashkent. (Sovfoto.)

include alfalfa, wheat, corn, rice, sesame, sugar beets, tobacco, mulberry trees for sericulture, melons, and a variety of fruits. Great apple orchards in the surrounding oasis have given the name Alma-Ata, "father of apples," to the capital of the Kazakh SSR (population of city about 300,000).

Most of the area outside of the oases is too dry for cultivation, although a considerable amount of nonirrigated grain farming is carried on in the north of Kazakhstan, which touches the black-earth belt, and on some of the rainier slopes in the southern mountain zone. Formerly the drier grasslands, the better-vegetated portions of the deserts, and the mountainous areas were given over to nomadic herding. Today, however, the Soviet government has settled most of the nomads in permanent villages, made possible in many instances by the drilling of deep wells to provide a dependable year-round supply of water. Livestock raising over most of Soviet Middle Asia is now more similar to ranching than to the traditional nomadism, although the herdsmen must often accompany the grazing animals for considerable distances as the latter are moved from one area of range to another. Cattle, sheep and goats are the principal types of livestock. Some camels are raised in the desert lowlands.

During recent decades Soviet Middle Asia has become increasingly important as a producer of minerals, particularly coal, nonferrous metals, and petroleum. Reserves of bituminous coal estimated at 50 billion tons, much of it high-grade coal suitable for coking, are found in the vicinity of the new city of Karaganda, located in the low uplands of central Kazakhstan. The Karaganda coal basin has become the third largest producer of bituminous coal in the USSR (after the Donets and Kuznets basins), and Karaganda itself has experienced a spectacular growth from a tiny village in 1926 to a city of 440,000 today. The coal mined here is mainly shipped to the Urals to supply the great metallurgical industries of that coal-deficient region. However, it also provides a basis for large-scale metallurgy in Middle Asia itself. Although an iron and steel plant utilizing local iron ore deposits is operating near Karaganda, the most important branch of metallurgy in the region is the smelting of nonferrous metals, especially copper, lead, and zinc. The largest copper reserves of the USSR are found in central Kazakhstan at Dzhez-kazgan, about midway between Karaganda and the Aral Sea, and at Kounrad, just north of Lake Balkhash. The lead and zinc deposits of the region, also probably the largest in the USSR, are mainly localized in the Altai Mountain foothills of eastern Kazakhstan around Leninogorsk (formerly Ridder). Each of the three places named is an important mining and smelting center. Impressive reserves of chrome, nickel, and high-grade petroleum in northwestern Kazakhstan, and smaller deposits of many other minerals scattered throughout the region add further to the picture of Soviet Middle Asia as an extremely rich and diversified mineralized area. Uranium is mined at a number of places in the Kirghiz and Tadzhik SSR's.

▶ The Soviet Far East

The Soviet Far East is a rather loosely defined regional name applied to the part of the USSR which borders the Pacific. The core of this outlying region is a strip of territory about 200 miles wide extending along the Pacific littoral from the important seaport of Vladivostok on the south to the smaller port of Nikolaevsk on the north. Here live about 3 million people, mainly Great Russians and Ukrainians.

Although the Soviet Far East as a region is predominantly mountainous or hilly, a sizable lowland is found west of the coastal mountains in the basin drained by the Amur River and its tributary, the Ussuri. This interior lowland, which lies open to the sea at either end, forms the core of the region. Five main cities are disposed in a north-south line along two important arteries of transportation, the Trans-Siberian Railroad and the lower Amur River. At the extreme south on the Sea of Japan is Vladivostok (325,000), the Pacific terminus of rail, air, and sea routes connecting the Soviet Far East with the western coreland of the USSR. Vladivostok is equipped with modern port facilities, and the harbor is kept open throughout the winter with icebreakers. The city also has important shipbuilding, metal-fabricating, and canning industries and is the main port for the Soviet fishing and whaling fleets in the Far East. About 50 miles north of Vladivostok on the Trans-Siberian Railroad is the smaller city of Voroshilov (150,000), a food-processing center located in a fertile rice- and soybean-growing district which forms the most important farming area of the Soviet Far East. The industrial and transportation center of Khabarovsk (325,000) is located at the confluence of the Amur and Ussuri Rivers about 400 miles northeast of Voroshilov. Here the Trans-Siberian Railroad turns south to Vladivostok and the Amur River turns north to the Sea of Okhotsk. To the northeast in the Amur Valley is situated Komsomolsk (140,000), generally considered to be the most important center of iron and steel milling in the Soviet Far East. It is a new city, dating from 1932. About 25 miles above the mouth of the Amur is the fishing port of Nikolaevsk (40,000). It was formerly an important naval base but has now been superseded by Sovetskaya Gavan (Soviet Haven), located to the south on the strait connecting the Sea of Okhotsk with the Sea of Japan.

The Pacific littoral north of Nikolaevsk is very mountainous and sparsely populated. Here on the northern shore of the Sea of Okhotsk are the small seaports of Okhotsk and Magadan. Magadan, founded in 1932 and now estimated to have a population of around 50,000, is the supply port for an important inland gold-mining district in the basin of the Kolyma River.

Prior to World War II the Soviet Union and Japan held the northern and southern halves, respectively, of the large island of Sakhalin, located immediately to the north of Japan. Since the war the USSR has incorporated southern Sakhalin and also the Kurile Islands, formerly Japanese-held. Sakhalin has considerable mineral wealth, including coal and petroleum, and important lumbering and fishing industries. The Kuriles are a sparsely populated chain of small volcanic islands forming an offshore screen between the Sea of Okhotsk and the open Pacific. Fishing is the main economic activity. At the north the Kuriles approach the remote peninsula of Kamchatka. This peninsula, like the Kuriles, is a region of active vulcanism, having many hot springs in addition to some 20 active volcanoes, one of which reaches a height of nearly 16,000 feet. Petropavlovsk (30,000) is a fishing port and naval base in southern Kamchatka.

The Soviet Far East is of relatively minor economic significance to the Soviet Union. This region is generally poorer in known mineral resources than the Urals, the Ukraine, or Kazakhstan, although the gold of the Kolyma Basin and the petroleum of Sakhalin have considerable economic importance, and deposits of coal, iron, lead and zinc, and other minerals are worked to some extent. Gold, fish, furs, and lumber are the major export products. Salmon and other commercial fish are abundant in the waters bordering the region and provide the basis for a fishing industry of major importance. These waters represent one of the four main fishing grounds of the USSR, the others being the Caspian Sea, Barents Sea, and Sea of Azov. Lumber exports from the region include not only the customary softwoods, but also oak and other hardwoods from the basin of the Ussuri River. A diversified development of relatively small-scale manufacturing in the Soviet Far East has lessened, though by no

A fur warehouse in the far northeastern arctic of the USSR. The view shows bear and fox pelts being aired and processed. (Sovfoto.)

means eliminated, the economic and strategic disadvantages accruing from the isolated position of this region with respect to the main centers of Soviet industry located thousands of miles to the west in the Slavic Coreland.

▶ The Northern Lands

To the north and east of the Agricultural Triangle, and west of, and partially including, the Pacific littoral are enormous stretches of coniferous forest (taiga) and tundra extending completely across the USSR from the Finnish and Norwegian borders to the Pacific. These outlying areas of wilderness may be designated for convenience as the Northern Lands, although parts of the Siberian taiga extend to the southern border of the USSR. The Northern Lands include more than half of the Soviet mainland and also a number of island groups in the Arctic Ocean, among which the two mountainous, fiorded islands

of Novaya Zemlya are especially well known.

These difficult lands comprise one of the most sparsely populated large regions of the world. Ordinary types of agriculture are largely precluded by the climate, although hardy vegetables and grains are grown in scattered localities and some dairy farming is carried on. Most of the people are supported by a few primary activities, including reindeer herding, hunting, fishing, trapping, lumbering, and mining. Towns and cities of any size are limited to a small number of sawmilling, mining, and transportation centers, found in most cases along the Arctic coast to the west of the Ural Mountains, along the major rivers, or along the Trans-Siberian Railroad between the Agricultural Triangle and Khabarovsk.

The largest city along the Arctic coast is Archangel (325,000), located on the Northern Dvina River about 25 miles from the

White Sea. This city is the most important sawmilling and lumber-shipping center of the USSR. Softwood lumber from Archangel moves south in large quantities to the coreland and overseas to foreign markets, mainly located in Western Europe. The city has direct rail connections with Moscow, and branching lines from Vologda, north of Moscow, reach Leningrad and the Urals. Archangel also has water connections with Leningrad and Moscow via the Baltic-White Sea Canal and the connecting Mariinsk Canal System. Despite its brief season of navigation (June to October), the city is one of the more important seaports of the USSR.

Another Arctic port, Murmansk, located on the northern shore of the Kola Peninsula west of Archangel, is the headquarters for important trawler fleets which sweep the Barents Sea in search of herring, cod, and haddock. The harbor of Murmansk is ice-free, thanks to the warming influence of the North Atlantic Drift, and the port has experienced a rapid growth from a population of less than 9000 in 1926 to an estimated 160,000 at present. It ships fish, lumber, and phosphates, and imports coal from the Soviet mining concession in Spitsbergen. Murmansk is the western terminus of the Northern Sea Route, a waterway developed by the Soviet government at considerable expense to provide a connection with Vladivostok via the Arctic Ocean. Despite the use of icebreakers and the provision of weather-forecasting and supply facilities, this route is navigable throughout its length for only a few weeks in the year and is used by a very limited amount of shipping. Most ships operating from Murmansk and Archangel go no farther east than the Yenisei River. A 900-mile rail line connecting Murmansk with Leningrad serves important mining districts in the interior of the Kola Peninsula and areas of lumbering in the Karelo-Finnish SSR. The Kola Peninsula is one of the more important mineralized areas of the USSR, pro-

ducing nickel, copper, and other metals, as well as phosphates from reserves of the mineral apatite estimated at 2 billion tons. The nickel and phosphate reserves of the peninsula are among the largest in the Soviet Union. The Kola Peninsula and the adjoining Karelo-Finnish SSR are physically a prolongation of Scandinavia, being in fact located on the same ancient, glaciated crystalline shield which underlies most of the Scandinavian Peninsula and Finland. The Karelo-Finnish SSR, with its thousands of lakes, short, swift streams, extensive softwood forests, and important forest industries, bears a close resemblance to adjoining areas of Finland.

Two important new mining centers have developed in the basin of the Pechora River east of Archangel. High-grade coking and heating coals are mined in this region in the vicinity of Vorkuta (30,000) and high-grade petroleum around Ukhta. These centers are connected by rail with Leningrad, Moscow, and the Urals, all of which are deficient in local supplies of fuel.

East of the Urals the city of Igarka (25,000) has become a sawmilling center second only to Archangel in importance. Igarka lies on the Yenisei River about 500 miles inland, but can be reached by ocean shipping during the few weeks of summer when the Yenisei is free of ice. Murmansk, Vorkuta, and Igarka are the largest cities in the world located north of the Arctic Circle. About 125 miles from Igarka to the north-northeast is the important mining town of Norilsk, credited with the largest nickel and platinum reserves of the USSR and also thought to be an important center of uranium mining. Few settlements of any special note occur north of the Arctic Circle between Norilsk and Bering Strait.

In central and eastern Siberia the unbroken taiga forest extends southward beyond the Trans-Siberian Railroad. A vast but sparsely-settled hinterland is served by four medium-sized cities spaced at intervals along the railroad: Krasnoyarsk (325,000) on the Yenisei River, Irkutsk (325,000) on the Angara tributary of the Yenisei near Lake Baikal, and Ulan-Ude (175,000) and Chita (175,000), east of Lake Baikal.

Important gold-mining centers are scattered throughout central and eastern Siberia. Although production figures are not definitely known, this part of the Soviet Union is considered to be one of the major gold-mining areas of the world. Mining activities are mainly centered in the basin of the Kolyma River, previously referred to under the Soviet Far East, and in the basin of the Aldan River, a tributary of the Lena. Large coal deposits are mined at Cheremkhovo on the Trans-Siberian Railroad west of Irkutsk, and a variety of metals, including tin, tungsten, molybdenum, manganese, lead, and zinc are secured in small to medium quantities from widely scattered mining areas tributary to the railroad. Large coal reserves in the basins of the Lena River, the Lower Tunguska tributary of the Yenisei, and the Bureya tributary of the Amur have scarcely begun to be exploited.

Aside from the irregularly distributed centers of lumbering, mining, and transportation, the Northern Lands are mainly occupied by non-Slavic peoples who eke out a living by reindeer herding, hunting, trapping, fishing, and, in the more favored areas of the taiga, by cattle raising and a precarious form of cultivation. The domesticated reindeer is an especially valuable source of livelihood for the tundra peoples, providing meat, milk, hides for clothing and tents, and serving as a draft animal. The Yakuts, a Mongoloid people inhabit-

ing the basin of the Lena River, are among the most prominent of the non-Slavic ethnic groups. Their political unit, the Yakut Autonomous Soviet Socialist Republic, is larger in area than any of the Union Republics except the Russian Soviet Federated Socialist Republic, within which it is contained. However, the Yakut Autonomous SSR has only an estimated 450,000 people inhabiting an area of 1,182,000 square miles. The capital city of Yakutsk, on the middle Lena River, has now an estimated population of 60,000 despite its exceedingly cold winters. A highway connects Yakutsk with the Trans-Siberian Railroad between Chita and Khabarovsk. Steamers on the broad and deep Lena River provide a connection with the Northern Sea Route during the warm season.

Although the efforts of the Soviet government to develop the Northern Lands have received much publicity and have achieved considerable success in the fields of mining, lumbering, and transportation, it seems probable that these lands will continue to be a thinly-settled frontier region for a long time to come. A considerable amount of experimentation has been carried on with quick-growing and frost-resistant crops and with various forms of hothouse culture, but it seems doubtful that these can form the basis for a really flourishing agriculture except in very limited areas. The problems of the Soviet Union in the foregoing respects are similar to those of Canada, and the efforts of the two nations to develop their northern territories will afford instructive comparisons in the coming decades.

PART 4
The Middle East

Introduction to the Middle East

14

The term Middle East, as used in this book, refers to an elongated region stretching for 6000 miles across northern Africa and southwestern Asia from the Atlantic Ocean to the borders of India, China, and Soviet Asia. This region includes some 30 different countries, but the majority of these are relatively small in area and population. Only six countries have populations of 10 million or more: West Pakistan, the largest, had some 34 million in 1951; Turkey, Egypt, and Iran have in the neighborhood of 20 to 23 million, Ethiopia-Eritrea,

about 16 million, and Afghanistan, about 13 million. Among the six countries Afghanistan is the smallest in area, with 250,-000 square miles (a little smaller than Texas), while Iran is the largest, with 630,-000 square miles. A number of Middle Eastern countries having populations of less than 10 million are impressively large in area. The largest country, the Anglo-Egyptian Sudan, has 967,500 square miles —nearly a third the area of the United States. Other countries exceeding Iran in area include Saudi Arabia, Algeria, and

Many ingenious devices are employed to secure water in the arid Middle East. The donkeys in this photo taken in Saudi Arabia, walk back and forth on the runway to pull up to the surface camel skins filled with water, which are automatically dumped into an irrigation ditch. [*Standard Oil Company* (N. J.).]

TABLE 13

MIDDLE EAST: AREA AND POPULATION DATA

COUNTRY	POLITICAL STATUS	AREA (THOUSAND SQUARE MILES)	POPULATION (MILLIONS)	DENSITY (PER SQUARE MILE: TO NEAREST WHOLE NUMBER)
Egypt	Independent Republic	386.2	21.43 (1952 Est.)	55
Saudi Arabia	Independent Kingdom	900.0	7.00 (1952 Est.)	8
Yemen	Independent Kingdom	75.0	4.50 (1953 Est.)	60
Iraq	Independent Kingdom	168.1	5.10 (1950 Est.)	30
Syria	Independent Republic	72.0	3.50 (1953 Est.)	49
Jordan	Independent Kingdom	37.0	1.33 (1952 Est.)	36
Lebanon	Independent Republic	3.9	1.32 (1952 Est.)	336
Libya	Independent Kingdom	680.0	1.15 (1952 Est.)	2
Totals: Arab League States		2322.2	45.33	20
Turkey	Independent Republic	296.2	22.46 (1953 Est.)	76
Iran	Independent Kingdom	630.0	19.56 (1952 Est.)	31
Afghanistan	Independent Kingdom	250.0	13.00 (1953 Est.)	52
West Pakistan[a]	Sovereign State of Commonwealth of Nations	311.4	33.80 (1951 Census)	109
Kashmir[a]	Disputed area between Pakistan and India	82.3	4.08 (1953 Est.)	50
Totals: Moslem, non-Arab states		1569.9	92.90	59
Israel	Independent Republic	8.0	1.65 (1953 Est.)	205
Ethiopia	Independent Empire	409.3	15.00 (1951 Est.)	37
Eritrea	Autonomous unit in Ethiopian-Eritrean Federation	45.8	1.10 (1951 Est.)	24
Totals: All Independent States		4355.2	155.98	36
Anglo-Egyptian Sudan	Territory under joint British-Egyptian administration pending independence	967.5	8.76 (1952 Est.)	9
British Somaliland	British Protectorate	68.0	0.64 (1952 Est.)	9
Aden	British Colony and Protectorate	112.0	0.90 (1952 Est.)	8
Cyprus	British Colony	3.6	0.50 (1952 Est.)	139
Oman	Sultanate (technically independent) under British influence	82.0	0.75 (1953 Est.)	9
Trucial Oman	Group of seven British-protected Sheikdoms	6.0	0.12 (1953 Est.)	20
Qatar	British-protected Sheikdom	4.0	0.02 (1953 Est.)	5
Kuwait	British-protected Sheikdom	6.0	0.17 (1953 Est.)	28
Bahrein	British-protected Sheikdom	0.23	0.11 (1953 Est.)	478
Totals: British dependencies and protected states		1249.3	11.97	10
Algeria	French Government General	846.1	9.14 (1952 Est.)	11
Tunisia	French Protectorate	48.3	3.60 (1952 Est.)	75
French Morocco	French Protectorate	151.0	8.19 (1953 Est.)	54

TABLE 13 (Continued)

MIDDLE EAST: AREA AND POPULATION DATA

French Somaliland	French Overseas Territory	8.5	0.06 (1951 Est.)	7
Totals: French possessions		1053.9	20.99	20
Spanish Morocco	Figures include the Moroccan Protectorate, Ifni Colony, and four cities governed as parts of Spain	18.5	1.21 (1952 Est.)	66
Spanish Sahara	Spanish Colony	105.4	0.04 (1952 Est.)	0.4
Somalia	Italian trusteeship under United Nations, pending independence	198.3	1.28 (1952 Est.)	7
Tangier	Zone under international administration	0.23	0.17 (1952 Est.)	733
Totals: Dependent areas		2625.6	35.66	13
Grand totals		6980.8	191.64	27

ᵃ Pakistan is divided into two sections separated by the Republic of India. West Pakistan and the disputed state of Kashmir are considered to be transitional between the Middle East and the Orient. East Pakistan has a very different type of natural environment and economy. For the purposes of this text it is not considered a part of the Middle East.

Libya. Areas, populations, and population densities of the Middle Eastern countries are given in Table 13.

Among the countries of the Middle East, importance is not necessarily a function of size. The new state of Israel has carved out a niche for itself despite the opposition of larger neighbors, and the rich petroleum deposits of Iraq, Kuwait, Bahrein, and Qatar have magnified the importance of these small countries in the eyes of other nations. Morocco, likewise, because of its strategic location, phosphate and other mineral deposits, and potentialities for agricultural and industrial development, ranks in world importance with countries which are larger in area, population, or both.

The margins of the Middle East are mainly occupied by oceans, seas, high mountains, and deserts: to the west the Atlantic Ocean; to the south the Sahara Desert, the highlands of East Africa, and the Indian Ocean; to the north the Mediterranean, Black, and Caspian Seas, together with mountains and deserts lining the southern land frontiers of the Soviet Union; to the east the Thar Desert of India and the great mountain knot of Inner Asia. The Middle East itself is mainly composed of arid or semi-arid plains and plateaus, together with considerable areas of rugged mountains.

Although this region exhibits much variety from place to place, two important factors help to give it unity: (1) the dominance of dry climates and (2) the Mohammedan or Moslem religion. The latter is the principal religion in all of the Middle Eastern countries except four: Israel, where Judaism prevails; Lebanon and Ethiopia, where ancient forms of Christianity are dominant; and the British-controlled island of Cyprus in the eastern Mediterranean, where the population mainly adheres to the Greek Orthodox Church. Even these four countries have Mohammedan minorities; indeed in Lebanon the Mohammedans constitute 45 percent of the population.

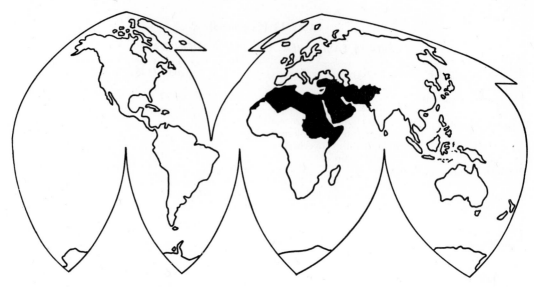

World location of the Middle East. (*Boggs Equal Area Projection, copyright A. J. Nystrom & Co.*)

World Importance of the Middle East

Throughout much of recorded history the dry and sparsely settled Middle East has been a major barrier interposed between the humid lands of Europe, eastern Asia, and trans-Saharan Africa. Even today no continuous rail line extends completely across the region in either a north-south or east-west direction, and motor highways are few and widely separated. The traveler crossing this part of the world does best to proceed by sea or air. One of the world's great trunk routes of sea transportation, the Mediterranean-Asiatic route, passes through the Middle East via the Suez Canal and Red Sea. Through traffic by air is also highly developed. The cities of Cairo, Istanbul, Beirut, Baghdad, Basra, Karachi, Tunis, and Algiers are important stops on international air routes crossing the region. Indeed Cairo, where major routes from Europe, southern Africa, and the Far East converge, is one of the world's greatest centers of air transportation.

However, the role of the Middle East as a barrier or transit land should not be over-emphasized. This region has made vital contributions to the world. The earliest known civilizations originated here, and the great monotheistic world religions of Judaism, Christianity, and Islam (Mohammedanism) arose here. Many of the well-known plants and animals upon which world agriculture is based were domesticated in the Middle East. "Most of the vegetable foods we eat originated in this area. Wheat, barley, and rye, of the small grains, and possibly millet. Broad beans, chick-peas, lentils, and vetches, of the legumes. Onions, leeks, garlic, of the lilies. Figs and the vine, and all the delicious varieties of muskmelon that cool and slake the thirsty traveler in the heat of summer. Pomegranates . . . ; olives and sesame for oil; apples, quinces, and pears, of the roses . . . ; peaches, plums, apricots, and almonds; walnuts, saffron. Dates in the desert oases and along the exotic rivers." [1] The list of common animals domesticated in

[1] Carleton S. Coon, *Caravan: The Story of the Middle East*. New York: Holt, 1951. P. 23. Used by permission of the author and the publisher.

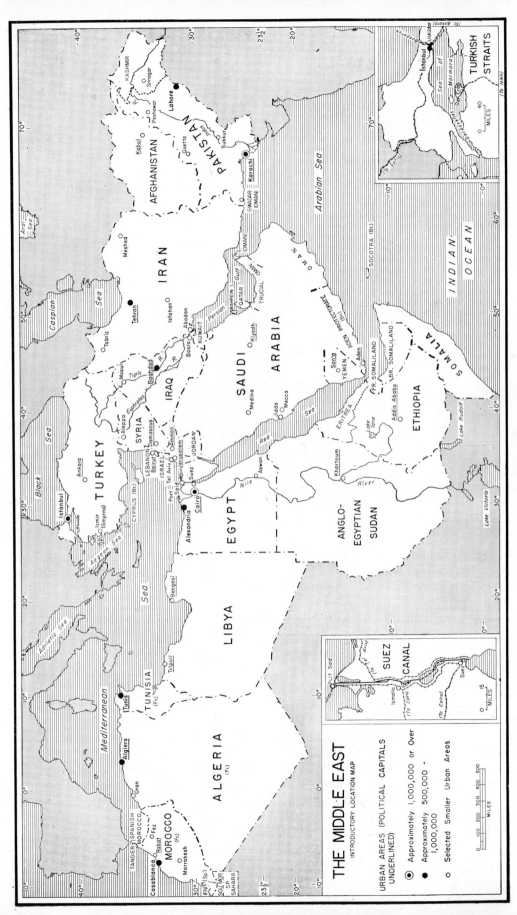

Index map of the Middle East.

A scene in the Middle Eastern deserts. Camels wait patiently as their Arab masters face meditatively toward Mecca and pray during one of the five prayer periods of the day which Mohammedans observe. (*Arabian American Oil Company.*)

this region includes horses, oxen, sheep, goats, pigs, and dogs. "We who eat roast beef on Sundays and pork with our beans seldom wonder whom to thank for these gifts, other than the ultimate and divine Source of all bounty. It was the ancient hunters and earliest farmers of the Middle East who first rounded up these animals and tamed them for their use. Try to imagine yourself on foot, armed with a bow and arrow, a length of cordage, and a stone ax, either alone or accompanied by a dozen

of your fellows, setting out to catch a wild bull in the forest or a wild sheep on the mountain crags." [2]

Despite its barrier nature, the Middle East has not lived in isolation, but for 50 centuries or more has had a history of vigorous interaction with the outside world. Most of the historic world empires have included portions of this region. Some of these empires originated inside the region and others outside. As a result the political and military role of the Middle East has

[2] *Ibid.*, p. 24. Used by permission of the author and the publisher.

alternately been that of conqueror and conquered. During modern times the main imperial powers have been Turkey, Britain, France, and Italy. The Turkish Empire was liquidated as a result of World War I and the Italian Empire as a result of World War II. France and Great Britain still have colonial holdings in the Middle East, but these nations have lost some of their possessions in recent years and perhaps will lose others before the current wave of anticolonialism in this region has run its course. Most of the Middle East is freer of foreign domination today than it has been for many centuries.

In our day the Middle East has become important to the world as a source of oil from vast deposits encircling the Persian Gulf. It has also achieved a certain notoriety for its collection of troublesome political problem areas—Palestine, Morocco, Kashmir, the Suez Canal Zone, to name a few of the more prominent ones. Several outside powers have important political, economic, and military commitments or in-terests in this region. The United Kingdom and France, for example, are vitally dependent on Middle Eastern oil. In addition, each of the latter nations still has colonial possessions in the area, and each is concerned with maintaining the security of lines of communication across the Middle East which afford connections with still other dependent territories or associated Commonwealth states in trans-Saharan Africa, southern and eastern Asia, and the Pacific Ocean area. The Middle East is also an area of considerable interest to the Russians, who hope to exploit its current unrest for their own political ends, and perhaps gain access to its oil deposits. Although the United States is farther away, this is likewise a region of great consequence to Americans, particularly in strategic terms. Oil, security of sea communications, and air bases such as those already established in Morocco, Libya, and Saudi Arabia would appear to be the primary American interests. American companies have invested large sums in oil facilities here.

The Strenuous Middle Eastern Environment

On the whole, nature has not been kind to the Middle East. This hot, dry region is notably deficient in natural resources. With a few conspicuous exceptions, water, wood, good soil, and mineral resources are in short supply almost everywhere.

▶ Dominance of Dry Climates

For the Middle East as a whole, the most critical resource deficiency is lack of moisture. Most of this region is part of the Dry World—a vast belt of deserts and dry grasslands extending across Africa and Asia from the Atlantic Ocean nearly to the Pacific. At least three fourths of the Middle East has an average yearly rainfall of less than 10 inches—an amount too small for most types of nonirrigated agriculture under the prevailing temperature conditions.

Some fair-sized areas bordering the Mediterranean Sea have 20 to 40 inches of rain, but most of it falls during the cool season. Only in the mountainous interior of Ethiopia and the southern part of the Anglo-Egyptian Sudan—areas not typically Middle Eastern in environment—does a rainfall of more than 20 inches coincide with optimum temperatures for crop growth.

▶ Temperature Regimes

Middle Eastern climates exhibit the comparatively large seasonal and diurnal ranges of temperature which are characteristic of dry lands. Summers in the lowlands are very hot almost everywhere. Many places regularly experience daily maxima of 100°F. for weeks at a time. Shade temperatures of 130° or higher have been re-

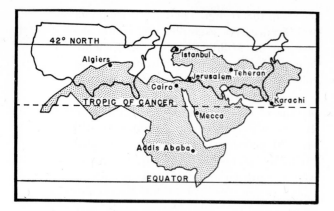

The Middle East compared in latitude and area with the United States.

corded in parts of the Sahara. Day after day a baking sun assails the parched land from a cloudless sky, and hot, dusty winds add to the discomfort of the inhabitants. Only in the mountainous sections or in some places near the sea do higher elevations or sea breezes temper the intense heat of midsummer.

Lower temperatures of the winter season bring relief from the summer heat, and the more favored places receive enough precipitation to grow winter wheat or barley and a limited number of other cool-season crops. In general, Middle Eastern winters may be characterized as cool to mild. However, fairly severe winters are experienced in the high interior basins and plateaus of Iran, Afghanistan, West Pakistan, and Turkey, and the temperature occasionally drops below freezing even in parts of the Sahara and Arabian Deserts that lie along the borders of the tropics. Only in the far southern, atypical climatic areas of the upper Nile Basin and Somaliland do the temperatures remain consistently high throughout the year.

The Middle Eastern deserts have exceptionally large diurnal (daily) ranges of temperature—one of the most characteristic features of desert climates. Clear skies, the relatively low humidity of the air, and the lack of a vegetation cover permit the sun's

rays to heat the earth rapidly by day, but also promote a rapid escape of heat from the earth at night. Extreme cases are recorded of places in the Sahara that have witnessed a maximum of well over 100° and a minimum of below 32° within a 24-hour period.

▶ *Types of Climate*

Maps showing climates classified by type reveal the Middle East to be predominantly an area of desert or steppe climate, with smaller fringing areas of mediterranean (dry-summer subtropical) climate, highland climate, and, in the extreme south, atypical tropical savanna climate.

The areas of *desert climate* include the great Sahara Desert of northern Africa, largest in the world; the immense desert which covers most of the Arabian Peninsula and extends northward into Iraq, Jordan, and Syria; and smaller deserts in Iran and Afghanistan and along the lower Indus River in West Pakistan. These areas exhibit characteristically low and erratic rainfall averaging 5 to 10 inches a year or less. Occasional violent downpours alternate with rainless periods lasting for months or years at a time. Although some of the precipitation sinks in the ground and thus replenishes the meager supply of ground water, most of it runs off quickly or is lost through evaporation. Such rainfall is of little or no use for agriculture. Scattered areas of desert exhibit the familiar dunes of shifting sand, but rocky or gravelly surfaces are far more common. The characteristic vegetation is composed of widely spaced woody shrubs, with occasional tufts of grass. Short-lived flowering annuals lend a touch of color to the landscape following the infrequent rains.

Areas of *steppe climate*, while dry, are better supplied with moisture than the deserts because of greater rainfall, less evaporation, or a combination of these. Such areas are classed as semi-arid rather than arid. An annual average of 10 to 20 inches

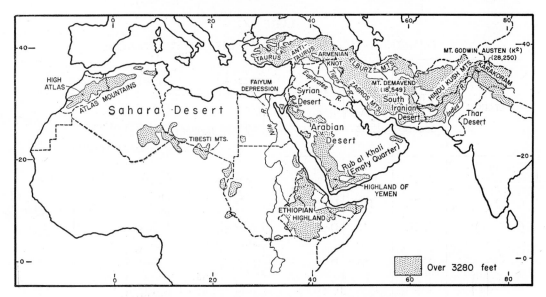

Principal highlands and deserts of the Middle East.

of precipitation is typical, though deviations occur at both the upper and lower ends of this scale. The natural vegetation is more closely spaced than in the deserts and includes a larger proportion of grasses. Thus better forage is available for livestock, and the steppes are far superior to the deserts as grazing lands. However, the undependable nature of the rainfall renders crop growing precarious except where irrigation water is available. The steppe climate characteristically occupies a zone of transition between the desert and more humid lands beyond. For example, two steppe zones, one on the north and one on the south, separate the Sahara Desert from areas of mediterranean climate and tropical savanna climate, respectively.

The Middle Eastern areas of *mediterranean or dry-summer subtropical climate* are principally confined to the borderlands of the Mediterranean Sea in northwestern Africa and southwestern Asia. It entirely encloses Lebanon and Cyprus. The most productive farming areas of Morocco, Algeria, Tunisia, Turkey, Syria, and Israel are found in this climate zone. Rainfall averaging 15 to 40 inches annually provides more moisture for crop growth than is available in the steppe climate, but the characteristic regime of rainy winters and dry summers is a handicap to agriculture. Both the climate and associated agricultural activities conform generally to the pattern already described for Southern Europe in Chapter 10.

Areas of *tropical savanna climate* are found near the equator in parts of the Anglo-Egyptian Sudan, Ethiopia, and Somaliland. This humid climate type, occupying the outer margins of the rainy tropics, is not typical of the Middle East. It is characterized by high temperatures the year round, a complete absence of frost, an annual rainfall averaging 20 to 60 inches or more, and a dry season lasting most or all of the winter half-year. The tropical savanna climate is described more fully in Chapters 16 and 23.

Highland climates, varying in character according to altitude and distance from the equator, are found in the higher mountain areas of the Middle East. Table 14 gives climatic data for some representative Middle Eastern stations. Note the unbalanced rainfall regime at all stations listed.

TABLE 14

CLIMATIC DATA FOR SELECTED MIDDLE EASTERN STATIONS

STATION	LATITUDE TO NEAREST WHOLE DEGREE	ELE-VATION ABOVE SEA LEVEL (FEET)	TYPE OF CLIMATE	AVERAGE TEMPERATURE (DEGREES F. TO NEAREST WHOLE DEGREE)			PRECIPITATION	
				AN-NUAL	JANUARY	JULY	ANNUAL AVERAGE (TO NEAR-EST INCH)	PERCENT OCTOBER-MARCH
Tehran (Iran)	36°N.	4002	Steppe	62°	35°	85°	9"	79%
Baghdad (Iraq)	33°N.	110	Desert	73°	48°	94°	6"	81%
Karachi (Pakistan)	25°N.	13	Desert	77°	67°	85° (June)	8"	17%
Cairo (Egypt)	30°N.	67	Desert	69°	54°	81°	1"	92%
Khartoum (A. E. Sudan)	16°N.	1247	Desert	85°	74°	92° (June)	6"	3%
Istanbul (Turkey)	41°N.	164	Mediterranean	57°	41°	74°	29"	68%
Algiers (Algeria)	37°N.	194	Mediterranean	64°	53°	77° (Au-gust)	30"	81%
Jerusalem (Israel-Jordan)	32°N.	2485	Mediterranean	63°	47°	75°	16"	93%
Mongalla (A. E. Sudan)	6°N.	1440	Tropical Savanna	81°	82°	78°	39"	23%
Addis Ababa (Ethiopia)	9°N.	8038	Tropical Highland	59°	56° (De-cember)	62° (April)	49"	13%

▶ Role of the Mountains in Water Supply

Mountains play a vital role in the economy of the Middle East. Indeed, by furnishing the principal supplies of water for irrigation and household use, they make life possible for most of the inhabitants of this dry region.

The mountains of the Middle East are found in three principal areas. (1) In extreme northwestern Africa the Atlas Mountains of Morocco, Algeria, and Tunisia lie between the Mediterranean Sea and the Sahara Desert. The High Atlas of Morocco reaches elevations of more than 12,000 feet

and has permanent snowfields. (2) A larger area of mountains occupies the northeastern quarter of the Middle East. It stretches across Turkey, Iran, Afghanistan, and West Pakistan, and includes the highest peaks in the region. The loftiest and best-known mountains in Turkey and Iran are the Taurus, Anti-Taurus, Elburz, and Zagros Mountains, which radiate outward from the rugged Armenian Knot in the tangled border country where Turkey,

A cedar forest in the Atlas Mountains of Morocco. Forests of this quality are found in only a few parts of the Middle East. (*French Embassy Press and Information Division.*)

Iran, and the Soviet Union meet. The higher summits in these ranges attain elevations of 10,000 to nearly 19,000 feet. The mountains in this quarter of the Middle East culminate in the great Hindu Kush mountain system of Afghanistan and West Pakistan, which has one peak reaching 25,-000 feet, and the Karakoram Range, in Kashmir, where Mount Godwin Austen (K²), second highest in the world, rises to 28,250 feet. (3) The third principal area of mountains is found in Ethiopia and Yemen, bordering the southern end of the Red Sea. The extensive highland of Ethiopia has a number of scattered summits higher than 10,000 feet, and at least one approximately 15,000 feet. The smaller highland of Yemen has peaks ranging from 7000 to slightly more than 12,000 feet. Lower, discontinuous mountain ranges extend northward from Ethiopia and Yemen along either side of the Red Sea.

Scattered mountain areas occur elsewhere in the Middle East, for example, the Tibesti Mountains in the central Sahara, which rise to 11,000 feet.

Water originating in mountain rainfall or snowfall often percolates for long distances underground and reaches the surface in springs or is drawn upon by wells in populated areas at the base of the mountains or beyond. Water supplies of this kind are ordinarily sufficient for only a limited local development of irrigation farming. Most of the larger irrigated districts depend on water carried from the mountains by surface streams, a few of which are among the great rivers of the world. The Nile, Tigris-Euphrates, and Indus Rivers provide water for many millions of farmers, and urban dwellers as well, in Egypt and the Sudan, Iraq, and West Pakistan. The earliest known civilizations arose in the valleys of these unique rivers, each of which has supported agriculture for at least forty or fifty centuries.

▶ The Scarcity of Wood

The Middle East is not noteworthy for a rich and varied flora and fauna. Once, long ago, this region was better supplied, but in the course of the many centuries that man has inhabited the Middle East, the original resources have become depleted. An especially critical shortage is a lack of timber. Extensive forests existed in early times, but overcutting and overgrazing have almost wiped them out. Timber has been cut faster than nature could grow it, and the young seedlings have been grazed off by sheep, goats, and camels, with the result that the forests have been unable to reproduce themselves. Lumber in commercial quantities can still be obtained from a few mountain areas, such as the Atlas region of French and Spanish Morocco and Algeria, but the total supply falls far short of the need.

Carleton S. Coon, a leading authority on the Middle East, has written as follows concerning the scarcity of wood: [3]

The fact is that except for China no part of the earth's surface seems to have been so denuded as the Middle East. We read of the orchard that was Morocco in Roman times and see barren hillsides. The Egyptians imported thousands and thousands of trunks of the cedars of Lebanon; and in every museum in the world which contains Egyptological specimens, pieces of that wood appear in the form of coffins or other types of furniture. Solomon used the cedar of Lebanon in building his temple. If you go to Lebanon today, you will see the cedar depicted on the flag of the republic and on the hats of its customs inspectors. But on Mount Lebanon itself, despite recent attempts at conservation and reforestation, not enough remains to furnish the timber for one Gloucester schooner.

. . . In Iran one is struck by the difference between the complete barrenness of the landscape which is either under culti-

---

[3] Coon, *op. cit.*, pp. 20–23. Used by permission of the author and the publisher.

vation or within walking distance of a village, and that of the uninhabited deserts. In the inhabited land children go out every morning with long-handled hoes and sacks to remove every spear of inflammable vegetation, including camel thorn, that the sheep and goats have left behind them; their work is thorough. In the desert, in places too distant from villages to warrant this attention, the traveler is impressed by the abundance of natural flora, in the form of sagebrush and dry stalks of aromatic annuals. Up on the eastern flank of the Elburz . . . I once saw some juniper trees which had been lopped for firewood. "Aren't these protected by law?" I asked a soldier who was with me. "Yes," he replied, "but the government cannot afford to station one of us beside each tree.". . .

It must be remembered that wood serves not only as building material but as fuel as well. Throughout the Middle East charcoal is the most prized fuel, for it gives a hot, smokeless flame, essential in houses designed for summer rather than winter habitation. It also is needed in metallurgy, pottery firing, and bread making. Most people use dung for fuel, for operations such as boiling soup or tea where a critical temperature of 1000° F. or more is not needed. Roasting meat, baking, smelting, and other technical operations requiring hotter fires are community or professional enterprises.

In Iran one of the most striking sights is the half-acre patch of dense poplar forest that grows up-ditch beside each village. These trees grow quickly, and their limbs cling close to the trunks; trees with 4-inch stems grow no more than 18 inches apart. No more efficient way of producing 20-foot poles quickly and on a minimum space could be found. These poplar poles are the standard units of material for rafters, door jambs, window frames, and the like. The forest has moved from the mountain to the valley.

It is easy for us, newly aroused to an interest in conservation, to decry the deforestation of the Middle East. We have lived in a rich land for periods ranging from one to three hundred years, depending on the part of the country, and we have wasted probably no more than half our natural resources in forest and topsoil during that time. In a far poorer environment, over a period of 5000 years and more, the peoples of the Middle East have destroyed only 90 per cent of it. What if they had proceeded at our pace!

► Shortage of Minerals

The Middle East is further handicapped, especially as regards industrialization, by a serious lack of mineral resources. Good deposits of coal are extremely rare. The region is rich in petroleum, but the principal deposits are confined to a few countries bordering the Persian Gulf. Although scattered deposits of metals occur throughout the Middle East, including fairly large reserves of high-grade iron ore in French and Spanish Morocco, Algeria, and Tunisia, few offer much prospect for large-scale exploitation. Good-sized deposits of salt are fairly common in the region, and French North Africa has abundant reserves of phosphate rock, useful as a chemical and fertilizer material. However, the general outlook for extraction of minerals in the Middle East is rather poor. Among the Middle Eastern countries, Turkey and French Morocco would appear to offer the best possibilities at present for industrialization based on a variety of local minerals, although neither of these countries is really outstanding as a producer of minerals in world terms.

The Middle Eastern Landscape

The landscape of this dry region alternates between green and brown, according to the presence or absence of water.

George B. Cressey has described the land surface as one might view it from a plane if one were flying by either of two alternate

This pipeline across the desert (Trans-Arabian Pipeline) carries oil for more than a thousand miles from fields on the shore of the Persian Gulf in Saudi Arabia to a shipping point on the Mediterranean Sea in Lebanon. (*Trans-Arabian Pipe Line Company.*)

These closely-spaced shafts (below) in Saudi Arabia mark the course of a tunnel used to carry irrigation water. The shafts make it possible for workmen to keep the tunnel free of sediment and debris. Similar devices are employed in parts of Iran. [*Standard Oil Company (N. J.).*]

routes across the heart of the Middle East: [4]

What does one see on a flight between Cairo and the Persian Gulf? For 5 hours, at 300 miles an hour, there is an almost total absence of life. As soon as one leaves the last irrigation ditch outside Cairo, the green of the Nile oasis instantly changes to the brown of the desert. One hour eastward there is a glimpse of the Red Sea. Then for 4 hours or more there is the desolation of Arabia. One looks down from the plane at sand dunes and bare rock. If there is an occasional stunted tree or water hole, it is not visible from the air. Not a trace of green is to be seen. Once or twice a keen eye will catch a group of a dozen mud houses, nothing more. This may be a place to study geomorphology, but it is not an attractive spot to make a living.

Then comes the green blue of the Persian Gulf, and one flies over the fabulous oil fields of Dhahran and Bahrein Island, with oil wells, refineries, docks, and air-conditioned comfort, American style.

Or fly from Cairo northeast to Tehran [Teheran], 7 hours away. Here there is plenty of desert, but more of interest. Such a route provides a better glimpse of the Suez Canal, and, in peace time, of Jerusa-lem and the Dead Sea. It is a commentary on the size of Palestine that while one is over the Dead Sea, the Mediterranean is still in sight. Across the Syrian Desert, planes follow one of the pipelines which bring oil from Iraq to the Mediterranean. This thin black line across the barren desert, with pumping stations every few miles, is a comfortable guide across a wilderness where one would hate to be forced down without water. Near Baghdad one crosses the thin green strips of cultivation along the Tigris and Euphrates. In places old irrigation works, long abandoned, stand out in the desert, and ruined cities recall the dramatic history of these valleys. Eastward across the mountains, snow-capped in winter, lies the barren plateau of Iran and the capital city of Tehran. Radiating down the broad alluvial fans one may notice heaps of earth at intervals of a hundred yards. These locate the shafts spaced along the underground tunnels called kanats or karez which bring irrigation water from water-bearing gravels at the base of the mountain. This route from Cairo crosses the Dead Sea depression, with a minus elevation of 1297 feet, and comes within sight of Mount Demavend at 18,549 feet. This is an area of contrasts.

Peoples and Ways of Life

The Middle East is principally inhabited by dark-haired peoples of the Caucasoid racial group. Especially important among the many languages spoken in the region are Arabic and other Semitic languages, Berber and other Hamitic languages, Turkish, Persian, and Urdu (spoken in West Pakistan). Most of the inhabitants of the Middle East are farmers or nomadic herdsmen. The principal areas of dense population are the irrigated valleys of the major rivers and the coast lands of the Mediterranean Sea. The few large cities are mostly political capitals or seaports. Only ten metropolitan cities have populations of approximately half a million or more—Cairo, Karachi, Istanbul, Tehran, Alexandria, Lahore, Casablanca, Tunis, Baghdad, and Algiers. Manufacturing is still mainly confined to handicraft industries, although modern factories are beginning to appear in some of the larger cities.

The Middle East, like other world regions, is sufficiently varied in its ways of living that generalizations concerning the culture of the region as a whole nearly always contain a certain amount of distortion. Nevertheless, a surprising amount of

---

[4] George B. Cressey, "The Land of the Five Seas." *Journal of Geography*, v. 51 (1952), pp. 222–223. Used by permission of the author and the *Journal of Geography*.

uniformity can be discerned in the modes of life pursued in places as far apart as Morocco and Afghanistan. In a broad way, it is possible to distinguish a "Middle Eastern culture" which is characteristic of the entire region in greater or less degree. This culture in its original form has been much affected by influences from Europe and America, particularly in the cities. However, much of the old culture still remains in rural areas and in the older sections of urban places. Some of the characteristic features of the traditional culture of the Middle East have been described as follows by Carleton S. Coon: [5]

Although late to take over the fruits of the industrial revolution, these countries originated two earlier and equally important crises without which the third could not have arisen: the neolithic revolution which brought in agriculture and animal husbandry, and the urban revolution which introduced city life, metalworking, and writing. For over 5000 years the peoples of these countries . . . have been experimenting in the arts of getting a living out of the landscape and getting along with each other. . . .

▶ City Life

Three major ways of life have arisen in concert with one another. One is city life, with thousands of skilled workers, specialists in all kinds of hand industries; with merchants prepared to handle both local and international trade; with palaces and courts in which the political institution functions; with mosques, churches, and temples housing the religious hierarchies, whose prime duty is to maintain the equilibrium of the whole society; and with universities and other educational institutions preparing students for both religious and secular leadership. . . .

Some of the cities, notably Mecca, Kerbela [Karbala], and Meshed, are centers of pilgrimage, and in them the mechanism of caring for religious visitors is well worked out. Pilgrims, coming from all parts of the Islamic world to the holy places, from the Philippines and Morocco, India and Bukhara and China, do much to fortify the unity of the countries with which we are concerned. On the pilgrimage, fellow devotees from different countries meet and converse and exchange ideas. Every year a number of pilgrims decide to stay in one of the countries en route, rather than going home. The uniformity of skills, of architecture, of music, and of literature in these countries reflects this annual intercourse. The pilgrimage has its political effect as well: those Moslems who are living under foreign domination see others who are free; they have a chance to compare their systems of government. The extent to which governments permit pilgrims to pass freely is an index of the security of each government.

▶ Village Life

From the life of cities one can move without pain to that of villages, for the city is a big village as well as a center of industry. The land on the outskirts of the city is tilled by farmers who commute in reverse, and they have done this since the days of Hammurabi. A village is a group of houses located near water and surrounded by agricultural land. It contains a dozen to several hundred families, usually closely related. If the village is on the flatlands, it is usually owned by a sheik or a landlord. While the sheik may be in residence, the landlord usually lives in the city, governing through a local, appointed agent who is in effect the mayor or headman. Rarely, such a village is free, in that the farmers own their land and select their own leader.

If the village is in the mountains, its inhabitants usually form part of a tribal system, and their allegiance is to their tribal chiefs. Since the plains are accessible and defenseless, lowland villagers are seldom noted as fighters, and are usually docile

---

[5] Carleton S. Coon, "Point Four and the Middle East." *Annals of the American Academy of Political and Social Science,* v. 270 (1950), pp. 88–92. One heading has been changed. Used by permission of the author and the *Annals.*

subjects of the central government, whatever it may be. The mountain villagers are relatively healthy, and more warlike, since they have some chance of defending their rocky hideouts, and are used to intervillage and intertribal raids and feuds arising from population pressure. The mountaineers often preserve some archaic form of speech, foreign to that of the dwellers on the plain, wear distinctive clothing, sing distinctive songs, nurse their children on distinctive tribal lore, and have long been a problem to shahs and sultans.

Some of these tribes are seasonally migratory. They pasture their animals in the mountain meadows in summer, and in the fall pack all their belongings onto horses, donkeys, and cattle, and move in a wild rush of dust and sheep dung down to the warmer plain, where they spend the winter pasturing their animals in the new grass which grows with the rain. In the spring they climb back to the mountains. This annual migration may involve the movement of several thousands of human beings and hundreds of thousands of animals over a distance of several hundreds of miles. The country through which they move is inhabited by sedentary people, with whom all kinds of conflicts could easily arise. Hence the tribe needs leadership and a competent private police force to keep all hands in line. This policing of the migration is the practical basis of the tribal organization, which follows patriarchal family lines. Since international boundaries often follow watersheds, and since mountain watersheds make prime summer pasture, many of these tribes are international; hence the worries of shahs and sultans.

▶ *Desert Life*

Another kind of nomadism exists in the deserts. The Baluchi, the Bedouin, the Tuareg, and other camel people of the South Iranian, Arabian, and Sahara deserts are probably the best known of all Middle Easterners to the American public, but the American public little realizes what complex lives the nomads lead. It is as true as it is trite to liken the desert to a sea and the camel to a ship. The agricultural communities along the shore serve as ports and havens to which the fleets of Bedouin come for victualing and re-equipping. But the ships carry their carpenters and machinists, and supply ships come out to service them when they are too busy to leave the banks.

Speaking less metaphorically, the camel nomads are not simple strangers at all, but Arabs or Berbers like their sedentary kinsmen, just as cowboys are Americans or Canadians, and not some special breed or nation. In years of good rainfall the desert provides bountiful pasture during the cool weather; in dry years there must be a scramble for greenery and for water, and in their scramble the strong may well push out the weak. We have had similar troubles over water holes and range in the West. In the good season, traders come out to live with the Bedouin and sell them the goods they need against livestock. At all seasons, a blacksmith will accompany each camp. He is no kin to the men he serves, and hence if they are raided, he, like the merchants, will not be harmed. Thus automatically the supply of metal tools and implements is assured.

If one walks down the streets and through the markets of any large [Middle Eastern] city, one is likely to see not only city men, but also villagers, mountain men, and camel men off the desert. . . . These people have come to town to see the sights and to trade. . . .

▶ *Some Details of Middle Eastern Material Culture*

Many of the picturesque details of Middle Eastern material culture are based on excellent common sense and a maximum utilization of scarce raw materials. Old-fashioned Moslems have little furniture in their houses. They take off their shoes when they enter a room, and sit on clean carpets. They have enough wool to weave carpets, but not enough wood to build bulky tables and chairs. Their food includes much butter, cheese, curds, and other milk products, but little meat. Milking animals in a land of little abundance is less extravagant than butchering them. Pigs have long been forbidden, and one must remember that in a barren land where all vegetable foods grown are needed to feed men, it would be antisocial to fatten a pig.

Old-fashioned Middle Eastern clothing is designed to give the wearer the maximum of comfort, privacy, and dignity. The jellaba of the North African keeps him warm in winter and cool in the hot sun; he can sleep in it, and shield himself from the public gaze when performing natural acts on a barren landscape. The chuddar of the Persian lady covers her decently, and conceals the state of her clothes underneath. On the street, the widow and the judge's wife look alike. Middle Eastern street clothing, by its uniformity and voluminousness, is an instrument of democracy. The shift to Western garb can hardly be in every sense an improvement.

Middle Eastern architecture, with its adobe walls and clever domes, creates out of local mud and a few sticks what we cannot erect here, from exotic materials, for a dollar a cubic foot—a comfortable home. Fuel is a huge bottleneck in the Middle East, and hence the scarcity of burnt brick. . . . We can teach the Middle Easterners little about noninstitutional building.

Individual Middle Eastern Countries and Their Characteristics

In this chapter the individual countries of the Middle East are briefly discussed. The discussion is organized in terms of regional groups of countries, as follows: (1) The Arab States and Israel, (2) The Oil Kingdoms, (3) Afghanistan and Turkey, (4) The Countries of Northwest Africa, and (5) Ethiopia and Somaliland. West Pakistan is discussed with the Indian Realm in Chapter 17.

The Arab States and Israel

Occupying the heart of the Middle East are eight countries—Saudi Arabia, Egypt, Iraq, Syria, Lebanon, Jordan, Yemen, and Libya—which are known collectively as the Arab States and are associated politically in the Arab League. In each of these

An aerial view of the Arabian American Oil Company's marine loading terminal at Ras Tanura, Saudi Arabia. Four tankers can load at one time at one of the piers and two at the other. (*Arabian American Oil Company.*)

Israel and its neighbors.

countries Arabic is the principal language and, except for Lebanon, Mohammedanism is the dominant religion. The Arab States often present a united front in world affairs, although quarrels of long standing among the member countries tend to hinder their functioning as a group. All of these countries are militarily weak, as was demonstrated in 1948 by the small new state of Israel, when that country was unsuccessfully attacked by five of its Arab neighbors.

▶ Israel and Its Neighbors

The immediate neighbors of Israel to the north and east are Lebanon, Syria, and Jordan (formerly Transjordan). The territory occupied by these nations, including Israel, was held by Turkey prior to World War I. When the Turkish Empire was liquidated following the war, Syria and Lebanon became French mandates under

the League of Nations, while Transjordan became a British mandate, as did Palestine, from which Israel was later formed. Syria and Lebanon secured complete independence in 1946 and Transjordan in 1948.

Palestine was partitioned between Israel and Jordan when Israel was constituted in 1948 as an independent homeland for the Jewish population of the world. A total of 708,000 Jewish immigrants, mostly from Europe and the Middle East, entered Israel between May 14, 1948, when the new state was officially proclaimed, and the end of 1952. Aided by outside capital, the Israelis have commenced to develop their small country as a modern state. Existing irrigation facilities are being supplemented by new projects, and industry is being developed. Industrialization is hampered, however, by a general poverty of industrial resources. The country is notably lacking in the mineral fuels, metals, and textile fibers. However, there are valuable reserves of salts suitable for chemical manufacture in the brines of the Dead Sea and in the Negev semi-desert, which occupies most of the southern half of the country. Many of the recent immigrants to Israel are skilled craftsmen, and types of industry are being developed to capitalize on these skills, for example, diamond cutting, and the manufacture of optical equipment, precision instruments, cosmetics, and pharmaceuticals. How much further the Israelis can develop their small, deforested, eroded, and mineral-poor country is a question. However, substantial progress has been made since independence, and Israel shows promise of becoming a truly modern, progressive, industrialized country.

Meanwhile, Israel's relations with her Arab neighbors continue to cloud the country's future. At the time of partition, over 700,000 Arabs whose ancestors had lived in Palestine for centuries were uprooted from their homes to make way for the expected influx of Jewish immigrants. These displaced families, settled in refugee camps in Jordan, Egypt, Lebanon, and Syria, and growing rapidly in numbers through natural increase, have been a major source of bad feeling between Israel and the Arab States. Other difficulties have arisen over the city of Jerusalem, partitioned between Israel and Jordan (population of Israeli side 150,000; Jordan side 75,000). Proposals by the United Nations to create an internationally administered zone including all of Jerusalem and Bethlehem, together with a corridor to the Mediterranean port of Jaffa, have met with no success. The problem of Jerusalem originates in the fact that the city is a holy place for all three of the monotheistic world religions, including Islam as well as Judaism and Christianity. Despite its perilous situation on the boundary with a hostile country, the Israeli-held New City of Jerusalem has been made the capital of Israel. The largest city and principal industrial center of the country, however, is Tel Aviv–Jaffa (400,000), on the Mediterranean coast. The leading seaport and second largest industrial center is Haifa (190,000 with suburbs), north of Tel Aviv.

Another major dispute between Israel and her Arab neighbors concerns the use of water from the Jordan River. This historic stream rises in Lebanon and Syria, and flows southward to the Dead Sea. The lower river forms the boundary between Israel and Jordan. Israel desires to use the water of the Jordan for hydroelectric development and irrigation, but Syria, Lebanon, and Jordan have expressed strong opposition to the projected diversion of the water.

Jordan, bordering Israel on the east, is desert or semi-desert country. The best farming areas and main centers of settlement are in the northwest. Syria and Lebanon, bordering the Mediterranean, receive considerably more rain, although most of it comes in the winter half-year. The principal farming districts of the latter countries are found on discontinuous coastal plains and interior uplands backed by mountain ranges and hills which act as a barrier to moisture-bearing winds from the Mediterranean, and thus create considerable orographic rain and snow. East of the mountains, precipitation diminishes rapidly until true desert is reached in interior Syria. The same general situation with regard to topography and rainfall holds true in Israel, although the interior hills are lower than in Lebanon and Syria. The farm products of these countries bordering the Mediterranean Sea are those characteristic of a mediterranean climate: wheat, grapes, olives, figs, citrus fruits, nuts, some cotton and tobacco, and wool. Irrigation or special dry-farming methods are necessary for summer cropping.

Western and northern Syria, Lebanon, Israel, and northwestern Jordan form the western half of the "Fertile Crescent," a historic strip of cultivable land between the Syrian Desert and the rugged highlands of Turkey and Iran. The eastern half of the Fertile Crescent is the plain of the Tigris and Euphrates Rivers, or the Plain of Mesopotamia, mostly in Iraq. Through the centuries, from the beginning of recorded history, this semicircle of land extending from the Persian Gulf to the Nile Delta has been followed by the main caravan tracks connecting Asia with northern Africa. It has also served as a pathway for marching armies—Assyrians, Persians, Egyptians, Macedonians, Romans, Crusaders, Arabs, Turks, and others have come this way at various times. The countries of the Fertile Crescent have probably been overrun by foreign armies more times than any other group of countries in the world. These are historic lands, with a record of civilized human settlement dating back for thousands of years. Damascus (335,000), the capital of Syria, is perhaps the oldest continuously occupied large city in the world. Somewhat larger than Damascus is another inland city, Aleppo (363,000), an ancient caravan center in northern Syria. The old

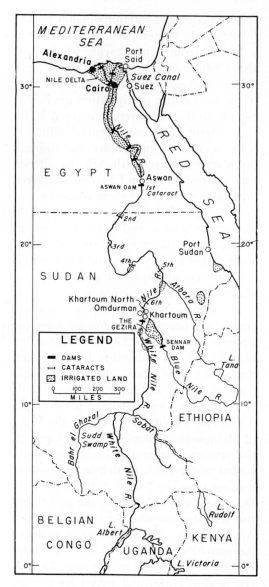

The Nile Basin.

▶ Egypt—The "Gift of the Nile"

At the southwest, Israel borders Egypt, which is probably the most influential of the Arab States. It is certainly the largest in population, having three times as many people as its nearest competitor, Saudi Arabia. This ancient land, the home of one of the oldest known civilizations, is described in the following excerpts from an article by two geographers, George H. T. Kimble and Dorothy L. Weitz: [1]

As long ago as 430 B.C., Herodotus observed in his *History* that "Egypt is an acquired country, the gift of the river." This characterization is just as valid today; for, with the exception of the Faiyum depression and some smaller oases in the Western Desert, the only part of Egypt that is regularly in cultivation is the 3½ per cent of the land that can be irrigated from the Nile. . . . In this small area, made up of the triangular delta north of Cairo and the narrow, ribbon-like valley to the south, live more than 95 per cent of Egypt's 20 million people. The rest live either in the oases or on the surrounding deserts in the wake of their wandering flocks.

Nowhere else in the world is the contrast between the desert and the sown so dramatic, or the transition from solitary waste to teeming valley so sharp. And nowhere else does the well-being of man hang by so tenuous a thread. Fortunately the "thread" never breaks. Formerly, it is true, the annual fluctuations of the Nile gave rise to constant anxiety, but the construction of the dam at Aswan in 1902, and the six supplementary barrages downstream, as well as the two upstream, have removed the grim specter of famine. Even so, the rises and falls of the water level are still the subject of as much comment among the *fellahin* [peasants] as the oscillations of the barometer are among the farmers of the prairies. Indeed, the Nile is to the Egyptian's conversation what the weather is to the American's.

Phoenician city of Beirut (380,000), on the Mediterranean, is the capital, largest city, and main seaport of Lebanon. Equipped with modern harbor facilities and an important international airport, Beirut is one of the busiest centers of transportation and commerce in the Middle East. Rail lines connect it with Syria and Israel.

[1] George H. T. Kimble and Dorothy L. Weitz, "Egypt." *Focus*, v. 2, no. 4 (1951), pp. 1–2. Used by permission of *Focus*, published by the American Geographical Society of New York.

The ancient Egyptians, who believed that the swelling of the Nile represented the tears of the goddess Isis shed in compassion for her rain-starved people, early learned to raise crops on the flooded margins of their river and to supplement the floods by means of simple water-lifting devices. In most parts of the Nile Valley the ancient *shaduf* (consisting of little more than a pole and bucket), the *saqia* (in which the water is raised by a rotary wheel furnished with buckets, powered by a beast of burden), and the Archimedean screw are still employed to fill the irrigation ditches. Thanks to these and more modern machinery, including the motor-driven pumps now coming into vogue, especially in the Delta, no less than 70 per cent of the total population of Egypt contrive to live off the soil. In few other places on earth is land cropped so intensively or so continuously. Two, and even three, crops are often raised off the same piece of soil in the course of a twelvemonth, and yields are generally high; for this the well-regulated water supply, the long-lasting fertility of the valley silts, and the growing employment of artificial manures are primarily responsible. Given a more lavish use of such manures, the demand for which at present outstrips the supply, even greater yields could be obtained.

Cotton, the long-staple Egyptian variety, is the leading commercial crop; although occupying only 20 per cent of the total cultivated area, it accounts for almost 80 per cent of the country's exports. Because of lively demand and high prices, it is especially favored on the large estates, on which, in fact, most of the cotton is grown. Where the *fellah,* attracted by the cash rewards, has tried to emulate his wealthy landlord, he has frequently finished the season with not enough grain to feed himself, and not enough money to buy it at the local market. The usual food crops are corn (a staple in the Egyptian diet), wheat, barley, rice, fruit, grain sorghum, and sugar cane.

For the fellah, life is hard. His tools are those of his ancestors—the hoe, the wooden plow, the hand sickle, and the threshing board. His dwelling is a crude, fly-infested, two-room mud hut sheltering family, water buffalo, and chickens alike. He owns little clothing and knows few comforts. He depends on the Nile for both drinking water and sewage disposal, and his wife and children collect dung for fuel. Like three-fourths of his fellow countrymen, he is afflicted with disease (notably hookworm, schistosomiasis, tuberculosis, and malaria). He is prolific, for his Islamic religion honors large families, and his children (numbering usually anywhere from four to seven) are a needed asset in the fields; but he can expect one out of every four babies born to him to die within the year. It is only the exceptional fellah who can read and write, and because of the insistent needs of his land and the exactions of his landlord, he is even reluctant to send his children to school.

Most of the land is held under an almost feudal landholding system. More than three-fourths of those actively engaged in agriculture either are landless or own tiny plots of less than one-half acre. Furthermore, the pressure of population has created a land hunger, forcing the price of additional land beyond the reach of the average cultivator, who must supplement his income with the low and uncertain wages of seasonal labor on the large cotton estates.

In 1952 the reactionary government of King Farouk was overthrown by a revolution sponsored by certain elements of the Egyptian Army. The revolutionary government proclaimed Egypt a republic and promised active measures to improve the land tenure situation and the general status of the peasantry. Such measures have a vital relation to industrial development, also being fostered by the new regime. An increased amount of industry is badly needed to raise the standard of living in the country—a result partially attainable by draining off some of the surplus labor from overcrowded rural districts. Rural population densities in Egypt are already 700–1000 or more per square mile, and the population is increasing rapidly. In order to develop properly, however, Egyptian industry needs the support of an adequate home market, which the impoverished peasantry cannot provide at present. As in many underdeveloped countries, industrial development in Egypt is hindered by the self-same poverty it could help to cure.

Further increases in industry will also be handicapped by a shortage of natural resources. Egypt has no forests or coal mines; oil deposits are present along the Gulf of Suez, but the production is not sufficient for the country's needs. One of the most promising mineral resources is a sizable reserve of iron ore in the vicinity of Aswan, several hundred miles up the Nile Valley from the Mediterranean. Egypt's first iron and steel plant was under construction near Cairo in early 1955. Phosphate, low-grade manganese ore, sodium salts, gold, and building stone complete the list of minerals known to be available in commercial quantities. Hydroelectricity from a new generating station scheduled for completion in 1958 at the Aswan Dam can help meet the need for increased sources of power, and nitrates secured from a new fixation plant at the same site will provide a much-needed fertilizer material. An immense new dam on the Nile to be constructed 4 miles south of Aswan Dam over a 10-year period commencing in 1955 will supply additional hydroelectric power as well as water with which to irrigate large new acreages of farm land.

In the past the development of industry has been handicapped by a lack of investment capital, and the new revolutionary regime has taken steps to encourage foreign investment. However, in late 1954 it was too early to forecast the ultimate success of such efforts, or the success of other measures designed to raise living standards in the country. The new government was known to be opposed by powerful interests, including many of the large landowners as well as the more reactionary Mohammedan leaders. Even among the more devout peasants, ideas of progress were apt to be condemned as dangerous or heretical.

About half a million workers are currently employed in industry, mainly in Cairo (2,100,000), the capital, and Alexandria (925,000), the principal seaport, located, respectively, at the head and western seaward edge of the Nile Delta. Textiles and food processing are the main branches of industry. "The new, Western side of Egypt is most in evidence in Cairo, Alexandria, and other urban centers; here air-conditioned apartment buildings (many of them built on erstwhile productive farmland), Parisian fashions, chromium-plated automobiles, American movies, and European sports command a wide and ever-growing acceptance." [2]

• *The Suez Canal Zone.* Recent years have seen bitter controversies between Egypt and the United Kingdom, which formerly held the country as a protectorate. One of the major disputes has concerned the Suez Canal Zone, legally Egyptian territory, but garrisoned by Britain up to 1954 under an agreement made with Egypt in 1936. Rising nationalism in Egypt following World War II led to repeated demands for the evacuation of all British forces and return of the Canal Zone to full Egyptian control. In the summer of 1954, after much negotiation, a settlement was reached whereby Britain agreed to remove its troops, but with the privilege of reactivating the Suez base in the event of an attack on any of the eight Arab League states or Turkey by an outside power. The island of Cyprus in the eastern Mediterranean was to replace the Canal Zone as Britain's major military base in the Middle East.

The principal focus of attention in the Suez Canal Zone is, of course, the canal it-

---

[2] Kimble and Weitz, *op. cit.*, p. 3. Used by permission of *Focus* and the American Geographical Society of New York.

self, which forms a vital link in Britain's sea communications to the Indian and Pacific Ocean areas, and is used by ships of many other nations as well. Unlike the Panama Canal, in which ships are raised or lowered to successive water levels by means of massive locks, the Suez Canal is entirely a sea-level canal with no lock facilities of any kind. The canal, which connects the Mediterranean with the Gulf of Suez and Red Sea across the low Isthmus of Suez, was completed in 1869 under the direction of a noted French canal builder, Ferdinand de Lesseps. The facilities are operated by a semi-private Egyptian corporation, the Suez Canal Company, in which the controlling financial interest is British but the actual management largely French. The concession granted the company by Egypt expires in 1968, at which time the canal will revert to the Egyptian government. The total length of the Suez waterway, including dredged approach channels and the Bitter Lakes, is 107 miles, with the average time required for passage being around 13 hours. In 1952 a record total of 83.4 million tons of cargo passed through the canal, as compared with 36.1 million tons through the Panama Canal in the 1952–1953 fiscal year. Petroleum, carried by three fourths of all northbound ships, is by far the largest single item of cargo. At opposite ends of the canal are the seaports of Port Said (178,000 with suburbs) on the Mediterranean and Suez (108,000) on the Gulf of Suez. A small subsidiary canal brings fresh water to the arid Canal Zone from the Nile.

▶ The Anglo-Egyptian Sudan

The future of the Anglo-Egyptian Sudan has provided a second major focus of controversy between Egypt and Britain. This vast, sparsely populated tropical country adjoining Egypt on the south began to be governed as a joint British-Egyptian condominium in 1899. Egyptian demands for British withdrawal, plus agitation by the Sudanese themselves, led to an agreement in 1953 whereby the Sudan would be allowed to choose between independence and some form of union with Egypt after a three-year transition period. Although Egypt has important cultural and historical ties with its neighbor to the south, the major Egyptian interest centers in the Nile River. It is in the Sudan that the Nile receives all of its major tributaries, and the river system offers considerable prospects for increased water control to bring more land into agricultural use in Egypt as well as the Sudan itself. More than a million acres of irrigated land are already under cultivation in the Sudan, mainly in the Gezira irrigation project south of Khartoum. Water for the latter project is supplied from the Sennar Dam on the important Blue Nile tributary, which rises in Ethiopia and enters the main Nile at Omdurman. By far the most important cash product of the Sudan is long-staple Egyptian cotton, grown under irrigation and exported, mainly to Great Britain, through the modern harbor facilities of Port Sudan (47,500) on the Red Sea. However, livestock raising on a subsistence basis is the principal means of support for the majority of the Sudanese population, many of whom are pastoral nomads. In 1952 the Sudan was estimated to have 5.5 million cattle, 1.5 million camels, 6 million sheep, and 4.3 million goats.

Most of the country is a vast plain, although a small, isolated mountain area in the extreme west rises at one point to 10,-000 feet. In both physical and cultural characteristics the Sudan is transitional between the Middle East and Negro Africa. There is a great contrast between the arid Saharan north, peopled by Arabic-speaking Moslems who are basically Caucasoid in racial characteristics though with some Negroid admixture; and the seasonally rainy equatorial south, with its grassy savannas and pagan Negroid tribes. The largest urban district, formed by the capital, Khartoum, and the adjoining cities of Omdurman and Khartoum North, is located toward the center of the country. The total population of the metropolitan area is now estimated at 335,000.

▶ Libya

Egypt's neighbor to the west, Libya, was formerly an Italian colony, but became an independent kingdom in 1951 following a postwar period of transition under United Nations supervision. Most of the country is a desert waste inhabited by a sparse nomadic population of Arabs and Berbers raising camels, sheep, and goats. Some cultivation is carried on in scattered oases and in a strip along the Mediterranean coast watered by occasional winter rains. An Italian-built motor highway follows the coast and connects Tunisia with Egypt. The coastal areas witnessed several important battles during the North African campaigns of World War II. The only cities of any size are the two main seaports, Tripoli (145,000) in the west and Bengasi (62,000) in the east. Tripoli serves as the winter capital of Libya and Bengasi as the summer capital.

The Oil Kingdoms

Two of the Arab League states, Saudi Arabia and Iraq, are rich in oil. The same is true of Iran and the tiny Arab sheikdoms of Kuwait, Bahrein, and Qatar, bordering Saudi Arabia on the east. All six of these countries are monarchies, although the actual power exercised by the ruler varies from country to country. Collectively, the six Oil Kingdoms contain most of the known petroleum deposits in the Middle East.

These deposits are vast in size and easily exploited. Although the total reserves are not known with certainty, they may possibly amount to as much as half of the world's remaining oil. In 1953 the proved reserves were reported to total 43 billion barrels, distributed by country as follows: Kuwait, 15 billion barrels; Saudi Arabia and Bahrein, 12; Iran, 9; Iraq, 6; and Qatar, 1. Most of the deposits lie in relatively close proximity to the Persian Gulf. This shallow, desert-rimmed arm of the Indian Ocean, about three times the size of Lake Superior, ranks with the Gulf of Mexico, Caribbean Sea, and Caspian Sea among the world's great centers of oil production and transportation. Today one fifth of the world's oil production comes from the Middle East. Royalty payments by the European and American corporations that produce and market the oil have added greatly to governmental revenues and are making possible a variety of projects to raise living standards among the people of these lands.

▶ Iran

Iran, perhaps better known as Persia, was the earliest of the Middle Eastern countries to produce oil in large quantities. The main oil fields are located in the southern part of the country some distance inland from the Persian Gulf. The oil facilities were originally developed by the Anglo-Iranian Oil Company, a British concern. This company built the world's largest refinery at Abadan (about 100,000 in 1950), an Iranian town some 40 miles north of the Persian Gulf. Abadan lies on the Shatt al Arab (formed by the junction of the Tigris and Euphrates Rivers), which is navigable for ocean-going ships. Crude oil from the Iranian fields reached the refinery by pipeline, and the refined products, together with some crude, were shipped away by tanker. In 1950 Iran produced more oil than any other Middle Eastern country. However, in 1951 as a result of anti-British agitation and a strong tide of nationalist feeling in Iran, the oil facilities were na-

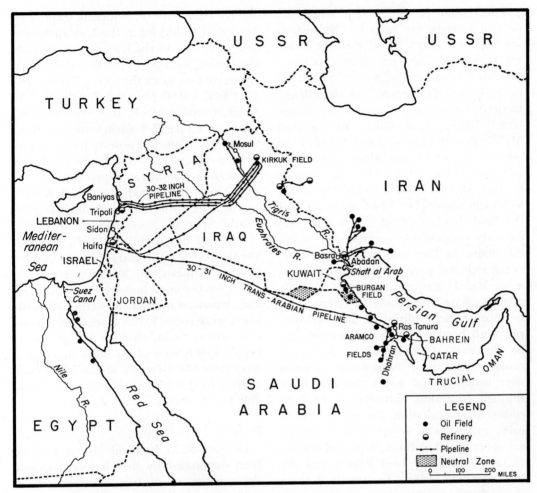

Principal oil fields, pipelines, and refineries of the Middle East. The four pipelines connecting the Kirkuk Field with the Mediterranean coast include (1) a 30–32-inch line to Baniyas in Syria, (2) a 16-inch and a 12-inch line to Tripoli in Lebanon, and (3) a 12-inch line to Haifa in Israel (not operating at the beginning of 1955 due to hostile Arab attitudes toward Israel).

tionalized, despite strong British protests. The British managers and technicians left the country, and Iranian production shortly declined to a very low figure. Not until the summer of 1954 was a compromise settlement of the dispute finally reached.

Like Egypt, Iran is a miserably poor country, and it could ill afford to lose the revenues from oil. The bulk of the land is rugged mountain or desert plateau. On the lowlands rainfall is sufficient for dry-field agriculture on a considerable scale only in northwestern Iran, which receives a mod-

erate amount of winter rain, and in a sheltered strip between the Elburz Mountains and the Caspian Sea which has a subtropical climate with heavy rain, especially in winter, and grows oranges, dates, rice, and cotton. Elsewhere in the country agriculture must depend mainly on irrigation. Eastern Iran, in particular, is extremely dry and barren. About two thirds of the crop acreage in Iran is devoted to either wheat or barley, while an estimated 4 million cattle and 18 million sheep comprise the bulk of the livestock.

The Iranian people, most of whom are peasant farmers, are beset by the customary Middle Eastern ills of drought, dusty winds, hunger, illiteracy, disease, poverty, and landlordism. Farming is by traditional methods with crude tools. In the villages modern conveniences and sanitation are largely lacking. Iran exhibits the common Middle Eastern picture of an ignorant peasantry living under conditions of grinding toil and almost intolerable poverty, contrasting sharply with a relatively small, well-to-do upper class which owns most of the land, holds most of the money, and exercises considerable control over political affairs. In Iran, however, the gulf between rich and poor is even wider than in most Middle Eastern countries. Sporadic attempts have been made in recent years to improve the condition of the rural people, both by the Iranian government and by outsiders. Considerably larger areas could be irrigated if the necessary facilities were installed, and much could be done through education, introduction of even rudimentary sanitation, the use of insecticides, provision of better seeds, increased use of artificial fertilizers, improved systems of farm credit and land tenure, and the like. However, efforts to introduce these things in the country have not met with conspicuous success, due to the lack of capital, the inertia and suspicion of the conservative Moslem peasantry, and the active or passive opposition of intrenched interests, particularly the more reactionary religious leaders and many of the owners of extensive tracts of land.

Iran borders the Soviet Union on the north, and several of the principal Iranian cities, including the capital and main industrial center of Tehran (619,000; including suburbs, about 1,000,000), are located relatively near the USSR. The Russians have long taken an active, and sometimes a very direct, interest in Iranian affairs. Parts of Soviet Middle Asia were taken from Iran in the nineteenth century, and the Russians have subsequently manifested territorial ambitions in the Iranian border province of Azerbaijan, which adjoins the Soviet Socialist Republic of the same name, and contains the second largest Iranian city, Tabriz (280,000). Besides the obvious attraction of oil, Iran represents for the Soviets a possible warm water outlet on the world ocean. Conversely, Iran is a possible avenue of approach for hostile forces in wartime. Considerable quantities of supplies from the United States and Britain reached the Soviet Union through Iran in World War II, thus demonstrating the viability of this particular "back door" to the USSR. For many years Iran was a buffer between Russian and British interests; today it has become a buffer between Russian and American interests as well. This militarily weak country, like Korea, Indochina, and Austria, is unfortunate enough to occupy a highly strategic position in a world struggle of Great Powers, and so it is bound to have its destinies controlled in considerable part by forces outside the country.

▶ Iraq

In Iraq, as in Iran, oil production has been dominated by British interests, and the government of Iraq has been under strong British influence for a long period (the country was a British mandate for a time after World War I). However, other nations besides Britain have been interested in Iraq oil, and the Iraq Petroleum Corporation, which is the main oil company, is jointly owned by British, American, French, and Dutch interests. The most important producing fields are in the vicinity of Kirkuk (143,000) in the northwestern part of the country. The oil is transported by pipeline to points on the Mediterranean coast, whence it is shipped by tanker to overseas destinations.

Iraq, formerly known as Mesopotamia, is essentially the broad plain drained by the Tigris and Euphrates Rivers, together with fringing uplands. In ancient times an elaborate system of irrigation works was developed here, but it was largely destroyed by Mongol invaders in the Middle Ages and has never been completely repaired. The plain of the Tigris and Euphrates supports a considerably smaller farm population today than the other historic Middle Eastern flood plains of the Nile and the Indus. Three food grains—wheat, barley, and rice—occupy most of the cultivated acreage. Barley is the leading export crop, amounting to 9 percent of all exports by value in 1952 (petroleum, 81 percent). Dates comprise a second important export crop, constituting 5 percent of all exports in 1952. Iraq produces and exports more dates than all other countries combined. The limited manufacturing of Iraq, mainly confined to agricultural processing and brickmaking, is centered in the historic capital city of Baghdad (552,000 with suburbs) on the Tigris River. The main seaport is Basra (206,000), located at the head of ocean navigation on the Shatt al Arab. Mosul (340,000) is an important market center in northwestern Iraq.

▶ Saudi Arabia

Oil production in Saudi Arabia has been developed by an American concern, the Arabian American Oil Company (Aramco). The oil fields are located on the shore of the Persian Gulf with the town of Dhahran the headquarters for the operations. Some oil is refined at near-by Ras Tanura or on Bahrein Island and shipped out by tanker, but most of it is transported in crude form to the Mediterranean port of Sidon, in Lebanon, via the great 30–31 inch Trans-Arabian Pipeline (TAPline), which, together with a 315-mile connecting Aramco line at its eastern end, is 1068 miles long.

Saudi Arabia occupies the greater part of the Arabian Peninsula, the homeland both of Arab civilization and of the Mohammedan religion. The country, an absolute monarchy ruled by an Arab king, lives under a system of law derived from the Koran.

Most of Saudi Arabia is a desert waste, particularly the Empty Quarter (Rub al Khali) in the southeast. The latter contains some of the largest areas of sandy desert in the world. There is not enough rainfall in Saudi Arabia to support permanent streams, but as in other desert areas there are many intermittent streams which carry water whenever it happens to rain. Many of these streams have some underground flow at slight depths even when the stream bed is dry, and shallow wells dug in the bed supply limited amounts of water for domestic use and irrigation. Although the best-known inhabitants of Arabia are the camel nomads or Bedouin, the majority of the people are oasis farmers. The latter are mainly found around the margins of the peninsula, where rainfall is a little greater than in the interior. Dates, wheat, and barley are the principal crops. The largest and best-known city of Saudi Arabia is Mecca (population variously estimated at 90,000 to 150,000), the birthplace of Mohammed and the principal holy city of Islam. Jidda (80,000), on the Red Sea, is the main seaport and point of entry for pilgrims to Mecca and other Arabian holy places. Riyadh (60,000), in the eastern interior, is the principal seat of the Saudi Arabian government, although Mecca is also recognized as a capital and foreign diplomatic representatives are quartered at Jidda.

Saudi Arabia is rimmed to the south and east by a collection of small countries which vary considerably in political status. They include the independent state of Yemen and the British-influenced sultanate of Oman, which have highlands receiving more rain than falls elsewhere in the Arabian Peninsula; the British colony and protectorate of Aden; and the Persian Gulf protected states of Trucial Oman, Qatar, Bahrein, and Kuwait, all under British influence. Kuwait has immense reserves of oil in the Burgan field, the world's largest. Bahrein and Qatar also have substantial proven reserves. The oil facilities in Kuwait are operated by joint British and American interests, in Bahrein by an American con-cern, and in Qatar by a subsidiary of the Iraq Petroleum Corporation. Qatar is the smallest producer of the three.

Afghanistan and Turkey

Afghanistan and Turkey also contain some oil, although the deposits do not compare in size with those of the countries bordering the Persian Gulf. These mountainous countries are Middle Eastern in many respects, but in other ways are transitional to other world regions. Afghanistan has been historically important as a buffer state between Russia and British India. The main overland routes leading from the Soviet Union to Pakistan cross Afghanistan; the country has no rail lines, but has access to Russian and Pakistani railroads which reach the Afghan borders. Afghanistan is remote from the main currents of world affairs. In physiography, climate, and economy it resembles Iran. Most of the people are concentrated in the eastern valleys around the capital, Kabul (310,000), and Kandahar (195,000).

In world terms, Turkey is considerably more important than Afghanistan. Once a decadent, reactionary Moslem state at the center of a disintegrating and corrupt empire, Turkey has undergone a transformation in recent decades and is becoming a modern country, with a political orientation toward Europe and America. It is briefly described in the following excerpts from a publication by the United States Department of State: [3]

The history of Turkey in the twentieth century has been a story of determination to maintain its independence and territorial integrity, to attain equal status with European states, and at the same time to achieve through Westernization a higher standard of living. . . .

▶ People and Land in Turkey

The pattern of society in Turkey, onto which a considerable amount of Westernization was grafted, resembled in many ways that of Western Europe prior to the industrial revolution. And Turkish society today is still relatively stable. That restless byproduct of industrialization, a large, landless, wage-earning class, has not yet developed. In fact, because of the population exchanges following World War I, even the dynamic byproduct of commerce and trade, a flourishing middle class, exists on only a small scale.

An educated upper-class Moslem group rules a large and devoutly Moslem peasant majority. Until the birth of the Turkish Republic the income of the ruling class came mostly from government positions or commissions in the army. Although these occupations were not on the whole profitable, they were considered socially more acceptable than trade. As a result, although there are a few large private fortunes in Turkey, the upper-class Turk usually has little surplus capital to invest in industry, even if he is interested in doing so. This lack of capital has contributed to the slow growth of industry in Turkey. . . .

The bulk of Turkey's national income comes from agriculture, in which more than 80 per cent of the people are engaged. There are few large landowners and few landless peasants, so that altogether Turkey's agricultural base is strong.

The average peasant in the interior of Turkey owns one or two small strips of land and his oxen and sheep. These provide him and his family with the bare essentials of life. He grows or makes nearly everything he uses. He lives much as people lived be-

[3] "Turkey: Frontier of Freedom." *Background,* June, 1952 (U. S. Department of State Publication 4633), pp. 1–5. One heading has been slightly altered.

fore industry developed in Europe. The center of his world is a tiny village, like the manor villages of medieval Europe, usually isolated from the main road for protection, with its one- or two-room cottages huddled together around a source of water.

His floor is covered with a handsome, hand-woven rug, but he has little furniture. He and his family sleep on mattresses on the floor. His animals sleep nearby, sometimes in the same room. Water for washing, cooking, and drinking is drawn from the village well.

Shortly after sunrise he sets out to cultivate his land, which may be as much as 7 or 8 miles away. The village shepherd gathers the sheep of the village and takes them out to graze on the pasture land which the villagers hold in common.

On the high Anatolian plateau, which covers most of central Turkey, the main crop is hard winter wheat, which can survive extremes of heat, cold, and drought. The farmer cuts the earth in shallow furrows with a wooden plow. He uses no fertilizer, and his crop yield is low.

Until the inauguration of the Turkish-American roads program a few years ago, most of the peasants in the interior were unable to get their crops to market. They therefore made little effort to raise surplus crops to exchange for money. The situation is now improved, but Turkey still lacks feeder roads in the interior and in the eastern portions of Anatolia.

In the coastal regions of the Mediterranean and Aegean and in some portions of the narrow Black Sea coastal plain, the soil is richer than in the uplands. The temperature is warmer and more even, the rainfall abundant. Here more intensive farming is practiced, and here are grown most of Turkey's export crops—cotton, tobacco, nuts, grapes, and figs.

In these regions are the few large estates employing agricultural labor by the day and using more modern farming methods. Villages are closer together and less primitive than in the interior. The peasants are more prosperous. There has long been a rudimentary road system which made it possible for farmers to get their crops to market.

There are about 40,000 small villages in all of Turkey, an area slightly larger than Texas. Population density averages about 85 persons per square mile along the coasts and 1 to 25 per square mile in the dry interior and mountainous eastern region.

Turkey's 21 million people cultivate only 16 per cent of the total land area. About 50 per cent, most of it in the interior, is used for grazing. Much of this upland needs only water to make it excellent crop and farm land capable of supporting many more people.

Slightly less than 20 per cent of the people live in cities. About 285,000 live in Ankara, seat of the Government. Izmir, the ancient Smyrna, is an important seaport of about 230,000, through which 70 per cent of Turkish exports pass. Istanbul, formerly Constantinople, at the crossroads of land and water traffic between Europe and Asia, is a city of a million.

The Turks who overran Asia Minor, Persia, northern Arabia, and Egypt from the eleventh to the fifteenth centuries were horsemen from the steppes of central Asia. Their numbers were small and they mixed with the natives of these . . . areas. When the Ottomans conquered the Balkan peninsula in the fifteenth and sixteenth centuries, Slav and other strains infiltrated small portions of the population. Thus, the inhabitants of Turkey today are a racial mixture.

The Republic has tried to bind these peoples together by enforcing the use of the Turkish language. Consequently, everyone, with the exception of some of the Kurdish minority, speaks Turkish. A further bond among the great majority of Turkish citizens is the Moslem religion. However, Turkey's non-Moslems, about 300,000 persons dwelling for the most part in Istanbul and Izmir, are guaranteed full equality by the constitution.

▶ *Turkey Turns West*

One of the earliest moves toward Westernization came in 1876, when dissatisfied leaders in the Ottoman Army forced a constitution and parliamentary government on the Sultan. A year later the Sultan set the document aside. But in 1908 a larger and more determined group, called the Young Turks, seized power and restored the constitution.

The Young Turks considered the rising German nation an efficient model of Western military and industrial prowess. The Germans, late arrivals on the industrial scene, were hungry for markets and raw materials. They ingratiated themselves, particularly with the Young Turks. They reorganized the Ottoman Army along Prussian lines. And they constructed a large segment of the Baghdad Railroad, connecting Berlin, Constantinople, and Baghdad, with the idea of tying the Middle East into a German-controlled Central European bloc. Thus, World War I found the Ottoman Empire solidly lined up with Germany and the Central Powers.

After World War I, all that remained of the Ottoman Empire was northern Anatolia and the Straits area, and the latter was placed under Allied control. The threat in 1919 to the continued survival of Turkey crystallized the resistance of the Anatolian peasants. Under Kemal Ataturk and a group of nationalistic Turkish officers, the peasants rose against foreign forces occupying the Turkish homeland.

Ataturk established a government at Ankara. In 1922 he made a treaty with the Soviet Union by which he got back the two Turkish border provinces which had been seized by Russia in 1878. He also finished establishing Turkish authority throughout the Anatolian peninsula. Thereupon, he declared the Sultan in Constantinople deposed. In 1923 the treaty of Lausanne, the only negotiated treaty of World War I, established the boundaries of Turkey essentially as they are today. In October of that year Turkey was formally proclaimed a republic with Kemal Ataturk its president.

The treaty of Lausanne . . . also provided for population exchanges between Turkey, Greece, and Bulgaria. Through them Turkey lost many relatively skilled farmers, almost all of Anatolia's skilled village artisans, craftsmen, and tradesmen,

and the experienced Greek merchants of the seaports. However, the Turks felt that to have a population homogeneous in language and cultural pattern more than made up for the loss. . . .

► The New Turkey

Turkey's revolution has not been merely a change in the head of government nor a change in the outward forms of government. It has been an historic revolt against traditional Ottoman Islamic authority. The revolt itself has been imposed from above by active, nationalistic elements of the ruling class. While as yet only a small percentage of the Turkish peasantry has felt its full effects, change is filtering down to lower levels.

Ataturk set about to separate church and state. At first he permitted the deposed Sultan's brother to remain as Caliph in Constantinople. (The ruler of the Ottoman Empire had been both Sultan and Caliph, spiritual head of the Moslems.) But in 1924 he abolished the caliphate. Four years later Islam ceased to be the state religion of Turkey.

Other moves designed to Westernize Turkey followed. The Turkish language was partially purged of its Persian and Arabic words. The Latin alphabet was adopted, and the Turks went to school to learn to read and write the new letters. Polygamy was abolished, though not retroactively, and civil marriage made compulsory. The old Moslem law was replaced by Swiss civil, Italian penal, and German commercial codes. Women were legally emancipated and later given the suffrage. The rudiments of a nation-wide compulsory education system were more firmly established. And everyone in Turkey acquired a family name.

Most members of the upper class, particularly the younger people, accepted the changes enthusiastically. The peasants accepted them somewhat reluctantly. When use of the fez was prohibited, they took to Western caps, which, worn backward, lend themselves admirably to the Moslem attitude of prayer with the forehead touching the rug.

Despite the measures directed against traditional Islamic forms, the Moslem religion remains as a matter of personal belief in Turkey. The new administration lifted the ban on the use of Arabic in religious services (Arabic is the traditional language of the Koran) and is permitting religious instruction in the public schools for those who wish it.

The Second World War came on a Turkey busy with its national and economic development. Ataturk had died in 1938. His successor was Ismet Inonu, who had been Prime Minister for much of the period since the founding of the Republic.

At the beginning of hostilities in 1939 Turkey signed a treaty of mutual assistance with the United Kingdom and France, which, however, stipulated that Turkey was not obligated to become a belligerent against the Soviet Union. This did not mean that the Turks had any sympathy with the Soviets. For centuries they have had a deep hatred of the Russians, which has become even deeper with the course of events under the Soviets. But the Soviet Union borders on Turkey, and Turkey was not looking for outside troubles.

Turkish possession of the straits—Bosporus, Sea of Marmara, and Dardanelles—connecting the Soviet-dominated Black Sea with the Aegean and Mediterranean has given rise to frequent controversies between Russia and Turkey. Russian chances of gaining a voice in the control of this strategic water passage by any means except force have seemed increasingly poor since World War II, as Turkey has gravitated toward the side of the Western nations and has become one of the strongest and most active members of the North Atlantic Treaty Organization. Aided by outside funds, chiefly of American origin, Turkey has not only increased its military preparedness, but has pushed its program of industrialization, road building, and the improvement of agriculture. The country appears to have sufficient mineral resources on which to base substantial increases in industry, including the largest deposits of good coal in the Middle East, some petroleum, fair-sized deposits of high-grade iron ore, and reserves of copper, chromium, manganese, antimony, sulfur, and salt. Nevertheless, Turkish industry is still in an early stage, and the country continues to depend mainly for a livelihood on the products of specialized subtropical agriculture, grain farming (increased mechanization helped make Turkey the world's fourth largest wheat exporter in 1952), and the raising of livestock. Turkey's impressively large livestock population was estimated in 1952 to include 10 million cattle, 26 million sheep, and 22 million goats.

The Countries of Northwest Africa

At the northwestern border of the Middle East are a group of countries which, though far removed from the core of the region, are nevertheless Middle Eastern in many essential characteristics. They include Algeria, French Morocco, and Tunisia, controlled by France; Spanish Sahara and Spanish Morocco, controlled by Spain; and the International Zone of Tangier, occupying a strategic location on the African shore of the Strait of Gibraltar.

Algeria, French Morocco, and Tunisia are the most important countries of this group. These areas came under French control in the nineteenth and early twentieth centuries, and France has expended large sums in their development. They have some excellent roads, a rail system, and modern port facilities at Algiers (490,000), Oran (275,000), Casablanca (682,000), Tunis (603,000; population figures for all cities include suburbs), and a number of smaller ports. The native population is mainly Moslem Arab and Berber. Although there is a considerable European population, mainly French, the Europeans are far outnumbered by natives except in the cities of Algiers, Tunis, and Oran.

The North African territories are economically valuable to France as sources of minerals, especially phosphate and iron ore, and products of Mediterranean agriculture such as wine, citrus fruits, wheat, early vegetables, and olives. Politically they are valuable as symbols of French prestige. They have differed in political status, Morocco and Tunisia being held as protectorates, while Algeria has been administered under an appointed Governor General as an integral part of the home country. Feelings of dissatisfaction with French rule, accompanied by sporadic outbreaks of violence, appeared to be increasing in late 1954 following French reverses in another colonial area, Indochina. Agitation for self-rule was especially strong among the native Mohammedan populations of Morocco and Tunisia.

Ethiopia and Somaliland

East of the Sudan section of the Nile Basin a great volcanic mountain mass rises steeply from the desert. Much of this mountainous area, the heartland of the empire of Ethiopia, lies above 10,000 feet and some peaks reach 14,000 feet. The highland receives heavy rains during the summer half of the year, rather than the winter rain characteristic of mediterranean climatic areas. Important Nile tributaries such as the Blue Nile, the Sobat, and the Atbara rise here. Temperature conditions vary from tropical to temperate as elevation increases. Thus crops varying from bananas, coffee, and dates through oranges, figs, and temperate fruits to cereals can be produced

A flat-roofed village at the base of barren mountains in the Atlas region of Morocco. (*French Embassy Press and Information Division.*)

without irrigation. Large expanses of upland pasture a variety of livestock, primarily cattle and sheep.

Ethiopia, together with Eritrea, is inhabited by an estimated 16 million people, of very diverse racial and cultural characteristics. Although dark-skinned, most of the population is descended from the Hamitic or Semitic branches of the Caucasian race. It is estimated that about 60 percent of the population adheres to the Coptic Christian faith, a very ancient branch which penetrated Ethiopia from Egypt, where there is still a sizable Coptic minority. The rest of the population is divided between the Moslem faith and a variety of more primitive pagan beliefs. This diverse population is held in relatively loose political union under the emperor of Ethiopia, whose seat is in Addis Ababa, the only sizable city in the country with a population estimated at about 400,000. Tribal forms of life remain important, and disputes are still often settled on a private basis with the rifle.

East of the mountain mass of Ethiopia, and partly included within the empire, lower plateaus and coastal plains descend to the Red Sea, the Gulf of Aden, and the Indian Ocean. Extreme heat and aridity assert themselves at these lower levels, and nomadic and illiterate tribesmen make a poor living from camels, goats, and sheep.

Ethiopia and its borderlands constitute a very marginal part of the Middle East. The latter is especially true of the rainy tropical Ethiopian highlands. However, the arid lowland sections possess many typically Middle Eastern characteristics, and the entire area has important cultural and historical links with the core of the Middle East in Egypt, the Fertile Crescent, and Arabia.

▶ European Imperialism

European powers seized coastal strips of this territory in the latter nineteenth century. Britain was first with British Somaliland in 1882, then France annexed French Somaliland in 1884, and lastly Italy asserted dominance over Italian Somaliland and Eritrea in 1889. The strategic importance of these holdings along the Suez–Red Sea route and adjacent to the independent native state of Ethiopia is obvious. Their economic importance is negligible.

Italy attempted to extend its domain from Eritrea over the much more attractive and potentially valuable land of Ethiopia in 1896, but the Italian forces were annihilated by the Ethiopian tribesmen at Aduwa. Forty years later, in 1936, a second attempt was successful. Hopes of developing the country's potential wealth and of using it as an outlet for surplus Italian population were frustrated in World War II, when the Italian empire in eastern Africa was conquered by British forces in 1941. Ethiopia was restored to independence and Eritrea was federated with it in 1952. Italian Somaliland (now called Somalia) was returned to Italy to be administered as a Trust Territory under the United Nations, pending independence in 1960.

▶ Problems of Ethiopian Development

The potential wealth of Ethiopia, including substantial reserves of gold, coal, copper, iron ore, and other minerals, remains undeveloped, though the emperor's government is doing what it can. A primitive transport system whose best parts are the 3000 miles of good road built by the Italians during their occupation is a major factor in keeping the country isolated and undeveloped. The French-built railroad from the port of Jibuti (17,000) in French Somaliland to Addis Ababa lacks feeder lines and has never proved as successful as hoped, although a large part of the coffee which comprises Ethiopia's major export does move through the port. Ethiopia is currently developing a motor road to the outside via its small Eritrean port of Assab. Other routes into the country are mere trails, and the easiest approach is by air to

Addis Ababa from Aden. Radio-telegraph communication to and from the country was only established in 1947. Under such circumstances one of the Middle East's and the world's areas of potential wealth re-mains in isolation and backwardness, though it should perhaps be added that the isolation has probably had something to do with its remaining in independence also.

16

Introduction to the Orient

The Orient (East) is used in this book as a regional name for the group of countries occupying the southeastern quarter of Eurasia. Besides countries on the mainland extending from India and Pakistan to Korea, the Orient, as herein defined, also includes an arc of island countries stretching for thousands of miles between Ceylon on the southwest and Japan on the northeast. To the north and northwest the landward margins of the Orient touch the Soviet Union. To the west lies the Middle East; to the east are the many islands of the Pacific World and, across the broad expanse of the Pacific Ocean, the distant shores of the Americas. To the southwest, across the Indian Ocean, lies Africa, its eastern margins and offshore islands now inhabited by more than three quarters of a million Orientals. The great peninsula of Europe is far away to the northwest at the opposite corner of the Eurasian land mass.

Regional Groups of Countries

For convenience in study, the countries of the Orient may be divided into a number of regional groups on the basis of such factors as proximity; environmental, economic, and cultural similarities; political relationships; or historical ties.

1. The *countries of the Indian Realm* include India, Pakistan, and the small Hi-

Terraced rice fields are the most characteristic and best known type of rural landscape in the Orient. The terraces in this view are located on the mountainous island of Java in the East Indies. (*Information Office of the Republic of Indonesia.*)

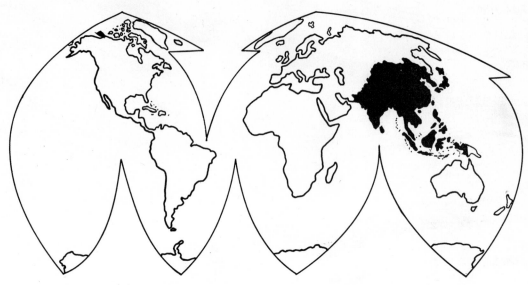

World location of the Orient. (*Boggs Equal Area Projection, copyright A. J. Nystrom & Co.*)

malayan states of Nepal, Bhutan, and Sikkim. Ceylon is often included with this group, although considered with Southeast Asia in the present treatment.

2. The *countries of Southeast Asia,* bordering India on the east, include the relatively small peninsular countries of Burma, Thailand (Siam), Indochina, and Malaya, the large island country of Indonesia, the smaller island countries of Ceylon and the Philippines, and a scattering of minor European island possessions, including British Borneo, Portuguese Timor, and Netherlands New Guinea.

3. The *countries of the Chinese Realm,* as considered herein, include Communist China, Nationalist China (Formosa and smaller islands), and, for convenience, the Mongolian People's Republic (Outer Mongolia), which now has closer political and economic relations with Russia than with China, although it has been considered historically a part of China. This regional grouping also includes the tiny European coastal possessions of Hong Kong (British) and Macao (Portuguese), which are largely Chinese in population, though not in political control.

4. The island nation of *Japan,* shorn of its former possessions, stands alone, as does its erstwhile colony, *Korea,* or at least South Korea, now that North Korea has been added to the roster of Communist nations.

The Colonial Background of the Orient

Modern European penetration of the Orient began at the end of the fifteenth century. The early comers established trading posts and gradually extended political control over limited areas near the coast. In the eighteenth and nineteenth centuries the pace of annexation quickened, and large areas came under European sway. By the end of the nineteenth century Great Britain was supreme in India, Burma, Ceylon, Malaya, and North Borneo; the Netherlands possessed most of the East Indies; France had acquired Indochina and a number of small holdings around the coasts of

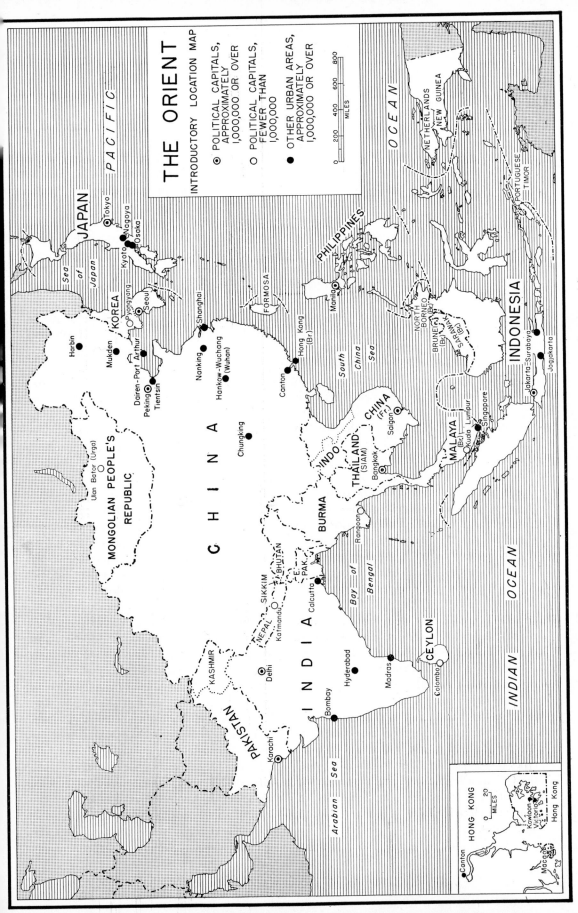

THE ORIENT

INTRODUCTORY LOCATION MAP

⊙ POLITICAL CAPITALS, APPROXIMATELY 1,000,000 OR OVER

○ POLITICAL CAPITALS, FEWER THAN 1,000,000

● OTHER URBAN AREAS, APPROXIMATELY 1,000,000 OR OVER

0   200   400   600   800
MILES

PACIFIC OCEAN

JAPAN
Tokyo
Nagoya
Kyoto
Osaka

Sea of Japan

KOREA
Pyongyang
Seoul

Harbin
Mukden
Dairen-Port Arthur
Peking
Tientsin

Shanghai

Nanking
Hankow-Wuchang (Wuhan)

Chungking

C H I N A

MONGOLIAN PEOPLE'S REPUBLIC

Ulan Bator (Urga)

Canton

Hong Kong (Br.)

FORMOSA

PHILIPPINES
Manila

South China Sea

BURMA

THAILAND (SIAM)
Bangkok

INDO CHINA (Fr.)
Saigon

Rangoon

NEPAL
SIKKIM
BHUTAN
Katmandu
E. PAK.
KASHMIR
Delhi

I N D I A
PAKISTAN
Karachi
Bombay
Hyderabad
Calcutta

Bay of Bengal

Madras

CEYLON
Colombo

Arabian Sea

INDIAN OCEAN

MALAYA
Kuala Lumpur
Singapore

NORTH BORNEO (Br.)
BRUNEI (Br.)
SARAWAK (Br.)

I N D O N E S I A

Jakarta
Surabaya
Jogjakarta

NETHERLANDS NEW GUINEA

PORTUGUESE TIMOR

HONG KONG
0   20
MILES

Canton
Kowloon
Victoria
Macao
Hong Kong

Provisional boundaries within Korea and Indochina shown by dotted lines.

India; and Portugal, the supreme colonial power of the Orient in the sixteenth century, had been displaced from her early holdings with the exception of Macao, a part of the island of Timor, and Goa and two other small holdings on the west coast of India. China, though retaining a semblance of territorial integrity, was forced to yield possession of strategic Hong Kong to Britain in the mid-nineteenth century and to grant special trading concessions and extraterritorial rights to various European nations and the United States. At the end of the century the Philippines, dominated by Spain after the mid-sixteenth century, passed into American control. The only Oriental countries of any importance to escape domination by the Western powers during the colonial age were: (1) Thailand, which formed a buffer between British and French colonial spheres in Southeast Asia; (2) Japan, which withdrew into almost complete seclusion in the seventeenth century, but emerged in the latter nineteenth century as the first modern, industrialized Oriental nation, and soon set about acquiring a colonial empire of its own; and (3) Korea, the "Hermit Kingdom," which also followed a policy of isolation from foreign influences from the early seventeenth century until 1876, at which time a trade treaty was forced on the country by Japan.

Especially in the later nineteenth century and the first four decades of the twentieth century, the Orient constituted an extraordinarily rich colonial area from which the Western nations extracted vast quantities of such valuable commodities as rubber, sugar, tea, copra, palm oil, spices, and tin, and in which Western manufacturers found large markets for cheap textiles, metalwares, and other inexpensive types of goods. The Westerners also found the Orient a fertile field for investment in plantations; transportation, communication, and electric power facilities; factories, and mines.

▶ Decline of Colonialism in the Twentieth Century

Western dominance of the Orient was ended in the twentieth century by a complex chain of circumstances, including (1) the weakening effects of conflicts among the Western nations in the two World Wars, (2) the rise of Japan to Great Power status, and its successful, though temporary, military challenge to the West in the early stages of World War II, and (3) the rise of nationalistic and anticolonial movements in areas subject to European control, such movements often being guided by Oriental leaders educated in Europe or America. By the end of World War II Western colonialism in China was a thing of the past, and following the war insistent native demands for independence led to Britain's relinquishing possession of the Indian Empire, Ceylon, and Burma to the new independent states of India, Pakistan, Ceylon, and Burma, and Holland's relinquishing control of the East Indies (except Western New Guinea) to the new state of Indonesia. Meanwhile the United States granted independence to the Republic of the Philippines in fulfillment of promises made before World War II, and Japan was forced to give up her extensive Oriental and Pacific empire. In 1954 a weakened and disorganized France was gradually losing its remaining control in Indochina. In the same year the remaining French possessions along the coasts of the Indian subcontinent were ceded to India, and repeated demands were being made by India for the return of the three small coastal possessions still held by Portugal. Only in British Malaya and Hong Kong did a European nation retain effective control over really important colonial territories.

In the Orient the twentieth century has witnessed a complicated series of revolutions within revolutions accompanying the decline of Western colonialism—revolutions directed by nationalists against decadent monarchical and aristocratic native governments, nationalist revolutions directed against European and Japanese colonialism, and Communist revolutions directed against native nationalists, weak imperial and feudal rulers, and outsiders. In late 1954 this condition of turmoil seemed far from ended, and the Orient remained one of the most unsettled and explosive areas of the political world.

The Varied Physiographic Setting

The stage on which the Oriental drama is being enacted is a complex intermingling of many types of topography—high, rugged mountains, arid plateaus and basins, humid hill lands and river plains, and a vast number of offshore islands rising from the floor of shallow seas. Although the picture is extremely complicated in detail, a certain order appears if the surface features of the Orient are conceived of as three concentric arcs or crescents of land—an inner arc of high mountains, plateaus, and basins; a middle arc of lower mountains, hill lands, and river plains; and an outer arc of islands and seas.

▶ The Inner Highland

The inner highland of the Orient is composed of the highest mountain ranges on earth, interspersed with plateaus and basins. At the south the great wall of the Himalaya, Karakoram, and Hindu Kush Mountains overlooks the north of the Indian subcontinent. At the north, the Altai, Tien Shan, and Pamirs separate the Orient from the Soviet Union. Between these mountain walls lie the sparsely inhabited Tibetan Plateau, over 15,000 feet in average elevation, and the great desert basins of Sinkiang and Mongolia.

▶ River Plains and Hill Lands

The area between the inner highland and the sea is principally occupied by river flood plains and deltas, bordered and separated by hills and relatively low mountains. The major components of the topography include (1) the immense plain of northern India, built up through countless ages by the Indus, Ganges, and Brahmaputra Rivers; (2) the hill lands of peninsular India, geologically an ancient crystalline plateau, but largely hilly in aspect, (3) the plains of the Irrawaddy, Chao Praya (Menam), Mekong, and Red Rivers in peninsular Southeast Asia, together with bordering hills and mountains, (4) the hill lands and small alluvial plains of southern China, (5) the broad alluvial plains along the middle and lower Yangtze River in central China and the mountain-girt Red Basin on the upper Yangtze, (6) the large delta plain of the Yellow River and its tributaries in north China, backed by loess-covered hilly uplands, and (7) the broad central plain of Manchuria, almost completely enclosed by mountains with low to moderate elevations. The floor of the Red Basin and the central plain of Manchuria are structural rather than river-made plains, and are rolling in aspect rather than flat.

▶ Offshore Islands and Seas

Offshore, a fringe of thousands upon thousands of islands, mostly grouped in great archipelagoes, borders the mainland. On these islands high interior mountains with many volcanic peaks are flanked by broad or narrow coastal plains where most of the inhabitants live. Three major archipelagoes include most of the islands—the East Indies, the Philippines, and the Japanese Archipelago. Ceylon, Formosa, and Hainan are large islands not included in an archipelago. Between the archipelagoes and the mainland lie the China Seas, and, to the north, the Sea of Japan. At the south-

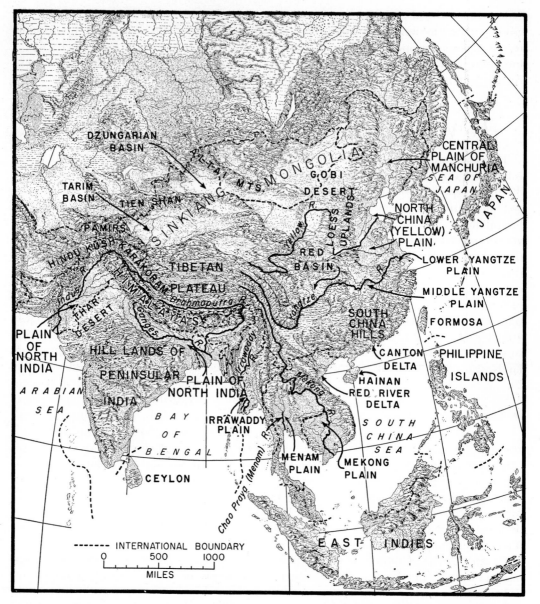

Major landforms of the Orient. (*Base map is a portion of A. K. Lobeck's* Physiographic Diagram of Asia, *copyright The Geographical Press, a division of C. S. Hammond & Company, Maplewood, N. J.*)

west the great peninsula of India projects southward between two arms of the Indian Ocean—the Bay of Bengal and the Arabian Sea.

The Pattern of Climates and Vegetation

In detail the climatic, like the physiographic pattern, is one of almost endless variety. However, two unifying elements are present throughout most parts of the

Orient inhabited by any considerable number of people. These are (1) the dominance of warm climates and (2) a characteristic monsoonal regime of precipitation.

▶ High Temperatures of the Inhabited Regions

In the parts of the Orient where most of the people are found, temperatures are tropical or subtropical and the frost-free season ranges from around 200 to 365 days. The principal exceptions are the northern part of China proper, Manchuria, North Korea, and northern Japan. In the latter areas the summers are warm to hot in the lowlands, but the growing season is generally less than 200 days and the winters are often severely cold. The arid basins and plateaus of Sinkiang and Mongolia also have a continental type of climate with warm summers and cold winters. The higher mountain areas and Tibetan Plateau have highland climates varying with the altitude and latitude. Permanent snowfields and glaciers are found at the higher elevations.

▶ The Monsoons

The precipitation varies from almost nothing in parts of the Thar Desert of western India and the Tarim Basin of Sinkiang Province in China to an average of more than 400 inches in the Khasi Hills of northeastern India. A monsoon climate, or at least a climate with monsoon tendencies, prevails nearly everywhere in the populous middle arc of plains and hills, and in many parts of the islands as well. Technically a monsoon is not, as some people imagine, a violent downpour of rain with accompanying winds and lightning (though such are often its effects), but is simply a current of air blowing fairly steadily from a given direction for several weeks or months at a time. Although conditions vary from place to place, the Orient is characterized in general by two monsoons: a summer monsoon blowing from the sea to the land and bringing high humidity and copious rain and a winter monsoon blowing seaward and bringing little or no rain and cool or cold, clear weather. The characteristic features of the monsoonal type of climate, then, are (1) the seasonal reversal of wind direction, (2) the strong summer maximum of rainfall, and (3) the long dry season, typically lasting from November to March or even longer.

In some areas the monsoon appears gradually; elsewhere it "breaks" or "bursts" with great suddenness. On the plains of India the appearance of the summer monsoon is preceded by a period of dry, stifling heat during April and May. This is ended abruptly with the break of the southwest monsoon, which has been described as follows. "The wind blows strongly from the southwest, very strongly over the sea; thick masses of cloud cover the sky, and the air is saturated with vapor. A downpour of rain with violent thunder and lightning initiates the rainy and moist conditions that will prevail for the next three months. The clouds help to shelter the earth from the sun and the streaming rain helps to cool the air; over most of India the temperature falls sharply. Living things feel a sense of relief, and the parched land drinks and becomes luxuriantly green again." [1]

▶ Types of Climate

Seven main types of climate in the Orient are customarily recognized in climatic classifications—tropical rain forest, tropical savanna, humid subtropical, humid continental, steppe, desert, and highland.

• *Tropical Rain Forest.* The rainy tropical climates of the Orient are found along or relatively near the equator. Consequently, high temperatures are experienced throughout the year in the lowlands. There is a com-

[1] W. G. Kendrew, *The Climates of the Continents.* New York: Oxford University Press, 1942. P. 125. Used by permission of the publisher.

plete absence of frost, and the year-round growing season offers the maximum possibilities for agriculture from the standpoint of temperature. However, the high temperatures and heavy rain promote rapid leaching and destruction of organic matter, with the result that most soils in the rainy tropics are relatively infertile despite the thick cover of deep-rooted trees and grasses they often support. Two main types of humid tropical climate, each associated with characteristic forms of vegetation, are recognized. These are (1) tropical rain forest climate and (2) tropical savanna climate. The main difference is the absence of a dry season in the former.

The *tropical rain forest climate* is typically found in lowlands within 5° or 10° of the equator. A rainfall of at least 30 to 40 inches, often 100 inches or more, is spread throughout the year so that every month has considerable rain. Average temperatures vary only slightly from month to month; Singapore, for example, exhibits a difference of only 3° between the warmest and coolest months. Monotonous, steamy heat prevails the year round, although excessively high temperatures of 95° or 100°F. or more are seldom or never experienced. Some relief is afforded by a drop of 10° to 25° in the temperature at night, and conditions are more pleasant along coasts subject to periodic sea breezes. White settlers from the middle latitudes have experienced considerable difficulty in maintaining health and vigor on a long-term basis in this climate zone. Not the least of the handicaps is the prevalence of malaria, sleeping sickness, dysentery, and other diseases.

The tropical rain forest produced by the climatic conditions described above is characteristically a thick forest of large broadleaf evergreen trees, mostly hardwoods, from 50 to 200 feet in height, and forming an almost continuous canopy of foliage. The trees are often entangled in a mass of vines, and dense undergrowth is found wherever sufficient light penetrates to the ground.

Tropical rain forest climate and vegetation are characteristic of most parts of the East Indies, the Philippines, and the Malay Peninsula. Rain forest vegetation is also found in certain other areas which experience a dry season, but in which the precipitation of the rainy season is sufficiently heavy to promote a thick growth of trees. The latter areas are found (1) along the west coast of India south of Bombay and along the south coast of Ceylon, (2) along the west coast of Burma, extending northward to the delta of the Ganges and Brahmaputra Rivers in India and East Pakistan, (3) along the east coast of Indochina, and (4) in parts of the northern Philippines.

• *Tropical Savanna.* Although the *tropical savanna climate,* like the tropical rain forest climate, is characterized by high temperatures the year round, this climate type is customarily found in areas farther from the equator, and the average temperatures vary somewhat more from month to month than is true of the rain forest climate. However, the most striking and important difference between the two climate types lies in the fact that the savanna climate has a well-defined dry season, lasting in some areas for as much as 6 or 8 months of the year. The annual precipitation is less, on the average, than in the rain forest climate; however, it is the seasonal distribution of the rain rather than inadequate total precipitation which represents the principal handicap for agriculture in the savanna lands. The savanna climate is typical of the greater part of the Indian subcontinent and Ceylon, the interior of Burma, practically all of Thailand, all of Indochina except the east coast, and eastern Java and smaller islands to the east. Much larger areas of this climate type are found in Africa and Latin America and a somewhat smaller area in northern Australia.

In the Orient the characteristic natural

TABLE 15

CLIMATIC DATA FOR SELECTED ORIENTAL STATIONS

STATION	COUNTRY	LATITUDE TO NEAREST WHOLE DEGREE	ELEVATION ABOVE SEA LEVEL (FEET)	TYPE OF CLIMATE	AVERAGE TEMPERATURE (DEGREES F. TO NEAREST WHOLE DEGREE)			AVERAGE PRECIPITATION		
					ANNUAL	JANUARY	JULY (OR WARMEST MONTH)	ANNUAL TO NEAREST INCH	PERCENT OCCURRING APRIL–SEPTEMBER (TO NEAREST WHOLE PERCENT)	PERCENT OCCURRING JUNE–SEPTEMBER (TO NEAREST WHOLE PERCENT)
Karachi	West Pakistan	25°N.	13	Desert	77°	67°	85° (June)	8″	83%	79%
Delhi	India	29°N.	718	Tropical Savanna	77°	58°	92° (June)	27″	85%	85%
Bombay	India	19°N.	37	Tropical Savanna	79°	75°	85° (May)	71″	96%	95%
Madras	India	13°N.	22	Tropical Savanna	83°	77°	90° (June)	51″	34%	30%
Calcutta	India	24°N.	21	Tropical Savanna	79°	67°	87° (May)	63″	87%	75%
Mandalay	Burma	22°N.	250	Tropical Savanna	81°	69°	89° (April)	33″	79%	58%
Singapore	Malaya	1°N.	8	Tropical Rain Forest	79°	78°	81° (May)	95″	45%	30%
Jakarta	Indonesia	6°S.	26	Tropical Rain Forest	79°	78°	79° (May)	71″	29%	15%
Canton	China	23°N.	29	Humid Subtropical	73°	57°	85° (August)	61″	81%	58%
Shanghai	China	31°N.	23	Humid Subtropical	59°	38°	81°	45″	69%	53%
Hankow	China	31°N.	121	Humid Subtropical	63°	40°	86°	50″	72%	47%
Chengtu	China	31°N.	1611	Humid Subtropical	62°	43°	79°	39″	90%	79%
Peking	China	40°N.	125	Humid Continental	54°	25°	80°	24″	93%	84%
Mukden	China (Manchuria)	42°N.	141	Humid Continental	47°	11°	78°	28″	84%	71%
Harbin	China (Manchuria)	46°N.	526	Humid Continental	39°	−1°	73°	19″	86%	73%
Tokyo	Japan	36°N.	19	Humid Subtropical	57°	39°	79° (August)	61″	63%	44%
Hakodate	Japan	42°N.	13	Humid Continental	46°	26°	69° (August)	46″	58%	45%
Kashgar	China (Sinkiang)	40°N.	4296	Desert	55°	23°	80°	3″	62%	41%
Urga	Outer Mongolia	48°N.	4347	Steppe	28°	−11°	63°	8″	86%	30%
Gyantse	China (Tibet)	29°N.	13,110	Highland	42°	24°	58°	12″	97%	90%

vegetation associated with the savanna climate is a deciduous forest of smaller trees than those found in the tropical rain forest. The forest growth deteriorates to scrub in the drier areas. Tall, coarse tropical grasses, the most common vegetation form in the African and Latin American savannas, are found in only limited areas, and even there are thought to have been produced by repeated burning of forest growth during the dry season. In parts of Southeast Asia long-continued burning has fostered pure stands of certain tree species peculiarly resistant to extinction by fire. Among these are a number of economically valuable types, especially teak, which is exploited on a considerable scale in Burma and Thailand. In the more densely populated and long settled parts of the Oriental savanna lands the natural vegetation has been so modified by centuries of human occupation that the original conditions are difficult or impossible to determine.

• *Climates Outside the Humid Tropics.* The climate of southern China (including the Yangtze Valley), southern Japan, and extreme southern Korea is customarily classified as *humid subtropical*. This climate type is characterized by warm to hot summers, mild or cool winters with some frost, and a frost-free season lasting 200 days or longer. The annual rainfall of 30 to 50 inches or more is fairly well distributed throughout the year, although monsoonal tendencies produce a dry season in some areas. The natural vegetation, now largely removed over extensive areas (especially in China), is a mixture of evergreen hardwoods, deciduous hardwoods, and conifers.

A generally comparable climate occurs in the southeastern part of the United States, although the strong Oriental tendency toward winter drought is not present in the latter area.

The northern part of China proper, most of Korea and Manchuria, and northern Japan have a *humid continental* type of climate marked by warm to hot summers, cold winters with considerable snow, a frost-free season of 100 to 200 days, and less precipitation than the humid subtropical areas. Most areas experience a definite dry season in winter. The predominant natural vegetation is a mixture of broadleaf deciduous and coniferous trees, although tall prairie grasses are thought to have formed the original cover in parts of North China and Manchuria. Many aspects of the humid continental climate of the Orient are duplicated in comparable latitudes of eastern North America. However, the American areas of this climate type lack the dry season in winter. The Orient has the long-summer subtype of humid continental climate except for northern Manchuria and extreme northern Japan, which have the short-summer subtype.

Steppe and desert climates, whose characteristics have been previously described in Chapters 12 and 14, are found in Sinkiang and Mongolia and in parts of western India and West Pakistan. A severe *highland climate* characterizes Tibet and adjoining mountain areas. Some of the higher mountains in the East Indies are also best classified as having highland climates.

Climate data for representative stations in the Orient are presented in Table 15, page 315.

Population and Economy of the Orient

Approximately half of the world's people now reside in the Orient. They range from some of the most primitive tribes on earth in the remoter highlands to peoples such as the Indians and Chinese who have been civilized for thousands of years and are the possessors of rich and varied cultures. Mongoloid peoples form a majority in China, Japan, Korea, Burma, Thailand, and Indochina, but the majority of the people in India, though darker skinned than Europeans, are considered to belong to the Caucasian race, and brown-skinned Malays or kindred peoples form a majority among the native inhabitants of the Malay Peninsula, the East Indies, and the Philippines. However, this cursory survey does little justice to the tremendous variety of racial stocks found in the region as a whole.

The picture with respect to religion is also complicated. Hinduism is dominant in India, although many other religions are practiced; while Mohammedanism is the dominant faith in Pakistan, Indonesia, parts of the southern Philippines, parts of outer China, and among the native Malays of the Malay Peninsula. Various forms of Buddhism are dominant in Burma, Thailand, parts of Indochina, and Tibet and Mongolia. Ceylon and Nepal divide between Buddhism and Hinduism. The situation in China is difficult to define precisely: there Buddhism, Confucianism, and Taoism all exert an important influence, often in the same household, and the same general situation prevails among the Koreans and the numerically dominant Annamese of Indochina. In Japan religious affiliations have been divided between Buddhism and the strongly nationalistic religion of Shintoism. The Philippines, with a large Roman Catholic majority, is the only predominantly Christian nation of the Orient. Christian communities do exist in various other areas such as Korea and India. Oriental religions (excepting Mohammedanism and Christianity, which are not indigenous to the region) may be broadly described as contemplative in nature, emphasizing meditation rather than active work for social betterment, and seeking converts with much less vigor than Christianity or Islam. Veneration of ancestors is a prominent feature, especially among the Chinese, Annamese, and Koreans. Often an elaborate ritual for everyday living is followed, the latter being particularly characteristic of the more orthodox Hindus.

The more primitive hill tribes are largely Animists.

▶ Distribution of Population

The densest populations of the Orient are found, generally speaking, on river and coastal plains, although surprisingly high densities occur in some hilly or mountainous areas. The higher mountains, steppes, deserts, and some areas of tropical rain forest are very sparsely inhabited.

Most countries in the Orient have experienced large increases in population during recent centuries, and especially since the beginning of the nineteenth century. Rural densities of 500 to 1000 persons per square mile are fairly common, and some of the more fertile irrigated areas support 2000 persons per square mile or even more. At present, high rates of population increase are found in many areas of the Orient, and a number of Oriental countries—most notably India, Japan, Pakistan, Indonesia, and China—are faced with serious problems of population support. Should present rates of population growth continue for a considerable period, the problem of finding enough food for so many millions will become increasingly critical. Partial solutions are offered by such measures as (1) industrialization to drain surplus population off the land and to provide exports with which to buy imported food, (2) reclamation of new farm lands, and (3) improved agricultural techniques to increase the yield of food per acre. However, each of these possibilities presents certain difficulties. The Oriental countries are not so well provided with resources for industrialization as some other nations of the world, and will encounter many problems in finding adequate markets for industrial exports. Only limited amounts of land suited to Oriental forms of agriculture are not now in use, and some countries, particularly Japan, already attain very high crop yields. However, other countries, notably India, offer considerable prospects for increased yields through better methods of farming. In the long run, artificial limitation of births may well prove the only answer to the population problem, aside, of course, from the age-old population checks of famine and disease. No important religious taboos against birth control appear to exist among the majority of Orientals, although the Oriental religions tend to place a premium on large families. Official government sanction has been given to "planned parenthood" in India and Japan. However, formidable difficulties await any attempt to institute birth control on a large scale among the poor, largely illiterate, and conservative peasant masses who constitute the bulk of the population in the Orient.

▶ Means of Livelihood

Japan is the only country of the Orient which has yet developed modern types of manufacturing on a really large scale. However, India, China, and Indonesia have considerably greater industrial resources than Japan and may be expected to become increasingly important as industrial nations. As yet the great majority of Orientals, including about two fifths of all Japanese, earn their living directly from the soil. Two important types of agriculture, plantation farming and shifting cultivation, are discussed in some detail in Chapter 18 on Southeast Asia, the Oriental area in which these forms of agriculture are the most prominent. In the steppes and deserts of outer China and West Pakistan nomadic herding and oasis farming are practiced. Most Orientals, however, make a living by laborious, painstaking cultivation of crops for home use on tiny plots of land that are watered by the monsoon rains. This type of production, commonly known as *intensive subsistence agriculture,* is built around the growing of cereals, although other types of crops are

raised. Where natural conditions are not suitable for irrigated rice, such grains as wheat, barley, millet, grain sorghums, or corn, are raised. However, irrigated rice is the grain which yields the largest amount of food per unit of area where conditions are favorable for its growth, and this crop is the agricultural mainstay in the areas inhabited by the great majority of Oriental people.

▶ Importance of Rice in the Oriental Economy

The nature and significance of rice growing in the Orient is briefly presented in the following selection by Smith and Phillips: [2]

The old adage that bread is the staff of life is a striking example of the ease with which a half-truth is perpetuated as a universal verity. The fact is that hundreds of millions of healthy and industrious men have never seen bread as we in the Occident know it, but that is no sign that these men are savage, barbarian, or heathen. Throughout the Orient from India to Japan, teeming millions obtain their carbohydrate from rice, which is low in gluten and will not make light bread. . . .

Since rice does not make light bread because it lacks the gluten, the Oriental boils the grain and eats it in that form. He flavors it with a bit of meat or fish if he can afford it; or uses curry, a hot seasoning preparation made in endless varieties. With peas and beans and some greens, rice furnishes almost the entire nourishment for hundreds of millions of people. Peas and beans are widely grown by almost all Eastern peoples who raise rice, and they are the substitutes for meat, milk, and cheese of the West, while the starch of rice is the substitute for bread, potatoes, and many puddings as well. . . .

• The Rice Environment

Among the environmental factors affecting rice production, water supply is most

---

[2] J. Russell Smith and M. Ogden Phillips, *Industrial and Commercial Geography,* 3d ed. New York: Holt, 1946. Pp. 428–434. Authors' footnotes and all headings except one have been omitted. One heading has been added, one word italicized in editing. Used by permission of the authors and the publisher.

An Indian villager carrying unthreshed rice from the fields. (*Technical Cooperation Administration, U. S. Department of State.*)

important, for the great bulk of all rice is grown under irrigation, the rice fields being submerged under approximately 6 inches of fresh, slowly moving water for at least 75 days. While the amount of water needed in a given area varies with such factors as rate of evaporation, relative humidity, and soil conditions, a total of 45 to 65 inches of water is generally required for rice production. . . . Furthermore, rice requires a mean temperature of more than 70°F. during the growing season of 4 to 6 months. Hence, rice is a product of the tropics and subtropics, most of it being grown in regions of reeking humidity with frequent, almost daily rains. . . .

Level land is obviously essential for irrigation, and where it is lacking man must create it artificially as he has done by laboriously building terraces on the steep hillsides in many parts of Japan, China, the Philippines, and the East Indies. Although rice is grown on a variety of soils, there must be an impervious subsoil to prevent the loss of valuable irrigation water by seepage. Ideal soil conditions are found on many an alluvial plain, where a topsoil of fertile and friable silt has been deposited above a layer of impervious clay.

Although rice is now produced in the tropic and subtropic lands of every continent, 95 per cent of the world's crop is grown each year in southern and eastern Asia. . . .

• The Technique of Rice Growing

. . . Lowland rice must be grown by irrigation, and the devices used in fitting and keeping the land for this service are among the greatest monuments of human diligence in the world. . . . In Ceylon, for example, the railway that goes from the seacoast to the highlands goes through an irrigated plain divided by low banks into ponds of small area—rice fields, each of which has by great labor been leveled so that the water may be of uniform and proper depth for rice growing. As the railroad climbs the slopes of the hills the rice patches continue, with smaller area and higher banks, turning at last into a giant flight of gentle water steps, one of the most beautiful landscapes that the world possesses. . . .

The common treatment of . . . lowland rice is alternately to flood it and draw off the water during the early periods of its growth. It is kept under water during a larger part of its development, the water being entirely drawn off as it ripens. The water must not become stagnant, and to keep it in motion it is the common practice on the hillsides to lead a stream to the top terrace, and let the water pass from terrace to terrace down the slopes. . . .

The labor of rice growing often involves the raising of plants in small seed beds and transplanting them in little bunches to the rice field itself. This work, as most of the other work in connection with terrace-grown rice, can be done only by hand. The small fields make it impossible to use such machinery as reapers and at times even the ox and water buffalo. . . .

When the Asiatic rice field is finally drained, the ripened grain is usually cut by hand, tied up in bundles, and allowed to dry. To accomplish this in moist places, it is often necessary to put the sheaves upon bamboo frames. It is usually threshed by hand with the aid of some very simple devices. One of these is a board with a slit in it. Drawing the rice through the slit pulls the grains from the heads and allows them to fall into a receptacle. The grain at this stage is called *paddy* because of a close-fitting husk not unlike that which protects the oat kernel. As with oats, these husks cause the grain to keep much better than when the husk is removed and the final husking of rice for home use is usually deferred until the time of use approaches. Among the Oriental people the husking of the paddy to prepare it for food is a daily occurrence, commonly done by hand. One of the commonest sounds throughout the East . . . is the pounding of a heavy mallet or pestle as it falls into a vessel full of paddy in the process of pounding the grain and loosening the husk.

17

The Indian Realm

In terms of present-day political units the Indian Realm includes the five countries of India, Pakistan, Nepal, Bhutan, and Sikkim. India and Pakistan are by far the largest of these countries in area and population. Nepal, Bhutan, and Sikkim are small states on the southern flank of the Himalaya Mountains. All three of the latter countries have strong economic and political ties with India (Bhutan and Sikkim are under formal Indian protection). The three Himalayan countries are mountainous, sparsely populated, and difficult of access. They are among the least known of the world's countries and have relatively little importance in world affairs. The large island of Ceylon off the southeast coast of the Indian peninsula is often in-

cluded with India and Pakistan in regional groupings. However, in many respects Ceylon is more similar to the countries of Southeast Asia, and is considered with the latter group in Chapter 18.

The outer frontiers of the Indian Realm lie in the Himalaya and Karakoram Mountains, highest in the world, to the north, and in the flanking ranges which trend south from the two ends of the Himalayan arc. Until 1947 it was customary to refer to the entire area now included within India and Pakistan as "India." Due to the size, complexity, relative isolation, and distinctive civilization of this area, it was often called the Indian subcontinent. For well over a century the subcontinent was the most important unit in the British colonial

Making cow dung cakes, India's universal cooking fuel. The number of cakes in the photo bespeaks a commercial rather than a household operation. (*Foreign Agricultural Service, U. S. Department of Agriculture.*)

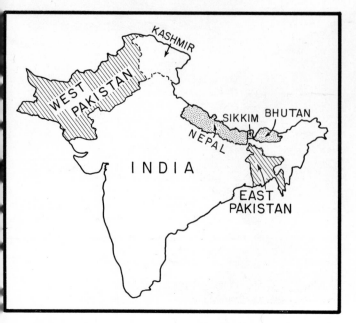

Political units of the Indian subcontinent. Pakistan is indicated by diagonal lines and the three Himalayan states of Nepal, Bhutan, and Sikkim by a dot pattern. The future status of Kashmir, disputed between India and Pakistan, remained undecided at the time of writing.

empire. Then in 1947 it gained freedom, but in the process became divided along religious lines into two sovereign nations, the predominantly Hindu nation of India, and the Moslem nation of Pakistan. Many of the outstanding characteristics of the subcontinent and the two new countries occupying it are summarized in the following selection from an outstanding book by a regional specialist on South Asia, W. Norman Brown: [1]

On August 15, 1947, the world received two new large, self-ruling nations, India and Pakistan. They were created by partition of the old British "Indian Empire" and began their separate and independent existence as Dominions within the British Commonwealth of Nations. Both remain members in the Commonwealth. Pakistan retains [a similar] relationship to the Commonwealth as do Canada and those other member countries which acknowledge a common allegiance to the British Crown. India, on inaugurating its new constitution on January 26, 1950, became a "sovereign, democratic republic," but remained a member in the Commonwealth in accordance with an agreement with other Commonwealth countries to recognize the King as the symbol of the Commonwealth association and as such the "head of the Commonwealth.". . .

Importance of India and Pakistan

The old India, before partition, had little voice in international affairs. Its foreign relations were conducted through the British Foreign Office; its internal administration was subject on the highest level to the British Parliament. What India or citizens of India thought was of slight significance outside India, and, until only a few years before 1947, of not much more within India itself. But when the new nations were created, this situation changed. Each acquired international importance as a great Asian power, whose friendship and cooperation are valuable to other nations.

▶ Area and Population

What is the basis for the two nations' importance? Briefly, it lies less in their present development than in potentialities, and derives from their area, population, resources, intellectual capacity, and strategic situation. First, is the simple matter of size. The old pre-partition India, a self-contained subcontinent, well isolated from

[1] Reprinted by permission of the publishers from W. Norman Brown, *The United States and India and Pakistan.* Cambridge, Mass.: Harvard University Press, Copyright, 1953, by The President and Fellows of Harvard College. Pp. 1–17. All headings and one editorial footnote have been added.

the rest of the world by difficult land barriers and seacoast, had about 1,581,410 square miles of territory, more than half the area of the United States. This is now divided unequally between India and Pakistan in a ratio of not quite 3.4 to 1, with some regions in dispute. The territorial claims of the two nations slightly exceed those of the old undivided India. India claims (Census of 1951) 1,221,072 square miles, including Kashmir, Junagadh, and Manavadar (whose status is in dispute with Pakistan), and is between one-third and one-half the size of the United States with its territorial possessions. Pakistan . . . claims (1951 Census estimate) 360,-780 square miles (excluding Junagadh and Manavadar) and is about the size of France, Italy, Switzerland, and the Netherlands combined. Pakistan is in two sections, at opposite sides of the subcontinent, a thousand miles apart. Of these, Western Pakistan is much the larger, having approximately 307,000 square miles. Eastern Pakistan has only about 54,000 square miles but is the more populous.

The population figures of the subcontinent are more suggestive than those of area. In 1951 India counted its population at 356,891,624, excluding Kashmir (4.02 million in 1941, estimated in 1950 to be 4.37 million) and some tribal areas in Assam (estimated at 560,631). This is more than double that of the United States. Pakistan, according to its 1951 Census estimate (released March 20, 1951), ha[d] 75,687,000, of whom 33,568,000 live[d] in Western Pakistan and 42,119,000 in Eastern Pakistan. The total population of the two nations was, therefore, estimated in 1951 at around 437.5 million, which is more than the combined populations of the United States, the Soviet Union, and the United Kingdom. . . .

▶ Industrial Potentialities

Economically India and Pakistan are far from having developed their industrial potentialities, though it is true that after World War II, with the eclipse of Japan,

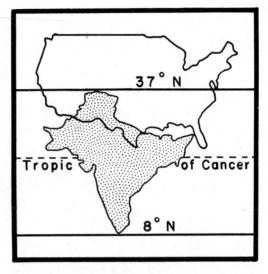

The Indian subcontinent compared in latitude and area with the United States.

India was, for the time being, the chief industrial producer in Asia. It is doubtful that these two countries separately or together could ever assume an industrial position in Asia comparable to that which Japan held before the war and may regain. Nevertheless, they have the resources for a development of notable size. India has extensive, high-grade deposits of iron, estimated at 20 billion tons. She has deposits of coal, estimated at 60 billion tons; little of this is useful in metallurgical activities. She has excellent resources in manganese, mica, and bauxite. Her largest industry is cotton textiles. She produces cement, paper, and some other industrial products. Pakistan has far fewer economic resources than India, but does have almost a world monopoly in raising jute, though the mills for processing it are located in India, Scotland, and the United States. It is estimated that India and Pakistan have combined water-power resources of about 27,000,000 horsepower. Though the subcontinent lacks a good supply of oil and has few deposits of non-ferrous metals, these and other necessities for industry can be imported from near by—oil from the Persian Gulf and Burma, the needed metals largely from Burma.

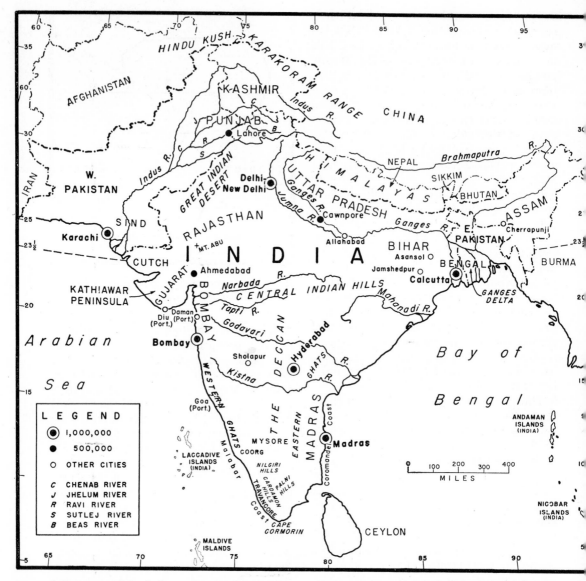

Index map of the Indian subcontinent. New Delhi is the capital of India and Karachi of Pakistan.

The population figures show that the subcontinent has a large labor supply. Not only is the source practically inexhaustible; Indian labor also has a tradition of skill celebrated in Europe since the times of classical Greece and Rome. Five centuries ago India was producing wares which induced technically less advanced Europe to seek a water route to that land. Hence the discovery of America! Early in the war in 1942 a United States Technical Mission to then unpartitioned India reported that, given a living wage, the Indian workman stood up well in comparison with industrial workers of Western countries.

► *Intellectual Achievements and Potentialities*

Besides economic potentiality, India and Pakistan have the prospect of significant intellectual accomplishment. In the Indian subcontinent flourish today two of the world's greatest historic civilizations—the native Indian and the imported Islamic. Of these the first has existed for more than four and a half thousand years. Islam, though younger in India, is the heir to a thousand years more of civilization in the Near East. Both of these have been supplemented in the subcontinent by Europeanism since it established itself militarily and politically in the latter half of the eighteenth century. Thought in India has never been static, nor has social custom. As Jawaharlal Nehru repeatedly points out in his *Discovery of India* (1946), it is just the adaptability of Indian civilization to new ideas and its conjunction of intellectualism with imagination which have enabled it to modify or abandon outworn institutions and maintain its vitality and strength by developing new ones. It is this same adaptability which makes India and Pakistan potentially strong for intellectual development in the modern world. It is reasonable to expect that in the future, as in the past, the Indian subcontinent will be intellectually creative and will rank with Europe and America in scientific, social, and humanistic accomplishment. It may rival, though not duplicate, the great Western nations.

▶ Strategic Location of the Subcontinent

Together with these possibilities of achieving world economic importance and intellectual distinction, the subcontinent happens also to hold a strategic position on the globe. It lies at the top of the Indian Ocean, commanding the lanes of sea traffic between Europe and Africa on one side and on the other, Southeast Asia, the Far East, and the Pacific lands. This situation gives it marked advantages for trade in a great section of the earth. If India and Pakistan expand their industry, they will have convenient foreign markets on each side for surplus exportable manufactures. In a military crisis they could, with their large resources of population and an expanded industry, strike out in either direction. . . .

▶ Elements of Weakness

But along with these potential sources of strength, India and Pakistan have serious elements of weakness. One is the conflict between the Islamic and Hindu communities which has now separated the subcontinent into two political entities and may lead to further strife. There are perilous divisions within each country between majority and minority social groups, between linguistic groups, between geographical regions. Today the economy of each is weak. Poverty is general, and sudden disaster can produce a famine, local or widespread according to the circumstances. The population problem is critical. Before these two countries can realize their potentialities, they must get these various problems under control.

A Land of Villages

India and Pakistan live today, as they have done in the past, primarily by means of agriculture, with relatively little supplement from industry. The imbalance is shown by the small number of industrial workers. Modern factories in the two nations employ only around 2 million persons, or by the most liberal interpretation of "factory" perhaps 2.5 million. This is about one-half of 1 per cent of the total population. Whether you travel in the subcontinent by rail, automobile, or air, you emerge suddenly from one of the few large cities to proceed for hundreds of miles across open country, dotted with drab little villages, lightened by only an occasional whitewashed Hindu shrine or Muslim [Moslem] mosque. Here and there you come to a small town. There is nothing to compare with the Atlantic coastal stretch of almost continuous urbanization from Boston to Wilmington or with some other American industrial areas, as around Pittsburgh and Chicago. Only about 6.5 per cent of India's population in 1951 and 5.0 per cent of Pakistan's lived in cities of a hundred thousand or over. In the United States the [comparable] urban percentage in 1951 was 32.0. Just as there are few cities and towns in India and Pakistan, so too there are few isolated rural dwellings like the farmhouses of the United States. Most of the people (over 87 per cent) live in the more than 650,000 villages, which are settlements of less than 5000 population, averaging about 520 each. Of the villagers much the greater part (about 70 per cent of the total population) are cultivators of the adjacent land; the others supply services or pursue handicrafts (weaving, pottery, metal work, oil pressing, or other). The country, as one sees it, consists of clusters or even long stretches of tiny fields, streaked with inarable land and jungle. Except at a few centers like Calcutta, Bombay, Madras, Jamshedpur, Asansol, Ahmedabad, Kanpur (Cawnpore), Sholapur, Karachi, factory chimneys are solitary or absent. . . . In the hills and mountains, where agriculture is more difficult, villages are fewer and smaller. In the deserts . . . they are still scarcer.

The Perennial Problem of Water Supply

Agriculture in almost every part of India and Pakistan has to depend upon a scanty or fickle water supply, and the possession of water is a perennial and never fully solved problem. Nowhere else do so many people put so much labor into getting water; and nowhere else is the problem of getting it more dramatic. In a region where great rivers can be used for irrigation, such as the Punjab or Sind, the water is impounded by huge dams or barrages and led off through canals. The major outlets are large; from these run off smaller canals, and from these still smaller ones, and so by graduated decrease until the water finally reaches the fields through minute capillary-like distribution. For part of the year many of these channels must be cut off, to save the water until it is needed later. At the latter time the peasants are busy throughout the day opening the sluices leading to their land so as to get the maximum flow during the hours for which they have contracted and to direct the water first to one part of their farms and then to another. This is the easiest of India's ways of using human labor to water fields, and the most certain. The rivers of north India are largely fed by the melting snows of the Himalayas and the rain that falls upon their southern ranges during the annual summer monsoon. At that time the clouds, after crossing the plains, have to rise, are cooled, and so are made to condense and precipitate their moisture. The flow of water in the rivers fluctuates from year to year, but in no year does it cease entirely. Hence, peasants who live in regions where there are river-fed irrigation systems are usually better off and less subject to crop failure and famine than those who must rely upon other sources.

In many parts of India and Pakistan the farmer gets water for his fields from a well. In North India he may use a great Persian wheel, filling the air with an interminable creaking, which dips an endless chain of earthenware pots into the water, raises them above ground level, and empties them into a trough from which the water flows through runlets to the land. A blindfolded camel or a pair of bullocks operates the mechanism, treading a tiny circle all day long while a man or boy stands by to keep them moving. Elsewhere a peasant may use a buffalo or a bullock or a pair of bullocks, which alternately raise and lower a leather sack into the water. There is a ramp built up to the well, rising above its mouth some six feet or more. Along it the bullocks tread forward and backward, relaxing the rope to which the sack is tied, and so letting it fall, then, when they reverse, raising it to the wooden crossbeam at the high end of the incline, where it is emptied into a channel to flow away. It takes one man to empty the sack, another to drive the bullocks. Very poor peasants who own no bullocks and cannot arrange to use those of a neighbor may operate such a well with only human labor, India's cheapest commodity, drawn from the ranks of the family.

In still other areas peasants raise the water with a sweep, like an Egyptian *shaduf*. This is a seesaw-like apparatus with a leather sack or an earthenware pot at one end of the beam and a counterpoise balanced at the other. All day long a man may walk back and forth along the beam, first lowering the container into the well and then raising it to the top, where another man empties it into a runway. Or at the extremity of the sweep there may be a bamboo pole with the vessel fastened to its end. A man stands beside the well forcing the pole down until the vessel is submerged, then letting it go so that the counterpoise can raise it to the surface. In South India one may see a channel or ditch full

of water, into which two peasants, often women, jointly dip a shallow scoop, rhythmically swinging it back and forth between them, lifting the water and emptying it in a higher channel through which it flows to the fields.

Throughout the land there are hundreds of thousands of "tanks," or artificial ponds, which are filled by the annual rains and serve in the dry season for irrigation, washing, even drinking. It is important to keep these tanks in good working order. Silt must not be left to accumulate; plants, such as the rapidly spreading water chestnut, must be prevented from choking them and absorbing the water supply. A tank has to be cleaned out regularly. But when it is cleaned, it is necessary to do the work carefully, so as not to dig out the bottom and let the water seep away. . . .

Physical Geography of the Subcontinent

What are the facts about the subcontinent's topography, its fertile plains, its river systems, its mountainous areas, its deserts, its basic water supply?

▶ The Outer Wall of High Mountains

The subcontinent is shaped roughly like a quadrangle—or, more precisely, like a pentagon, though the fifth side is disproportionately short. One long point of the figure is the Deccan peninsula projecting sharply southward into the Indian Ocean, with the Arabian Sea on its west and the Bay of Bengal on its east. The rest is mountain-bound. Along the northwestern side, now held by Pakistan, is a protective barrier of hills and desert, generally difficult for armies or peoples on the trek, yet penetrable at various points, and providing the chief means of ingress to India by land throughout recorded history. The northern side is a concave arc of lofty mountains, containing the world's highest peaks. It bars both the peoples and the cold winds of the land beyond and at the same time blocks the rainclouds of India from reaching Central Asia, where in consequence large areas remain desert. These ranges are

geologically young and they and the nearby plains are disturbed by frequent tremors and occasional disastrous earthquakes, such as those in Bihar in 1934 and Assam in 1950. On the east the short fifth side is the Burma frontier, whose jungle-covered mountains and dangerous marshes are all but impassable.

▶ The Northern Plain

Inside the northwestern and northern walls is the great plain of the subcontinent. It starts at the Arabian Sea with the peninsula of Kathiawar in the present Republic of India, and extends, first, slightly west of north to Sind in Pakistan. There it bends to a little east of north and continues for about 700 miles to the Himalayas, including all of Western Pakistan except some mountain areas. It then turns eastward into India, to follow a curved course below the Himalayan chain, crossing the breadth of the country and coming to an end against the hills of Assam and Eastern Pakistan and the coast of the Bay of Bengal.

This plain varies from 80 to 200 miles in width. In its sweeping course it contains the greatest of India's river systems. In the west is the Indus, which rises on the northern side of the Himalayas, flows westward behind them to round their end, separating them from the Karakoram and Hindu Kush ranges, and then drives inside the northwestern frontier down to the sea. The Indus is fed by the five rivers of the Punjab ("Land of Five Streams"), one of which (the Sutlej) also rises north of the Himalayas not far from the source of the Indus, but, unlike it, finds a route directly through them. The four others (Jhelum, Chenab, Ravi, Beas) rise in the range and flow directly to the lowlands. In the upper Punjab the moderate rainfall and the irrigation based upon its rivers support an extensive agriculture. Farther south, in the lower Punjab and Sind, rainfall is scanty, varying from ten to twenty inches annually and in many places being even less. Here agriculture is impossible except with the aid of irrigation. This has been practiced for millennia, but never on a scale to support a large population. Today there are great systems of irrigation in this region, and others are under construction or planned. East of the long course of the Indus is the Great Indian [Thar] Desert. . . .

The northern part of the Great Indian Plain, often called Hindustan, contains the Ganges-Jumna (Jamna) river system, which only a low rise of ground separates from the Indus system. The soil of this region is a deep alluvial deposit. Its two main rivers, the Ganges and the Jumna, rise on the lower side of the Himalayas and curve southeast in gradually converging arcs until they unite at Allahabad. From there the Ganges continues eastward to Bengal, absorbing many tributaries, to join the Brahmaputra. This last, like the Indus and the Sutlej, rises on the northern side of the Himalayas, but, as though to polarize the Indus, flows eastward to turn and circle the eastern end of the mountain chain, where it finds an opening, reverses itself, and flows southwest. It and the Ganges unite and form an immense delta. Their waters reach the Bay of Bengal through many mouths, steadily depositing silt, and today as for millennia in the past continu-

ally projecting the land area into the bay.

The part of the northern plain east of the Punjab, already favored by its rivers, is in normal years also well watered by seasonal rains. It is the most desirable part of India and has always been the goal of invaders. Its population density is close to 600 per square mile and, though it comprises only about one-sixth of the subcontinent's total area, it contains about two-fifths of its total population.

▶ *Peninsular India*

Below [south of] the northern plain is a complex highland, the upper end of which is embraced by the two descending extremes of the plain. Along its northern part are various ranges of low hills, of which the highest peak, Mount Abu, is 5651 feet in elevation. These make the Central Indian terrain difficult to penetrate and permit it to support only a moderately dense population. Indian literature has for 2500 years spoken fearfully of the wild jungles and the primitive peoples in this area. . . .

Still farther south is the part of the plateau known specifically as the Deccan ("South"), which comprises most of the triangle of peninsular India. This tableland (varying from about 1000 to 2500 feet in elevation) tilts gently from west to east. Its great rivers rise on the western side, flow eastward across it, and empty in the Bay of Bengal. It is not well watered, either by streams or by rainfall, and much of its area is rocky or has soil of only inferior quality. Nevertheless it supports around 200 persons to the square mile.

The Deccan is bordered on east and west by low ranges of mountains known as Ghats ("Steps"). The Western Ghats, a kind of seaboard scarp, which have a few peaks of approximately 5000 feet but average around 3000 feet, descend in thickly forested, bold declivities to the seaboard. The southern part of this shoreline, known as the Malabar coast, is one of the best-watered, most fertile, and most thickly populated parts of India, having over 800 persons to the square mile. On the other side of the peninsula the Eastern Ghats, averaging about 1500 feet in altitude, are less picturesque. They lead down to another well-watered, productive, and thickly inhabited plain, wider than that on the west and known as the Coromandel coast. The central plateau terminates in clusters of hills called the Nilgiris ("Blue Mountains") and Palni, which respectively have peaks as high as 8640 and 8841 feet. Finally, . . . at the extreme south, are the Cardamon Hills. Beyond these last is Cape Comorin, the southernmost point of India, east and south of which lies the fragrant island of Ceylon. . . .

Role of the Monsoon Rains

The most important climatic feature of the subcontinent is the annual southwest monsoon, which brings "the rains" and gives India 90 per cent of its heaven-dispensed water. So impressive has this phenomenon been upon India's consciousness that in her languages the commonest words for year primarily mean "rain" or "rainy season." The southwest monsoon blows, with some variation each year, during the four months of June through September, when the high sun heats the land rapidly and the hot air rises so that a low-pressure area is created and cool air flows inland from the sea. As it comes in from across the Indian Ocean, it is laden with moisture. . . . One arm of the monsoon strikes the hills of the lower western (Malabar) coast of India, rises, cools off, and precipitates its water heavily. But by the time it has crossed the Western Ghats, it has lost most of its moisture and has little left to precipitate upon the Deccan behind them. Northerly along this coast the indrawn winds dispense their water in smaller and smaller amounts as the Ghats become lower, until they deposit scarcely any when they reach Cutch, just below the Tropic of Cancer, and Sind, which the clouds hasten across, hoarding their treasure for Kashmir, seven hundred miles to the north. Hence Gujarat, which is the region north of Bombay, is productive, rich, and thickly settled, but beyond it Cutch, Sind, Rajasthan, and parts of the Punjab, being almost rainless, are dry and thinly peopled except where irrigated from the Indus.

The other arm of this monsoon rounds the southern end of India and Ceylon and proceeds north up the Bay of Bengal. It strikes the eastern coast unevenly, but gives fair coverage to the coastal plain lying between the Eastern Ghats and the Bay. When it gets to the head of the Bay of Bengal, it fans out to west, north, and east. The winds which blow westward water the inland areas of eastern India and the long northern plain of Bengal, Bihar, Uttar Pradesh, and the Punjab. They reach also into the center of the country. As they proceed westward, they steadily lose moisture until very little is left for the upper Punjab, especially the part which lies in Pakistan. They beat against the length of the first ranges of the Himalayas, rising and cooling and exhausting their last moisture on their southern side. This rainfall, in the years when it is sufficiently abundant, soaks the deep alluvial soil, fills the streams, which in the dry season are but thin trickles in wide sandy beds, transforms them into roaring floods, and happily makes the northern plain for the time a mass of fertile mud.

The currents of the monsoon which go to the north, northeast, and east drench Bengal and Assam, especially the hills in the latter area. . . . Over 800 inches have been recorded in a single year at Cherrapunji in the Khasi and Jaintia Hills.[2] This heavy precipitation fits the slopes of the mountains for tea gardens.

Additional rain comes to certain parts of India during the months of November and December, when there is another monsoon,

[2] *Editorial Note.* The average yearly rainfall at Cherrapunji is 428 inches, making this one of the rainiest spots on earth.

this one blowing from the northeast. Over most of the country these winds are dry, with only occasional light rainfall known as "mango showers." They make the winter season in northern India a time of cool weather with almost unbroken sunshine and a comfortable temperature, ideal for tourists but of no help to the peasant if the southwest monsoon has been deficient and his crops need water. In South India the case is different. The part of the northeast monsoon which comes inland from across the Bay of Bengal carries moisture which it has absorbed from that body of water and then precipitates. It waters the coastal plain and succeeds in carrying much of its charge across the low Eastern Ghats into the rest of Madras, and into Coorg, Mysore, and Travancore. With this supplement to the rainfall of the southwestern monsoon the area is able to support a good deal of intensive agriculture. Nevertheless, neither monsoon brings the region just east of the Western Ghats very heavy rainfall, and each monsoon is fickle. There is no certainty of adequate rain to guarantee full crops, and often, as in the five-year stretch 1947–1951, there is short supply, and the area is in difficulty.

If "the rains," that "annual gamble" from the southwest, are "normal" and wide-spread, the subcontinent is prosperous. That is, people do not actually suffer starvation; the government can collect the land revenue; the peasantry do not have to borrow from the village moneylenders at a ruinous rate of interest and may even do something toward reducing the principal of their debts. But if the rains are scanty in any area or fail, not only do the fields get no direct water from heaven; the sources of irrigation dwindle too. Rivers fall; the village tanks are not replenished; the water table is lowered; wells dry up. So, too, if in Northern India, the rains are too full and make the rivers flood, as in 1950, seed may be washed out, cattle carried off, villages destroyed, and ruin come upon the peasantry and their land. Where there is irrigation from snow-fed streams, as in the Punjab, the case is not so desperate, for the mountain slopes always get a share of rain, which ultimately collects in the rivers. Elsewhere the inevitable result is poor crops or none at all. Agriculture stops; food is exhausted; there follows "distress," "scarcity," or "famine"; and relief must be brought in from outside. Such conditions have been reported since the third century B.C., just after India's historical records start; the case has not been different since. . . .

The Extent and Effects of Poverty

The bulk of the village population gets only the most meager living in terms of food, clothing, and shelter. Urban factory labor lives no better, possibly worse. Without seeing Indians in their villages, towns, and cities, it is difficult for a Westerner to visualize the extent and effect of their poverty. And if the average American visitor wants to remain sensitive to the conditions in which the masses of the people live, it is well for him not to stay in the country long. Very quickly the want, the disease, the discomfort, the misery, become only accepted facts.

In 1946 the Government's Health Survey and Development Committee . . . reported the average individual diet figure to be 1750 calories a day (against a needed 2400 to 3000 calories), which was "ill balanced" as well as low and it estimated that 30 per cent of India's families were seriously undernourished. In prewar years, with food supply at "normal," the Director of the Indian Medical Service (Sir John Megaw in 1933) estimated that 41 per cent of the people were "poorly nourished," that is, endured continued semistarvation. . . .

For clothing a gauge may lie in the consumption of cotton textiles—almost all clothing in India and Pakistan is of cotton. The average for personal clothing and household purposes combined was about 13.5 yards per year in 1949–1950; in prewar years it was about 16 yards; figures given for the world consumption of textiles are 42 yards a person; for the United States 64 square yards of cotton textiles alone.

Housing is equally inadequate. In the villages most dwellings are made of mud and wattle or sun-dried brick, crowded together in an irregular huddle, affording little protection from the winter cold, the burning heat of summer, and the torrents of the rainy season. The average floor space per person in the villages is impossible to determine. In industrial urban areas surveys in 1938 showed it to be less than 28 square feet in Bombay, about 43 square feet in Ahmedabad, about 24 square feet in Sholapur. Most urban workers with their families were living in one-room tenements; in 1931 in Bombay 74 per cent, in Karachi 58, in Kanpur (Cawnpore) 63; in London at the same time it was 6.0 per cent. Often the quarters were without a chimney or a window, with no lights or water supply, and no sanitary arrangements. Conditions can hardly be better now, since living costs have gone up more rapidly in intervening years than wages, and the urban population has increased, while little new housing has been erected. Every city, at least during the present century, has had a large number of people with no housing at all, who sleep each night in the open.

In typical village and urban dwellings furniture scarcely exists. A house, or hut, has a fireplace consisting of a few bricks or stones or molded clay set to form three sides of a rectangle over which a pot or pan can be placed; it may also contain a few metal cooking vessels and some primitive implements for farming or the pursuit of a handicraft. That is likely to be all. Scavenging is a function of the village dogs. With these basic handicaps to health go heavy incidence of disease and paucity of preventive and curative medicine.

The combined effect of poor diet, insufficient clothing, substandard housing, lack of medical resources, is a high mortality rate. The 1941 Census of India gave a figure of 21.8 per 1000 (against 10.6 in the United States), but some critical studies of the data by competent demographers set it much higher, that is, at 31.2 per 1000. Life expectation at birth, according to actuarial calculations published in the Indian Census Reports, averaged in 1941 31.8 years (it was estimated at about 26.7 in 1931), as against approximately 60 for whites and 48 for Negroes in the United States (1929–1931). The brevity and ills of life in India have often been held responsible for her preoccupation with religion, emphasis upon family organization, and intense desire to have progeny and have it early in life, thus conducing to early marriage. In our time they look like an invitation to extremist remedies, such as communism or any other that claims to have a quick cure for social ills.

For some five millennia man in the Indian subcontinent has not merely held his own against the disadvantages which nature puts upon him, but has searched out and utilized means to maintain a life of high achievement in the arts of civilization. If on the spiral of history South Asia once was more accomplished in those arts than the West but now is less so, it may again reach a position of equality. That, at least, is the hope of many citizens of India and Pakistan. But the two young nations started life after a wearying struggle to achieve independence, and a destructive conflict between Hindus and Muslims, the ill effects of which still continue. With no time granted for recuperation, they have had to attack their basic living problems, build new sources of national strength, and assume international responsibilities. Their resources and energy have not yet been equal to the demands.

The "basic living problems" which India and Pakistan must attack are among the most difficult and pressing to be found anywhere in the world. Though the various problems are closely interrelated, they may be classified for convenient discussion under the headings of agricultural problems, industrial problems, problems of social relations, and population problems. In the following discussion the major problems are viewed against the general economic and social order of the subcontinent.

Agricultural Characteristics and Problems

From the standpoint of total production of agricultural commodities the Indian subcontinent is clearly one of the world's outstanding agricultural areas. Although the available data are not sufficient for figures to be stated with great accuracy, the subcontinent produces something like the following proportions of some of the world's major agricultural commodities: well over 90 percent of its jute, over one third of its peanuts, between one third and one half of its tea, close to one third of its rice, about one fifth of its millet and sugar, about one tenth of its tobacco and cotton. In addition, the area produces an unknown but very high percentage of the world's grain sorghums and contains probably between one fifth and one fourth of its cattle.

However, this huge total production has to be balanced against the fact that around a sixth of the world's people live in the subcontinent and are mainly engaged in agricultural production. Average production per man and per acre is low, despite the pressing need for food indicated by chronic undernourishment among large segments

A family kitchen in the forested Central Indian hills. Dried cow dung is a more common fuel than wood in most parts of the subcontinent. (*Technical Cooperation Administration, U. S. Department of State.*)

of the population, coupled with periodic famines in various areas. The magnitude of the food problem does not become fully apparent until it is realized that the average citizen of the subcontinent is more poorly fed now than he was 50 years ago and that total production of the major food crops has tended to decline somewhat since about 1920. Meanwhile the population has been steadily increasing. Between 1931 and 1941 the subcontinent registered a total gain of about 51 million, and between 1941 and 1951 a gain of 49 million. Thus it will be seen that since 1931 the population has increased at an average rate of about 5 million a year, without a compensating increase in food production.

▶ Major Crops of the Subcontinent

Between 70 and 85 percent of the cultivated land of the subcontinent is ordinarily planted in food grains. Rice is the most important single crop, being the favored grain in most areas where the water supply is adequate. Rice growing is especially characteristic of the lower Ganges and Brahmaputra Valleys and the eastern and western coastal lowlands of the peninsula. These are the areas where water supply is most adequate and the population is densest.

Immense quantities of low-grade cane sugar are produced for household use in the Indian subcontinent. The bullocks in the photo are supplying motive power for a small sugar cane press. Crushed cane pulp in the foreground will be used for fuel. (*Foreign Agricultural Service, U. S. Department of Agriculture.*)

Wheat is the leading grain in the upper Ganges Valley and in West Pakistan. The Punjab, divided between West Pakistan and India, is especially noted as a wheat-growing area. Millet and grain sorghums are favored in areas where rainfall is deficient and adequate water is not available for irrigation. Such conditions are found over considerable areas in the interior of the Deccan, and this is the principal producing area for millet and sorghums. For the most part all of these grain crops are produced on a subsistence basis, for home or local consumption. Only a small percentage will ordinarily enter the channels of a more widespread trade.

To secure the funds with which to attack their various problems, India and Pakistan need to increase their volume of exports. This has involved them in an agricultural dilemma. The available land is badly needed for food production, yet their exports rest mainly on the production of certain commercial crops. Should the land be used for food, with consequent injury to exports and hence to the supply of funds and equipment needed for development, or should it be devoted to export crops, with consequent deterioration in the food supply? The answer is difficult. The major commercial crops at present are cotton, produced mainly in West Pakistan and near Bombay in India; jute, a coarse fiber produced mainly in East Pakistan and to some extent in the lower Ganges Valley in India; various oil-bearing seeds and nuts, peanuts being especially important; and tea, produced on a plantation basis in Assam and to a lesser degree in the far south of the peninsula.

▶ Some Economic Consequences of Partition

Hindu India and Moslem Pakistan chose to go their separate ways without regard for economic consequences. With respect to agriculture Pakistan finds itself in a somewhat better situation than India. Western Pakistan usually produces a small surplus of grain to offset the deficit which is ordinarily experienced in East Pakistan. For export Pakistan has the cotton of the Indus Valley and the jute of East Pakistan. The latter area included much the larger share of the jute-producing areas in pre-partition India.

India is in a poorer relative position agriculturally due to the loss of the Indus Valley cotton and grain surpluses and the jute of East Bengal. Recently India has been trying to make up for the loss of the jute by expanded jute production in West Bengal. Cotton production in India is not great enough to completely supply the existing textile industry. Thus only tea and oilseeds are left to India as major agricultural exports. Complicating India's agricultural situation still further is the fact that the country was left at partition with the majority of the areas most chronically deficient in food production. The interior Deccan, with its low and uncertain rainfall, is an important case in point.

▶ Low Productivity of the Individual Farmer

The shortage of food and the extreme degree of rural poverty over the subcontinent are closely related to the individual farmer's lack of productivity. One of the reasons for the latter is the small size of farms. In the years between 1891 and 1941 the average size of farm in that part of India for which statistics are available decreased from 2.23 acres to 1.90 acres. Many "farms" total less than a single acre. Many peasants have been detached completely from the land and have come to form a growing landless rural "proletariat."

Even if the individual farmer made the most of his small holding his total production could not be large, but this is far from the case. His time is often wasted in traveling between parts of his holding which are widely separated, for fragmentation of farms into numerous small, separated plots has been the rule. Cases are recorded where one acre has been split among the holdings of sixteen different cultivators. The efficiency of his labor is decreased by lack of adequate equipment. It has often been noted that the plows of many farmers in the subcontinent are no more than iron-shod sticks which merely scratch the soil rather than turn it over. Tillage is retarded in some areas by lack of adequate draft power, despite the huge number of cattle, principally oxen and water buffaloes, whose primary function is to serve as draft animals. The Hindu prohibition on the killing of cattle and the lack of scientific animal husbandry combine to keep great numbers of useless animals alive which compete with work animals for the sparse forage. A large but undernourished and relatively ineffectual animal population is the result.

On his small holding the farmer of the Republic of India obtains some of the world's lowest crop yields. Rice yields in India appear to be the lowest in the Orient and the lowest for any sizable producer anywhere; wheat yields averaging 10 to 11 bushels per acre are the lowest for any major producer and among the lowest anywhere. Yields in Pakistan are generally somewhat better than in India, but still below the world average. Such low yields are the result of poor techniques of cultivation, lack of scientific seed selection, and the poverty of the soil. Most of the soils now in use have been intensively worked for many centuries without adequate provision for maintaining their fertility. They have been leached by the concentrated rains of the monsoon season, and they receive little or no fertilizer. Most farmers cannot afford artificial fertilizers, and animal manures must ordinarily be used as fuel for cooking due to the lack of wood over extensive areas long since deforested.

That the low average yields of the subcontinent are not absolutely necessary is shown by the success that has attended experiments aimed at increasing them. Village projects set up by the Indian and Pakistani governments, often with American financial aid, have succeeded in raising yields more than 50 percent through improved farming techniques, including the provision of better, though simple, equipment and a modest amount of fertilizer.

However, before much in the way of permanent improvement can be accomplished, the peasant must have some incentive to improve and must be able to obtain credit on reasonable terms. Incentive for many peasants has been decreased by a landlord system whereby the peasant holds his land only as a tenant and must pay for its use with anywhere from one sixteenth to one half of his produce. In addition, the economic insecurity of the peasants has led to a very large proportion, and in some areas the majority, being permanently in debt to the village moneylender. Studies of different areas have shown interest rates varying from 9 to 300 percent. It is recognized by responsible persons in India and Pakistan that these conditions must be altered in order to offer at least a minimum of hope to the cultivator if he is to exert himself toward improvement. Without such exertion on the part of individual farmers, any program for solving the agricultural problems of the subcontinent seems doomed from the start.

► Possibilities of Land Reclamation

One obvious path toward solving the problem of greater food production is the reclamation of additional land to be farmed. The actual possibilities seem quite uncertain and are a matter of great debate, both among natives of the subcontinent and outsiders. For many years the cultivated acreage has expanded very slowly despite great and increasing need. Present farming methods seem incapable of coping with the aridity, roughness, and lack of fertility which characterize large areas not now farmed. Modern mechanized methods, especially in connection with increased irrigation, hold considerable promise, but would be expensive to install. Most experts seem to feel that reclamation alone is far from being an adequate solution to the problem, though it may represent one important factor in a solution. Several major projects are currently underway.

Industry and Its Problems

In the partition of the Indian subcontinent, India received almost all of the area's developed capacity in modern industry as well as the great bulk of its mineral and power potential. Pakistan was left with a much smaller industrial plant and a poorer complement of industrial resources.

India, however, has a sizable industrial structure. In the Orient it is probably second to Japan in total industrial development, although China might dispute this ranking. The labor force employed in factories in India can be placed at between 2 and 3 million men. In addition, an unknown number of millions are still employed in handicraft production.

▶ The Major Industries

The chief branches of Indian factory industry are cotton textiles, jute, and iron and steel. Modern cotton mills employ about 600,000 workers. The industry is concentrated in the cities of Bombay (2,839,000 with suburbs), Ahmedabad (788,000) and neighboring areas along or near the west coast, and in Madras (1,416,000) and vicinity in the south. Of basic importance to cotton manufacturing are the large home market, abundant and extremely cheap labor, hydroelectric power available from stations in the Western Ghats and the Nilgiri Hills, and a large domestic production of cotton. However, although India normally ranks below only the United States and possibly the Soviet Union in total amount of cotton grown, the domestic production is inadequate for the needs of the cotton industry and considerable amounts are imported, principally from Western Pakistan. Indian cotton textile production not only supplies most of the needs of the domestic market, but is sufficient for large exports throughout southern Asia.

The jute industry is closely concentrated in and near the largest city of the subcontinent, Calcutta (3,750,000 with suburbs). Around 300,000 workers are employed in the industry, which lost nearly all of its raw material base when the jute-growing areas of East Pakistan were partitioned off from India. This fact makes it imperative for India and Pakistan to cooperate in order for the industry to survive at its present level, and a certain amount of cooperation has in fact been evident since partition. But the two nations have also shown a definite tendency to compete in jute production, evidenced by Indian attempts to increase the acreage in jute in West Bengal and Pakistani attempts to increase the number of jute-manufacturing plants in East Bengal. The subcontinent has almost a world monopoly on the growing of jute, which is used principally for making gunny sacks and other coarse bagging. The tall, slender jute stalk, which requires hot weather and flooded land for growing, and abundant labor for harvesting, finds ideal conditions in the low, swampy, tropical, densely populated delta lands of the lower Ganges and Brahmaputra Rivers. Jute manufactures represent the most important single item of Indian exports, and raw jute occupies the same position in the export trade of Pakistan.

The iron and steel industry of India is concentrated in the northeastern corner of the peninsular uplands somewhat over a hundred miles west and northwest of Calcutta. The main centers are at Jamshedpur (218,000) and near Asansol. In this vicinity occurs the most valuable concentration of mineral resources on the subcontinent, including iron ore, coking coal, manganese, and tungsten. These resources have drawn modern industry into an area which is one of the least developed in India, inhabited largely by primitive tribesmen. The Tata Iron and Steel Works at Jamshedpur, developed by the famous Tata family of Indian industrialists, became the largest single steel-producing unit in the British Empire during the period between World Wars I and II.

The Indian iron and steel industry is not large by world standards. In 1952 it produced an estimated 1.2 percent of the world's pig iron and an estimated 0.8 percent of its steel. Before World War II there was some export of pig iron, although a certain amount of steel had to be imported. Since the war, both iron and steel production have generally been insufficient for increased Indian demand, and expansion of the industry to at least the point of national self-sufficiency has become a major objective of the Indian government. The available mineral resources seem adequate for this objective to be reached, since India is one of the world's richest nations in iron ore and manganese and has enough coal to support present plans for expansion. However, good coking coal is not overly abundant, and the securing of an adequate supply of coke presents an important long-term problem for Indian metallurgy. A number of Indian areas other than the corner of peninsular India where present development is centered have important deposits of minerals, including iron ore, but the utility of most such deposits is lessened by remoteness from supplies of coal.

The meager industries of Pakistan are mainly confined to a few cotton-milling,

food-processing, and cement factories, together with the traditional handicraft industries. The country is extremely poor in mineral resources, although some deposits of petroleum and chromite exist, and substantial reserves of salt and other chemical raw materials provide the basis for a possible expansion of chemical manufacturing. Most of the present industries and known mineral resources are in West Pakistan.

▶ The Need for Further Industrialization

Although it seems doubtful that Pakistan can achieve more than a very modest development of industry in the immediate future, the potentialities of India are considerably greater. The total industrial development in the latter country so far is by no means negligible, but the degree of industrialization is quite small considering the resources available and the large population to be supported. This is reflected in the low degree of urbanization. In 1951 only five urban areas in India numbered more than a million inhabitants: the major seaports and industrial centers of Calcutta, Bombay, and Madras, already named, and in addition the metropolitan area formed by the capital, New Delhi, and adjacent Delhi (1,191,000 for the combined cities); and the largest city of the Deccan, Hyderabad (1,085,000). In Pakistan only the capital city and main seaport of Karachi (1,118,000) had over a million inhabitants, with the second-ranking city of Lahore numbering 850,000.

The Republic of India has a great need to develop her substantial industrial resources, not only to provide more goods for the population, but also to absorb some of the increasing labor force and, especially, to bring about a reduction in imports other than food. India's major resource deficiencies are a lack of petroleum and nonferrous metals, but these do not appear to present a decisive obstacle to further industrialization. Many areas are remote from coal deposits, so that high priority is being placed on hydroelectric development wherever feasible. Besides providing power, the reservoirs attending such developments can aid in the expansion of agriculture by making it possible to irrigate more land. India hopes to double its irrigated area.

Problems of Social Relations

On a physical map the Indian subcontinent looks like an obvious physical unit, marked off from the rest of the world by its mountain borders and seacoasts. Yet the social complexity of this area is so great that the apparent physical unity has never been paralleled by over-all political unity except during a relatively brief period in the nineteenth century and the first half of the twentieth century.[3] During this time political unity was imposed from outside by Great Britain. Even so, however, a great variety of small to fairly large political units under native rulers retained varying degrees of autonomy, although all of these native states were ultimately under British control. As soon as British power was withdrawn, the divisive force of conflicting social groups again asserted itself and the subcontinent split into two nations. At present the governments of both India and Pakistan have serious problems to overcome in reconciling the aims and aspirations of sharply divided groups within their respective countries, as well as in creating satisfactory relations between the two new countries themselves.

▶ Religious Divisions and Conflicts

The major social divisions within the subcontinent are in religion and language. Of these, religious divisions have generally appeared the more important and have received by far the greater attention. The most serious division has been between the two major religious groups, the Hindus and the Moslems. Hinduism is a religion native to the subcontinent and was the dominant religion at the time Islam made its appearance. It has continued to have the largest number of adherents. Hindus are estimated to number about 290 million at the present time as compared with around 100 million Moslems.

Islam made its appearance in the subcontinent as a proselytizing and conquering religion in the eighth century A.D. Periodic later invasions penetrated the relatively weak northwestern frontier until at the peak of Islamic power in the sixteenth and seventeenth centuries the Mogul Empire dominated most of the subcontinent. British penetration of India was aided by the internal disintegration of this Mohammedan empire in the eighteenth century.

Seldom have two large groups with such differing beliefs lived in such close association with each other. To Islam's uncompromising monotheism and insistence on uniformity in religious beliefs and practices, polytheistic Hinduism opposes the view that a variety of religious observances is consistent with the differing natures and social roles of human beings. To Islam's essential intolerance of all other faiths, Hinduism opposes an essentially tolerant attitude. To Islam's belief in its divine mission to convert all men to the true religion, Hinduism opposes the belief that proselytizing is essentially useless and wrong. To Islam's democratic belief in the essential equality of all believers, Hinduism opposes a social system founded on the inequalities of caste. To Islam's use of the cow as food

---

[3] Most of the subcontinent was politically unified during at least three periods prior to unification under the British, *i.e.*, during the Maurya Empire (third century B.C.), Gupta Empire (fourth century A.D.), and Mogul Empire (middle sixteenth century to early eighteenth century A.D.). However, even in these periods the extreme south of the peninsula tended to remain independent.

and for sacrifice, Hinduism opposes the view that the cow is an especially sacred animal and must under no circumstances be killed. The exuberant and noisy celebrations of the Hindu faith are a great contrast to the austere and silent ceremonials of Islam. Bloodshed has sometimes resulted when a Hindu parade with its jingling bells and firecrackers disturbed the solemnity of Mohammedans gathered for a particularly sacred religious rite.

The antagonism to be expected between such differing groups was intensified when the formerly subordinate Hindus came, un-der the British occupation, to dominate most Indian business as well as the civil service. Many Moslems feared the results of being incorporated into a single state with the Hindu majority, and their demands for political separation led to the creation of two independent states on the subcontinent rather than one. The creation of Pakistan in two widely separated parts was due to the distribution of the main areas of predominantly Moslem population at the time of partition. Immediately preceding and following partition violence broke out between the two peoples on a

Among the Hindus the cow is a sacred animal. The cows in the photo are on the sidewalk of a business street in Calcutta. Such scenes are common in Indian cities. (*John Morgan of the Charleston, W. Va., Gazette.*)

huge scale, and hundreds of thousands of lives were lost in wholesale massacres before the new governments could establish control. Mass migrations between the two countries involved some 12 million people, most of whom became a burden on the country of their choice until they could be resettled, a task not completely finished at the time of writing.

Partition of the subcontinent has left a minority of a few million Hindus in East Pakistan and probably 40 to 50 million Moslems in India. In addition, India has religious minorities of some importance in about 7 million Christians, living mainly in the south of the peninsula, and about the same number of Sikhs, concentrated mainly in the Punjab. Smaller numbers of Jains, Parsees, Jews, and Buddhists are present, mainly in India. Perhaps the most significant, though not the largest, of these groups is the Parsees. Though numbering only somewhat over a hundred thousand, mainly in Bombay, this group has attained wealth and economic power in India far out of proportion to its numbers. The Parsees derive originally from Persia, although the group has been in India for more than a thousand years. Their religion is the ancient Persian faith of Zoroastrianism.

• **The Kashmir Question.** The great religious conflict of the subcontinent between Moslems and Hindus has now been principally transmuted into a problem of international relations between Pakistan and India. Co-operation, especially in the economic sphere, is in the interest of both nations, but a heritage of ill will has yet to be overcome. Relations between the two countries are particularly disturbed by the fact that partition cannot yet be regarded as complete, since the fate of one of the most important parts of the subcontinent still hangs in the balance. This is Kashmir, in the northwestern corner of the subcontinent. Both Pakistan and India have claims of some legitimacy to Kashmir, or at least

to parts of it, and failure to settle its status by peaceful negotiation has led to local undeclared warfare which has threatened at times to erupt into a full-scale war between the two nations. At the time of writing an uneasy cease-fire agreement was in effect and the fate of the area was still undecided. Kashmir has only about 4.1 million people (77 percent Moslem in 1941), its importance being chiefly strategic and economic. Its frontiers border Tibet, Sinkiang, and Afghanistan, though in difficult territory, and it controls the upper reaches of most of the rivers on which the agriculture of West Pakistan depends for irrigation and which that country hopes to develop for hydroelectric power.

• **The Problem of Caste.** In the Republic of India, serious internal problems of religious division still exist, not only between the Hindus and minority groups, but within the body of Hinduism itself. One of the fundamental features of Hinduism has been the division of its adherents into the most elaborate caste system ever known. This system is described in the following paragraphs by Brown: [4]

Every Hindu is in traditional theory born to a caste, in which he must remain for life, and he is bound to live by its rules, subject to severe consequences for failure. A caste is a hereditary, endogamous group, which has a name of its own and some special traits of occupation, cult, or custom, giving it a separate place in the system. A man must take his wife from his caste—there are a few well-defined exceptions—usually can eat only with caste fellows, and is ranked in the social scale by the nature of the traditional customs of his caste. . . .

Caste stratifies Hindus into more than 2000 mutually exclusive groups, most of which, however, have limited geographical extent, so that no more than 50 to a couple of hundred may exist in any single locality. At the top of the caste hierarchy are the

---

[4] Reprinted by permission of the publisher from Brown, *op. cit.*, p. 30.

Brahmans, whose various castes include about 6.4 per cent of the Hindus; at the bottom are the Untouchables . . . forming about 21 per cent. The Brahmans define social position, officiate in religious ceremonies, have custody of sacred lore, and enjoy marked privileges.

Modernization of India comes inevitably into conflict with this rigid social system. Brahman privileges are being increasingly threatened and in some areas have been restricted by law. Untouchables, so called because their touch has been held to defile a high-caste Hindu, now number almost 60 million and must be drawn into a modern economic system in ways which undermine restrictions on their caste. Their cause has been championed for both moral and "practical" reasons by Indian leaders of higher caste, and they have themselves organized politically to better their position. Agitation from below and reaction from above combine to create friction as the rigidity of the caste system loosens under the impact of modern conditions and needs. Especially in the cities the close intermingling of large numbers of people in factories, rooming districts, public eating places, and public transportation has been a major factor in hastening the disintegration of the caste structure, although the latter is still strong in the villages.

▶ Language Divisions

Language supplements religion as a divisive factor in India and Pakistan. The present languages of the subcontinent fall into two chief groups, the Aryan languages in the north, and the Dravidian languages in roughly the southern half of peninsular India. The various languages within each of these two groups are fairly closely related

to each other. Languages claiming more than 10 million speakers each at the latest count include three languages of the Dravidian group—Telugu, Tamil, and Kanara—and eight languages of the Aryan group—Hindi, Bengali, Bihari, Marathi, Punjabi, Rajasthani, Gujarati, and Oriya. Dozens of other languages and dialects are spoken by lesser numbers of people. Although bi- and tri-lingualism are common, the difficulties of communication created by so many languages are obvious. Such difficulties are increased by the fact that not more than 10 to 20 percent of the population can be regarded as literate in any language, even by the simplest of tests.

English has become the *lingua franca* of the subcontinent, or at least of the educated classes. However, only about 1 percent of the population is literate in it. This fact plus nationalist feelings has led to a desire to adopt some native tongue as an official language (the business of both governments is now mainly carried on in English) to be propagated as a common medium of instruction and communication. Disputes have naturally arisen in each country as to which language should be chosen. India has apparently decided on Hindi, which is spoken by the largest linguistic group (some 80 million), but this decision on the part of the Indian government has resulted in strong protests, especially from the Dravidian south, and the actual adoption of Hindi as the official language is set for some years in the future. In Pakistan Urdu, a language similar to Hindi but written with Perso-Arabic script, is dominant in the west and seems the most likely candidate for a future national language, although it has a strong competitor in Bengali, the language of East Pakistan.

Population Problems

In the 50 years between 1901 and 1951 the population of the Indian subcontinent increased by 153 million people or about

54 percent. Between 1931 and 1941 it increased by 51 million or about 15 percent. Between 1941 and 1951 it increased by 49

million or about 13 percent. It has been authoritatively estimated that, if the present rate of increase continues, the subcontinent will have 840 million people by the year 2005.

Actually, this rate of increase is not outstandingly high; in fact it is probably lower than the rate for the world as a whole. But the base from which the increase takes place is so large that the total increment is very great. In addition, the growth of population has not here been accompanied by corresponding increases in agricultural and industrial production so that the standard of living has visibly deteriorated in the last 50 years. Thus it is commonly argued that the subcontinent is overpopulated and becoming more so, though opponents of this view say that the basic trouble is with production and not with population. It is a fact, however, that when gains have been made in production or new areas have been opened to cultivation, the growth of population has soon outrun the increased means of subsistence so that the ultimate result has been simply a larger number of people living under conditions similar to or worse than those existing previously.

Whatever the basic cause of the subcontinent's poverty, few students of the matter would fail to agree that a sharp check on population increase is highly desirable. Few also would fail to agree that the basic cause of increase is a very high birth rate, since the death rate remains quite high despite some diminution in recent years. Thus the governments of India and Pakistan face the problem of bringing their large and mostly illiterate populations to a knowledge of birth control and a desire to use it in lessening the rate of increase. In so doing they must counteract traditional religious views placing a premium on large families, as well as the desire for children as a source of additional labor on the subcontinent's intensively worked farms.

18

Southeast Asia

Southeast Asia, from Ceylon on the west to the Philippines on the east, is a region of peninsulas, islands, and intervening seas. East of India and south of China, between the Bay of Bengal and the South China Sea, the large Indochinese Peninsula, occupied by Burma, Thailand (Siam), and Indochina, projects southeastward from the continental mass of Asia. From it the long, narrow subpeninsula of Malaya extends another 900 miles toward the equator. Ringing the south and east of this continental projection are thousands of islands, among which Sumatra, Java, Borneo, Celebes, Mindanao, and Luzon are outstanding in size. Another large island, New Guinea, east of Celebes, is culturally a part of the Melanesian archipelagoes of the Pacific World.

However, the western half of New Guinea, held by the Netherlands, is claimed by the Southeast Asian country of Indonesia and may be considered a marginal part of Southeast Asia in a political sense. To the west the island of Ceylon, while merely a detached part of the Indian subcontinent in a geologic sense, may be considered as the western outpost of the Southeast Asian region from the standpoint of economic development, culture, and climate.

Southeast Asia, thus conceived, exhibits a complex political pattern of independent states and European colonial holdings. The independent states include Ceylon, Burma, Thailand, Indonesia, and the Philippines. Of these only Thailand dates its present independence farther back than 1946. The

Puddling a bed for rice seedlings in Thailand. Women reduce the soil to creamlike consistency with their feet, while men perform the heavier task of breaking ground. (*Foreign Agricultural Service, U. S. Department of Agriculture.*)

Introductory location map of Southeast Asia.

remnants of colonialism include French Indochina, British Malaya and Singapore, British Borneo, Portuguese Timor, and Netherlands New Guinea. The three last-named territories are of minor significance. All are mountainous, and British Borneo and Netherlands New Guinea have extensive areas of swamp. British Borneo, economically the most important of the three, occupies the northwestern third of the island of Borneo. It consists of three separate political units, the colonies of Sarawak and North Borneo, and the protected state of Brunei. The population is divided between native tribesmen and immigrant Chinese and Malays. Rubber and petroleum are the main exports. Portuguese Timor, largely an area of scrubby monsoon forest, occupies the eastern half of the island of Timor, plus a small exclave on the northwestern coast. The remainder of the island is a part of Indonesia. The Portuguese section is a largely neglected remnant of the extensive Oriental empire that Portugal possessed in the sixteenth century. Netherlands New Guinea is a thinly populated expanse of tropical rain forest and high mountains occupying the western half of the island of New Guinea. Most of the inhabitants are primitive tribesmen. There are about 8000 Europeans. Some petroleum is produced in the northwestern part.

Area, Population, and Environment

It is approximately 4000 miles from Ceylon to central New Guinea and 2500 miles from northern Burma to southern Indonesia, but the total land area of Southeast Asia is only about 1,745,000 square miles, or slightly more than half the area of continental United States. The population of the region is estimated at about 186 million, giving a density of 107 per square mile—an average which embraces very great extremes within the region. Area and population data for the individual political units are given in Table 16.

► Relative Sparseness of Population

While the average population density of Southeast Asia is about twice that of the United States, it is little more than a third the density of India-Pakistan or China proper. This relative sparseness of popu-

TABLE 16

SOUTHEAST ASIA: AREA AND POPULATION DATA

POLITICAL UNIT	AREA (THOUSAND SQUARE MILES)	POPULATION (MILLIONS: 1952 OR 1953 ESTIMATES)	DENSITY (PER SQUARE MILE: TO NEAREST WHOLE NUMBER)
Ceylon	25.3	8.10	320
Burma	261.7	19.05	73
Thailand	197.7	19.56	99
Indochina	272.4	30.50	112
Federation of Malaya	50.6	5.61	111
Crown colony of Singapore	0.2	1.12	4977
Indonesia	575.9	78.16	136
Philippines	115.6	21.65	187
British Borneo	78.7	0.96	12
Netherlands New Guinea	159.4	0.75	5
Portuguese Timor	7.4	0.46	62
Total	1,744.9	185.91	107

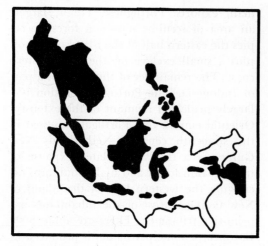

Southeast Asia compared in area with the United States.

Index map of the Southeast Asian mainland.

lation is apparently of long standing. It has been estimated that all of Southeast Asia contained only about 10 million people around the year 1800. To some extent the relative lack of population may be attributed to the isolation of the region by land, since in the north the Indochinese Peninsula abuts on high, rugged, and malaria-infested mountains. Over a period of centuries the forebears of most of the present inhabitants entered the area as recurrent thin trickles of population, crossing the mountain barrier under pressure, usually as refugees driven from previous homelands. But the region was known in early times by the Chinese, Japanese, and Indians; trade has moved through it for many centuries; and some early immigrants reached it by sea, particularly from India. Yet widespread dense populations did not develop.

▶ Environmental Difficulties

It seems likely that the difficulties imposed by the natural environment within Southeast Asia have a primary bearing on the relative sparseness of population. Certainly these difficulties are formidable. The most significant of them derive from the fact that the region is a truly tropical one marked by continuous heat, torrential rains, a prolific vegetation cover difficult to clear and keep cleared, soils which are generally poor and leached, and a high incidence of disease. The unfavorable agricultural effects of a four- to six-months-long dry season in the Indochinese Peninsula and scattered smaller areas in the islands are accentuated by a high rate of evaporation imposed by the tropic heat. Although modern Western scientific knowledge and technology have mitigated the effects of these conditions somewhat and have stimulated a tremendous population increase in the last 150 years, unaided primitive techniques proved unable to maintain large populations. Early civilizations were unable to expand widely or even to maintain themselves, as is evidenced by the monumental ruins found in a few parts of the region. In other places climate and vegetation have almost destroyed even the vestiges of early civilizations, cities, and states.

The lush vegetation of Southeast Asia masks the infertility of most of its soils, an infertility that becomes apparent and generally increases rapidly when the land is cleared and cultivated. Heat and humidity speed bacterial and chemical action so that the humus in the topsoil is rapidly destroyed and the mineral plant foods become thoroughly depleted by leaching. In addition, erosion is so rapid that the rivers generally carry enormous volumes of mud and silt, eventually to be deposited on flood plains and deltas at or near the sea.

The mountainous nature of the terrain over much of Southeast Asia creates further difficulties. In addition, the East Indies and Philippines experience frequent volcanic eruptions and earthquakes, and the northern Philippines and eastern Indochina are often afflicted by the violent wind- and rainstorms known as typhoons. However, these spectacular and destructive natural phenomena have probably constituted only minor hindrances to the growth of population except in very limited areas.

The Economic Pattern

The overwhelming majority of the people of Southeast Asia are farmers. Industry has made even less headway than in India or China, and certainly far less than in Japan.

▶ Shifting Cultivation

A permanent form of agriculture has proved extremely difficult to establish in most parts of this mountainous tropical realm. Much of the land is used only for a shifting, primitive subsistence form of cultivation in which fields are cleared and used for a few years and then allowed to lapse back into jungle while the cultivator moves on to clear a new patch. The cultivators are generally in a primitive state with regard to both agricultural techniques and social organization. Clearing is ordinarily accomplished by fire, and the crops are often grown with little or no cultivation. Unirrigated rice is usually the principal crop, although corn, beans, and root crops (such as yams and cassava) are also grown. Agricultural activities are often supplemented by hunting and gathering in the forest. These migratory subsistence farmers ordinarily differ ethnically from adjacent settled populations, for they are the remnants of peoples driven to refuge in the back country by stronger invaders. Since it is estimated that 15 years are generally necessary for an abandoned clearing to regain its fertility, it is obvious that only a small proportion of the land can be cultivated at any one time; therefore, populations living under such conditions must necessarily be sparse.

▶ Densely Populated Districts of Sedentary Agriculture

Most of Southeast Asia's people live, often in extremely dense clusters, in scattered areas of permanent sedentary agriculture. Such areas form the core regions of the various countries and stand in striking contrast to the relatively empty spaces of the adjoining districts. A superior degree of soil fertility appears to have been the main locational factor in most instances. In Southeast Asia soils of better than average fertility have ordinarily resulted from one or more of the following factors:

1. The presence of lava and volcanic ash of proper chemical composition to weather into fertile soils.

2. The accumulation and periodic renewal of plant nutrients washed from up-

stream areas and deposited on river flood plains and deltas.

3. A slowing down or seasonal reversal of the leaching process in areas having a distinct dry season and relatively low rainfall.

4. Occurrence in some areas of uplifted coral platforms which weather into a superior soil.

A few areas of Southeast Asia exhibit fairly dense populations without any corresponding soil superiority. Such areas are ordinarily characterized by a plantation type of agriculture based on crops adapted to poor soils, such as rubber.

Side by side with the present areas of dense settlement, some of which are seriously overcrowded, are sizable areas still undeveloped despite the fact that they apparently are capable of supporting large populations. Their development must wait until the need for their utilization becomes sufficiently great and the available resources sufficiently large to encourage large-scale clearing of forests, draining of swamps, and construction of irrigation systems. It also must await the initiative and resourcefulness of a sufficient number of people who are willing to leave established homes and accept the risks of pioneering in areas often plagued by relatively low and undependable rainfall and/or malaria.

The typical inhabitant of the present areas of permanent sedentary agriculture is a subsistence farmer whose main crop is wet rice, grown with the aid of natural flooding or by irrigation. In some drier areas unirrigated millet or corn, the latter especially in Indonesia and the Philippines, take the place of rice. The major crop is supplemented, to a degree tending to vary positively with the pressure of population, by secondary crops which can be grown on land not suited for rice or other grains. Prominent secondary food crops include coconuts, yams, cassava, beans, and garden vegetables. If the year is a good one, a portion of the produce may be sold, and some farmers grow a secondary crop such as tobacco, coffee, or rubber primarily for sale. Fish are an important component of the food supply and a considerable source of income, not only along the coasts but also inland along streams, lakes, and artificial fish ponds.

▶ The Role of Commercial Agriculture

Subsistence production in Southeast Asia exists side by side with an important development of commercial agriculture, directed mainly toward supplying commodities for export. The region is one of the world's major supply areas for tropical plantation crops as well as a supplier of surplus rice to other parts of the Orient. These commercial elements in Southeast Asian agriculture are principally the result of Western colonial enterprise in the region.

European imperialism in Southeast Asia began in the sixteenth century. Until the nineteenth century, however, the principal interest of the newcomers lay in the region's strategic location on the route to China, and they were generally content with effective control over scattered patches of land along the coasts and with gleaning for trade such surpluses of value as the native economies happened to offer. But during the nineteenth century increasing populations and an expanding technology in Europe and North America greatly enlarged the demand for products of tropical agriculture. Consequently, effective European political control was forcibly extended over almost the whole of Southeast Asia, and European capital and knowledge were applied to bring about a rapid increase in production for export. Certain indigenous commodities, such as copra and spices, were given increased emphasis, and a number of entirely new crops were introduced, a case in point being the rubber seedlings smuggled out of Brazil in 1876 and introduced into Malaya in 1879.

The usual method of introducing commercial production was to establish large estates or plantations managed by Europeans but worked by indigenous or imported Oriental labor. Development of these large commercial farming enterprises was assisted not only by the favorable climate, but also by the availability of land in a relatively empty part of the Orient and by the amphibious nature of the topography, which made possible a close dependence on cheap, efficient, and easily established transportation by water. The major difficulty to be overcome was in most cases the recruitment of an adequate labor force from a population already fully engaged in food production and not sufficiently pressed by poverty and hunger to be easily attracted from the communal life of the villages into labor for wages on the plantations. The eventual solution to the latter problem in many areas was large-scale importation of contract labor from India and China.

Plantation activity came to have widespread repercussions on the economic life of the natives themselves, for many native farmers and ex-estate laborers learned by example and entered commercial production on their own account. Even shifting cultivators could plant a few rubber trees and return when the trees reached the producing stage, 7 to 10 years later, to tap them for latex if the price warranted.

Smallholders of the foregoing types now command an important share in the export production of most plantation commodities.

The list is very long of plantation-type commodities that have been produced in Southeast Asia on a medium to large scale at one time or another. Wide fluctuations have occurred from time to time in the crops grown, the centers of production, the amounts exported, and the prosperity of the producers. These shifts have been occasioned by such factors as fluctuating world demands, intraregional and interregional competition, changing political conditions, and the occasional ravages of plant diseases. This general situation has prevailed not only in Southeast Asia, but in plantation areas throughout the tropical world. Excluding rice, the major agricultural exports from Southeast Asia together with the main producing countries at the present time are indicated in Table 17. A smaller development of some of the major commodities listed in the table has occurred in various Southeast Asian countries other than those indicated. In addition, a variety of other products such as tobacco, kapok, cinchona (the natural source of quinine), spices, and sisal enter the total export picture. In the supply of some of these lesser commodities such as

TABLE 17
EXPORTS OF MAJOR SOUTHEAST ASIAN PLANTATION-TYPE AGRICULTURAL COMMODITIES

COMMODITY	APPROXIMATE PERCENT OF WORLD EXPORTS ORIGINATING IN SOUTHEAST ASIA	PRINCIPAL EXPORTING COUNTRIES IN SOUTHEAST ASIA WITH APPROXIMATE PERCENTAGE OF WORLD EXPORTS
Rubber	90–100%	Malaya-Singapore: 40–50% Indonesia: 20–30%
Tea	40–50%	Ceylon: 30–40% Indonesia: 5–10%
Abaca	90–100%	Philippines: 90–100%
Copra and coconut oil	50–60%	Philippines: 25–35% Indonesia: 25–35%
Palm oil	30–40%	Indonesia: 20–30% Malaya: 5–10%
Sugar	5–10%	Philippines: 5%

kapok, cinchona, and certain spices, South-east Asia is the world's leading region.

Political convulsions since 1941 have ef-fected great changes in the commercial ag-riculture of this region. Especially notable has been the great decline and only partial recovery of Indonesian export production as a consequence of war and revolution, coupled with the new government's em-phasis on increased production of food for use within the country. Prior to World War II Indonesia was second only to Cuba as a sugar exporter and second only to the United States as a tobacco exporter, but postwar exports of both of these commodi-ties have been relatively insignificant.

▶ *Commercial Rice Farming*

One very significant aspect of Western influence on the economy of Southeast Asia has been the stimulation of commercial rice farming in certain areas that were formerly unproductive. The development of planta-tion agriculture, mining, and trade pro-vided a market for rice by bringing into existence a large class of people who worked for wages and had to buy their food. Dur-ing the same period Western economic, medical, and sanitary innovations helped bring about an enormous increase in Ori-ental population generally and a growing demand for food. Western technology made possible the bulk processing and movement of rice, and aided in the development of drainage, irrigation, and flood control fa-cilities needed to produce it on a large scale in areas previously undeveloped. As a consequence of these developments an Asian pioneer movement took place into certain areas capable of greatly expanded rice pro-duction. Among these latter areas three have gained outstanding importance in commercial rice growing: the deltas of the Irrawaddy, Chao Praya, and Mekong Riv-ers, located in Burma, Thailand, and south-ern Indochina, respectively.

Almost impenetrable swamps and un-controllable floods had kept these deltas thinly settled previously, as other swampy areas in Southeast Asia are, but adequate incentives and methods for pioneering have turned them into densely settled areas within the past century. Despite grow-ing populations, the farms in these areas are larger than is common in the Orient, and the surplus of rice is such that 60 per-cent or more of the world's total rice ex-ports generally originate in the three deltas. In the years before World War II Burma ranked first among the world's rice ex-porters, generally accounting for about a third of the world total, and was followed by Thailand and French Indochina, each supplying approximately another 15 per-cent of world exports. Unsettled conditions in Burma and Indochina during the war and postwar periods have led to a serious decline in rice production and exports, especially in Indochina. Thailand, on the other hand, has experienced fewer political and military difficulties and has been able to greatly expand its output and exports of rice. In 1952 Thailand, Burma, and Indo-china accounted respectively for 28, 26, and 4 percent of the world's total rice exports.

These exports of the basic food of the Orient have gone mainly to India, China, Japan, and to other nations within South-east Asia. City populations, especially near the coast, and laborers in plantation and mining areas are the principal consumers of imported rice. The vital need for such imports to make up for deficiencies in domestic production has given Burma, Thailand, and Indochina great significance in the eyes of other Oriental nations, and indirectly in the eyes of all nations inter-ested in Oriental affairs. Nor is that sig-nificance lessened by the fact that full de-velopment has not yet been reached in any of the surplus rice-producing areas.

▶ *Production and Reserves of Minerals*

Southeast Asia has considerable mineral wealth, much of which remains essentially unexploited. Tin and petroleum are the principal minerals to be exploited thus far. This region produces and exports about 60 percent of the world's tin: 35 percent from Malaya, 20 percent from the islands of Banka and Billiton in Indonesia, and most of the rest from southern Thailand. Oil is produced on the islands of Sumatra, Java, and Borneo in Indonesia, the region's main producing country, as well as in British Borneo, Burma, and Netherlands New Guinea; but the total regional production amounts to only about 1 percent of the world total. However, added significance is given to Southeast Asian oil by the possibilities of expansion and its status as the most important source between the Persian Gulf and California.

About 5 percent of the world's bauxite is produced in the Rhio Archipelago of Indonesia, about 10 percent of its chromite in the Philippines, and about 10 percent of its graphite in Ceylon. Iron ore is fairly abundant in the region. It is exported from the Philippines and Malaya in relatively small quantities, is worked on a very small scale in Thailand, and is available in Indochina. In addition, there are present in the region, and often worked on at least a minor scale, a great range of other mineral resources: gold and silver; the alloys tungsten, nickel, and manganese; the major non-ferrous metals lead, zinc, and copper; and others.

Production of minerals thus far has been almost entirely for export, with Western Europe, Japan, and the United States representing the principal markets. Use of Southeast Asian mineral resources for industrialization within the region itself would face the handicap of a shortage of coal suitable for large-scale metallurgy. Lignite is present, especially in Burma and Thailand, and low-grade bituminous coal is mined in Sumatra, Borneo, and the Philippines, but the only metallurgical coal known in the region is the anthracite of northern Indochina. Electricity produced from low-grade coal and lignite and by utilization of the region's sizable resources of water power, although a necessity for future industrial development, could hardly replace metallurgical coal in heavy industry. Nevertheless, Southeast Asia appears to have the resources for a considerable expansion of both mining and manufacturing, in addition to its undoubted and perhaps more important potential for further expansion of agriculture. But like most underdeveloped areas, this region faces serious problems in securing the necessary labor, capital, and markets to make economic expansion a success.

Distinctive Qualities of the Individual Countries

While the countries of Southeast Asia have many broad similarities, each has also its own distinctive qualities. Each exhibits a different combination of environmental features, native and immigrant peoples, economic activities, and culture traits. Many of the dominant characteristics and problems of these countries are the outcome of 400 years of European imperialism, but in no two countries have the influences and results of imperialism been the same. The following brief portraits of the major countries in the region will perhaps be sufficient to give an idea of the distinctive characteristics of each.

► Ceylon

The island of Ceylon consists of a coastal plain surrounding a knot of mountains and hill lands in the south central part. Most of the people live either in the wetter southwestern portion of the plain, in the hilly areas of the south center, in the dry Jaffna Peninsula of the north, or in a limited area on the east central coast. Coconuts and rice are the major crops of the low southwestern coast and Jaffna Peninsula, while tea and rubber plantations dominate the economy of the uplands, Colombo (425,000), in the southwest, is the capital, chief port, and only large city.

Centuries of recurrent invasion from India were followed by Portuguese domination in the early sixteenth century, Dutch in the seventeenth, and British from 1795 until 1948. In the latter year Ceylon was granted independence as a dominion in the British Commonwealth. This eventful history plus the island's long-standing commercial importance on the sea route around southern Asia has given Ceylon a polyglot population. The two major ethnic groups, distinguished from each other by language and religion, are the predominantly Buddhist Sinhalese, making up about 70 percent of the population, and the Hindu Tamils, constituting about 20 percent. The Tamils, whose main center of settlement is the Jaffna Peninsula, are descendants of early invaders and more recent imported laborers from southern India. In addition to the numerically superior Sinhalese and Tamils, there is a remnant of Arab population and the Burghers, descendants of Portuguese and Dutch settlers. About 10 percent of the people are Mohammedans and about 5 percent Roman Catholics. In the interior a few thousand tribesmen known as Veddas practice shifting cultivation. Despite some antagonism among the various ethnic groups, Ceylon has enjoyed a long period of comparative civil peace.

The economy of Ceylon is rather highly commercialized, with three export crops, coconuts (920,000 acres), rubber (655,000 acres), and tea (561,000 acres), occupying two thirds of the land under cultivation. Most of the remaining acreage is in rice, but the production is insufficient to feed the growing population of Ceylon, and considerable amounts of rice are imported. Much potential agricultural land is currently unused, and the government is at-

tempting to reduce food imports by expanding rice production through the establishment of modern irrigation works. Relatively prosperous export industries and stable political conditions seem to favor these and other forward-looking projects. However, an increase in the island's total population from 5.3 to 8.1 million since 1931 has considerably aggravated the food problem.

▶ Burma

Burma centers in the basin of the Irrawaddy River and includes surrounding uplands and mountains. Within the basin are two distinct areas of dense population, the Dry Zone, around and south of Mandalay (173,000), and the Delta, focusing on the capital and major seaport of Rangoon (600,000). The Dry Zone has been the historical nucleus of Burma. The annual rainfall of this area (33.2 inches at Mandalay) is exceptionally low for Southeast Asia and there is a dry season of about 6 months. The people are supported by mixed subsistence and commercial farming, with millet, rice, cotton, beans, peanuts, and sesame as major crops. During the past century the Dry Zone has been surpassed in population by the Delta, where a commercial rice-farming economy now supplies most of the country's exports. The Irrawaddy River forms the main artery of transportation uniting these two core areas.

The native Burmese, most of whom live in the Irrawaddy Basin, number only about 70 percent of the country's total population. Prior to World War II around 1 million Indians (about equally divided between Hindus and Moslems) lived in the Delta as laborers, merchants, moneylenders, and owners of farm land, much of it rented to Burmese tenants. The number of Indians is apparently less at present due to a homeward migration to India during the war. The Shan Plateau to the east is inhabited by two distinct groups, each accounting for between 5 and 10 percent of the country's population—the Shans to the northeast and the Karens to the southeast and in the delta of the Salween River. Some of these people eke out a meager livelihood by shifting cultivation in the hills, although the majority are plain and valley dwellers growing irrigated rice. A variety of hill-dwelling tribes inhabit the Arakan Mountains of the west and the northern highlands. Most of these people are shifting cultivators. Burma is predominantly a Buddhist country, with about 90 percent of the total population adhering to this religious faith.

Burma was conquered piecemeal by Great Britain in three wars between 1824 and 1885. In 1948 it abandoned all formal ties with Britain and became an independent republic. Japanese conquest and Allied reconquest in World War II were succeeded by a period of civil war following the establishment of an independent Burma. At one time no less than eight different rebellions were in progress. Communist agitation has been an important cause of disaffection, and also ethnic separatism, especially among the Karens. The country is being gradually reduced to order, but its economy has been badly damaged. Shipments of rice, principally to India, Japan, Malaya, and Indonesia, currently account for more than three fourths of all exports by value.

▶ Thailand

Thailand, formerly known as Siam, centers in the delta of the Chao Praya River, often referred to as the Menam (a Thai word meaning River; the full name as used in Thailand is Menam Chao Praya). The annual floods of this river irrigate the commercial rice production that forms the mainstay of the country's economy. More than nine tenths of all cultivated land in Thailand grows rice, and this one product constitutes around half of all exports by value. Rubber and tin, the second- and third-ranking exports, contribute respec-

tively about one fourth and one tenth of the total. On the lower Chao Praya in the most densely populated part of the country is the capital, main port, and only large city, Bangkok (about 1,200,000 with suburbs). Areas outside of the delta region are more sparsely populated, largely by sedentary agriculturalists, although some shifting cultivators are present. These areas include mountainous territories in the west and north, inhabited mainly by Karens and a variety of mountain tribes, and the dry Korat Plateau to the east, populated by the Thai and related Laotian and Cambodian peoples. To the south in the Kra Isthmus, a part of the Malay Peninsula, live some 650,000 Malays. An estimated 95 percent of the population of Thailand adheres to the Buddhist faith, the only significant exception being the Malays, who are Moslems.

The Thai monarchy enjoys the distinction of being the only Southeast Asian country to preserve its independence throughout the period of Western colonialism. Its success appears to have been largely due to its position as a buffer between British and French colonial spheres. A number of border territories were lost, however, mostly inhabited by peoples related to the Thai, and the government of the country has exhibited irredentist tendencies for many years. These ambitions were temporarily gratified by the Japanese at the expense of Burma, Indochina, and Malaya in return for Thailand's cooperation during World War II. However, the areas in question were reclaimed by their previous possessors at the end of the war, and irredentism has not been much in evidence in official statements by the Thai government since 1946–1947.

The major ethnic minority of Thailand is Chinese. About 3 million Chinese are resident in the country and are claimed as citizens both by Thailand and by China. The Chinese control much of the country's rice trade and other business, and have ex-

A scene on a plantation in the rubber belt of Malaya. Records are being made of the amount of latex (rubber sap) collected by each tapper. (*British Information Services*.)

tensive interests in the rubber plantations and tin mines of the Malay Peninsula section. This situation has roused a considerable amount of ill feeling on the part of the Thais, and makes the loyalty of the Chinese a matter of considerable importance. Thus far, however, Thailand has escaped serious civil conflict, just as it escaped serious involvement in World War II.

► Indochina

Indochina, commonly called French Indochina, consists of three Associated States of the French Union: Cambodia, Laos, and Vietnam, the latter partitioned in 1954 into North Vietnam, held by the native Viet Minh Communists, and South Vietnam, held by a French-supported native government. Pre-partition Vietnam, the largest of the three Associated States, comprised a total of three historically distinct regions: Tonkin, Annam, and Cochin-China. Tonkin, the northern region, includes the densely populated delta of the Red River and a surrounding frame of sparsely populated mountains. Annam, in the center, includes the sparsely populated Annamite Cordillera and numerous small, densely populated pockets of lowland along its seaward edge. Cochin-China, to the south, consists principally of the densely populated delta of the Mekong River. The state of Cambodia includes principally the plains along and to the west of the lower Mekong River, together with mountainous fringes to the northeast and southwest. Laos is a mountainous country pressed between Vietnam, Thailand, Burma, and China.

Three quarters of the population of Indochina is made up of the people traditionally known as Annamese, although Vietnamese is now the more common and preferred term. They are closely related to the Chinese in both language and religion. Their religion is somewhat difficult to categorize: like the majority of Chinese they practice ancestor worship and have been much influenced by the precepts of Confucianism. The Annamese inhabit the heavily populated delta lands and coastal plains in all three of the major regions of Vietnam, and constitute 90 percent of that state's 25 million people. The Cambodians are the second ethnic group in numbers. They practice the Buddhist religion. Cambodians comprise the great majority of the approximately 4 million people in their own state, and they represent an important minority in adjoining Cochin-China. About 1 million Thais are distributed almost evenly between Laos, where they form the dominant group, and the mountains of Tonkin. Over a million people belong to various primitive tribes living in the mountains of Vietnam and Laos. About a third of a million Chinese, mostly merchants, are found for the most part in Saigon-Cholon (1,700,000), Indochina's major port and metropolis, although some live in the northern cities of Hanoi (238,000 with suburbs) and Haiphong (143,000 with suburbs) in the delta of the Red River.

France conquered Indochina by stages between 1858 and 1884. In the course of these conflicts the French extinguished an Annamite empire covering the approximate territory of present-day Vietnam, and defeated the Chinese, whom the Annamese called to their aid. In 1893 Laos and in 1907 the western part of Cambodia were taken from Thailand.

The French colonial administration proved relatively ineffective from the standpoint of economic development, though it did succeed in opening the Mekong delta lands of Cochin-China for commercial rice production. A considerable number of other commercial crops were introduced, both into native agriculture and on plantations, but a really large export production was never attained. Mineral resources of coal, iron, tin, tungsten, manganese, zinc, and phosphates were developed either on a small scale or not at all. Two agricultural products provided nearly two thirds of all exports by value in 1952: rubber (36 percent) and rice (28 percent). As in the case of other French colonial possessions, the economy of Indochina has been closely tied to that of France.

The end of the Japanese occupation in 1945 found a Communist-dominated native government in power in Vietnam, which demanded independence from France. In 1946 fighting broke out between the Communist faction and the French, who set up a native government of their own. Support for the French cause was never overly strong, despite the eventual granting of considerable powers of self-government to Vietnam, Cambodia, and Laos. Communist military successes compelled France to cede Tonkin and northern Annam to the rebel government in 1954.

▶ Malaya

Malaya, whose highly commercialized economy based on tin and rubber makes it Britain's most valuable colonial holding, is a federation, under British protection, of nine native sultanates and two "settlements." The country occupies the southern end of the mountainous Malay Peninsula. Singapore, governed separately as a crown colony, is a small island at the tip of the peninsula. The island has slightly more than a million inhabitants, most of whom live in the city of Singapore. One of the world's great seaports, Singapore is the major entrepôt of Southeast Asia and Britain's main naval base in that region.

Singapore lies at the eastern end of the Strait of Malacca, the major passageway through which sea traffic is funneled between the Indian Ocean and the China Seas. Malacca city, on the west coast of the peninsula bordering the strait, was a Portuguese stronghold from 1511 and was held by the Dutch from 1641. British control over the strait was established in 1824, but was exercised from Singapore, founded five years earlier. As tin, rubber, and other commercial products became important in the latter nineteenth and early twentieth centuries, Britain gradually extended political control over the whole of present-day Malaya. The native states were successively acquired as protectorates between 1874 and 1909, the northern four being detached from Thai suzerainty in the latter year.

The tin-mining industry of Malaya was pioneered in the latter nineteenth century largely by Chinese interests, though these are now overshadowed by British concerns. A line of rich tin deposits along the western foothills of the mountains was made accessible by the building of railroads. Rail transportation to the ports and increasing world demands for rubber to be used in the new electrical and automotive industries led to a large development of rubber plantations in the first decades of the twentieth century. Consequently, a densely populated tin and rubber belt has developed in the foothills between Malacca (55,000) and the hinterland of Penang (189,000). Within this belt the inland city of Kuala Lumpur (250,000) has developed as an important commercial center and the capital of the Federation of Malaya.

The native Mohammedan Malays, constituting about half of the Federation's population, have played only a minor role in the development of commercial agriculture and mining. For the most part they are subsistence rice farmers inhabiting small coastal deltas along both sides of the peninsula. The tin and rubber belt is populated largely by Chinese, who comprise about 40 percent of the population of the Federation, and by Indians, mainly Hindu, who constitute another 10 percent. Three quarters of Singapore's population is Chinese. These Chinese and Indian immigrants to Malaya and Singapore are mostly commercial farmers, wage workers, and businessmen.

Antagonisms among the various ethnic groups have made evolution toward self-government difficult, although the area is slowly moving in that direction. On the other hand, recent Communist terrorist activities have apparently failed to attract widespread support among the people.

▶ Indonesia

Indonesia is by far the largest and most populous of the countries of Southeast Asia. Its several thousand islands comprise about one third of the region's land area and contain about 40 percent of its total population. The large population of Indonesia results from the enormous concentration of people which has developed on the island of Java. Here live at present an estimated 50 million people, representing nearly two thirds of Indonesia's population and more than a fourth of the population of all Southeast Asia. The island's population density is more than 1000 per square

mile; in contrast the remainder of Indonesia, which is nearly 11 times larger than Java in area, has only a little more than half as many people and an average population density of just over 50 per square mile.

The extraordinary concentration of population on this one island can be partly accounted for by the superior average fertility of its soils, the best of which have been derived from materials poured out by the many volcanic peaks. However, it also is the result in good measure of the centering of Dutch colonial activities in Java. Other islands of Indonesia (with the notable exception of Borneo) have areas of volcanic soil, but such areas, while generally more densely populated than adjoining nonvolcanic areas, seldom attain the extremely high population densities found on Java. The economic development of some islands has undoubtedly been handicapped by the unfriendly nature of their coastlines, which present a front of coral reefs, steep cliffs, or extensive swamps, and thus create difficulties of access.

The Dutch East India Company, having ousted the Portuguese and bested the British, secured effective control of Java in the seventeenth century. Large sections of the remaining islands, however, were not brought under control until the nineteenth century; the conquest of northern Sumatra was only completed in 1904. Strenuous efforts to develop and exploit the natural wealth of Java were undertaken by the government of the Netherlands with the introduction of the Culture System in 1830. Under this system forced contributions of land and labor were required of Javanese farmers for the intensive production of export crops under Dutch supervision. The system was undeniably harsh but, from the Dutch point of view, successful. Although the Culture System was abolished in 1870 native commercial agriculture continued to expand along with plantation production, and a means of support for increasing numbers of people was provided. Thus the introduction of the Culture System appears to have set off not only a great increase in the output of export commodities, but also the enormous rise in Java's population, which has multiplied tenfold in slightly more than a century.

Development of the other main islands began later and has been less intensive. Nevertheless the eastern coastal plain of Sumatra, inland from the great fringing swamp, has now surpassed Java in the production of two major commercial crops—rubber and palm oil. Java and eastern Sumatra are overwhelmingly the most important areas of commercial agriculture; in fact the remaining islands of Indonesia, considered as a group, lead in the production of only one major export crop—coconuts. Borneo, interior Celebes, and the mountainous western section of Sumatra are the habitat of primitive tribes who gain a meager subsistence from shifting cultivation and associated hunting, fishing, and gathering activities. Five areas outside of Java and Sumatra exhibit an uncommon density of agricultural settlement. These are the island of Madura, adjoining Java on the northeast and sharing its intensive commercial development although lacking its volcanic soils; the two volcanic islands of Bali and Lombok east of Java, given over largely to intensive subsistence cultivation; and the volcanic southwestern and northeastern arms of Celebes.

Irrigated rice, often grown on picturesque terraces in the mountainous areas, is the most important food crop of Indonesia. It is supplemented by such subsistence crops as sweet potatoes, cassava, corn, peanuts, and soybeans. As has already been indicated, the country is an important producer of certain minerals, notably tin (from the islands of Banka and Billiton between Sumatra and Borneo), oil (from Sumatra, Java, and Borneo), and bauxite (from the Rhio Archipelago between Sumatra and Malaya). The leading Indonesian exports by value in 1952 were rubber (46 percent), petroleum products (20 percent), tin (9 percent), copra (6 percent), and palm oil, tea, pepper, coffee, and tobacco making up most of the remainder.

The superior commercial importance of Java and Sumatra is indicated by their greater urban development. The Indonesian capital of Jakarta, formerly Batavia, located near the western end of Java, is now estimated to have a population of about 3 million, considerably more than any other city in Southeast Asia. Two other cities on Java, Jogjakarta and Surabaya, were estimated in 1951 to have more than a million people, while the cities of Bandung and Semarang were estimated at 800,000 and 530,000, respectively. The main cities on Sumatra are Medan and Palembang, currently estimated at 500,000 and 300,000, respectively. In the remaining islands the only sizable city is Makassar, in southwestern Celebes, estimated at 400,000. An important share of the business of these cities is carried on by Chinese immigrants and their descendants, the only alien group of much numerical significance. The number of Chinese in Indonesia is generally placed at about 2.5 million, and they form for the most part an urban commercial class.

Increasing Indonesian nationalism before and during the Japanese occupation of World War II led to a bitter struggle for independence from the Netherlands following the war. Independence was eventually won after considerable fighting and political intercession by outside powers. In the settlement of 1949 with the Dutch, Indonesian claims to the large undeveloped territory of Netherlands New Guinea were left unsatisfied. However, the new country has had difficulty in establishing peace and order within the area it already controls. Ethnic diversity has been at least partially responsible for the unsettled conditions. While about 90 percent of all Indonesians are listed as Mohammedan, the population exhibits great cultural differences in other

Prominent buildings in Jakarta, the capital of the Republic of Indonesia and former capital of the Netherlands East Indies. In right foreground, the building of the Netherlands Trade Society, left foreground, the Java Bank. At top left, the Jakarta railway station. (*Information Office of the Republic of Indonesia.*)

respects, as reflected in the fact that over 200 languages and dialects are currently in use. Consequently, ethnic separatism has played an important part in the affairs of the new state, with a special degree of antagonism existing in some localities against the numerically and politically dominant Javanese. Armed conflict of at least a desultory kind has been almost constant since independence, and even Java has not returned to the state of internal security known under the Dutch. Since 1942 the Indonesian economy has suffered greatly from war, military occupation, and general political disorder, but the size and natural wealth of the country give promise for the future.

▶ The Philippines

The Philippine group includes over 7000 generally mountainous islands, but the two largest islands, Luzon and Mindanao, almost equal in size, account for two thirds of the total area. Most of the mountainous districts are inhabited by a sparse population of relatively primitive shifting cultivators, although in northern Luzon the Igorot tribes have developed a spectacular and world-famous system of wet rice cultivation on terraced mountain sides.

Most of the population is concentrated in three areas, as follows:

1. The Visayan Islands in the center of the archipelago, where soils derived from volcanic materials and uplifted corals support an intensive subsistence agriculture based on rice and corn. Negros Island in this group is a major center of plantation sugar production.

2. The plains extending from south of Manila to Lingayen Gulf and thence north along the west coast of Luzon. Rice is the

main food crop of these plains, and sugar, much of it produced on small native farms, is the main commercial product.

3. The southeastern peninsula of Luzon. Subsistence rice and commercial coconut production are basic to the economy here except in the extreme southern part, where large plantations utilize volcanic soils to produce a major share of the Philippines' output of abaca or Manila hemp.

The Philippines were a Spanish colonial possession from the latter sixteenth century until 1898, and with the exception of the Japanese occupation of 1942–1944 were controlled by the United States from 1898 until 1946, when independence was granted. The Spanish legacy is still important in the country. Ever since its founding in 1571 the Spanish capital of Manila (now 1,375,000 with suburbs) has been the metropolis and only large city of the islands. The society created by Spain was composed of a relatively small upper class of Hispanicized Filipino landowners and a great mass of landless peasants. Problems created by the maldistribution of agricultural land have remained as a major source of difficulty for the new Republic of the Philippines. Discontented peasants gave much support to a Communist-led revolt after World War II, which was being suppressed in 1954 through the granting of land, generally on sparsely populated Mindanao, to surrendered rebels. In the Philippines Spanish missionary activity succeeded in creating the only Christian nation in the Orient. Today an estimated 80 percent of the population is listed as Roman Catholic, while another 10 percent adheres to other Christian denominations. Spanish Catholicism failed to penetrate only the most remote mountain areas, still pagan, and southern Mindanao and the Sulu Archipelago, where the Mohammedan Moros successfully resisted Spanish control for 300 years.

The American period, although it began with the suppression of a Philippine independence movement, eventually brought independence, along with economic development and tutelage in democracy. The growth of the major Philippine export industries—coconut products, cane sugar, and abaca—was stimulated by preferential treatment in the American market. In the 1930's a large degree of self-government was granted, full independence was promised for 1946, and legislation was passed in the American Congress to cushion the economic effects of independence by continuing the preferential treatment of Philippine exports to the United States. At the same time education was furthered so that even now English serves as the medium of instruction in Philippine schools and serves to some extent to bridge the gap between the diverse linguistic groups of the population. One of the most widely used native languages, Tagalog, has been selected as the principal base for an official national language. It is taught in all of the schools.

The Chinese Realm

China is the largest country of the world in population and is exceeded in area only by the Soviet Union and possibly Canada.[1] It is mainly an agricultural country, and possibly produces a greater total volume of crops than any other nation. Like several other countries of the Orient it has a serious problem of rural overpopulation. This problem might be partially solved by industrialization, and the resources are pres-

ent for a considerable development of industry. However, modern types of manufacturing have not been developed to any marked degree as yet, except in scattered areas. Inadequate transportation has been one of several important handicaps to the development of large-scale industry. China has a common land frontier with no less than eleven other countries, all of which, except the Soviet Union and India, are

[1] The population of China, including Formosa and Tibet, has commonly been estimated at 450 to 500 million. In November, 1954, the government of the Chinese People's Republic (Communist China) announced the results of the first nationwide census, taken as of July 30, 1953. Figures reported by the government showed a total of 590 million people for mainland China plus Formosa (574 million by direct count, the remainder added

by other means). For details see George B. Cressey, "Changing the Map of China," *Economic Geography,* v. 31 (1955), p. 15. Estimates of China's area range from 3,643,000 square miles to 3,877,000 square miles. The area of the Soviet Union is officially reported as 8,600,000 square miles and that of Canada as 3,846,000 square miles (land and fresh water) or 3,610,000 square miles (land area only).

Extensive terracing of hillsides for use as rice paddies has been the direct result of population pressures in China as well as in other parts of the Orient.

relatively small and weak. The country has been almost continuously involved in wars and revolutions for nearly half a century, the last period of comparative peace having occurred prior to 1911. China is a very old country with a long record of achievement in philosophy, literature, and the arts. However, the Chinese have not shared to any great degree in the scientific and technological advances which have been so marked a feature of Western culture in modern times. For about a century prior to World War II China was dominated by various other nations and at times was virtually reduced to a colonial status—a fact which was, and is, bitterly resented by many Chinese.

The foregoing facts about China have gained added significance for the world at large with the recent emergence of mainland China as a military power under Communist rule and allied with Soviet Russia. The full meaning of this development has yet to be unfolded, but there can be no doubt that Communist China has become a new and extremely important factor in world affairs. In the Korean War which

China compared in latitude and area with the United States.

the Communist Chinese entered late in 1950, this Asian country put troops in the field whose performance against a modern Occidental army removed any lingering doubts as to the ability of Asians to utilize effectively modern weapons and methods of warfare. Thus under the new Communist regime, China, which had been largely a negative quantity as a military nation in modern times, has suddenly thrust itself upon world attention by force of arms.

Historical Background

In order to understand the significance of China's new role in the world, a certain amount of historical perspective is needed. This perspective, up to the beginning of war with Japan in 1937, is briefly supplied in the following selection: [2]

► Early China

The foundations of Chinese history go back many centuries before the Christian era. The unification of the people into an empire came in the third century B. C. Since that time there have been many dynasties, some of them dynasties of conquering rulers leading nomadic peoples from the north, some of them native rulers. There were periods of weak central government characterized by wars between feudal states. The area known as China has shrunk and grown with the changing fortunes of these dynasties. Under the Mongol rulers of the Yuan dynasty (1280–1367) the boundaries of China were extended to the borders of Europe and encompassed Manchuria, Korea, Indochina, Burma, and Tibet. The Ming dynasty (1368–1644) that followed the Mongol rule was under native sovereigns and in this period some of the conquests of the Mongols were lost. Manchu rule replaced the Mings in 1644 in another period of aggressive expansion. Un-

---

[2] *Geographical Foundations of National Power* (Army Service Forces Manual M 103–3). Washington: Government Printing Office, 1944. Pp. 1–3.

One footnote has been omitted and two headings have been added.

der this rule the boundaries again extended into Tibet, Central Asia, and other areas lost during the Ming dynasty. Much of this territory was very loosely held and allegiance amounted to sending tribute to the Imperial Court at stated times. The Republic of China dates from 1911. In the revolution that brought about this change of dynasty native control was re-established. However, China was subjected to almost continuous civil war from the Revolution [to the outbreak of war with Japan in 1937]. . . .

The civilization that grew within the areas known as China was of a very high order. Learning was held in great regard, and officials were scholars, appointed to their posts under a democratic examination system that was fairly well developed as early as the sixth century. Literature, philosophy, poetry, and the arts flourished and rose to high levels of excellence. An ingenious handicraft system produced objects of great beauty and delicacy as well as sturdy objects for daily use.

Transportation and communications were well organized and amazingly swift. Post offices were set up at short intervals along the main roads and letters were carried by relays of riders on horseback so that the Emperor in Peking was informed within a very few days of events occurring on the outer edges of his empire. This stage post system began in the Han period before the Christian era. Public inns also served the main highways and were open freely to all who had occasion to travel, and there were stores of fodder for the horses. Some of the more important roads were paved with stones. In the Sui dynasty in the 6th century the Grand Canal was built to connect the north and the south. It was rebuilt in the 13th century by the great Khublai Khan to improve communications between the capital and the Yangtze Valley and to facilitate the administration of the empire. Great use was made of the rivers as means of internal communication. The Yangtze and its tributaries were then, as they are now, important factors in the life of the nation.

The Chinese felt no need of the outside world. Their civilization was superior to that of neighboring lands and was drawn upon and borrowed from by those lands. It reached also into the outside world and influenced distant cultures. Japan took from China her written language and much of her art and literature and industry, Korea also drew heavily on Chinese culture. China gave the world silk and paper and many medicines, the art of printing, the magnetic needle, gunpowder, and many other things. Chinese philosophy reached far beyond the widest borders of the empire.

▶ Contacts with the West

Influences from the outside world did come in and affect Chinese culture. Some of these influences came in by way of the conquering barbarians from the North; some came through peaceful trade; some were brought back by Chinese forces that had moved into the outer regions in the waves of empire expansion. Buddhism came from India and Christianity from the West, and they have had a wide and deep influence upon Chinese thinking and upon Chinese art. China also received many gifts from the outside, including cotton, which has become the primary fiber of her economy. By the 11th or 12th century, the use of the compass brought more sailing ships to China's shores, and by the 16th century contact with Europe by sea had become frequent.

China's self-sufficient economy had little interest in these first visitors from the West and the trade that they wanted. Even later, when the British East India Company tried to develop a trade, because they wanted China's tea and silk, pottery, lacquer, and cotton cloth, there was little besides silver that they could use in exchange—silver and a few luxuries and trinkets like watches and clocks. Their woolen cloth could find no market. The Chinese were not interested in the staple products of the West. America traded ginseng and silver for China's silk and teas in the early trade.

The Chinese were not eager for trade with the West. They erected a barrier to commerce comparable to the Great Wall they had built against the northern invaders in the first years of the Empire. This wall against commerce was a strict control of all trade by sea through the Co-hong, a Guild system operated under strict supervision of a commissioner, or emperor's merchant, appointed by the throne. Under Guild regulations foreign commerce was permitted only through the port of Canton. For many years this strict monopoly held the foreign traders under control. The advance of industrialization in the West, however, was a much stronger force than the Emperor's trade monopoly.

Early in the 19th century the invention of the steamship broke down the barrier of the Pacific Ocean. The Western Nations had advanced in their industrial development and were looking for markets, not for a luxury trade, but for the disposal of a large surplus production in exchange for China's tea and silk. For many decades their factory-made goods could find no market in China. They were inferior in quality to China's handmade products, and they were also sometimes more costly. The lighter weight cotton cloth for work clothes was not as elegant as the finer cloths still being spun by skilled native craftsmen. Gradually the factory goods improved in quality and cheapened in price, and the disintegration of China's great handicraft economy began. As the factory goods came into the coastal cities and displaced the handmade goods of the country, the economy was thrown out of adjustment. Following on the heels of the goods themselves, new industrial methods were imported into the coastal cities under foreign influence. The new methods established on the shores of China offered more serious competition to the old industries than the foreign factory goods, and the disintegration of the old order was hastened.

The superior ships and weapons of war of the Western nations forced political and economic concessions from isolationist China. Hong Kong was lost to the British and Macao to the Portuguese. The French secured a lease on Kwangchowan; the Germans, a lease on Chiao-hsien (Kiaochow); the Russians, Liaotung in Manchuria. Japan obtained the Nansei (Ryukyu) Islands, Taiwan (Formosa) and the Pescadores by arbitrary annexation or military conquest. Concessions were granted to foreign powers in Shanghai, Tientsin, Hankow and many other so-called "treaty ports." Railway concessions were yielded to the Russians and Japanese in Manchuria, the British, French, Belgians, and Americans in China proper. Mining rights went to British, German, and French nationals. Legation Quarters were set up in Peking with special privileges for the foreign powers. . . .

▶ *The Chinese Revolution and Subsequent Events*

The Revolution that brought in the establishment of the Republic of China came about in 1911. The years that have followed the Revolution have been marked by both civil wars and foreign invasion. The old economy has continued to disintegrate, while a new economic structure has been slow to build under the competition offered by the more industrialized nations.

From 1911 to 1931 the new Nationalist government of China was mainly occupied with the task of consolidating its control over the country. This involved a series of military actions against various local rulers or "warlords" who had seized power in local and provincial areas during the breakup of the Manchu empire. During this period Chiang Kai-shek came to the fore as the leading political figure in China. After the middle 1920's the Nationalist government was engaged in a struggle with Communist forces operating principally in the hilly regions of southern China and the northwest.

In 1931 Manchuria was invaded and taken over by Japan, and in 1937 the Japanese provoked a full-scale war with China. Although the Chinese forces fought heroically, they were unable to check the better-armed and better-trained Japanese. As a result the government was obliged to retreat to the far interior. Here it managed

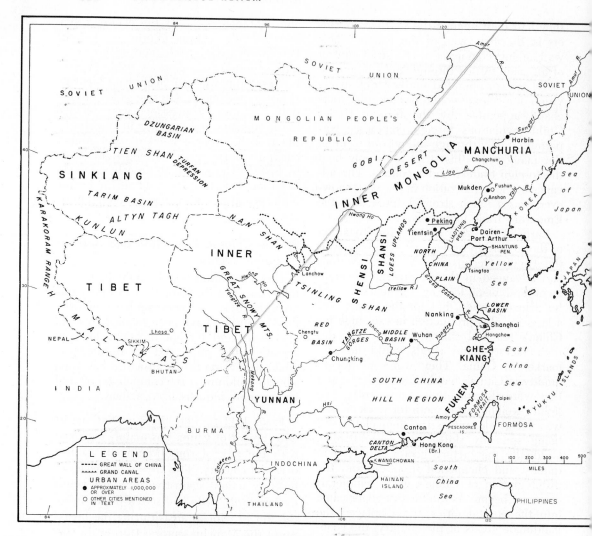

Index map of China. Political capitals are underlined.

to hold out, aided by a trickle of supplies from the outside, until final defeat of Japan by the Allies in 1945. Meanwhile the Chinese Communists were also fighting the Japanese, and there was a temporary lull in the struggle of the Nationalists and the Communists against each other. However, after 1945 fighting on a large scale developed between Nationalist and Communist forces in Manchuria and North China. Although aided in this struggle by American equipment and supplies, the Nationalist government lost the support of large segments of the population, and the Nation-

alist armies gradually melted away. In 1949 the government, together with its remaining forces, fled to Formosa. In early 1955 Formosa, the neighboring Pescadores Islands, and a scattering of small islands along the immediate mainland coast were still in Nationalist hands. Continuing hostilities between the Communist and Nationalist factions made the general area of the Formosa Strait an important focus of tension in the world-wide power struggle between the Communist and anti-Communist nations. Aid was being given the Nationalists by the United States.

Major Areal Divisions

China is vast in size, but like all extremely large countries contains a great deal of unproductive land. This is found mainly in the western and northwestern parts of the country in Tibet, Sinkiang, and Mongolia. These outlying areas are principally composed of high mountains and plateaus, together with great expanses of arid or semi-arid plains where rainfall, generally speaking, is insufficient for agriculture. This dry, sparsely settled country offers a marked contrast to the better-watered, densely settled parts of China which lie nearer the sea. In a general way, then, China can be divided into the Outlying Regions, or Arid China, on the west, and the Chinese core region, or Humid China, on the east. Humid China, the "China that matters" in world terms, contains the great bulk of China's population, and most of its natural resources and productive capacity.

Arid China

A rough boundary between Humid and Arid China would be a line drawn from the northeastern corner of India to the northern tip of Manchuria. In a general way this line corresponds to the line of 20 inches average annual rainfall. "Except in parts of Manchuria, most of the country east of this line is densely populated and the people are predominantly Chinese; west of the line the population is nearly everywhere sparse, large tracts are uninhabited, and many of the people are non-Chinese, chiefly Mongols, Tibetans, or Turks. Nearly everywhere east of the line crops are raised without dry-land irrigation; west of it grazing largely takes the place of agriculture, which is confined to scattered oases where water for irrigation is available along belts between mountains and dry plains." [3] The principal regions west of the line include Tibet, Sinkiang, and Mongolia.

► **Tibet**

Tibet is essentially a vast mountain-rimmed plateau which averages nearly 3 miles in elevation and is the loftiest inhabited region on earth. It is bordered to the south by the Himalayas, to the northwest by the Karakoram Range, to the north by the Kunlun, Altyn Tagh, and Nan Shan Ranges, and to the east by the Great Snowy Range or Szechwan Alps. Many of the great rivers of Asia rise in Tibet, and the southern and eastern margins of this region are cut by deep canyons through which these rivers escape to the sea. Eastern Tibet, particularly, is extraordinarily difficult country to traverse, for the traveler must pass in succession the canyons of the upper Yangtze, Mekong, and Salween Rivers, together with mountain ranges separating these streams. All of the major mountain ranges which border Tibet are extremely high and rugged, with many snowcapped peaks of 20,000 feet or over. The world's highest peak, Mount Everest (29,002 feet), is situated in the Himalayas on the border between Tibet and Nepal. Since the latter part of the Manchu period a political division has been recognized between Inner or Nearer Tibet, and Tibet proper, sometimes referred to as Farther Tibet. Inner Tibet adjoins Humid China, and has been more closely controlled by the Chinese central government than Farther Tibet. The latter

---

[3] *Geographical Foundations of National Power, op. cit.,* p. 5.

The palace of the Dalai Lama in Lhasa, the principal city and capital of Tibet. This massive structure, the Potala, symbolizes the importance of the Lamaist branch of the Buddhist religion throughout a vast area in Tibet, Sinkiang, and Mongolia. (*Eastfoto.*)

is the stronghold of the Lamaist branch of Buddhism, which has its principal holy place at Lhasa, the Tibetan capital (estimated population about 20,000). This city is located on a tributary of the upper Brahmaputra River in southeastern Tibet. The region of Lhasa is the lowest part of Tibet and contains, in sheltered valleys, the only considerable areas of agricultural settlement. Barley, a hardy grain requiring only a short growing season, is the main crop. Elsewhere the Tibetan population consists mainly of nomadic herdsmen; the yak is the characteristic domesticated animal, and sheep and goats are raised. Tibet is an extremely rough, inaccessible, little-known area. In past times the Chinese central government has taken an interest in Tibet due to the prevalence of Lamaism not only in Tibet itself, but also in Mongolia. However, the hold of China over Tibet has been very tenuous during the twentieth century, although the Chinese Communists, since their accession to power, have taken steps to bring the country more firmly within the orbit of the central government. Estimates of the area and population of Tibet vary widely. Nearer Tibet has perhaps 430,000 square miles and a population of 5 million (1953 census); Farther Tibet has about 350,000 square miles and a population reported at 1.3 million in the 1953 census.

▶ Sinkiang

Sinkiang adjoins Tibet on the north. Politically, Sinkiang is a province of China. It has an area of roughly 700,000 square miles and a 1953 census population of 4.9 million. In physical terms, Sinkiang consists essentially of two great basins, the Tarim Basin to the south and the Dzungarian Basin to the north. These basins are separated by the lofty Tien Shan range of mountains. The Tarim Basin is rimmed to the south by the mountains bordering Tibet, and the Dzungarian Basin is enclosed on the north by the Altai and other ranges along the southern border of the Soviet Union. Both basins are arid or semi-arid. The Tarim Basin, particularly, is dry, being almost completely enclosed by high mountains which block off rain-bearing winds. The Tarim Basin is occupied by the Taklamakan Desert, perhaps the driest region in Asia. The basin varies in altitude from 2000 to 6000 feet above sea level; the smaller adjoining Turfan Depression drops to 928 feet below sea level. The Dzungarian

Basin averages about 1000 feet in elevation, is more open than the Tarim Basin, and has somewhat more rain, though not enough for much agriculture.

The settled population of Sinkiang is concentrated in oases at points where streams from the high mountains debouch on the basin floors. These oases, located around the edges of the great basins, are connected by ancient caravan routes providing a passageway across Central Asia from Humid China to the Soviet Union, Afghanistan, and Kashmir. The most important routes follow the northern and southern piedmonts [4] of the Tien Shan. The route across the Dzungarian Basin along the northern flank of the Tien Shan is followed by a motor highway connecting Lanchow in northwestern China proper with railheads lying in Soviet Middle Asia. During the Japanese war a trickle of sup-

---

[4] A piedmont is a belt of country at an intermediate elevation along the base of a mountain range.

plies reached China from the Soviet Union via this route. Sinkiang has at times been a debatable territory between China and Russia. It has tended to be drawn into the economic orbit of Russia by the close proximity of Russian rail connections, as contrasted with Chinese railheads, which are far away to the east. The population is predominantly Moslem and non-Chinese and has long been restive under Chinese rule.

► Mongolia

Although it is not politically united, the area north of the Great Wall of China and west of Manchuria, extending northward to the southern border of the USSR, is customarily referred to as Mongolia. It is dominantly a country of vast plains which are occupied by desert or dry grassland. The plains areas are known locally as *gobis,* and have given their name to the Gobi Desert, which occupies much of Mongolia. A large part of Mongolia is included in the Mongolian People's Republic, often referred to

Herding sheep at the base of arid mountains in Sinkiang. Note the sparse pasturage. (*Eastfoto.*)

as Outer Mongolia. Although the latter area has traditionally been considered a part of China, since 1924 it has been a separate country organized along Soviet lines and under strong Soviet influence. It includes an area of about 626,000 square miles but is estimated to have only around 900,000 people.

The part of Mongolia nearest the Great Wall is known as Inner Mongolia and is definitely a part of China. Parts of Inner Mongolia are desert, but immediately north of the Great Wall is a belt of grassland which receives enough rain in wet years for a precarious agriculture. For centuries Inner Mongolia, like other grassland areas along the dry margins of world agriculture, has been a zone of competition and conflict between grain farmers on the one hand and graziers with their flocks and herds on the other.

Prior to World War II Inner Mongolia was considered to include four provinces immediately north of the Great Wall with an aggregate area of approximately 400,000 square miles and a total population of perhaps 7 million. However, the Communist government of China has now established a new Inner Mongolian Autonomous Region which includes the major portion of the old Inner Mongolia and also includes areas detached from the western part of what was formerly considered to be Manchuria. This new Autonomous Region had a 1953 census population reported at 6.1 million.

Humid China

Humid China, the core region of the country, includes the densely settled parts of China south of the Great Wall, and also includes Manchuria. The 18 ancient provinces of China south of the Wall are often referred to by outsiders as "China proper," although the Chinese themselves do not employ the term. China proper includes two major divisions, North China and South China, which differ from each other in various physical, economic, and cultural respects. Although each area exhibits much variety from place to place, South China may be characterized in general as subtropical, humid, hilly or mountainous, with irrigated rice as the main crop, while North China is continental, subhumid, has larger stretches of level land, and depends mainly on nonirrigated grain crops other than rice. The North Chinese are typically taller, heavier, more purely Mongoloid, wear warmer clothing during the cold winters, and are considered to be somewhat slower in thought and action and less excitable by nature than the inhabitants of South China. Many more languages and dialects are current in South China than in North China (mainly localized in the hilly coastal districts between Shanghai and Canton), although the majority of Chinese in both areas speak regional varieties of the same basic language. Farms are larger, streets and roads wider in North China, and oxen or camels are the characteristic draft animals rather than the water buffalo of South China.

The two major regional divisions are briefly described in the following selection: [5]

▶ North China

North China is subhumid, average annual precipitation ranging from 17 inches in the Loess Upland to 21 inches in the North China Plains. But owing to the very high variability from year to year the area is subject to famine from droughts and floods. The winters are cold, the summers hot. . . . The people depend on millet, kaoliang (a sorghum), and wheat as their

---

[5] *Geographical Foundations of National Power, op. cit.,* pp. 1 and 6–8. One footnote has been omitted and one heading added.

primary food. The great plain of the unruly Yellow River (Hwang Ho) dominates the region and is densely populated. Chinese civilization originated and developed in this area. . . .

North China . . . comprises two very different subregions: (1) the uplands of the interior and (2) the great alluvial plain of the Hwang Ho, or North China Plain, with the included uplands of Shantung.

• The Uplands

The Hwang Ho (Yellow River), which rises in Tibet, drains the western portion of the uplands; thence it makes a great swing far to the north into the steppes of Mongolia, where it turns back south through the uplands, only to make a right angle bend to the east, 200 miles before flowing out into the plain. The upland area as a whole was the historic frontier zone between China proper and the dry lands of inner Asia. Much of the region is covered with deep deposits of loess, which the Chinese descriptively call "Yellow Earth," an exceedingly fine-grained, but fertile soil, laid down by the wind. The scarce and unreliable rainfall renders agriculture precarious, however. In periods of drought famine occurs. Conversely, when a series of years brings more than average rain, much of the steppe borderland can be tilled, and farmers push out into it. . . .

• The North China Plain

The North China Plain is an immense complex delta. The Hwang Ho shifts its course from time to time, reaching the sea first to the north and then to the south of the Shantung hills. Numerous tributaries and ditches cross the Plain. These waterways are shallow and most of them are fordable and they have generally been diked in an effort to keep them within bounds during flood season. As the river deposited silt and debris, the dikes were built higher and higher to keep above the rising water level until the bed of the stream in many sections is above the level of the surrounding country. This situation placed the residents of the area in a precarious position. Few rivers are subject to such violent floods as the Hwang. Hardly any of its waters, shallow and full of shifting sand bars, are navigable for large craft.

The country is so dry that it is a yellow and dusty land except during spring and early summer. There is generally sufficient rain, however, to bring crops to bearing without irrigation. . . .

▶ South China

South China is a different world from that of the North. Its abundant rainfall and warmer climate make it lush and green at times of the year when North China is parched with drought or withered with cold. Much of South China is hilly or mountainous. The principal lowlands are the three large basins drained by the Yangtze River and the smaller Canton delta section.

• The Yangtze Basins

The three Yangtze Basins are set off from each other by narrows in the river valley. The Lower Basin is a delta merging with that of the Hwang Ho. The Middle Basin is likewise largely built up of river sediments and is flat, low, and dotted with lakes. The soil of these two basins is not quite as fertile as that of the North China Plain, but the more abundant rainfall insures a good crop every year and provides water for the irrigation of rice, which cannot be extensively grown farther north because of the long, cold winters. The third or Red Basin lies farther upstream, separated from the Middle Basin by a mountain wall through which the river has cut a deep gorge. The Red Basin stands several hundred feet above the Middle and Lower Basins and is a land of hills, among which lies the highly productive Chengtu plain.

The Yangtze Basins are set off from North China by a combination of barriers. On the east the many rivers and lakes of the delta flats form a considerable obstacle. Farther west, first a range of hills and then the Ch'in Ling (Tsinling) mountains, which rise to more than 10,000 feet, mark the border zone. These barriers are crossed by minor trails in many places, but the main highways for traders and warriors are few and have remained little changed since

A view of the important seaport of Canton in South China. Note the sampans clustered along the waterfront. Many Chinese families live permanently on such boats. (*Eastfoto*.)

the beginning of China's history. Even the construction of canals and railroads has not altered the pattern of the principal connecting routes. . . .

Throughout its course in China proper the Yangtze River is broad, deep, and, in places, swift. It is the backbone of the Chinese communication system. The lower part of its course is paralleled by railroads, but the river itself constitutes the sole through connection between the three basins. It has always carried naval vessels as well as trading ships. Large ocean craft can ascend to Nanking at all seasons. Ships drawing ten feet of water can continue, at all seasons, to Hankow, the metropolis of the Middle Yangtze Basin, and river craft drawing seven feet can ascend to Ichang at the foot of the gorge. Chungking, 1300 miles from the river mouth, is the head of year-round navigation for small power vessels. The gorge between Chungking and Ichang is hazardous because of rocks, whirlpools, and the swift current, and specially constructed, powerful steamers are required for its navigation. . . .

Cut off by mountain masses, the Red Basin was not annexed to China until the fourth century B. C. It is more readily defensible than any other productive part of the mainland of East Asia. A barrier of lofty mountains and the gorge of the Yangtze itself aid its defense against ground forces attempting invasion from the east. In productivity, the Red Basin combines characteristics of South and North China, growing both rice and wheat. . . .

• *The Canton Delta*

The principal river of China's far south is the Hsi, or West, River, a shorter stream than either the Hwang or the Yangtze. Its course is through uplands, except where its delta merges with those of lesser streams to form the Canton delta, a densely populated lowland, smaller in area than those farther north. This lowland, which is separated from the Yangtze by a wide belt of hills and low mountains, was not finally incorporated into China until the time of the Tsin and Han dynasties, nearly 1000 years after the basins of the Hwang Ho and

Middle and Lower Yangtze had been consolidated. . . .

• The Hill Lands

The coastal zone between the deltas of the Yangtze and the Hsi is so difficult to penetrate that it was not annexed to China until the third century A. D. The range of relief is between 1500 and 2500 feet, although some peaks rise to 6000 feet. The rivers are short, swift, and unnavigable, and each basin constitutes a unit isolated except on the seaward side. The size of the towns at the river mouths is limited by the productivity of the basins they serve. Agriculture is restricted to small and scattered valley lands. The coast is dotted with fishing hamlets. This is the only section of China in which the people have taken much interest in seafaring.

Most of Yunnan, the southwesternmost province of China proper, is a deeply dissected plateau some 6000 feet high. In the long history of the southward advance of the Chinese, it was the area most recently penetrated. Many primitive groups still live there unassimilated to the Chinese way of life, and intermittent guerilla warfare persists in places between these native folk and Chinese settlers.

▶ Cities of Humid China

Relatively few large cities exist in China considering the enormous population total of the country. The lack of great metropolitan areas is largely a reflection of the predominantly rural character of China,

A view of blast furnace Number 7 at Anshan, Manchuria. This city is the largest center of iron and steel production in China. (*Eastfoto.*)

the relatively small foreign trade, and the underdeveloped status of Chinese industry. By far the largest city, and second largest in all Asia, is the major seaport and industrial center of Shanghai (6,000,000), located on a navigable tributary of the Yangtze near the mouth of the latter stream. Three other metropolitan areas including a million people or more are spaced at intervals along the Yangtze. They include (1) Nanking (1,300,000), the capital of Nationalist China prior to 1937 and again from 1945 to 1949, (2) the industrialized conurbation of Wuhan (Hankow and Wuchang, population of metropolian area 1,300,000), and (3) Chungking (1,100,000) in the Red Basin, the capital from 1937 to 1945. South of the Yangtze the only "million city" of China is the seaport of Canton (1,500,000) in the Hsi delta. Two other cities numbering more than a million are found near the northern edge of the North China Plain. They are Peking (2,240,000), the capital before 1911 and again since 1949, and the important seaport of Tientsin (2,000,000), located on the Yellow Sea 70 miles southeast of Peking. A number of large cities in Manchuria are described in the following section.

▶ *Manchuria*

Manchuria is the part of Humid China north of the Great Wall. To the west are the Mongolian steppes and deserts; to the east Manchuria is separated from the Sea of Japan by Korea and Russia. In recent times this area has claimed an important share of world attention, chiefly through its role as a zone of rivalry and conflict among China, Russia, and Japan. Russian interest in Manchuria has been connected with the Chinese Eastern Railway, a shortcut across northern Manchuria between Vladivostok and the Trans-Siberian Railroad east of Lake Baikal, and with the naval and port facilities of Dairen–Port Arthur, which the Russians have used extensively at various times. The Japanese

were attracted to Manchuria as a source of supply for coal, iron, aluminum, timber, and other industrial resources, as a source of surplus foodstuffs, as an expanding market for Japanese manufactures, and as a promising area for capital investment. After the Russo-Japanese War of 1904–1905, mainly fought in Manchuria, Japan was increasingly active in the area, and took over actual control in 1931 with the establishment of the puppet state of Manchukuo. For the Chinese, Manchuria has served as an outlet for surplus population migrating from south of the Wall. Movement of Chinese colonists into Manchuria began centuries ago, but gained greatest momentum after 1900. Millions of Chinese farmers migrating to this area have made it one of the twentieth century's major zones of pioneer agricultural settlement. However, possibly the greatest significance of Manchuria to the present Communist government of China lies in a considerable development of heavy industry left by the Japanese, and the best rail network in China, begun by the Russians and later taken over and expanded by Japan.

In physical terms Manchuria consists of a broad, rolling central plain surrounded by a frame of mountains which seldom rise higher than 6000 feet. The mountains on the east, north, and southwest are forested and contain much valuable timber, including oak and other hardwoods as well as conifers. The central plain, oriented northeast-southwest, is approximately 600 miles long by 200 to 400 miles wide. The northern portions of the plain are drained by the Sungari River, a tributary of the Amur, and the southern portions by the Liao River, which flows to the Yellow Sea. The soils are relatively deep, dark-colored, and very fertile, and the summer rainfall of 15 to 25 inches is generally sufficient for the crops that are grown. Conditions are not favorable for irrigated rice, except in limited areas of the extreme south, and the winters are generally too severe for winter grains. However, spring-sown wheat, millet, kaoliang, corn, and barley do well during the relatively short but warm frost-free season of 150 to 180 days. Large acreages are devoted to soybeans, a versatile leguminous crop which provides protein food for both men and livestock, is an important source of vegetable oil, and enriches the soil through the addition of nitrogen. Manchuria was the world's largest exporter of soybeans for considerable periods prior to World War II. Manchurian farms are larger, the density of the agricultural population is less, and much greater possibilities for future mechanization of agriculture are offered than in the parts of Humid China south of the Great Wall.

The industries of Manchuria are mainly centered in or relatively near the largest city, Mukden (2,000,000) in south central Manchuria. Mukden is a diversified center of metal-fabricating and agricultural-processing industries. The largest center of iron and steel production, however, is Anshan, about 50 miles southeast of Mukden. The principal reserves of iron ore in China are found in a belt which crosses southern Manchuria. The ore is mostly low-grade with an average iron content of around 35 percent. However, sizable pockets of richer ore occur along or near the Korean border. Substantial deposits of high-grade bituminous coal also occur in Manchuria, although the total estimated reserves are much smaller than those of China south of the Great Wall, and only an estimated 10 percent of Manchurian coal is suitable for coking. The largest center of coal mining is Fushun, about 20 miles east of Mukden, where a bed of coal more than 400 feet thick is mined by open-pit methods. In general, Manchuria appears to have the coal and iron resources for substantial increases in heavy industry, although the reserves are not outstanding on a world basis.

The major cities of Manchuria are spaced at intervals of 150 to 250 miles along the main north-south rail axis. In north central Manchuria is the important rail junction of Harbin (1,000,000), where the railroad from Mukden intersects the Russian-built east-west line connecting Vladivostok with the Trans-Siberian Railroad east of Lake Baikal. About midway between Harbin and Mukden is the industrial and transportation center of Changchun (550,000). South of Mukden at the tip of the Liaotung Peninsula are the major seaport of Dairen and the nearby naval base of Port Arthur, forming together a metropolitan district with an estimated population of around one million.

Manchuria, including Jehol (a province immediately north of the Great Wall) and excluding sections now incorporated in the Inner Mongolian Autonomous Region, has an area of some 344,000 square miles and a population (1953 census) of 46.9 million.

The People and Economy of China

The 1953 census total of 590 million people reported by the government of Communist China (see footnote, page 360) is regarded with skepticism by some population analysts. Nevertheless, there appears to be no doubt that China has the largest population of any country. In recent years, population experts, basing their opinions on sample studies, have generally employed figures of 450 to 500 million, a total substantially greater than the 357 million reported for the Republic of India in the 1951 census.

Some important characteristics of the Chinese people and the economy which has supported them up to the present period of Communist domination are presented in the following selection: [6]

---

[6] *Geographical Foundations of National Power, op. cit.,* pp. 11–13. Six headings have been omitted.

[The population of China is very unevenly distributed]; six-sevenths of the total population is concentrated in one-third of the area. The east is densely populated, especially in the lower valleys of the Hwang Ho and the Yangtze, and the rice growing area south of the latter. The country is overpopulated in relation to its agricultural resources. Much of the sparsely populated outer area is unsuited to cultivation, and in China proper as a whole less than one-third of the people live in cities. The large peasant population live in small villages near their land.

In spite of their lavish use of human labor and their inherited skill, Chinese farmers cannot wring an adequate living from the cultivated area at their disposal. The yield per acre is relatively high, but the output per worker is low, and the standard of living is at the margin of subsistence. Famine, disease, and war consequently take a devastating toll.

The low average productivity of Chinese labor is not due to lack of ability. In the traditional handicraft industries Chinese workers display great taste and skill, and they are capable of becoming skilled industrial workers when employed under favorable conditions. The obstacles to achieving such favorable conditions have been peculiarly difficult to overcome because of the generally disordered economic conditions and the social habits of the Chinese, which discouraged individual initiative and responsibility. The high degree of illiteracy has been a further handicap. . . .

Because the Chinese have not kept pace with the West in the development of a machine-age civilization, the average American is too likely to jump at the superficial conclusion that they are primitive and backward. They are backward with respect only to certain material possessions and technical accomplishments by which the Western world sets great store. Their culture as reflected in many of their arts, in the tone of their thought, and in their philosophical outlook on fundamental problems of life, though different, is as rich and as mature as ours.

It is true, however, that conservatism and political passivity have been national characteristics of China. These may be due partly to China's long isolation in the past, but they are unquestionably also due in large measure to qualities in the Chinese people associated with the economic conditions under which they live. Most of the Chinese are desperately poor. Peasant and city dweller alike pass their lives in endless, dogged toil. Their cheerful endurance under hardships and their amazing powers of recuperation after floods, famines, and wars are elements of strength, but the mere struggle for subsistence is so all-consuming of time and energy that there is little opportunity for the development of wider interests and broader outlook. The average peasant family has occupied the same farm for countless generations, and each generation strives to carry on as its predecessors have done. Because travel is difficult and costly and because there is no reason for him to travel, the peasant seldom leaves his home community unless called into military service. Each community keeps to itself and ancient dialects and other cultural peculiarities persist. Deeply attached to his local "good earth" and to the graves of his ancestors, the Chinese peasant is unconcerned over what is going on in other parts of the country. He knows little of politics and cares less for them. China's weak national cohesion, together with the backwardness of her systems of production and transportation, has [in the past] left her a prey to the ambitions of other nations. . . .

▶ *Agriculture, Fishing and Forestry*

Approximately 80 percent of the population of China proper is engaged in agriculture. It is essentially an industry of peasant cultivators who work in family units to provide their daily food. The average farm is about . . . 3.5 acres, varying in size from province to province—in the congested southeast from one-third to one-half an acre per person—and is scattered in minute plots over considerable area. . . .

China proper may be divided into two major agricultural regions, each including several smaller ones. South of the Yangtze

THE PEOPLE AND ECONOMY OF CHINA

the climate is subtropical and humid, and rice is the principal crop with silk, sugar, and tea as supplements. There, double cropping and water-farming in valleys and on terraced hillsides is typical, and water buffalo are used as draft animals. So much of the region is mountainous that only about 18 percent of the land is under cultivation. The cultivable parts are so fertile, however, that they support an extremely dense population. North of the Yangtze–Hwang Ho divide, where the winters are severe and drought is frequent, dry farming is practiced, and wheat, millet, kaoliang, beans, and maize are the principal crops. Oxen are the draft animals. Nearly 45 per cent of the land is under cultivation, but it is so much less intensively cultivated than in the south that the northern crop area supports a population only about half as dense. The small amount of grazing land in China proper—about 5 percent of the cultivated area—is in the northwest where wool is raised and exported. Between the two principal agricultural regions lies an intermediate zone where both rice and wheat are grown.

Throughout China proper the forest land has been largely denuded of trees in the desperate search for fuel and timber. . . . Less than 10 percent of the land is now forested, and soil erosion is a most serious problem, made worse by the fact that the wild grass growing on much of the former forest land is harvested for fuel. The largest accessible forests of commercial value are found principally in Manchuria. . . .

Although sea fishing is confined largely to the indented sections of the coast, especially off Fukien and Chekiang provinces, many fish are caught in the carefully stocked streams, lakes, and small artificial ponds scattered over the farmland. . . . The most common meats are chicken and pork.

Among industrial raw materials, Chinese agriculture, before 1937, provided small exportable surpluses of raw cotton, raw silk, wool, vegetable oils, hides and skins. Among the food exports, egg products, tea, some vegetables, and fruit were notable. In the future when improved internal trans-

portation, economic stability, and the application of modern scientific knowledge have made specialization more widespread, these commercial crops may well become of far greater importance than hitherto.

▶ Mineral Resources

China is the only country of the Far East of which the coal fields are of world importance, and, although not so rich as was once supposed, the estimated reserves are much greater in extent than those of Great Britain. Much of the coal is of good quality. Coking coal is obtained from a number of the deposits. The important coal-bearing areas are in the interior, the principal one centering in Shansi within the right-angle bend of the Hwang Ho; another is found in Shensi province to the southwest. Most of the production, however, is in the northeastern provinces of China proper and in Manchuria. . . .

For many years it was thought that the petroleum resources of China were negligible. In 1934, however, the National Geological Survey of China announced an estimate of a total reserve of 4337 million barrels in China proper and Manchuria, including oil recoverable from shale. These reserves are as yet undeveloped, except for the production of oil from shale in Manchuria. . . .

The potential resources of water power are probably not remarkable, although the mountainous southern provinces are fairly well endowed. . . .

The iron ore reserves of China are not outstanding. . . . More than half the reserves are in Manchuria where most of the ore is of low iron content; of the remaining reserves a little more than half are in the northeastern part of China proper and the rest in the lower Yangtze Valley. The chief producing mines are in Manchuria where an iron and steel industry was built by the Japanese. . . .

Other metals of note produced in China include tin, antimony, tungsten, and manganese. Although these resources are a valuable contribution to the world supply of these by no means common minerals, they do not justify hopes of a future great industry based upon them. The largest deposits are in South China. . . .

▶ Manufacturing

The industrial development of China in the modern sense began just before the turn of the century but was greatly accelerated in 1905 when foreign powers obtained the right to establish factories in the Treaty Ports. By 1937 three kinds of industrial regions had developed: (1) the treaty port cities along the coast where both foreign and Chinese-owned modern plants, producing chiefly textiles and tobacco, flourished side by side with smaller native establishments in the Chinese quarters; (2) the river valleys and railway zones where industrial development was growing and industrial plants were largely foreign-owned, especially by Japanese; and (3) the interior, where the traditional handicraft industries still prevailed. These local trades were usually on a very small scale and often combined with agricultural occupations. Perhaps the most notable was the raising, spinning, and hand-weaving of cotton, a method by which a large part of the country's cotton cloth was produced. Large-scale production existed in coal mining, textiles, cement, paper, flour milling, iron and steel making, soap making, and the generation of electric light and power. It may be expected that . . . these will develop more fully in the future and that light manufactures of various kinds, the making of railway and electrical equipment and of chemical fertilizers will also expand. . . .

▶ Railroads

The railroad system in China proper is grossly inadequate for the needs of a modern nation. In 1937 the main lines and branch lines totaled a little more than 6000 miles in contrast to Great Britain which has over 20,000 miles of track. Moreover, in China the rolling stock was out of date and insufficient, and the service was erratic, and the charges were high. The railroad network consisted chiefly of a framework of through lines in the eastern coastal provinces. The southwestern provinces of China proper had no rail connections with the rest of the country nor had they more than a few miles of short lines for local use. With unimportant exceptions all the railway lines have been owned and operated by the national government since 1911. In contrast with the rest of China, Manchuria was better equipped with a network of railroads that in 1940 totaled 7380 miles. . . .

▶ Highways and Inland Waterways

Although through routes known to have persisted since prehistoric times cross the Chinese realm, they have normally carried only luxury goods, aside from local trade. Most of them are mere tracks for camels, bullocks, or human porters. Even the motor roads of recent construction are hardly to be described as through routes. Nowhere are they paved except in the vicinity of the cities in which foreign influence has been strong. The larger part are merely graded and become dusty in dry weather and rutted after heavy rains. . . .

The highways of China proper in use in 1936 totaled somewhat more than 56,000 miles, of which less than 12,000 miles represented paved roads. At the same time there were nearly 7000 miles of highway in Manchuria and about 5500 in the outer territories of Mongolia, Sinkiang, and Tibet. In the eight western provinces of China proper, with a total area of over one million square miles and a combined population of nearly 100 million people, there were but 13,000 miles of roads in 1936. The network covered the eastern half of the country with reasonable density and routes reached the western provinces with only a few breaks.

In 1937, the length of navigable inland waterways in China was estimated at 11,250 miles. Most of these are in the eastern half of China proper. The Chinese, with flat-bottomed boats, make use of many additional streams not ordinarily considered navigable. Many small canals have been constructed, some of them centuries ago. . . . Throughout the history of China, water transportation has been of great importance. . . . The principal north-south route consists of the ancient Grand Canal from Tientsin southward for 700 miles to Hangchow (south of Shanghai) and the principal east-west route of the Yangtze. The Yangtze's importance as an artery connecting the coast with the interior cannot be overstated. Large ocean steamers proceed up the river as far as Hankow and smaller vessels still further to Ichang, a thousand miles from the sea. Above Ichang the river rapids are negotiated by specially constructed powerful steamers. Native craft make use of the river for 1630 miles, more than half of its length. Numerous tributaries are navigable by native craft, broadening the breadth of the area served to an enormous territory.

Mainland China has now embarked on a program of large-scale national planning modeled after that of the Soviet Union. A Five-Year Plan was initiated in 1953. Agricultural holdings of landlords and the wealthier peasants were almost completely expropriated between 1949 and 1953 and turned over to farm tenants and small landowners. However, a heavy tax burden has replaced the rents formerly collected by the landlords. Creation of a society of small landowning farmers is in all probability an intermediate step, just as in the USSR at a comparable stage. The apparent goal is a collectivized agriculture, and collectivization has begun, though information regarding it was very fragmentary in early 1955. Industrial emphases in Communist Chinese planning appear similar to those of the USSR up to the present—in other words, a rapid expansion of mining, heavy industry, and machine construction; improvement of internal transportation and power facilities; and exaction of the utmost effort from industrial workers. The announced aim is to create an industrialized nation in the shortest possible time. Trade is being increasingly oriented toward the USSR. A considerable amount of political reorganization has taken place, much of it along Soviet Russian lines. Thus economically and politically mainland China has become an integral part of the vast bloc of Communist nations stretching from mid-Europe to Southeast Asia.

Formosa

Since 1949, interest in Formosa (Portuguese, "beautiful") has been more widespread than formerly, due to the presence there of the Chinese Nationalist government and its remaining armed forces. Formosa is separated from the coast of South China by the Formosa Strait, about 100 miles wide. From 1895 to 1945 the island was governed by the Japanese, who developed its economy as an adjunct to that of Japan, and called the island by its ancient Chinese name of Taiwan.

The area of Formosa, including the Pescadores and other small neighboring islands, is approximately 13,900 square miles. The population, largely Chinese, was estimated at 10 million in 1951. High mountains rise steeply from the sea on the eastern side of the island, but slope on the west to a broad coastal plain bordering the Formosa Strait. Formosa lies on the northern margin of the tropics, and its temperatures are further moderated by the warm, northward-flowing Kuroshio or Japanese Current. Irrigated rice, the main food crop, is favored by the hot, humid summers of the lowlands and by an abundance of irrigation water provided by streams originating in the mountains. Some of the higher mountain areas receive nearly 300 inches of rainfall a year. Cultivated land, mostly found on the western coastal plain, occupies about a fourth of the total area of the island. Rice accounts for more than half of the total crop acreage. Two rice harvests a year are commonly secured from the same field. Sweet potatoes are also a major food crop. Sugar cane was developed on a plantation basis by the Japanese as the major export crop. Cane sugar represented 58 percent of all exports by value in 1952. Other agricultural exports include rice, tea, tobacco, peanuts, pineapples, bananas, and oranges. Japan took most of the prewar exports and took 50 percent of all exports in 1952.

Formosa has substantial reserves of minerals, including coal, some petroleum and natural gas, salt, sulfur, copper, and gold. Many short rivers descending from the highlands furnish the hydroelectric power upon which the industries of the island mainly depend. The Japanese developed a fair amount of industry, including sugar and petroleum refining, the manufacture of chemical fertilizers and cement, and pulp and paper making based on extensive tracts of pine forest in the highlands. About three fourths of the island is forested in either broadleaf evergreens or conifers. Among the many valuable forest trees is the camphor tree, which has given Formosa practically a world monopoly of natural camphor. However, the natural product has now been jeopardized by the development of synthetic camphor.

The capital and largest city of Formosa is Taipei (estimated population 539,000 in 1951), located in the interior near the northern end of the island.

Japan and Korea

Until the middle of last century the island nation of Japan played little part in world affairs. In fact, from the beginning of the seventeenth century until the middle 1850's Japan lived in almost complete isolation, shut off by government decree from the outside world. In 1853, however, the visit of an American naval squadron under Commodore Matthew Perry led to a change of policy. The old era of isolation was ended, and Japan entered a new age of industrial and commercial development and territorial expansion. By the middle 1930's Japan had become a leading industrial and trading nation, had acquired a sizable empire, and had taken a prominent place among the military and naval powers of the world.

Had its leaders followed another course, Japan, the first Oriental nation to develop a modern economy along Occidental lines, might have led its Asiatic neighbors into an age of unprecedented progress and prosperity. But the influence of the military was increasingly strong as the twentieth century progressed, and Japan became committed to a program of territorial expansion through military conquest. A grandiose design was conceived for a "Greater East Asia Co-Prosperity Sphere"—a euphemism for a greatly expanded Japanese Empire, to include China and the rich tropical lands of Southeast Asia. Eventually, however, the Japanese leaders overreached themselves with an attack on the United States at Pearl Harbor, and in 1945 Japan

The busy harbor of Yokohama symbolizes the importance of Japan as a maritime and trading nation. (*Japan Travel Bureau.*)

JAPAN

INDEX MAP

● CITY OF 750,000 OR MORE (POLITICAL CAPITAL UNDERLINED)

- - - APPROXIMATE BOUNDARIES OF CORE REGION

Limit of Rice

HOKKAIDO

Sea

of

Japan

Hakodate

NORTHERN JAPAN

PACIFIC

OCEAN

HONSHU

Limit of Orange

KANTO PLAIN

Tokyo

Yokohama

KOREA

Sea of Japan

Strait of Shimonoseki

Hiroshima

Nagasaki

Moji

Kyoto

Nagoya

MT. FUJI

Osaka

Kobe

Shizuoka

SHIKOKU

Inland Sea

SOUTHERN

JAPAN

LIMITS OF RICE AND ORANGE AFTER ACKERMAN

100 Miles
100 200 Kilometers

KYUSHU

COPYRIGHT BY ERWIN RAISZ, 1944.

went down to complete military defeat at the hands of the United States and its Allies. Following the Japanese surrender the country was occupied by Allied forces, mainly American, and remained under occupation until a peace treaty went into effect on April 28, 1952. The Japanese, like the Germans, have faced an enormous task of rebuilding since the war, and with their

trade diminished and their former empire gone, must cope with staggering problems of readjustment and survival.

Japan's eventful history has seen cycles of racial and cultural immigration, nation-building, withdrawal into seclusion, emergence as an imperial power, and military defeat and occupation. Some pertinent aspects are summarized below.

Historical Background

The racial and ethnic origins of the Japanese are somewhat obscure. They are thought to be descended from a number of different Mongoloid and Malayan peoples who reached Japan from other parts of eastern Asia at various times in the distant past. An earlier people, the Ainu, were driven into outlying areas where remnants still exist, principally in Hokkaido, Sakhalin, and the Ryukyu Islands. Some of the Ainu may possibly have been assimilated by the invading peoples. The oldest surviving Japanese written records date from the eighth century A.D., but Japanese traditions extend back to the reign of Jimmu Tenno, the First Emperor, whose accession is ascribed to the year 660 B.C., although modern scholars have placed the date some centuries later. The acceptance of these traditions has been an important factor in Japanese psychology, since they ascribe a divine origin to the imperial family (Jimmu Tenno was supposedly descended from the Sun Goddess) and thus call attention to Japan as "the Land of the Gods."

The early emperors gradually extended control over all of their island realm. A society developed based on subsistence agriculture and organized into warring clans. By about the twelfth century the emperors were being pushed into the background by powerful military leaders, or *shoguns,* who actually controlled the country while the emperors remained as figureheads. Meanwhile the provinces were ruled by nobles or *daimyo,* whose power rested on the military prowess of lesser nobles, the *samurai.* Thus evolved a governmental system resembling in some ways the European feudal system of medieval times.

▶ Early Contacts with Europe

The adventurous and wide-ranging Europeans of the Age of Discovery reached Japan in the first part of the sixteenth century. In the 1540's came the Portuguese, and after them came representatives of other European nations. These early comers were mainly merchants and Roman Catholic missionaries. Both groups were well received. The merchants were allowed to set up trading establishments and open an active commerce, and the missionaries were allowed to preach freely and even received a certain amount of governmental favoritism. There were an estimated 300,000 Japanese Catholics by the year 1600.

However, these early promising contacts were eventually nullified. Even while they were occurring, a series of strong military leaders were imposing internal unity and central authority on the disorderly feudal structure of Japanese society. By 1600 the Tokugawa family had acquired absolute power, which it retained until 1868. This period is generally known as the period of the Tokugawa Shogunate. In order to maintain power and stability the early Tokugawa Shoguns desired to eliminate all disturbing social influences. The latter included the foreign traders and missionaries. In addition, the shoguns seem to have feared that the missionaries were the forerunners of an attempted conquest by Europeans, especially the Spanish who held the Philippines. Consequently, the traders were driven out, and Christianity was almost completely eliminated in bloody persecutions during the early part of the seventeenth century. After 1641 a few Dutch traders were the only Occidentals allowed in Japan, and even they were carefully segregated on the small island of Deshima in the harbor of Nagasaki. Japan settled under the Tokugawa into two centuries of isolation, peace, and stagnation.

▶ Westernization and Expansion

When the foreigners again made a serious attempt to open Japan to trade, two centuries later, the growing strength of the outside nations could not be thwarted by a Japan which had fallen far behind in the arts of both war and peace. This time the United States took the lead, and visits in 1853 and 1854 by American naval squadrons under Commodore Matthew Perry resulted in treaties opening Japan to trade with the United States. The major European powers were soon able to obtain similar privileges. Some of the great feudal authorities in southwestern Japan were strongly opposed to the new policy, but their opposition was quelled when coastal areas under their control were bombarded by American, British, French, and Dutch ships in 1863 and 1864.

These events so weakened the faltering power and prestige of the Tokugawa Shogunate that in 1868 the ruling shogun was overthrown by a rebellion. The revolutionary leaders restored the legitimate sovereignty of the emperor, who took the name Meiji or "Enlightened Rule." Thus the revolution of 1868 is generally termed the Meiji Restoration. Since that time Japan has generally been ruled, despite the forms of democracy, by relatively small groups of powerful men manipulating the machinery of government and the prestige of the emperor. Efforts were made by the American occupation authorities to establish a truly democratic system after World War II. Whether these efforts have achieved any lasting success is at present a question on which there is considerable difference of opinion.

The men who came to power in 1868 and the able Emperor Meiji himself were true revolutionaries in that they aimed at a complete transformation of Japan's society and economy. They saw that if Japan were not to fall under the control of the Western nations, its demonstrated military impotence would have to be remedied. They saw also that this would require a reconstruction of the Japanese economy and of many aspects of the social order. These tasks were approached with energy and

intelligence. Feudalism was abolished, though not without the necessity of suppressing a bloody revolt in 1877. Thus was cemented the power of a strong central government which could be used as an instrument for remodeling the country. Such a government was an institution that no other Oriental people possessed as an instrument of modernization and resistance to foreign encroachment.

The new government set about the task of having its subjects learn and apply the knowledge and techniques which the Occidental countries had been accumulating during the centuries of Japan's isolation. Foreign scholars were brought to Japan, and Japanese students were sent abroad in large numbers. A constitution, modeled largely after that of imperial Germany, was promulgated, the forms of representative government were instituted, and the legal system was remodeled to bring it into greater conformance with Occidental practices. On the economic side the government used its financial power, largely derived from oppressive land taxes, to foster industry in a variety of ways. Railroads, telegraph lines, and a modern merchant marine were constructed, and banks and other financial institutions were developed. Light industry was stimulated as a means of providing exports, and basic heavy industries were gradually developed. Wherever private interests could not achieve the desired economic development unaided, the government provided subsidies to private companies, or else built plants and operated them until they could be acquired by private concerns.

So spectacular were the results achieved that in forty years Japan had become the first Oriental nation in modern times to attain the status of a world power. The Japanese have often been spoken of in a derogatory fashion as mere imitators, but this seems unjust. It is obvious that rapid and excellent imitation was called for in the situation that confronted Japan, and the

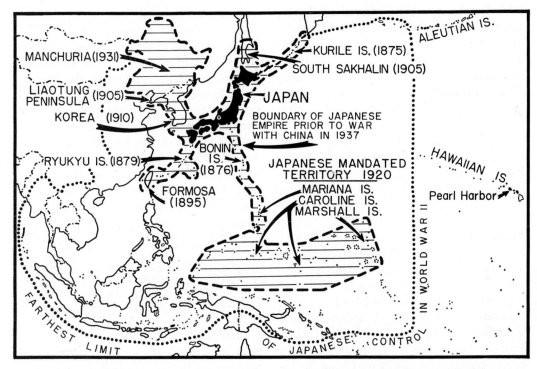

Map showing overseas areas held by Japan prior to 1937 and the line of maximum Japanese advance in World War II.

scope and success of that imitation represents a major accomplishment achieved in the face of great difficulties imposed by cultural inertia and the country's poverty in natural resources.

▶ The Japanese Empire

In the political sphere, Japan soon abandoned the stay-at-home policy of the Tokugawa period, and presently emerged as an imperial power. Between the early 1870's and World War II the country pursued, with only brief interruptions, a consistently expansionist policy, and by 1941 Japan controlled one of the world's most imposing empires. The major components of the Japanese Empire, in the order of their acquisition, were as follows:

1. The Kurile Islands. Acquired from Russia in exchange for Japanese abandonment of claims on Sakhalin, 1875.

2. The Bonin Islands. Annexed without opposition, 1876.

3. The Ryukyu Islands. These had had a semi-independent status under the overlordship of both Japan and China. They were occupied, despite local and Chinese protests, in 1879, and Japan was confirmed in ownership by China in 1895. The Ryukyus, together with the Bonins and the Kuriles, were incorporated into Japan as part of the homeland.

4. Formosa. Acquired from China in the Sino-Japanese War of 1894–1895.

5. Korea, the Liaotung Peninsula, and southern Sakhalin. Acquired as a result of victory over Russia in the Russo-Japanese War, 1904–1905. With Russian influence and pressure checkmated, Korea became a Japanese protectorate, though it was not formally annexed to the Japanese Empire until 1910. China remained the nominal sovereign over the Liaotung Peninsula, but Russia had forced China to lease Port Arthur and near-by territory to Russia, giving that country actual control, in 1898.

This leasehold was transferred to Japan. With Russia no longer able to intercede, Japan was able to extort from China numerous economic and political privileges throughout southern Manchuria, placing that area definitely within a Japanese "sphere of interest," though leaving China still the legal sovereign.

6. The Caroline Islands, Marshall Islands, and Mariana Islands. These Pacific island groups were former German possessions, except for the island of Guam in the Marianas, an American possession since 1898. When World War I broke out in Europe, Japan joined the Allied side and seized the German holdings in the Orient and the Pacific north of the equator. The peace settlements after the war confirmed Japanese occupancy of the islands under a mandate of the League of Nations. While the other major powers were embroiled in Europe, Japan was able, in addition, to exert pressure successfully on China for increased economic privileges, especially in Manchuria, Inner Mongolia, and northern China proper. Although Japan had occupied former German-controlled territory in China on the Shantung Peninsula, she was induced by Chinese and international pressure to evacuate that area in 1922.

7. Manchuria. Conquered in the course of hostilities with China lasting from 1931 to 1933. Manchuria became the Japanese protectorate of "Manchukuo." At the same time further Japanese privileges were extorted in Inner Mongolia and northern China proper.

8. Most of northern, central, and coastal China proper. These areas were overrun in 1937 and 1938. The war with China which Japan precipitated in 1937 contin-

ued, however, until 1945 without additional significant Japanese gains. Instead, Japan found it difficult to control the territory already conquered due to steadily increasing guerilla warfare by the Chinese.

9. French Indochina. Occupied without resistance during 1940 and 1941, after the conquest of France by Germany.

10. The empire was brought to its greatest extent by a series of rapid conquests between December 1941, and the summer of 1942, after the Japanese had entered World War II by attacking the Hawaiian Islands. These conquests included Guam and Wake Islands, the Philippines, Hong Kong, Thailand, Burma, Malaya, Singapore, the East Indies, much of New Guinea, the Admiralty, Bismarck, Solomon, and Gilbert Islands, and part of the Aleutian chain.

After 1942 Japan was generally in retreat, and 1945 found her shorn of the overseas territories acquired during nearly 70 years of successful imperialism. The motives of Japanese expansionism were mixed, including a tradition of national superiority and "manifest destiny," the desire of military officers to aggrandize themselves and gain complete control of the Japanese government, and a desire on the part of various elements in Japan to gain assured markets for Japanese goods and assured sources of materials. Though the methods of gaining them may have been illegitimate, the desire for materials and markets was solidly based on need. The postwar world, as well as Japan itself, is faced with the very real problem of how Japan is to exist if, shorn of empire, the nation cannot gain access by peaceful processes to the prerequisites for its economic life.

The Japanese Homeland

Postwar Japan is a nation of some 86.7 million people (1953 official estimate) occupying four main islands and numerous smaller islands with an aggregate area of approximately 142,300 square miles. The Japanese homeland is briefly described in

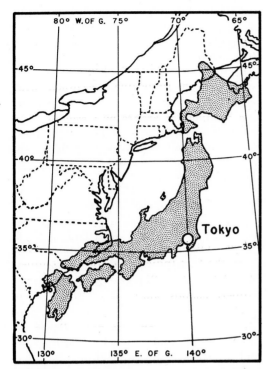

80° W.OF G. 75°   70°   65°
45°   45°
40°   40°
                          Tokyo
35°   35°
30°   30°
130°   135° E. OF G.   140°

Japan compared with eastern United States in latitude and area. (*After a map by E. O. Reischauer.*)

the Army Service Forces Manual: [1]

The homeland of Japan proper consists of four large volcanic islands—Honshu, Hokkaido, Shikoku, and Kyushu—and several hundred smaller islands in the same arc-shaped chain.

. . . Honshu, the largest island, has an area a little less than the combined areas of New York and Pennsylvania but with more than double their population. Hokkaido, lying in about the same latitude as Maine, has approximately the same area and [five] times the population. Shikoku, in the general latitude of South Carolina, has less than one-fourth the area but double the population. Kyushu, between the same parallels as Georgia, has one-fourth the area and [more than three] times the population. . . .

► Climate and Basic Natural Resources

The climatic conditions in Japan proper are not altogether comparable to those of points in corresponding latitudes in the eastern United States. On the whole, the winters are colder in Japan and the annual precipitation is heavier. This may be accounted for partly by the presence of a cold current which extends farther south in winter than in summer on both sides of the Japanese islands, and by their position in the path of the monsoon winds. Within the islands, differences in latitude produce marked climatic differences, and the great variation in altitude produces much local diversity irrespective of latitude. Along the southern and southwestern shores the climate is humid and subtropical; the winters are mild and the summers uncomfortably hot and oppressive. North of Tokyo the winters grow progressively colder. . . . Seasonal variations are particularly marked in the north and in the interior basins.

Nature was not generous to the Japanese. In a country where [2 out of 5] people engage in agriculture, nearly five-sixths of the land is too rugged for cultivation. The Japanese have been able partially to supply themselves with rice and other cereals, but only by the most intensive use of the arable soils. Forests cover [more than] half the land surface but do not supply all the kinds of wood needed. The many varieties of fish in the adjacent seas furnish a large part of the protein food consumed in Japan, as well as a valuable export.

. . . The hydroelectric energy generated from the mountain streams of Japan compensates only in part for the lack of petroleum and the poor quality of the coal. The raw materials for heavy industry are far from abundant. [Half or more of the country's requirements of nearly all the metals, including iron, must be imported.] The cotton textile and rubber manufacturing industries are wholly dependent on

---

[1] *Geographical Foundations of National Power* (Army Service Forces Manual M 103–2). Washington: Government Printing Office, 1944. Pp. 125–131. Six headings have been omitted and two headings slightly altered. Population figures and com-

parisons quoted in original source have been brought up to date. One editorial note has been added. The spelling of "Kwanto Plain" has been altered to read "Kanto Plain." Some changes in italicizing have been made.

foreign sources of raw cotton and raw rubber. . . .

► Contrasts Between North and South

The contrast between areas north and south of the 37th parallel is in part due to differences in climate and in part to the earlier settlement of the south. Southern Japan was settled early in the Christian era. There, particularly around the shores of the Inland Sea, the features considered typical of the Japanese landscape are found: a dense population living in lightly-constructed dwellings, tiny farms, with fields of paddy rice on the bottomlands, small terraced fields on the hill slopes, and tea gardens and mulberry groves on the uplands. The settlement of the north began much later and proceeded gradually, in spite of the pressure of population and the scarcity of arable land in the south. The expansion of manufacturing after 1868 has been much more significant in the south, and the concentration of population in the lowlands there has been greatly augmented.

► Highlands and Lowlands

About three-quarters of the area of Japan proper is composed of hill land or mountains of which the slopes are usually too steep and the soils too thin for normal cultivation. Scores of volcanic cones in various stages of activity provide some of the highest elevations. The mountain streams are short, swift, shallow, and generally unnavigable. They are chiefly important as sources of hydroelectric power and irrigation water for the populous lowlands.

The typical Japanese plain is an isolated area of alluvial soil deposited by rivers in mountain basins or by rivers and waves in coastal indentations. There is no continuous lowland belt along the shores of the islands. Because of shallowness and divided channels, the lowland streams are of little use for navigation, but their elevated beds make gravity irrigation simple. . . .

The marginal lowlands at the heads of bays or other openings upon the sea contain most of the arable land, most of the population, and the centers of trade, industry, and political and cultural life. Those of the north are less fully developed than those of the south.

► The Core Area of Japan

The core area of Japan proper is an irregular zone about 800 miles long, extending westward from the Kanto Plain through Nagoya to Osaka and thence along both shores of the Inland Sea to northwestern Kyushu.

The *Kanto (Tokyo) Plain* has an importance in the national life comparable in many ways to that of the English lowland and the Paris Basin, although it is of much more recent occupation. Tokyo [6,278,000 according to the 1950 census; Greater Tokyo was estimated at 7,300,000 in 1953] is the third largest city in the world and the national . . . capital. The Kanto Plain on which it stands is the largest lowland in Japan (2500 square miles). . . . On the Plain there are more than 80 cities and towns with populations exceeding 10,000. Tokyo and Yokohama, both on tidewater, together comprise the second industrial center of Japan and the commercial center not only for the plain itself, but for all of northern Japan.[2] The regions to the north and west are tapped by a network of railroads. . . .

South of the Kanto Plain the *Sun-en Coastal Strip* runs along the Pacific shore. This lowland, composed of rather small, isolated deltas separated by spurs of rocky

---

[2] *Editorial Note.* Yokohama (951,000; this and all subsequent figures for Japanese city populations are according to the 1950 census) was developed originally as a deep-water port for Tokyo, which was handicapped by a shallow harbor. However, the harbor of Tokyo itself has now been improved to accommodate most deep-sea vessels. The two cities together form a diversified industrial center. Lighter industries predominate, but there is a considerable amount of heavy industry. Much of the latter was developed during or immediately prior to World War II.

A winter scene in the mountains of western Honshu near the Sea of Japan. The buildings in the picture are those of a hot-spring resort. (*Japan Travel Bureau.*)

hills, has been for several centuries a thoroughfare between Kyoto and Tokyo. It is traversed by the famous old Tokaido highway and the modern railroad. The mild winters and heavy precipitation in summer have favored the cultivation of mandarin oranges and tea. Half of the Japanese tea crop is grown there and is refined, blended, and packed in the castle town of Shizuoka [239,000].

The *Nobi (Nagoya) Plain* which lies at the head of Ise Bay, 160 miles west of Tokyo, is second only to the Kanto Plain in area. Although third in importance as an industrial center, it has a higher population density than the Kanto Plain. The harbor of Nagoya [1,031,000] is shallow and silted, and the city, unlike Tokyo and Osaka, lacks a connecting deep-water port.

Farther west, the *Kinki District* at the eastern end of the Inland Sea has the longest record of compact human habitation and contains the earliest capitals. The district is the primary industrial area of the nation today and the site of three of the largest cities—Osaka, Kyoto, and Kobe.

Osaka [1,956,000; Osaka-Kobe metropolitan area 4,425,000] is 230 miles west of Tokyo on the bayhead delta of the broad, diked Yodo River and its numerous tributaries. Like Tokyo, the city has a network of canals and a shallow, silted harbor. Many of its modern Occidental buildings are supported on piles or metal drums. Its facilities for water transportation have contributed to the industrial pre-eminence of modern Osaka. So, too, have its excellent rail facilities, its level expanse of plain, and its large labor supply.

Kobe [765,000] is on deep water, 16 miles down the bay from Osaka. Like Yokohama, its rival deep-water port, Kobe was brought into existence by the demands of the modern commercial and industrial era. It has become a relatively important manufacturing center, specializing in metal industry, especially shipbuilding. . . . The coastal strip on which it is built is too narrow to allow much industrialized settlement, however.

Inland Kyoto [1,102,000], the capital from 794 to 1869, has been little changed by the Industrial Revolution. Large factories are forbidden by law. The city retains much of its ancient splendor, making it a center in peacetime for millions of pilgrims and tourists. The handicrafts of the feudal period—the making of lacquer, porcelain, bamboo articles, cloisonné, bronze, and silk textiles—survive as cottage and workshop industries.

Along the deeply indented shores of the *Inland Sea* there are innumerable alluvial lowlands and river deltas. The Sea is, in its way, as historic and beautiful as the Mediterranean. Settlements crowd the diminutive plains and adjacent hill slopes. The density of population and the scarcity of arable land have led to the artificial terracing of the hillsides, sometimes to elevations of several hundred feet. . . . The toil of generations of a single family is recorded in the stones or terraces inclosing a bare half acre of good loam. . . .

The Sea varies from 20 to 40 miles in width. . . . Hundreds of small intercoastal and interisland boats [carry] on a thriving local trade, and the entire length of 230 miles [is] traversed by trans-Pacific steamers and coastwise freighters plying between the coal fields of northern Kyushu and the factories of the eastern cities.

The *Northern Kyushu Coastal Strip,* . . . extending . . . west from Moji [125,000] on the Strait of Shimonoseki, holds the greatest concentration of heavy industry in Japan. Most of the coal is supplied by the Kyushu mines. Other raw materials—some coking coal . . . , iron ore, pig iron, steel scrap, petroleum, etc.—are brought in by sea. Coal from the Kyushu fields and steel for fabrication are sent out by the Inland Sea route to the Osaka and Nagoya industrial areas and even to Tokyo.

Japan's Population and Economy

Although a little smaller in area than the state of California, postwar Japan is the world's fifth most populous country. A population aggregating more than half that of the entire United States must be supported in a nation whose total acreage of cultivated land amounts to only a little more than 23,000 square miles—approximately the area of the state of West Virginia. No other important country approaches the over-all Japanese figure of approximately 3740 people to be supported per cultivated square mile. Furthermore, the Japanese population is currently increasing at a rate of approximately a million a year, and may reach a total of 100 millions by 1970. Although land reclamation on a considerable scale appears possible, the best lands of Japan are already fully occupied, and there seems no real prospect of counterbalancing the rise in population simply through bringing additional land into cultivation. Japan must already import about a quarter of its total food requirements as measured in calories, and could not feed even its present population from home production except at the barest starvation levels.

A century and a half ago Japan, already a crowded land, had a population now estimated at around 30 million. However, increases in the population were kept in check by disease and starvation and by the almost universal practices of abortion and infanticide. A rapid growth of population after 1868 was made possible by industrialization which provided exports of manufactured goods with which to purchase imported food. Today, however, with its overseas empire gone and stiff competition in world markets to be expected from other industrial nations, Japan's prospects for trade seem more uncertain than formerly, and the nation must look increasingly to other measures, including all possible increases in agricultural production and artificial limitation of births, in order to cope with its mounting problems of population support.

▶ Agriculture and Fisheries [3]

Even for Japan to supply three quarters of its current caloric needs from domestic production has required an intensive agriculture giving some of the world's highest yields, together with associated development of the world's largest fishing industry. More than nine tenths of all cultivated land is devoted to food crops. Irrigated rice is the basic crop nearly everywhere, including most parts of the northern island of Hokkaido. Wherever conditions of climate, water, and soil will permit—which includes the greater part of the irrigated acreage south of 38°N.—double cropping, or the planting of a second crop on the same field following the rice harvest, is practiced. In limited areas of the south where the growing season is unusually long, irrigated rice is grown as the second crop. However, in most areas rice is followed by winter wheat or winter barley, and in some cases by vegetables or white potatoes. Only an estimated 54 percent of the total cultivated area of Japan is irrigated. Crops grown in nonirrigated fields include a variety of grains: barley, wheat, millet, buckwheat, oats in Hokkaido, and some nonirrigated rice south of 38°N. Potatoes stand next to the grains in acreage and production: white potatoes in northern Honshu and

[3] Text material under this heading is principally based on Edward A. Ackerman, *Japan's Natural Resources and Their Relation to Japan's Economic Future* (Chicago: University of Chicago Press, 1953), especially pp. 55–78. This excellent reference work is provided with a great number of valuable maps, graphs, and tables, as well as 287 photographs portraying characteristic landscapes, natural resources, economic activities, and other aspects of Japanese life.

A Japanese peasant harvests a rice crop near Tokyo. (*Foreign Agricultural Service, U. S. Department of Agriculture.*)

Hokkaido, and sweet potatoes in southern Honshu, Kyushu, and Shikoku. Various kinds of beans and most of the common vegetables are also important dry-field crops. Double cropping is practiced on nonirrigated as well as irrigated fields wherever possible. Intertillage—the growing of two or more crops simultaneously in alternate rows—is common. Most Japanese farms have at least a few fruit trees. Persimmons, pears, and apples are the most common fruits, although mandarin oranges are widely grown along the Pacific and the Inland Sea south of about 37°N. Specialty crops grown in certain areas include mulberry trees, used for feeding silkworms, and in addition such crops as tea, sugar cane, tobacco, peanuts, flax, hemp, pyrethrum, and peppermint. Sugar beets are raised in Hokkaido, and along the Inland Sea are grown the reeds used for making mats which provide the universal floor covering in homes throughout Japan. On the whole, the variety of Japanese agricultural production belies the customary pic-

ture of Japan as almost exclusively a rice-growing country. Nevertheless, rice is a basic component of every Japanese meal, and provides nearly three fifths of the total calories in the Japanese diet.

Probably no nation surpasses Japan in over-all intensiveness of agricultural development. Farms average only 2 acres in size, except in Hokkaido with its harsher climate, where the average rises to 11 acres. In order to feed his family the Japanese farmer must utilize every means of extracting the highest possible yields from the scanty acreage at his disposal. The prevailing conditions are pictured in the following selection from an important book on Japan by Edwin O. Reischauer: [4]

Japanese methods of agriculture, involving as they do an immense amount of arduous hand labor, seem primitive and inefficient to most Americans. With our simple faith in machinery we often feel that mechanization of agriculture in Japan would not only save labor but would also increase production. Unfortunately, saving

[4] Reprinted by permission of the publishers from Edwin Oldfather Reischauer, *The United States and Japan.* Cambridge, Mass.: Harvard University Press, Copyright, 1950, by The President and Fellows of Harvard College. Pp. 58–59.

labor in a densely populated land like Japan means nothing unless the labor saved can be profitably employed in other tasks, and the concept that production can be increased by mechanizing farming is a complete fallacy as far as Japan is concerned. Tractors are used to a slight extent in the island of Hokkaido, but they are of little use in the narrow hillside terraces and tiny paddy fields that make up so much of Japan's farm land. And even on the broader stretches of flat fields, mechanization of the sort common in this country would on the whole decrease the yield rather than increase it. Machines have not been invented which till the soil as effectively as the great Japanese hoe with its two-foot blade. Nor have machines been invented which can equal the skill and loving care of the individual farm wife transplanting rice seedlings by hand. It would be as practical to mechanize the growing of flowers around an average suburban home in this country as to mechanize a Japanese farm. . . . with the prolific farmer and his family lavishing as much work . . . on each square yard . . . as an American family would on its prize flower bed. . . .

Actually, Japanese farming stands at a high level of achievement, given the special relationship of man to land existing in Japan. The tools and techniques used, while recklessly extravagant of manpower, make the most of every cultivable scrap of land, which is as it must be wherever men are overabundant and land is scarce. Machines are used on a small scale for certain farm tasks but only where they do not reduce the yield. With government aid, better seeds have been developed and are utilized widely. Most important of all, fertilizer, which is essential to make Japan's infertile and overworked soil produce, is used lavishly and when available in close to maximum quantities, considering the cost of fertilizers, which has in recent years risen to about 20 per cent of the total cost of agricultural production in Japan. While chemical fertilizers and soybean cakes from Manchuria were commonly used before

the war, the most universally available and therefore most widely used fertilizer in Japan . . . still is night soil. In the tight Japanese economy nothing can be wasted. As the cities grow, they require more food, but at least they produce in return more night soil with which to grow more crops and incidentally to impart that unfortunate olfactory atmosphere to Japan's farm lands which contrasts so sharply with their pleasant visual impression.

More than nine tenths of the total calories in the Japanese diet are supplied by starchy foods, including rice, other grains, and potatoes. Livestock products are of very minor importance, although dairying has been developed to some degree in Hokkaido. Fish are the principal source of protein and along with rice are an important element in most Japanese meals. A variety of valuable food fish are present in the waters surrounding Japan, and Japanese fishermen range widely throughout the North Pacific Ocean. The annual fish catch considerably exceeds that of any other nation in both tonnage and value.

▶ Outstanding Importance of Forestry and Wood Products

The varied local environments of Japan support a wide range of valuable tree species, including broadleaf evergreens in southern Japan, a mixture of broadleaf deciduous and conifers in central and northern Honshu and southern Hokkaido, and conifers in northern Hokkaido and at higher elevations farther south. About three fifths of the entire country is forested, and the Japanese, short of mineral resources, make use of wood in almost endless ways. The largest single use of wood is for fuel, accounting for about two thirds of all the wood consumed in Japan. The significance of forestry and wood industries has been described by Reischauer: [5]

Next to men and the power resources of coal and water, wood is probably Japan's

[5] Reprinted by permission of the publishers from Reischauer, op. cit., pp. 74–77.

greatest natural resource. With over half the land devoted to forest, Japan is among the more heavily forested of the civilized countries of the world and unquestionably the most heavily forested of the populous lands. Her poverty in agricultural land has meant a larger proportion of terrain preserved from the farmer's hoe. The country is rugged, but little of it is too high for forest growth, and relatively warm temperatures throughout most of the forest lands plus ample rainfall everywhere mean excellent growing conditions.

But the ratio of men to forest land in narrow Japan, while not so disastrous as the ratio of men to agricultural land, is precarious. The per capita acreage of forest land is only about one-fifth that of the United States. With timber lands so limited and with so little else to treasure, the Japanese have been forced to tend their forests with a care undreamed of in a land like ours, which has been more bountifully provided by nature. Up until the outbreak of war with China, attempts were made to cut no more than the annual growth, and reforestation over the years had gradually expanded the forest area. In the three southern islands, artificially planted forests account for about one-fifth of the total, making curious patterns of symmetrical rows of conifers, like some great corn field, in the mountain fastnesses of Japan. Careful cutting and planting practices have spread over the hills a patchwork pattern of different types and sizes of timber, resembling the patchwork patterns of agricultural land. The ratio of men to land in Japan has left man's imprint even on her wild mountains and rugged hills.

Japan is almost as dependent on a maximum yield from her forest lands as from her farms. While far richer in wood than are many of the lands of Asia and Europe, she depends upon her wood supply for greater and more vital services than does any other nation. The chief of these is for building material. . . . Despite tile, thatch, or tin roofs, mat floors, paper and glass sliding partitions, and walls made in part of mud plastered on bamboo lattice, wood forms the framework and bulk of the building materials in every house. The frequency of serious earthquakes throughout the land makes the utilization of stone or brick for houses somewhat hazardous. Lightly built wooden houses will sway safely with the motion of the tremor, where more rigid walls of stone or brick crack and fall. . . .

As an industrialized nation, Japan needs huge quantities of wood for railroad ties, telegraph poles, and mine timbers. The petty handicraft uses of wood and bamboo, which must be classed with it as a forest product, are numberless. Short of other materials, the Japanese use wood and bamboo for a thousand things for which we can afford to employ more costly materials. Japanese buckets may not be oaken but they are still made of wood. Simple wooden chopsticks take the place of our more complicated cutlery. Bamboo, an unbelievably versatile material, turns up in hundreds of surprising and ingenious uses. Japan also depends on wood, normally converted into charcoal, for what little heating her houses have and for cooking fuel whenever city gas supplies, made from coal, are not available. The Japanese, by holding their hands and wrists over charcoal braziers or by placing their feet in or close to specially designed heating devices, derive a considerable amount of . . . cheer from a tiny spot of heat in an otherwise frigid house. . . .

And over and above these direct uses of forest products is the growing demand for wood pulp. The Japanese have had a famous paper industry for about a thousand years and have developed some ingenious uses for paper. Pasted on sliding partitions and screens, it is an important architectural material. Long ago the Japanese, who suffer a great deal from winter colds, developed the sanitary use of fine paper tissues in place of the handkerchief. As a nation of voracious readers today, they absorb huge quantities of paper for books, magazines, and newspapers and would use far more if they could get it. As a great producer of paper as well as rayon, Japan's capacity for pulp consumption is almost unlimited.

▶ Manufacturing Industries and Industrial Resources

Silk manufacturing based on domestic silk was the first Japanese industry to be adapted to large-scale mechanized production during the period of industrialization following 1868. Japanese silk found a ready market in Europe and the United States, and the revenues from silk exports helped greatly in providing the necessary capital for industrial development in general. Mechanized production of cotton textiles based on imported cotton was also introduced very early, and large quantities of cheap cotton goods were soon being marketed among the peasant populations of eastern and southern Asia. Textile production is still of major importance in the industrial structure of Japan, although Japanese industry has shifted increasingly to the manufacture of metalwares in the twentieth century. The new emphasis has been achieved in spite of a striking poverty of mineral resources. Aside from ordinary grades of building stone, sand, and clay, the only major minerals present in reasonably adequate quantities are coal, copper, chromite, manganese, zinc, gold, silver, sulfur, gypsum, and magnesium. About three fourths of the total iron ore requirements are customarily met by imports. Fortunately, the power requirements of the country can be met from either domestic coal or hydroelectricity, although Japan has only a little petroleum and natural gas. Japanese coal, mainly found in Kyushu and Hokkaido, is mostly low-grade bituminous. Although difficult to mine because of thin and broken seams, the annual production is sufficient for most Japanese needs. High-grade metallurgical coals, however, must be imported. The remaining reserves of coal in Japan are sufficient for only a century or two at present rates of consumption. They are supplemented by hydroelectricity produced at hundreds of small generating stations along the many short but torrential rivers of Japan. Among the world's countries, Japan is exceeded only by the United States and Canada in developed hydroelectric capacity.

Besides a reasonably adequate base of domestic power resources, Japanese industry benefits from a large reserve of cheap labor supplied by an overpopulated countryside. The farmers of Japan also provided an early basis for industry in another respect, for much of the original government-sponsored industrialization was financed by revenues from land taxes. Such taxes were often oppressively high, and were an important factor in an increasing rate of farm tenancy and indebtedness after 1868.

The national pattern is one of small industrial establishments employing 5 to 10 workers or less. Larger factories employing hundreds of workers are most common in the Osaka industrial area.

The nature, significance, and future prospects of Japanese industrial development have been summarized as follows by Reischauer: [6]

Japan's industrial progress . . . has been no steady, inevitable growth, based solidly on obvious economic advantages, as in the case of America's rise to industrial leadership. It has been more like the erratic progress of a broken-field runner, fighting his way against great odds by a quick getaway, brilliant improvisations, and daring reversals of the field. Utilizing to the fullest her one advantage over the West of cheap manpower and her one advantage over Asia of greater industrial skills, she has threaded her precarious way toward industrialization between the far greater industrial potential of the West and the still cheaper labor of the rest of Asia. With her industry-swollen population, there can be no turning back. She cannot even stand still, for her less industrialized neighbors are always threatening to catch up with

---

[6] Reprinted by permission of the publishers from Reischauer, *op. cit.,* pp. 80–81.

her and wipe out the technical advantages on which her people now live. . . .

Japanese industry, which has only men and power to support it, will inevitably be forced more and more into the fields in which materials count least and labor and skills count most. Japan must go increasingly into the fields in which her cheaper labor costs give her an advantage over the West while the greater skills of her workers give her the edge over the rest of Asia. This means less emphasis on textiles and a growing emphasis on industrial art products, precision instruments, fine machinery, shipbuilding and ship repairing, and the like, which require a high ratio of skilled labor to materials. But even with the most careful rationalization of her industrial potential, the future of Japanese industry is certainly precarious. Even with determined efforts to maintain technical leadership over the rest of Asia on one side, balanced on the other by a willingness to accept a far lower standard of living than the industrialized peoples of the West, the Japanese have ahead of them . . . a very uncertain future.

But, whatever may be the ultimate fate of Japanese industry, it has already laid a heavy imprint on Japan and the Japanese. It has made Japan into a land of huge cities and sprawling factories, of whirring machines and crowded commuters' trains.

Korea

A discussion of Japan's former colony, Korea, is included in the present chapter for convenience and also on the basis of certain instructive comparisons which the two countries afford. In racial characteristics, language, and culture the Koreans are distinct from the Japanese, and certainly no bonds of sentiment exist between the two peoples. There is much evidence that the majority of Koreans disliked and resented Japanese rule, and a number of armed uprisings occurred during the period of Japanese occupation.

▶ Liabilities of Korea's Geographical Position

Korea is a country with an unfortunate geographical position. This relatively small country is surrounded by larger and more powerful neighbors that have frequently been at odds with each other and with the Koreans. Korea adjoins China along a land frontier which follows the Yalu and Tumen Rivers. It faces Japan across the Korea and Tsushima Straits, which have a combined width of only 120 miles. In the extreme northeast Korea borders the Soviet Union for a short distance.

For many centuries the Korean Peninsula has served as a bridge between Japan and the Asian mainland. From an early time both Japan and China have been interested in controlling this bridge, and since Korea has generally been weaker than either, its history has generally been that of a subject or vassal state. Although the Japanese have held or exercised considerable influence in parts of Korea since at least the early centuries of the Christian era, the influence of China was generally uppermost until the latter nineteenth century. At this time Chinese power waned, Japanese power increased with modernization, and Russia began to make itself strongly felt in eastern Asia. Korea became an object of contention among these powers. Japan emerged victorious in the struggles that followed, ousting the Chinese from Korea, as well as from certain other areas, in the Sino-Japanese War of 1894–1895, and ousting Russia from Korea and southern Manchuria in the Russo-Japanese War of 1904–1905. From 1905 until 1945 Korea was firmly under Japanese control, being formally annexed to the Japanese Empire in 1910.

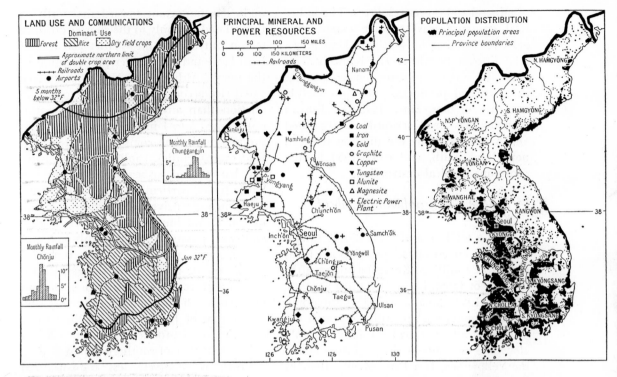

Maps showing major geographical features of Korea. (From Focus, by courtesy of the American Geographical Society of New York.)

Japan lost Korea along with the rest of its empire when it surrendered to the Allies, ending World War II, in 1945. In accordance with prearranged agreements Russian forces occupied Korea north of the 38th parallel of north latitude and American forces south of that line. Although it had been understood that Korea was to become a unified and independent country, no agreement could be reached between the occupying powers as to the establishment of a Korean government. Accordingly, separate governments were set up in north and south Korea under the aegis of the respective occupying powers: in the south, the Republic of South Korea, under the auspices of the United Nations; and in the north the Democratic People's Republic of Korea, which became a Communist satellite. The occupying powers withdrew the bulk of their forces in 1948 and 1949.

In 1950 North Korea attacked South Ko-

rea in force, and United Nations units, mainly American, entered the peninsula to repel the aggression. In the latter part of that year, when the North Koreans had been driven back from the southern part of the peninsula almost to the Manchurian border, Communist China entered the war and drove the United Nations forces south of the 38th parallel. Then the Chinese and North Koreans were in turn driven back slightly north of the parallel, where a stalemate developed which lasted until an armistice was arranged in the summer of 1953.

Few lands have ever been more devastated than Korea after several years of warfare covering the length and breadth of the peninsula. The tragedy is all the greater in that Korea is not a poor land by nature. During their period of control the Japanese developed transportation, agriculture, and industry, the latter from a sizable base of mineral and power resources. The industrial structure was to some extent integrated with that of southern Manchuria. The Korean people received few benefits from these developments, however, since the increased production was put mainly to Japanese uses. Since 1945 the Korean economy has been seriously disorganized and handicapped by the division between north and south, and since 1950 by the enormous physical destruction.

▶ A Brief Geographical Sketch of Korea

With a total area of some 85,000 square miles and an estimated population (1953) of 28 to 29 million, Korea has three fifths the area of Japan but only a third as many people. Like Japan, Korea is predominantly mountainous or hilly, although the proportion of level lowland, found mainly along the west side of the peninsula facing the Yellow Sea, is a little greater than in Japan. On the east or Sea of Japan side of Korea, mountains rise steeply from a very narrow coastal plain. The highest elevations are found in the northeast, adjoining Manchuria, where a few summits rise to around 8000 feet or slightly higher.

The long axis of the Korean Peninsula is oriented north-south, and thus Korea, like Japan, exhibits a climatic contrast between a continental north with severe winters and a relatively short growing season, and a subtropical south with milder winters and a longer frost-free season. However, because of its closer proximity to the continental mass of Asia, southern Korea has somewhat colder winters and a shorter growing season than southern Japan. Nevertheless, the climate of South Korean lowlands permits double cropping, with the main crops being irrigated rice, grown in the summer, and barley, planted in the fall on the drained rice fields or other dry fields. The climate in most parts of North Korea is too severe for winter grains, and the growing of irrigated rice becomes increas-

ingly less important toward the north—a fact related not only to the shorter growing season but also to the smaller acreages of level land and the smaller precipitation of the north. Although in North Korea irrigated rice accounts for a greater total production than any other single crop, it is outweighed 5 to 1 in acreage and 4 to 3 in production by the combined total of dry-field grains (millet, kaoliang, wheat, corn, and barley) and soybeans. Vegetables and hardy fruits, particularly apples and pears, are grown extensively throughout the peninsula. Other important crops are cotton and sweet potatoes, grown mainly in South Korea, and white potatoes, restricted mainly to the north. Thus the general situation with regard to distribution of crops between north and south is somewhat similar to that of Japan, although the variety of agricultural production in South Korea is less than that of southern Japan.

Korea is relatively less industrialized than Japan, and an estimated three quarters of the people gain a livelihood directly from the soil. The proportion of cultivated land is a little greater than in Japan, but nevertheless amounts to only a fifth of the total area of the country. Farming methods are less advanced, less fertilizer is used, and the average yields are significantly lower than in Japan, although much improvement in these respects was experienced during the period of Japanese rule. With its more favorable climate and larger proportion of level lowland, South Korea supports more than twice the population of North Korea on a considerably smaller total area. Estimated areas and populations in 1953 were: South Korea, 37,000 square miles, population 19,400,000; North Korea, 48,000 square miles, population 9,000,000.

Although South Korea produces nearly two thirds of the total estimated volume of crops, North Korea is the more important industrially. Most of the iron and steel, chemicals, hydroelectric power, and forest manufactures of Korea are produced in the north. Industry in South Korea is confined largely to cotton textiles and processed foods. The greater industrialization of North Korea is related to its larger endowment of industrial resources, including high-grade coal, much of it anthracite, substantial reserves of iron ore, most of the country's hydroelectric power potential, and the most valuable forests of Korea, principally coniferous species growing on the higher lands adjoining Manchuria. The principal mineral resource of South Korea is coal, although the quality is generally poorer and the reserves smaller than in North Korea.

The war-shattered South Korean capital of Seoul is the largest city of Korea. Its population was estimated at 712,000 in July 1953, as contrasted with 1,640,000 in 1949. Other important cities of South Korea include the seaport and temporary wartime capital of Pusan (474,000 in 1949) on the Korea Strait, the inland textile manufacturing and agricultural market center of Taegu (314,000 in 1949), and the port of Inchon (266,000 in 1949), located on the Yellow Sea 20 miles west of Seoul. Pyongyang (500,000 in 1949) is the capital, largest city, and most important industrial center of North Korea.

The resources and production of prewar north and south Korea were complementary to a high degree, and the division of the country at the 38th parallel has posed difficult problems of economic readjustment for both areas. Insistent future demands for reunification may be anticipated, and not altogether on economic grounds, for the Koreans, north and south of the parallel, are one people sharing a common culture and common historical traditions and they have exhibited strong feelings of nationalism on many occasions in the past.

PART 6
The Pacific World

The Pacific Islands

The Pacific World is mostly water. The Pacific itself, the largest of the oceans, is bigger than all the continents and islands of the world put together. Nevertheless, it has been a relative backwater of world commerce. Major shipping lanes reach in only around the margins, and the products afforded by the multitudinous islands and the sparsely populated island continent of Australia are not very great in total volume.

Prior to World War II the Western world had built up a legend about the Pacific and its islands as a kind of utopia. At an early time some of the islands did have an idyllic and very appealing quality to visitors from Europe and America. How-

ever, on many islands the native peoples were reduced in numbers and their cultures disrupted by a long period of unrestrained exploitation on the part of traders, whaling crews, labor agents ("blackbirders"), and other outsiders before the outside governments claiming jurisdiction began to impose tardy measures of regulation. On many islands, also, whatever idyllic quality remained was shattered by the military actions of World War II.

As here conceived, the term "Pacific World" is generally restricted to Australia, New Zealand, and the islands of the mid-Pacific lying mostly between the Tropics. The Pacific islands bordering the mainland of the Orient, the Soviet Union, and the

---

A coral atoll in the southwest Pacific. Note the lagoon beyond the large island in the center foreground. The coral reefs bordering the atoll are outlined by the white water. (*Australian News and Information Bureau.*)

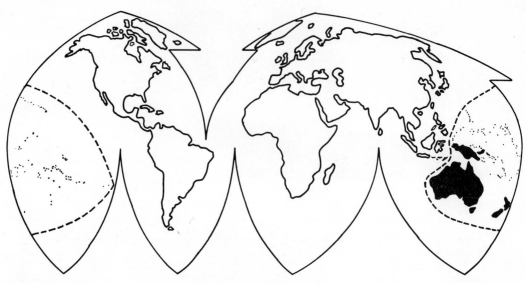

World location of the Pacific World. (*Boggs Equal Area Projection, copyright A. J. Nystrom & Co.*)

Americas are excluded on the basis of their close ties with the adjoining continents, while large areas of the eastern and northern Pacific which contain few islands and are seldom visited can largely be discounted. Australia and New Zealand are sufficiently different from the tropical island realms to the north to be possibly considered a separate world region, but are included in the Pacific World on the basis of their strong political and economic interest in the tropical islands, the ethnic affiliations of their original inhabitants with the peoples of those islands, and their insular character. Even on continental Australia most of the population lives in two clusters, in the southeast and southwest, which are islandlike in that they are connected with each other and with the outside world mainly by sea.

Melanesia, Micronesia, Polynesia

The Pacific islands are commonly divided, mainly on an ethnic basis, into three principal realms: Melanesia, Micronesia, and Polynesia. The islands of *Melanesia* (Greek: "black islands"), bordering Australia, are relatively large. New Guinea, the largest, is about 1500 miles long and 400 miles across at the broadest point. In general, these islands are extremely hot, damp, and disease-ridden and are overgrown with dense rain forest and jungle. From the standpoint of climate and health few places in the world are less attractive than certain parts of Melanesia, although in exposed locations near the sea somewhat more favorable conditions may be found, particularly in the Fiji Islands and New Caledonia. *Micronesia* (Greek: "tiny islands") includes hundreds of small islands scattered about in the central and western Pacific north of the equator. Prior to World War II Micronesia was held by Japan under a mandate from the League of Nations, except for the Gilbert Islands, which were a British possession, and Guam, a United States possession. Since the war the former Japanese islands have become the Pacific Islands Trust Territory, administered by the United States. *Polynesia* (Greek: "many islands") occupies a greater expanse

TABLE 18

SUMMARY OF MAIN PACIFIC ISLAND GROUPS

ISLAND REALMS	MAIN ISLAND GROUPS	WELL-KNOWN INDIVIDUAL ISLANDS OR ATOLLS	CONTROLLING POWERS
Melanesia		New Guinea	Australia, Netherlands
	Bismarck Archipelago	New Britain	Australia
		New Ireland	
	Solomon Islands	Guadalcanal	Britain, Australia
		Bougainville	
	New Hebrides Islands	Espiritu Santo	British-French Condominium
	Fiji Islands	Viti Levu	Britain
		Vanua Levu	
	Loyalty Islands		France
		New Caledonia	France
Micronesia	Caroline Islands	Kusaie	United States
		Ponape	
		(Palau, Truk, Yap are noteworthy island groups)	
	Mariana Islands	Guam	United States
		Saipan	
	Marshall Islands	Bikini	United States
		Eniwetok	
	Gilbert Islands	Tarawa	Britain
Polynesia	Hawaiian Islands	Oahu	United States
		Hawaii	
		Maui	
	Ellice Islands		Britain
	Tonga Islands		Britain
	Samoa Islands		New Zealand, United States
	Marquesas Islands		France
	Tuamotu Archipelago		France
	Society Islands	Tahiti	France
	Cook Islands		New Zealand

of ocean than either Melanesia or Micronesia. It is shaped like a rough triangle with the corners at New Zealand, the Hawaiian Islands, and remote Easter Island.

Each of the three island realms contains a number of distinct island groups. The major island groups, together with some of the more noteworthy individual islands in the groups, and the nations exercising political control, are indicated in Table 18.

The Native Peoples

It is commonly accepted among anthropologists that the original inhabitants reached the Pacific World from the mainland of Asia, the first migrants arriving in Melanesia and Australia thousands of years ago.[1] Four successive racial stocks are distinguished among the migrants into the islands: (1) Negritos, a short, dark, and

[1] There is some evidence that the early inhabitants of Polynesia may have migrated there from the Americas. A spectacular attempt to lend credence to this theory was the voyage of the raft *Kon-Tiki*, navigated by Thor Heyerdahl and five companions from Peru to the Tuamotu Islands in 1947. An account of this journey was published by Thor Heyerdahl in *Kon-Tiki: Across the Pacific by Raft* (Chicago: Rand McNally and Co., 1950).

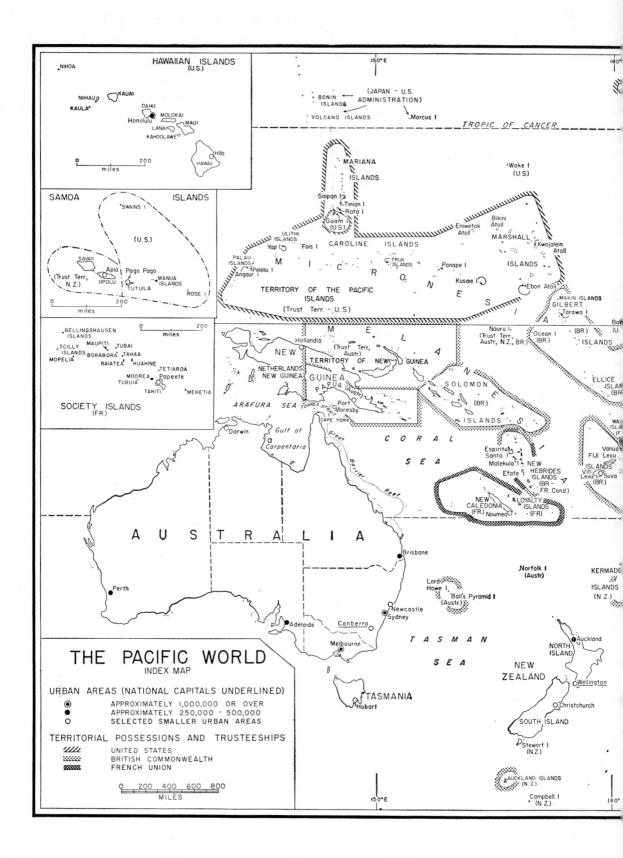

HAWAIIAN ISLANDS
(U.S.)

NIHOA
KAUAI
NIIHAU
KAULA
OAHU
Honolulu
MOLOKAI
LANAI
MAUI
KAHOOLAWE
Hilo
HAWAII

200
miles

SAMOA   ISLANDS
SWAINS I.
(U.S.)
SAVAII
Apia   Pago Pago
(Trust Terr., N.Z.)   UPOLU   MANUA
TUTUILA   ISLANDS
ROSE I.
200
miles

BELLINGSHAUSEN ISLANDS
MAUPITI   TUBAI
SCILLY ISLANDS   BORABORA   TAHAA
MOPELIA   RAIATEA   HUAHINE
TETIAROA
MOOREA   Papeete
TUBUIA   TAHITI
MEHETIA
200
miles

SOCIETY ISLANDS
(FR.)

150° E   180°

(JAPAN - U.S. ADMINISTRATION)
BONIN ISLANDS
VOLCANO ISLANDS   Marcus I.
TROPIC OF CANCER

MARIANA
ISLANDS
Wake I.
(U.S.)
Saipan I.
Tinian I.
Rota I.
Guam (U.S.)
Eniwetok Atoll
Bikini Atoll
MARSHALL
Kwajalein Atoll
ULITHI ISLANDS
Yap I.   Fais I.   CAROLINE   ISLANDS
PALAU ISLANDS   M   I   C   R   TRUK ISLANDS   Ponape I.   ISLANDS
Peleliu I.   Angaur I.   O   Kusaie I.   Ebon Atoll
TERRITORY OF THE PACIFIC ISLANDS   N   MAKIN ISLANDS
(Trust Terr. - U.S.)   E   GILBERT   Tarawa I.
S   I   A
M   E   L   Nauru I.   Ba
Hollandia   (Trust Terr., Austr., N.Z., BR.)   Ocean I.   (BR.)   (U.
(BR.)   ISLANDS
NEW   (Trust Terr., Austr.)   A
NETHERLANDS   TERRITORY OF NEW   GUINEA   N   ELLICE ISLAN
NEW GUINEA   GUINEA   E   (BR.
PAPUA (Austr.)   SOLOMON   S
ARAFURA SEA   Port   (BR.)   I   WA
TORRES STRAIT   Moresby   ISLANDS   ISLA
CAPE YORK   C   O   R   A   L   (F
Darwin   Gulf of   Espiritu   Vanua
Carpentaria   S   E   A   Santo   FIJI Levu
Malekula I.   NEW   Viti ISLANDS
Efate   HEBRIDES   Levu   Suva
ISLANDS   (BR.)
(BR. - FR. Cond.)
Great   NEW   LOYALTY
CALEDONIA   ISLANDS
(FR.)   Noumea   (FR.)
Barrier
A   U   S   T   R   A   L   I   A
Reef
Brisbane
Norfolk I.   KERMADE
(Austr)   ISLANDS
Perth   Lord   (N.Z.)
Howe I.
Ball's Pyramid I.
(Austr.)
Adelaide   Canberra   Newcastle   Auckland
Sydney   NORTH
Melbourne   T   A   S   M   A   N   ISLAND
NEW   Wellington
B   S   E   A   ZEALAND
TASMANIA   Christchurch
Hobart   SOUTH ISLAND
Stewart I.
(N.Z.)

THE   PACIFIC   WORLD
INDEX MAP

URBAN AREAS (NATIONAL CAPITALS UNDERLINED)
⊙   APPROXIMATELY 1,000,000 OR OVER
●   APPROXIMATELY 250,000 - 500,000
○   SELECTED SMALLER URBAN AREAS

TERRITORIAL POSSESSIONS AND TRUSTEESHIPS
////   UNITED STATES
:::::   BRITISH COMMONWEALTH
▓▓▓   FRENCH UNION

0   200   400   600   800
MILES

AUCKLAND ISLANDS
(N.Z.)
150° E   Campbell I.   180°
(N.Z.)

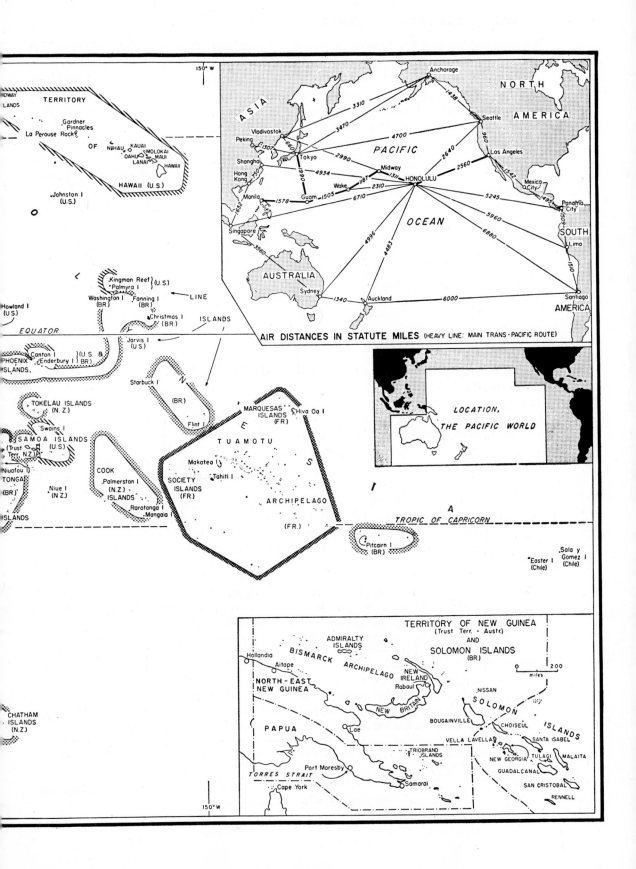

TERRITORY

Gardner
Pinnacles
La Perouse Rock
OF
NIIHAU KAUAI
OAHU MOLOKAI
LANAI MAUI
HAWAII

HAWAII (U.S.)

Johnston I
(U.S.)

O

MIDWAY
ISLANDS

ASIA

Anchorage
3310 1438
3470
Vladivostok 4700 Seattle
Peking
1307 5660 2640 990 AMERICA
PACIFIC
Shanghai Tokyo 2990
4934 Midway 2560 Los Angeles
Hong 750 1311 1542
Kong 1060 1187 HONOLULU Mexico
Manila Wake City
1578 Guam 1505 2310 5245 1435
652 6710 Panama
Singapore OCEAN 5960 City
3560 4996 6880
4483 SOUTH
Lima
150
AUSTRALIA
Sydney 1340 Auckland 6000 Santiago
AMERICA

AIR DISTANCES IN STATUTE MILES (HEAVY LINE: MAIN TRANS-PACIFIC ROUTE)

NORTH

AMERICA

LOCATION,
THE PACIFIC WORLD

Kingman Reef } (U.S.)
Palmyra I
Washington I Fanning I
(BR) (BR)
Howland I Christmas I
(U.S) (BR.)
EQUATOR LINE ISLANDS

Jarvis I
(US)
Canton I } (U.S. &
Enderbury I BR)
PHOENIX
ISLANDS

Starbuck I N

TOKELAU ISLANDS (BR.)
(N. Z.) Flint I E
Swains I MARQUESAS
SAMOA ISLANDS ISLANDS Hiva Oa I
(Trust (U.S.) (FR)
Terr. N.Z.) TUAMOTU S
Niuafou I COOK Makatea
TONGA Palmerston I Tahiti I
(BR) Niue I (N.Z.) SOCIETY
ISLANDS (N.Z.) ISLANDS ARCHIPELAGO
Rarotonga I (FR.)
Mangaia I
ISLANDS (FR.) TROPIC OF CAPRICORN A

Pitcairn I Sala y
(BR) Gomez I
Easter I (Chile)
(Chile)

CHATHAM
ISLANDS
(N.Z.)

TERRITORY OF NEW GUINEA
(Trust Terr. - Austr.)
AND
ADMIRALTY SOLOMON ISLANDS
ISLANDS (BR.)
Hollandia BISMARCK ARCHIPELAGO 0 200
Aitape NEW miles
NORTH-EAST IRELAND
NEW GUINEA Rabaul NISSAN
NEW BRITAIN SOLOMON
BOUGAINVILLE CHOISEUL ISLANDS
PAPUA Lae VELLA LAVELLA SANTA ISABEL
TRIOBRAND NEW GEORGIA TULAGI MALAITA
ISLANDS GUADALCANAL
Port Moresby SAN CRISTOBAL
TORRES STRAIT Samarai RENNELL
Cape York

150° W

frizzy-haired people; (2) Ainoids, a generally Caucasoid people, although excessively hairy, with lighter skins than the Negritos, and wavy hair: (3) Veddoids, dark-skinned and wavy-haired; (4) Indonesians,[2] a people of mixed Caucasoid and Mongoloid stock with light brown skin, black wavy hair, and medium to short stature. The Indonesian peoples, possibly intermixing with earlier immigrants, settled Micronesia and probably Polynesia, as well as mixing with other peoples in the more complex amalgam of Melanesia.

Over a long period the Micronesians and Polynesians became relatively distinct from each other and relatively homogeneous throughout their separate spheres. The people of each area came to speak dialects of a single basic language and to share many features of a common culture. In Melanesia, on the other hand, complex and varied mixing of successive migrant groups has led to an extremely confused racial and cultural pattern. Racially the Negroid element is generally dominant, though often diluted by other elements. A variety of languages and dialects are found, and anthropologists have distinguished literally hundreds of fairly distinct cultures. Some of the tribes, especially in the remote interiors of the larger islands, are extremely primitive.

Types of Islands

The almost countless islands scattered across the Pacific vary widely in size, type, and utility. Three main categories of islands are now recognized according to origin: coral islands, formed of the skeletons and living bodies of small marine organisms; volcanic islands, formed by submarine eruptions; and continental islands. These major categories, grouped into further subclasses, have been described as follows by an American anthropologist, Douglas L. Oliver, in an outstanding book on the Pacific islands: [3]

From man's point of view, physical setting consists of several elements: the form of the land and the nature of the soil, the quality of the climate, the types and dispositions of plants, and the presence of animal life. In Oceania these components are variously combined to produce seven major types of islands, differentiated according to the limits they imposed upon the islanders and their primitive technologies:

1. *Treeless Atolls or Coral Islands* (typical examples are Canton, Johnston, and Howland Islands). Grass and herbs provide survival food for castaways and small parties of fishermen, but the lack of good soil and drinking water renders these land specks unsuitable for permanent native settlements. Sea birds and fish abound and, if drinking water were present, human life could be sustained indefinitely on these islands; but for the most part the vegetation-loving Oceanic natives have avoided them. On the other hand, the very conditions which discouraged native settlers and made these islands bird refuges resulted in the deposit of valuable guano fertilizer and produced ready-made runways for twentieth-century aircraft.

2. *Dry-forest Atolls or Coral Islands* (typical are most of the Marshall and Ellice Islands, and many of the Tuamotus and northern Cooks). Strand flora, together with some arable soil and fresh water, make these islands habitable for limited numbers of people; rich marine resources

---

[2] This anthropological term should not be confused with the same term now used in a political sense to refer to citizens of the new country of Indonesia.

[3] Reprinted by permission of the publishers from Douglas L. Oliver, *The Pacific Islands.* Cambridge, Mass.: Harvard University Press, Copyright, 1951, by The President and Fellows of Harvard College. Pp. 12–14. Italicized portions numbered and capitalized in editing.

Some of the wilder aspects of Melanesia are portrayed in this view from Papua, the southeastern quarter of the large island of New Guinea. Note the luxuriant, tangled growth of the tropical rain forest rising above the long thatched hut occupied by members of an entire village. (*Australian News and Information Bureau.*)

supplement the scanty vegetable and fruit diets. However, overpopulation is a constant threat, and crowded native communities have sought solutions in mass emigration and in infanticide. Yet despite the paucity of resources on these islands, some communities have developed intricate and aesthetically pleasing arts and crafts, utilizing every material at their disposal. They have, moreover, appeared to compensate for the limitations imposed upon their economies by evolving exceedingly complex institutional relations.

3. *Luxuriant, Moist Atolls or Coral Islands* (typical examples are the Gilbert and Tokelau Islands, Swains Island, Fanning, Ebon, Ulithi, and Nissan). These are the lush and beautiful "tropical isles" of romantic novel and motion picture. They have sufficient soil to support cultivation of taro

and bananas, in addition to the coconut palms and breadfruit grown also on the dry islands.

4. *Raised-coral Islands* (typical examples are Makatea, Niue, Ocean, Nauru, Angaur, Peleliu, and Fais). These islands were formed out of successive elevations of old coral reef and are composed of limestone covered by thin layers of soil which support low and dense stands of dry-land flora (medium-sized trees, small trees, shrubs, vines, ferns, and so forth). Rough pitted limestone surfaces and tangled growth make these islands difficult to cross. Fresh water in the form of springs and streams is usually lacking, and cave pools or rain-catchment basins provide drinking water. Coconuts and other food plants grow fairly well in the scattered pockets of soil, but frequent droughts are a menace to

native agriculture. Since many of these islands contain rich phosphate deposits, they have assumed an economic value far surpassing that of any other kind of island of comparable size.

5. *Unweathered Volcanic Islands* (typical examples are the northern Marianas and Niuafoo). Because the weathering of these islands has not progressed far, there is considerably less soil on them, and hence less vegetation, than on the "older" weathered volcanic islands. Most forest growth is limited to the valleys and the ridges are covered with grasses and smaller plants. Native populations can and do thrive in moderate numbers on these islands; usually the little soil present is rich and supports luxuriant growths of coconuts and other food plants.

6. *Weathered Volcanic Islands* (typical examples are the Hawaiian, Society, and Samoan Islands). These islands, some of them rising thousands of feet above sea level, contain many kinds of environment: wide strands, brackish and fresh water swamps, gentle and steep slopes, extensive lava fields, and so forth. They are subjected to great variation in rainfall. Plant life is extremely varied. Nearly every kind of growing thing or growing condition needed by man to develop complex technologies is to be found. Minerals alone are lacking.

Certain "mixed" islands, including Guam, Saipan, Rota, and Mangaia, possess characteristics of both weathered volcanic and raised-coral settings.

7. *"Continental" Islands:* New Guinea, Viti Levu, New Caledonia, Espiritu Santo, Guadalcanal, Bougainville, New Britain, New Ireland, and most other large islands in the Melanesian archipelagoes. These islands are formed of continental rocks complicated by volcanic intrusions and possess even wider varieties in environment and plant life than the volcanic islands. Their richer, mineral-bearing soils support nearly every kind of vegetation. Their high mountains, dense forests, and broad swamps have encouraged the existence of numerous isolated native communities, favoring the development of cultural and even racial diversity.

▶ *"High" and "Low" Islands*

A somewhat simpler distinction is commonly made between the "high" and "low" islands of the Pacific. Some of the characteristics of these two types of islands are elaborated in the following selection by an American geographer, Otis W. Freeman: [4]

In the Pacific one of the most distinctive things, that is constantly emphasized by residents and visitors, is the difference between "high" and "low" islands. The "high" islands, mostly of volcanic origin, abound in food as compared with the "low" islands of coral origin. The mountainous islands are large in proportion to the land area of coral atolls, have a variety of trees, plenty of water, fertile soil, and can support considerable populations. The low islands have few plants except the coconut palm, little or no drinking water, scanty soil, and each coral isle can support few inhabitants. . . .

The major seaports of the mid-Pacific are located on the larger islands. No city of real size and importance is built on a coral atoll, although such localities may serve as first class air and sea bases. Only Honolulu [235,000] and three cities in New Zealand exceed 100,000 in population. Hilo [27,000] on Hawaii, Noumea [20,000] in New Caledonia, Suva [25,000] on Fiji, Papeete [12,000] on Tahiti, and Apia [15,000] on Samoa are smaller cities of importance as seaports and commercial centers. The high islands in the trade winds are generally healthful and a considerable tourist trade exists in Hawaii and to a less extent in Fiji and Tahiti. Health conditions in the wet tropical islands of the Solomons and New Hebrides are not so favorable, malaria and many other diseases being prevalent. . . .

On the volcanic islands large sugar plantations have been developed by the Americans on Hawaii, the British at Fiji, and the Japanese on Saipan in the Marianas. . . . In none of these islands were the natives

---

[4] Otis W. Freeman, "The Pacific Island World." *Journal of Geography,* v. 44 (1945), pp. 22–28. Used by permission of the author and the *Journal of Geography.* City populations added in editing.

numerous enough or willing to work on the plantations so that outside labor had to be imported. In Hawaii Chinese and Portuguese were first used but today Japanese and Filipinos do the work. In Fiji, Indians, mostly of the Hindu faith, were brought in and now number almost as many as the native Fijians. At Saipan the Japanese brought in their own people. The natives . . . produce little for sale from the land—most of their farming is of a sustenance nature.

On the high islands the natives originally lived in villages rather than on individual farms, and the custom is still generally followed. Each valley commonly supported a village which by preference was located on the beach or as close to the sea as the topography permitted. . . .

As mentioned, a variety of food could be produced on the high islands. . . . Pigs furnished most of the meat to supplement the starchy foods, fruit and fish. The seedless breadfruit, plantain, taro, yam, and sweet potato were the chief native sources of starch. These have now been supplemented by arrowroot, cassava, and improved varieties of bananas. Sugar cane, coffee, papaya, mango, lime, orange, lemon, shaddock, and ginger are among the useful plants introduced by Europeans. Cattle and goats are found on the larger islands where grasslands exist. . . .

• Coral Atolls

The "low" islands are made of coral and usually have an irregular ring shape around a lagoon. Such an island is called an atoll.

Fishing is a basic means of livelihood throughout the Pacific islands. This view shows native fishermen in the Triobrand Islands, east of New Guinea, arriving at a beach where part of their catch will be bartered for yams (center foreground) raised by inland villagers. Note the characteristic outrigger canoes. (*Australian News and Information Bureau.*)

Generally the coral ring is broken into many pieces, separated by channels leading into the lagoon, but the whole circular group is commonly considered one island, although quite often individual names are given to the larger islets. . . . The coral atolls are wholly within the tropics as the reef-forming organisms can only survive in warm waters.

Two leading theories have been advanced to account for the coral atolls. That of Charles Darwin has three stages: (1) the coral builds a fringing reef around a volcanic island, (2) the island slowly sinks and the coral reef is built upward and forms a barrier reef separated by a lagoon from the shore, (3) the volcanic island has sunk out of sight and a lagoon occupies the former land area whose outline is reflected in the roughly oval form of the atoll. . . . Another theory is that of Sir James Murray who would have the coral forming a reef on the outer limits of a shallow submarine platform. Likely most such platforms would result from erosion of a volcanic island, so would have the approximately oval shape of a volcanic peak.

No matter how they may have been formed, the geographer finds that the atolls have similar characteristics wherever they occur, although in size they vary. Many are only a few miles in diameter, while a few huge affairs up to 50 to 100 miles across occur. . . . Some coral islands lack the central lagoon, which has either been filled to become land or the island itself has been elevated enough for the feature to disappear. . . .

. . . The greatest concentration of atolls is in the Tuamotu Archipelago (also called the Paumotu, Low, and Dangerous Archipelago). The atolls of the Marshalls are arranged in two parallel chains, an eastern and a western. The Gilberts, Ellice, and Tonga Islands are atolls, as are the Union (Tokelau), Cook, and Phoenix groups. In addition there are many isolated low isles of coral. . . . Frequently the atolls follow an arcuate course and rise at intervals from a submarine platform or uplift, likely a zone of volcanic activity. . . . While the barrier reefs of the atolls protect ships in

the lagoons from currents and waves, they are themselves a great danger to navigation, especially as charts of Polynesia and Micronesia are often incomplete and inaccurate. . . . Occasionally some atoll is completely overwhelmed by a hurricane and the giant waves associated with it that may wash entirely over the low land and destroy most of the palms and inhabitants. . . .

The soil of the low islands is broken from the coral by the waves and winds. It is thin and poor, and few plants except coconuts can grow on it or withstand the infiltration of the salt sea into the ground water supply. On the more barren islands, coconuts, the rather poor fruit of the pandanus, and fish are the only available foods. Sometimes the natives by much labor construct a garden of artificially fertile soil. Within a stone wall or pit . . . all available plant waste and other refuse is collected to supply needed humus to the sterile coral sand. . . .

Copra is the only export from most coral islands. Chinese traders are the usual collectors of the commodity and in most villages the store is run by a Chinese who may be married to a native woman. The copra is usually shipped to large centers on sloops, luggers, or other sailing vessels. . . .

Pearls and pearl shell are quite frequently obtained from the lagoons of atolls in the Tuamotus and other groups. Tortoise shell is sometimes available. Dried sea slugs, called trepang or beche du mer, are sometimes prepared for export to China where they are eaten.

The most significant animal life on the low islands consists of birds. . . . Birds have sometimes been slaughtered for their feathers, and both eggs and birds are eaten, although they have a fishy flavor. However, the most valuable product of the birds is guano and indirectly phosphate rock. On the low islands in the trade winds, rain is too scanty to wash away the bird droppings and other refuse which accumulate and change to the brownish guano that is a valuable fertilizer because it is high in nitrogen and phosphorus. On some islands, notably Nauru and Ocean, just south of the equator, the phosphorus from the guano has interacted chemically with the coral limestone to form phosphate rock. This is quarried and exported to the temperate zone to use on depleted soils. Nauru and Ocean Islands, together with Christmas Island, 2000 miles to the east, supply one-tenth of the world's output of phosphate rock.

Relations with the West

Europeans began to visit the Pacific islands early in the Age of Discovery. Spanish and Portuguese voyagers were followed by Dutch, English, French and, later, American and German. Many famous names are connected with Pacific exploration, including those of Magellan, Tasman, Bougainville, La Perouse, and Cook. By the end of the eighteenth century virtually all of the important islands were known.

For a long period the European governments exercised only nominal control over the islands, and the natives were subjected to the unrestrained abuses of whaling crews, sandalwood traders, indentured labor contractors ("blackbirders"), and other adventurers. On island after island European penetration presented the dismal spectacle of decimation of the natives and disruption of their cultures. The intruders introduced new diseases, alcohol, opium, forced labor, and firearms which greatly increased the slaughter in tribal wars. Although the introduction of better tools and medicines, as well as the work of missionaries and the belated attempts of the imperial governments to give the natives a "new deal" must be entered on the other side, the balance sheet for four and a half centuries of Western influence in the Pacific islands does not reflect much credit on the outsiders.

In recent times Western personnel and capital have been attracted to the islands by mining and plantation agriculture. Although in general the islands are notably deficient in mineral resources, there are some exceptions. The phosphate resources have already been described. In addition, gold has been found in the Solomons, the Fijis, and, especially, in New Guinea. The French island of New Caledonia is particularly outstanding in mineral reserves and exploitation, with deposits of nickel, chrome, cobalt, iron ore, and other minerals.

A "Coconut Civilization"

Most tropical plantation crops have been attempted in the islands at one time or another, with varying degrees of success. However, two crops—sugar and coconuts—have gained much greater importance than any others. Of the two, sugar leads in value of production, but coconuts are by far the more widespread and fundamentally important in the lives of the people. The growing of coconuts and the trade in copra provide a common denominator for a large part of the island world, which has been said with considerable justice to have a "coconut civilization." The latter is described in the following selection by Douglas L. Oliver: [5]

South Seas sugar statistics are far more impressive in tonnage and in value than those of the South Seas coconut, but sugar's influence is limited to Hawaii, Fiji, and pre-war Saipan-Tinian, and only whites and immigrant Asiatics benefit directly from it.

[5] Reprinted by permission of the publishers from Oliver, op. cit., pp. 135–136.

The influence of the coconut, however, stretches from Truk to Tonga and from Hiva Oa to Hollandia, and directly or indirectly affects the life of nearly every islander in this vast area. . . .

Coconuts require year-round warm temperature, a well-drained soil, and plenty of moisture and sunlight; they grow best of all in low altitudes near the coast. The palm grows out of the mature, fallen nut, and requires from eight to ten years to reach the bearing stage. After that it lives for nearly 80 years and bears nuts at the rate of about 50 a year for 60 or 70 years.

The mature nut consists of a hollow kernel of oily white meat, one-half inch thick, encased in a hard woody shell. Around this is a fibrous husk one-half to two inches thick. The cavity of the unripe nut is filled with a thin "milk," a nutritious and refreshing beverage with a tangy taste. As the nut matures, this "milk" is absorbed into the coconut meat, which when dried and removed from the shell becomes the copra of commerce.

Throughout Oceania the coconut leads a double life. In one way it is a source of food, shelter, and income which helps support native life nearly everywhere. In another way, however, it has been the instrument by which white men have done most to change native life.

To islanders the milk of the unripe coconut is a prized beverage, the only one, in fact, on many islands lacking potable water or rain catchments. The meat is scraped from the shell and eaten either by itself or mixed into puddings of taro and yams and sago. Or, the oil is squeezed from the meat and used as a food, an unguent, or a cosmetic. The hollowed shell becomes a flask, the clean-scraped shell a cup or a spoon or a material for carved ornaments. Cord is manufactured from the fibrous husk; furniture, utensils, and building timbers from the tough trunk. Leaves are used to thatch huts or weave baskets; and even the pith of the palm is eaten when for some drastic reason the palm is felled. On islands nearer to Asia's influence, the sugar-rich sap is drawn off by tapping the flower bud and is allowed to ferment into inebriating toddy. To deprive an islander of his coconut palms is to take away much of the basis of his living. Even the white man's world would be a much poorer place without them.

From the copra of commerce oil is expressed to produce margarine, cooking and salad oils, fine soap, and cosmetics. Copra cake, the residue after most oil has been expressed, is an important stock food rich in protein. Coir mats and rugs are manufactured from the fibrous husks, and coconut-shell charcoal is the best vapor absorbent known, especially valuable for absorbing industrial odors, for recovering gasoline and benzol from the air, and for use in gas masks. In the manufacture of soap, coconut oil plays a unique role; it hardens well, and its highly soluble acids possess exceptional lathering qualities, even in salt water. It has consequently become a favorite for toilet and salt water soaps and for soap chips. And, in addition to all these, consider how empty life would be without coconut pie!

But most of these good things are end products, processed in factories thousands of miles from the islands. With the exception of a few tons of coconuts used in the local manufacture of desiccated coconut and some locally used cooking oils, most palm products leaving the islands do so in the form of copra.

Copra is merely coconut meat removed from the shell and dried sufficiently for shipping. To obtain it, mature nuts may be picked from the palm or they may be collected after they have fallen. Then the whole coconut is split in half and the meat either immediately cut out of the shell or allowed to dry a bit before removal. Excess moisture must then be removed from the meat by some method of drying, and the resulting copra bagged in hundred-pound sacks for overseas shipment.

▶ Organization of the Copra Industry

In 1951 the Pacific islands, exclusive of the Philippines and Indonesia, accounted for some 8.8 percent of the total world production of copra, as compared with 38.9

Loading bags of copra and drums of coconut oil for export at the wharves in Suva, the capital and principal port of the Fiji Islands. (*British Information Services.*)

percent for the Philippine Islands, 18.7 percent for Indonesia, and 9.2 percent for Ceylon. Despite the relatively minor role of Oceania on a world basis, however, copra is of the utmost local importance throughout the islands, customarily being the leading industry in employment, value of product, and general effect on the lives of the islanders. The organization of the industry varies a great deal from one island or island group to another, but in general three principal types of production can be distinguished: by natives, by small planters, and by large corporations.

1. *Native production* is of some importance in the copra industry of every island group and is the dominant form of production in many groups. Natives gather the nuts, prepare the copra, and sell it to middlemen for marketing. The middleman is generally the local storekeeper and is usually either a Chinese or a white man. He in turn disposes of the copra to larger firms for overseas shipment. A peculiar aspect of native production is the tendency of the natives to produce less when the price is high, since they have not yet developed acquisitive habits, but instead are concerned only with a small but steady income.

2. *Small planter production* involves the "independent" operation of a single plantation by one of the many white men who have come into the islands for this purpose. Such a plantation will ordinarily comprise plantings amounting to several hundred acres of trees, and will employ up to a hun-

dred workers living in barracks. The workers are usually natives but are sometimes imported Asians. Often the plantation is quite isolated. The small planter type of enterprise is declining due to high production costs and hazards, coupled with widely fluctuating world prices which the planter can do nothing to control and against which he generally has little by way of a financial reserve. Planters complain of a chronic shortage of labor and its lack of efficiency, which they maintain is partly due to government regulation of working conditions, including wages. In addition, their position is made more precarious by a plenitude of diseases and insect pests capable of seriously damaging the groves and sometimes not even susceptible of control by organizations having much greater resources than those of the small planter.

3. *Production by large corporations* has been of increasing importance. British concerns are generally the most important, but those of a number of other nations are also in the field. Outstanding names are Lever Brothers, Burns Philip Company, Ltd., and W. R. Carpenter Company, Ltd. Such concerns own many separate plantations and usually operate such facilities as shipping lines, stores, and warehouses. They may, as in the case of Lever Brothers, have world-wide interests. Their financial resources apparently allow them to operate successfully in an industry becoming more and more difficult for the small planter.

Whatever the form of production, the total impact of the copra industry on the Pacific islands is summed up thus by Oliver:[6] "For better or for worse, the simple process of obtaining the meat and the oil of the coconut to spread on Western bread and bathe Western bodies has had greater influence on recent Oceanic history than any other factor."

---

[6] Reprinted by permission of the publishers from Oliver, *op. cit.*, p. 142.

Australia and New Zealand

The basic kinship of the Commonwealth of Australia and the Dominion of New Zealand, although often expressed in friendly rivalry, is widely recognized and is indicated in common usage of the term "Anzac Countries" to refer to the two collectively. This kinship is derived from similarities in population, cultural heritage, political problems and orientations, type of economy, and location.

Cultural, Political, Economic, and Locational Similarities of Australia and New Zealand

Both Australia and New Zealand are products of British colonization and are strongly British in ancestry and culture.[1]

The Australians and New Zealanders speak English, live under parliamentary forms of government, claim the British sovereign as

---

[1] Both New Zealand and Australia contain surviving minorities of pre-white native inhabitants. The primitive Negroid inhabitants of Australia were slaughtered or driven into outlying areas by the whites. Today they number about 75,000, in contrast to an estimated 300,000 at the beginning

---

Vast areas of level grazing land are found in the central lowlands of Australia. The above view of sheep grazing was taken in northwestern New South Wales. (*Australian News and Information Bureau.*)

TABLE 19

AUSTRALIAN AND NEW ZEALAND EXPORT AND IMPORT TRADE WITH THE UNITED KINGDOM AND THE UNITED STATES

	AUSTRALIA	NEW ZEALAND
Percent of Exports [a] to		
United Kingdom	39	66
United States	8	10
All Other Countries	53	24
Percent of Imports [a] from		
United Kingdom	53	60
United States	10	7
All Other Countries	37	33

[a] Percentages are based on total value, 1950.

their own, attend schools patterned after those of Britain, and attend the Anglican Church in greater numbers than any other. Both countries, like Britain, are socialistic "welfare states," with comprehensive social security standards and benefits, although in the development of this aspect of their society Australia and New Zealand actually preceded Britain and were world pioneers along with the Scandinavian countries. Both Australia and New Zealand have exceptionally high standards of living, ranking generally in a class with the United States and Canada in this regard.

Although they are fully independent nations, loyalty to Britain is an outstanding characteristic of the Anzac Countries. This loyalty is expressed in their membership in the Commonwealth of Nations and was plainly evident at the outbreak of both World Wars, which Australia and New Zealand entered immediately in support of Britain. However, since World War II, when a threatened Japanese assault on their homelands was mainly frustrated by American forces, the two countries have also sought closer relations with the United States. Close international ties with strong and friendly outside powers, especially naval powers, are extremely important to the Anzac Countries due to their small populations and remote insular locations, far distant from other Western and white nations. Australia's 8,753,000 people plus New Zealand's 2,047,000 (1953 estimates for both countries) amount to a smaller total than the population of the New York metropolitan area. In view of the latter fact, it is understandable that the two countries look with some apprehension at the awakening masses of the neighboring Asian countries to the north, whose teeming and land-hungry populations stand in striking contrast to the comparative emptiness and material abundance of Australia and New Zealand.

Australia and New Zealand are also tied closely to Britain and the United States by trade. Basic to the economies of both countries are exports of a few primary products, principally wool and wheat in the case of Australia and wool and dairy products in the case of New Zealand, coupled with extensive imports of manufactured goods. The greater part of this vital trade is with the United Kingdom and the United States, a fact brought out clearly in Table 19.

Physical and Climatic Characteristics of Australia

Australia is not only a country, but an island continent with an area, including the offshore island of Tasmania, of nearly 3 million square miles. It is exceeded in

---

of white settlement in 1788. Efforts are being made to preserve this remnant, found mainly on reservations in the tropical north, but the decline in numbers is still continuing. In New Zealand the native inhabitants were the Maori, a Polynesian people. Not so primitive as the Australian aborigines, and more warlike, their hold on the land was broken only by a bloody war between 1860 and 1870. At present the Maori, who seemed destined for extinction about 1900, are achieving something of a renaissance. Their numbers have increased from 40,-000 at the turn of the century to 120,000 today. While still something of a depressed group in New Zealand, their economic and social situation is much better than that of the apparently vanishing Australian natives.

area by only five countries: the Soviet Union, Canada, China, Brazil, and the United States. However, most of the continent is very sparsely populated, and in terms of total population Australia is a relatively small country. The sparseness of Australia's population and its concentration into a comparatively small part of the total land area are closely related to the continent's physical characteristics, among which aridity (accentuated by high temperatures and rapid evaporation) and low average elevation are outstanding. On the basis of climate and relief, Australia may be divided into four major natural regions: (1) the humid eastern highlands, (2) the tropical savannas of northern Australia, (3) the "mediterranean" lands of southwestern and southern Australia, and (4) the dry interior.

► The Humid Eastern Highlands

Australia's only major highlands extend along the east coast from Cape York to southern Tasmania in a belt 100 to 250 miles wide. Although complex in form and often rugged, these highlands seldom reach elevations of 3000 feet. Their highest summit and the highest point in Australia is Mount Kosciusko, which attains only 7328 feet. The highlands and the narrow and fragmented coastal plains at their base constitute the only part of Australia which does not experience a considerable period of drought each year. However, although onshore winds from the Pacific bring appreciable rain each month, the strong relief reduces the amount of agricultural land in this most favored of Australia's climatic areas. South of Sydney and at higher elevations to the north the climate is commonly classified as marine west coast (humid marine), despite the location. North of Sydney higher summer temperatures change the classification to humid subtropical, while still farther north, beyond approximately the parallel of 20°S., hotter temperatures and greater seasonality of rain cause essentially subhumid conditions.

► Tropical Savannas of Northern Australia

Northern Australia, from near Broome on the Indian Ocean to the coast of the Coral Sea, receives heavy rainfall during a portion of the (Southern Hemisphere) summer season, but experiences almost complete drought during the winter six months, or more, of the year. This highly seasonal distribution of rainfall is essen-

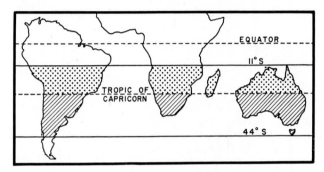

Australia compared in latitude and area with southern Africa and southern South America.

tially the result of monsoonal winds which blow onshore during the summer and offshore during the winter. The seasonality of the rainfall, combined with the tropical heat of the area, has produced a savanna vegetation of coarse grasses with scattered trees and patches of woodland. The effect of the long season of drought in reducing agricultural possibilities is compounded by the poverty of the soils and by a lack of highlands sufficient to nourish large perennial streams for irrigation. The alluvial and volcanic soils which support large populations in some tropical areas are almost completely absent in northern Australia.

► "Mediterranean" Lands of Southwestern and Southern Australia

The southwestern corner of Australia and the lands around Spencer Gulf have a mediterranean or dry-summer subtropical type of climate with subtropical temperatures, winter rain, and summer drought. In winter the Southern Hemisphere belt of

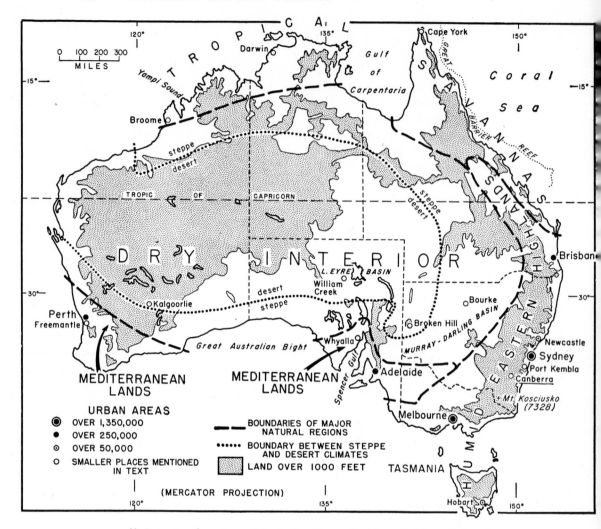

Major natural regions of Australia. The national capital is underlined.

the westerly winds shifts far enough north to affect these districts, while in summer this belt lies offshore to the south and the land is dry. Crops introduced from the mediterranean lands of Europe generally do well in these parts of Australia, but the agricultural possibilities of the Australian areas are limited by the lack of high highlands to catch moisture and supply irrigation water to the lowlands.

▶ The Dry Interior

The huge interior of Australia is desert, surrounded by a broad fringe of semi-arid grassland (steppe) which is transitional to the more humid areas around the edges of the continent. Altogether, the interior desert and steppe cover more than half of the continent, and extend to the coast in the northwest and along the Gulf of Carpentaria and the Great Australian Bight. This tremendous area of dry land is too far south to get much rain from the summer monsoon, too far north to benefit from rainfall brought by the westerlies in winter, and is shielded from Pacific winds by the eastern highlands. Here again the lack of highlands is unfortunate from a climatic point

TABLE 20

CLIMATIC DATA FOR SELECTED AUSTRALIAN STATIONS

NATURAL REGION, CLIMATE TYPE, AND STATION	LATITUDE TO NEAREST WHOLE DEGREE	ELEVATION ABOVE SEA LEVEL (FEET)	AVERAGE TEMPERATURE (DEGREES F. TO NEAREST WHOLE DEGREE)			PRECIPITATION	
			ANNUAL	JANUARY (OR WARMEST MONTH)	JULY (OR COOLEST MONTH)	ANNUAL AVERAGE TO NEAREST INCH	MONTHS AVERAGING LESS THAN ONE INCH OF PRECIPITATION
Humid Eastern Highlands							
Humid Subtropical							
Brisbane	27°S.	137	69°	77°	59°	45"	0
Marine West Coast							
Melbourne	38°S.	115	59°	68° (Feb.)	49°	26"	0
Tropical Savannas							
Darwin	12°S.	97	83°	86° (Nov.)	77°	61"	5 (May–Sept.)
Cape York	13°S.	69	79°	80°	76° (Aug.)	82"	5 (June–Oct.)
Mediterranean Areas							
Adelaide	35°S.	140	63°	74° (Jan., Feb.)	52°	21"	2 (Jan.–Feb.)
Perth	32°S.	197	64°	74° (Jan., Feb.)	55°	35"	5 (Nov.–Mar.)
Dry Interior							
Bourke	30°S.	92	69°	85°	52°	15"	2 (July–Aug.)
William Creek	29°S.	250	69°	83° (Jan., Feb.)	53°	5"	12

of view. Approximately the western half of Australia is occupied by a vast plateau of ancient crystalline rocks, but its general elevation is only from 1000 to 1600 feet and its few isolated mountain ranges are too low to materially influence the climate or supply perennial streams for irrigation. To the east, between the plateau and the eastern highlands, the land is still lower in the great central lowland which stretches across the continent between the Gulf of Carpentaria and the Great Australian Bight. The effect of elevation on the climate is shown by the fact that the lowest part of this lowland and of Australia, the Lake Eyre Basin, is the driest part of the continent. Another part of the lowland, however, the Murray-Darling Basin, contains Australia's only major river system and has the most extensive development of irrigation works on the continent.

Temperature and precipitation data for the four major natural regions of Australia are presented in Table 20 on page 419.

▶ The Small Proportion of Arable Land

One very important result of the widespread seasonal or total aridity and of the occupation of most of the only truly humid area by highlands is that Australia offers very little good agricultural land relative to its total area. Although some estimates place the proportion of potentially cultivable land as high as 15 percent of the total, the Australian government now classifies only about 2 percent of the land as arable with another 1 percent "potentially productive." In addition, 4 percent is classed as forest and woodland, while about 46 percent is classed as meadows and pastures and about 47 percent as wasteland. These figures give Australia an arable area which is only about one-fourteenth as large as the arable area of the United States, a country of comparable size, and is actually less than that of a number of countries with a small fraction of Australia's total area, such as France, Spain, Poland, and Italy.

The distribution of population in Australia generally follows that of arable land. Thus most of the country's small population is found in the humid eastern highlands and coastal plains, especially in the cooler south; in the areas of mediterranean climate; and in the more humid grasslands adjoining the southern part of the eastern highlands and the mediterranean areas.

Australia's Economy and Population

Australia is one of a few countries in the world which are highly industrialized and are at the same time important exporters of raw materials and food. There is an obvious similarity to the United States and Canada in this respect. But Australia, despite employment of a larger proportion of its labor force in industry than the United States, is predominantly an importer of manufactured products rather than an exporter like the United States. In the latter respect Australia is more like Canada, although Australia is more industrialized in proportion to the size of its population than is Canada. There are various other points of similarity between these two countries. Both are large countries with relatively small populations. In both, the population is mainly distributed around the periphery, a fact related to the large amounts of poor and undeveloped land which both possess in the interior. Both countries have a disproportionately high rank in world trade, both have close connections with Britain and with the United States, and both have high standards of living. One important difference, however, lies in the fact that Australia is able to produce a greater variety of foodstuffs than is Canada because of greater environmental variety. Canada, for example, has no tropical or subtropical climates.

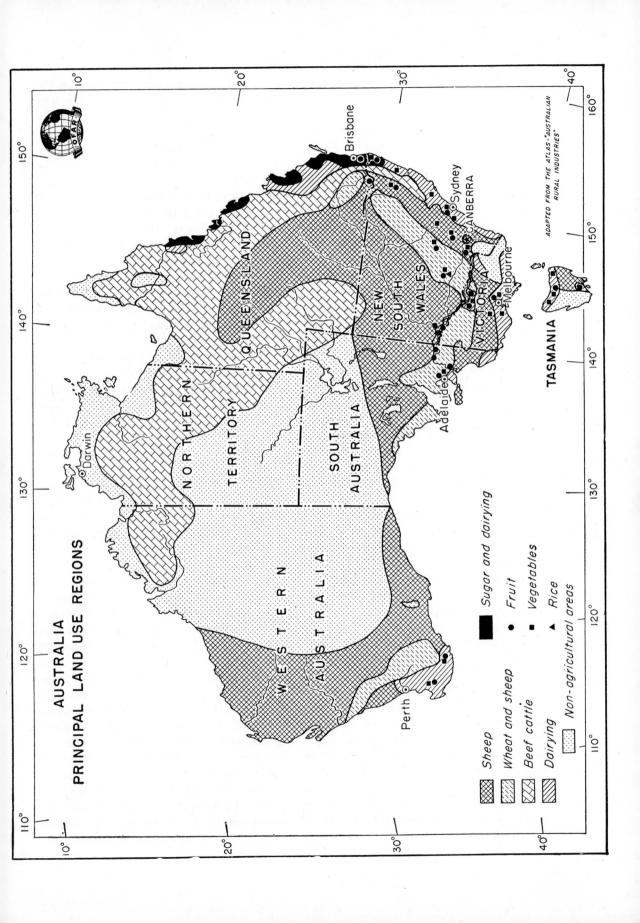

AUSTRALIA
PRINCIPAL LAND USE REGIONS

Sugar and dairying
Fruit
Vegetables
Rice
Non-agricultural areas

Sheep
Wheat and sheep
Beef cattle
Dairying

ADAPTED FROM THE ATLAS "AUSTRALIAN RURAL INDUSTRIES"

Brisbane
QUEENSLAND
Sydney
CANBERRA
NEW SOUTH WALES
Melbourne
VICTORIA
TASMANIA
Adelaide
SOUTH AUSTRALIA
NORTHERN TERRITORY
Darwin
WESTERN AUSTRALIA
Perth

► *Agriculture and the Pastoral Industries*

The sectors of the Australian economy which regularly produce a surplus for export are grazing, agriculture, and mining. Such a result seems a logical outgrowth of a situation where eight and three-quarter million people have at their command the natural resources of an entire continent, albeit a poor continent from the standpoint of agriculture. The existence of large and dependable markets for Australian primary products in Europe, the United States, and elsewhere, coupled with cheap and efficient transportation by sea to those markets, and the possession by the Australian people of the necessary technical skills and equipment to exploit the continent on an extensive basis, utilizing a minimum of labor and a maximum of land and equipment, makes the emphasis on surplus production and export of primary commodities seem even more logical. Australian agricultural and pastoral output per man is estimated to be twice that of the United States.

• *Sheep and Cattle Ranching.* Sheep ranching has always been the most important of Australia's rural industries. When the first settlement was planted at Sydney in 1788, the intention of the British government was merely to establish a penal colony, with the expectation that enough agriculture would be carried on to make the colony self-sufficient in food and perhaps provide a small surplus of some products for export. While self-sufficiency proved difficult to obtain in the early days due to the poverty of the leached soils around Sydney, it was soon discovered that sheep did well. At the time the market for wool was rapidly expanding with mechanization of the woolen textile industry in Britain. Thus, Australia found its main export staple in the early years of the nineteenth century. Sheep graziers rapidly penetrated the interior of the continent, and by 1850 Australia was already the largest supplier of wool on the world market, a position it has never lost.

Sheep raising has been tried practically everywhere in Australia that there seemed to be any hope of success. Much of the interior has been found too dry, parts of the eastern mountain belt too rugged and wet, and most of the north too hot and wet and with too coarse a forage in summer. Thus the sheep industry has become localized. It is concentrated mainly in a crescentic belt of territory which follows roughly the gentle western slope of the eastern highlands from the northern border of New South Wales to the western border of Victoria. New South Wales has over 40 percent of the Commonwealth's sheep, and Victoria between 15 and 20 percent. Beyond the main belt of concentration the sheep industry spreads on poorer pastures north almost to the Gulf of Carpentaria and west into South Australia. A minor area of production rims the west coast from about latitude 16°S. to beyond Perth, with the greatest concentration relatively near the latter city. The sheep ranches or "stations" in Australia vary in size from a few hundred to many thousands of acres. They are generally larger on the poorer pasture lands, that is, outside the main belt of production.

The main product of the Australian sheep stations is wool. The importance of wool in the country's economy is indicated by the fact that it ordinarily constitutes more than half of the total value of all Australian exports. Its importance to the world is indicated by the fact that Australian wool normally amounts to about a quarter of the total world production and over half of the total production of high-quality Merino wool. In addition, Australia has been able, since the development of refrigerated transport, to export considerable quantities of mutton and lamb.

Land in Australian which has not been found suitable for sheep or for a more intensive form of agriculture is generally devoted to cattle ranching. Such lands include particularly those of the north, with hot, humid summers and coarse forage. The main belt of cattle ranching extends in an east-west arc across the northern third of the country. The greatest concentration is in Queensland, which contains over half of the cattle, other than dairy animals, in Australia. On many of the remote ranches, especially in the Northern Territory, the labor force is composed of remnants of the black aboriginal population of Australia.

The beef cattle industry is not as important to Australia as the sheep industry. It is difficult to market first-class beef from a remote tropical area. Variability in weather, poor pasturage in the dry season, tropical insect pests and diseases, and drives of hundreds of miles to market are among the factors that retard the industry. Nevertheless, Australia supplies its own needs for beef, and exports appreciable quantities of meat as well as hides for tanning.

• *Wheat Farming.* After wool, wheat is Australia's most important export, generally supplying around 15 percent of all exports by value. As in the case of wool, wheat surpluses are largely a reflection of Australia's aridity and low density of population. In contrast to wool, however, wheat production did not begin as the result of a search for export staples. Wheat was the key crop in early attempts to make the settlement at Sydney self-sufficient. The soils along much of the coastal margin of Australia are leached and poor, though capable of much improvement through application of fertilizer. In the early years the colony almost starved as a result of wheat failures, and the problem of grain supply was not really solved until the development of the colony, now the state, of South Australia. There, fertile land and a favorable climate were found near the port settlement of Adelaide, so that wheat could be grown and shipped by sea to other coastal points.

In the decade of the 1860's, Australia passed from a deficit to a surplus position in grain production. Thereafter, wheat farming expanded rapidly. Among the factors making this expansion possible were (1) the development of the mechanical reaper and other types of machinery suited to extensive wheat farming, (2) the building of railroads inland from the ports, (3) scientific work in plant breeding and soil fertilization, (4) the enactment of legislation under which some of the large grazing estates were divided into smaller farms, and (5) an expanding European market. The main belt of wheat production spread from the eastern coastal districts of South Australia into Victoria and New South Wales, generally following the semi-arid and subhumid lands which lie inland from the crests of the eastern highlands. Thus the main wheat belt has come to occupy nearly the same position as the main belt of sheep production. In fact, the two types of production are very often combined in this area. A second, less important wheat belt has developed in the southwestern corner of the continent inland from Perth. The combined exports from these two areas have normally been sufficient to give Australia fourth rank among the world's wheat exporters, after the United States, Canada, and Argentina. It should be emphasized that Australian wheat production is an extensive and highly mechanized form of agriculture, characterized by a small labor force, large acreages, and low yields per acre, although very high yields per man.

• *Dairy Farming.* Though not as important as grazing or wheat farming for the export trade, dairying is now the leading type of agriculture in Australia in terms of employment. It has developed mainly in the humid coastal plains of Queensland, New South Wales, and Victoria. Originally oriented entirely toward the local market, it has been mainly a response to the striking urbanization of the country's coastal districts and the necessity of a relatively high

A view of Melbourne, Australia's second largest city and port. The railroad yards in the center lie between the wharves and the downtown business district of the city. (*Australian News and Information Bureau.*)

return per acre to defray the expense of clearing heavily forested land. Dairying has now become well established as the dominant type of farming in most of these coastal areas and regularly produces a small export surplus beyond the requirements of Australia itself.

• *Fruit Growing.* When Australia was settled it was found not to have any native fruits of commercial value. Consequently, the fruit-growing industry which now exists is based entirely on plants transplanted to the Australian environment. The range of climates allows production of both tropical and mid-latitude fruits, the most important items being pineapples from Queensland, bananas from New South Wales and Queensland, citrus fruits mainly from New South Wales, grapes for wine and table use produced under irrigation in the Murray Basin and near Adelaide, and apples and pears produced especially in Tasmania and Victoria. The home market is abundantly supplied with all these fruits, and there is normally a considerable export.

• *Sugar Production.* Australia is also an export sugar producer, though at a cost. Sugar production was begun on the coastal plain of Queensland in the middle of the nineteenth century to supply the Australian market. Laborers were imported from Melanesia to work in the cane fields on what often amounted practically to a slave basis. When the Commonwealth of Australia was formed in 1901 by union of the six states (New South Wales, Victoria, Queensland,

South Australia, Western Australia, Tasmania), Queensland was required to repatriate the imported "Kanaka" laborers in the interest of a "white Australia." However, since it was felt that production costs would be considerably raised by the use of exclusively white labor, the Commonwealth gave Queensland in return a high protective tariff on sugar. Operating behind this protective wall, the sugar industry has prospered in a tropical area where it was once argued that no white man could survive for very long at manual labor in the fields. Most of the original large estates have been divided into family farms worked by individual white farmers. This system of agriculture is very unusual for a commercial cane sugar area. The Queensland sugar area is also unusual in the fact that it is probably the most thoroughly tropical area yet settled by white men doing hard manual work without benefit of native labor.

▶ Urbanization and Industrialization

While grazing and agriculture produce the great bulk of Australia's exports, most Australians are city dwellers, and the high degree of urbanization is one of the country's outstanding characteristics. In December 1952 the populations of the five largest cities were estimated as follows: Sydney 1,621,000; Melbourne 1,393,000; Brisbane 445,000; Adelaide 422,000; and Perth, including its port, Freemantle, 309,000. Thus 34 percent or one out of every three Australians were in the two largest cities, and 48 percent in one of the five largest cities. When smaller cities and towns are added the Australian population may be counted as approximately 70 percent urban.

It will be noted that all of the five largest cities are seaports and that each is the capital of one of the five mainland states of the Commonwealth. One of the reasons for the striking degree of urban development and its concentration in the port cities is the heavily commercial nature of the Australian economy. A large proportion of the production from the country's rural areas is destined for export by sea. In addition, much of Australia's internal trade moves from port to port by coastal steamer. Growth of the respective capital-city ports has been further stimulated by the fact that each state originally built its own individual rail system focusing on its particular port. Since the different states used different gauges in building their rail lines, necessitating expensive break of bulk at or near state frontiers, each major port tended to effectively dominate the business of its own state. (The rail system is now being changed by substitution of a standard gauge throughout the Commonwealth.)

Among other things, the high degree of urbanization in Australia is indicative of a high degree of industrialization. A relatively small labor force is needed for the extensive forms of agriculture and grazing which are characteristic of Australia. As a means of supporting an increased population, the Australian government has encouraged industrial development. The latter has been viewed as highly desirable, not only as a means of giving Australia a population more in keeping with the size and resources of the continent, but also as a means of providing more adequate armaments for defense and of securing greater stability through a more diversified and self-contained economy.

The rise of industry was facilitated by the formation of the Commonwealth, which gave a unified internal market and tariff protection for developing industries. Industrial progress has also been facilitated by the fact that the continent was able to provide many of the natural resources needed for the development of manufacturing. Australia produces many different economic minerals in at least small quantities. The most serious deficiencies appear to be in petroleum (the first major oil strike was made in 1953), and in the fertilizer minerals of nitrate, phosphate, and potash. The deficiency in fertilizers, how-

Coal is one of Australia's most valuable natural resources. The coal mine in the photograph is located on the coast of New South Wales about 60 miles south of Sydney. (*Australian News and Information Bureau.*)

ever, is alleviated by Australia's possession of phosphate-rich Nauru Island in the Pacific as a joint Trust Territory with the United Kingdom and New Zealand.

• *The Australian Iron and Steel Industry.* Of outstanding importance among Australian minerals are the basic materials for the iron and steel industry. Both coal and iron are ample in quantity and quality. Every Australian state mines some coal, but the major known reserves are near the coast in New South Wales and Queensland. The main developed coal field outcrops on three sides of Sydney. Steel mills have been built to the north of Sydney at Newcastle (135,-000) and to the south at Port Kembla. To these mills iron ore is brought from deposits slightly inland from the port of Whyalla in South Australia. Pig iron has been produced at the latter port since 1941. New and rich deposits of ore are now in process of development on several islands in Yampi Sound. New steel capacity is projected in Western Australia using this ore and coal from that state. Not only are the necessary raw materials for the Austral-

ian steel industry relatively abundant, but they are located so near the sea that transportation costs are quite low and Australian steels are among the cheapest in the world. Aided by low-cost steel and tariff protection, an increasing variety of metal-fabricated goods is being produced in the country.

• *Production of Nonferrous Metals.* Most of the remaining production of minerals comes from the eastern highlands or the ranges branching off or outlying to the west. Lead and zinc lead in value of production. Australia produces surpluses of both, accounting for close to 15 percent of the world's lead production, and between 5 and 10 percent of its zinc. The lead-zinc mines at Broken Hill in western New South Wales constitute one of the world's most famous mining districts and have played an important role in Australia's economic development. The Broken Hill Proprietary Company, which developed these mines, later branched into steel production, which it now monopolizes in Australia, and then into numerous other fields. This one company now forms the backbone of the entire Australian industrial system, controlling about a third of all the capital invested in private manufacturing companies in Australia. Besides lead and zinc, the Broken Hill mines yield silver, once the major product, cobalt, cadmium, and sulfur. At various other locations in and near the eastern highlands gold, copper, tin, and oil shale are produced.

The western part of the continent leads in the production of only one important mineral, gold. The Kalgoorlie field of Western Australia produces over half of the Australian output, which now amounts to only 2 or 3 percent of the world total, although in the 1850's strikes in Victoria made Australia temporarily the world's largest gold producer and stimulated a threefold increase in the continent's population within 10 years.

• *Relative Inefficiency of Australian Industries.* Despite the extent of Australian industrialization, and despite considerable advantages with regard to raw materials, Australia is still an importer of most kinds of manufactured goods. This appears to be partly a reflection of a high standard of living bolstered by the earning power of agriculture and grazing. It is also related to the fact that the country is so small in population that its factories cannot produce and distribute on a large enough scale, and therefore at sufficiently low unit costs, all of the various kinds of goods which are needed. Furthermore, much of the industry which has been developed is relatively inefficient. It has been estimated that the average Australian industrial worker produces only about one third as much as his American counterpart, and it seems certain that much Australian industry could not exist without tariff protection from the lower prices of foreign competitors. Consequently, the wisdom of encouraging manufacturing has often been questioned. However, political and defense considerations are involved, and it can be argued that expansion of the population and domestic market will eventually allow Australian industries to achieve greater efficiency.

New Zealand

New Zealand, over 1000 miles southeast of Australia, consists of two large islands, North Island and South Island, separated by Cook Strait, and a number of smaller islands. North Island is smaller than South Island but contains the majority of the population, which numbers slightly more than 2 million. Since the total area is approximately 104,000 square miles, the population density averages about 20 per square mile. New Zealand is thus a sparsely populated country, although not so much so as Australia.

▶ Physical and Climatic Characteristics

Rugged terrain is found throughout much of New Zealand. The topography of South Island is dominated by the Southern Alps, often cited as one of the world's most spectacular mountain ranges. These mountains present large areas above 5000 feet and many glaciated summits above 10,000 feet. The mountains of North Island are less imposing and extensive, but many peaks exceed 5000 feet.

The highlands of New Zealand lie in the Southern Hemisphere belt of westerly winds and receive abundant precipitation. Lowlands generally receive over 30 inches

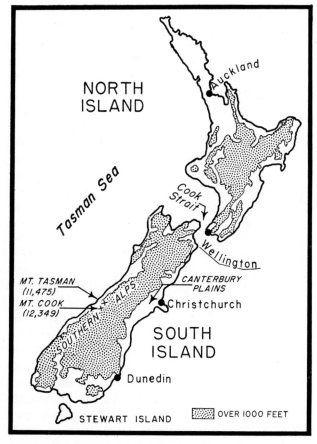

Index map of New Zealand. The national capital is underlined.

Dairy cattle on a well-kept pasture in New Zealand. The volcanic cone in the distance is Mount Egmont on North Island. (*New Zealand Embassy*.)

of precipitation, fairly evenly distributed throughout the year, and highlands often receive over 130 inches. Precipitation drops to less than 20 inches in small areas of rain shadow east of the Southern Alps. Temperatures are those of middle latitudes, moderated by the pervasive maritime influence. The result is a wet temperate climate commonly classified as marine west coast, with warm month temperatures generally averaging 60°–70°F. and cool month temperatures 40°–50°F. Highland temperatures are more severe, and a few glaciers are found on both islands.

▶ Importance of the Pastoral Industries

Rugged terrain and excessive precipitation in the Southern Alps and the mountainous core of North Island have resulted in almost a total absence of population from a third of New Zealand and have rendered about a fifth of the country completely unproductive, except for the notable attractions offered by the mountains to a budding tourist industry. Well-populated areas are restricted to fringing lowlands around the periphery of North Island and

along the drier east and south coasts of South Island.

The climate of New Zealand lowlands is ideal for growing grass and raising livestock, and almost half of the country's total area is maintained in pastures and meadows which support a major sheep and cattle industry. The outstanding importance and productivity of the pastoral industries in New Zealand is indicated in the following facts:

1. These industries completely dominate New Zealand's exports. In 1951, for example, wool, dairy products, and meat accounted for 52, 26, and 13 percent, respectively, of the total value of exports.

2. New Zealand ordinarily stands near or at the top among the world's countries in per capita trade.

3. New Zealand generally ranks first in the world in the export of cheese, mutton, and lamb, second in butter, and third in wool.

4. The earning power of its pastoral exports has been a major factor in New Zealand's exceptionally high standard of living, since they pay for the varied im-

ports which the country requires. Not only manufactured goods are imported, but also considerable quantities of food. Only about 3 percent of New Zealand is ordinarily in cultivation, and most of that is devoted to the growing of supplemental animal feeds.

The Canterbury Plains on the drier eastern side of South Island contain the largest acreages of cultivated land and are the main wheat-growing section.

▶ Industrial and Urban Development

In New Zealand as in Australia, however, basic dependence on the pastoral industries is accompanied by a high degree of urbanization and active attempts to develop manufacturing. The conditions and purposes fostering urban and industrial development in the two countries are quite similar. New Zealand's resources for manufacturing do not equal those of Australia, but coal, iron, and a number of other minerals are present in at least modest quantities, and there are very considerable potentials for hydroelectric power development. Considerable possibilities for forest production also exist, although the magnificent natural forests of New Zealand are now seriously depleted and imports of forest products are required. To an even greater degree than Australia, New Zealand has the problem of a small internal market militating against mass production at low cost. Most of the present manufacturing industries are high-cost producers protected by tariffs and thus maintained at the consumer's expense.

A somewhat lower degree and a much smaller scale of urbanization than in Australia is indicated by the 1951 populations of the five largest New Zealand cities: Auckland 329,000; Christchurch 174,000; Wellington (the capital) 133,000; Dunedin 96,000; Hutt 75,000. These figures assign 26 percent of New Zealand's population to the two largest cities and 42 percent to the five largest, a somewhat smaller proportion in each case than in Australia.

PART 7
Africa

Introduction to Africa

Africa is the largest in area of the major world regions discussed in this book. It covers approximately 11.7 million square miles (including Madagascar), and thus is nearly four times as large as continental United States. However the estimated total population was only 210 million in 1952–1953, giving an average density of 18 per square mile, as compared with an estimated 160 million (1953) or 53 per square mile in the United States.

The population of Africa, like that of most other extremely large regions, is very unevenly distributed. Approximately four fifths of the people are contained in the fourteen most populous political units. In approximate order of population these are Nigeria, Egypt, French West Africa, Ethiopia-Eritrea, Belgian Congo (including Ruanda-Urundi), Union of South Africa, Algeria, Anglo-Egyptian Sudan, French Morocco, Tanganyika, Federation of Rhodesia and Nyasaland, Kenya, Mozambique, and Uganda. Area and population data for the individual political units are given in Table 21. A map of African population distribution shows five conspicuous areas of especially dense population. These are (1) the borderlands of the Gulf of Guinea in West Africa, including Nigeria and portions of the political units to the west, (2) the Nile Valley in Egypt and the Anglo-Egyptian Sudan, (3) the coastal fringes of northwest Africa in Morocco, Algeria, and Tunisia, (4) the areas bordering the East African lakes, including portions of Kenya, Tanganyika, Uganda, the Belgian Congo, and Nyasaland, and (5) the eastern third of

A familiar sight on the Congo River are paddle wheelers which ply the river stopping at the native villages along the way to discharge supplies and pick up cargo. (*Belgian Government Information Center.*)

TABLE 21

AFRICA: AREA AND POPULATION DATA

POLITICAL UNIT	POLITICAL STATUS	AREA (THOUSAND SQUARE MILES)	POPULATION (EST. MILLIONS)	DENSITY (PER SQUARE MILE: TO NEAREST WHOLE NUMBER)
Spanish Africa		137.5	2.24	16
Spanish Morocco [a]	Protectorate and Colony	18.5	1.21 (1952)	66
Spanish Sahara	Colony	105.4	0.038 (1952)	0.36
Spanish Guinea	Colony	10.8	0.20 (1952)	19
Canary Islands	Two Provinces of Spain	2.8	0.79 (1950) [b]	282
Portuguese Africa		795.3	10.83	14
Angola	Overseas Province	481.4	4.11 (1950) [b]	9
Mozambique	Overseas Province	297.7	5.73 (1950) [b]	19
Portuguese Guinea	Overseas Province	13.9	0.51 (1950) [b]	37
São Tomé and Principe	Overseas Province	0.37	0.06 (1950) [b]	162
Cape Verde Islands	Overseas Province	1.56	0.15 (1950) [b]	95
Madeira Islands	Administered as Districts of Portugal	0.31	0.27 (1950) [b]	867
Belgian Africa		925.6	15.83	17
Belgian Congo	Colony	905.0	11.76 (1952)	13
Ruanda-Urundi	Trust Territory Administered with Congo	20.6	4.07 (1952)	198
French Africa		4245.6	51.76	12
Algeria	Government General	846.1	9.14 (1952)	11
Morocco	Protectorate	151.0	8.19 (1953)	54
Tunisia	Protectorate	48.3	3.60 (1952)	75
French West Africa	Group of 8 Overseas Territories	1805.2	17.36 (1951)	10
Togoland	Trust Territory	21.5	1.03 (1952)	48
French Equatorial Africa	Group of 4 Overseas Territories	969.1	4.44 (1952)	5
Cameroons	Trust Territory	166.5	3.13 (1951)	19
French Somaliland	Overseas Territory	8.5	0.06 (1952)	7
Madagascar	Overseas Territory	227.6	4.37 (1951)	19
Comoro Islands	Overseas Territory	0.83	0.17 (1951)	200
Réunion	Overseas Department	0.97	0.27 (1952)	278

British Africa		2999.4	75.12	25
Nigeria	Colony and Protectorate	338.6	30.00 (1953)	89
Cameroons	Trust Territory Administered with Nigeria	34.1	1.50 (1953)	44
Gold Coast	Colony and Protectorate	78.8	4.00 (1952)	51
Togoland	Trust Territory Administered with Gold Coast	13.0	0.41 (1952)	31
Sierra Leone	Colony and Protectorate	27.9	2.00 (1951)	72
Gambia	Colony and Protectorate	4.0	0.29 (1952)	71
Kenya	Colony and Protectorate	225.0	5.76 (1952)	26
Tanganyika	Trust Territory	362.7	7.94 (1952)	22
Uganda	Protectorate	94.0	5.26 (1952)	56
Zanzibar	Protected Sultanate	1.0	0.27 (1952)	267
British Somaliland	Protectorate	68.0	0.64 (1952)	9
Bechuanaland	High Commission Territory	275.0	0.29 (1952)	1.06
Swaziland	High Commission Territory	6.7	0.20 (1952)	30
Basutoland	High Commission Territory	11.7	0.58 (1952)	50
Mauritius and Dependencies	Colony	0.82	0.53 (1952)	643
Federation of Rhodesia and Nyasaland	Includes Protectorates of Northern Rhodesia and Nyasaland and Self-Governing Colony of Southern Rhodesia	490.6	6.68 (1952)	14
Anglo-Egyptian Sudan	Condominium, Pending Independence	967.5	8.77 (1952)	9
Other Dependencies				
Somalia (Former Italian Somaliland)	Italian Trust Territory, Pending Independence	198.3	1.28 (1952)	6.5
Tangier	Internationally-Administered Zone	0.23	0.17 (1952)	733
South West Africa	Former Mandated Territory Integrated with Union of South Africa	317.7	0.43 (1951) [b]	1.4
Sovereign Nations				
Union of South Africa	Sovereign State of British Commonwealth	472.5	12.65 (1951) [b]	27
Egypt	Independent Republic	386.2	21.43 (1952)	55
Libya	Independent Kingdom	680.0	1.15 (1952)	1.7
Ethiopia-Eritrea	Independent Empire	455.1	16.10 (1951)	35
Liberia	Independent Republic	43.0	1.50 (1953)	35
Grand Total		11656.5	210.48	18

Note: Apparent discrepancies in totals are due to rounding of figures.
[a] Figures include Northern and Southern Zones of Moroccan Protectorate, Ifni Colony, and five North African cities administered as part of Spain.
[b] Census figures.

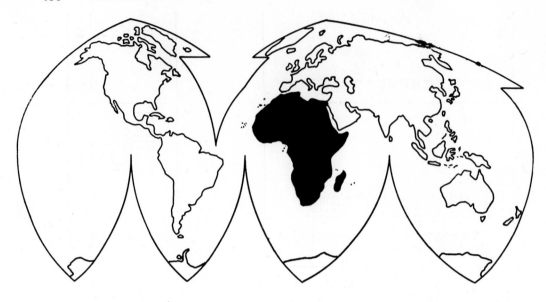

World location of Africa. (*Boggs Equal Area Projection, copyright A. J. Nystrom & Co.*)

the Union of South Africa. Each of the five major zones of dense population is a key area in the political and economic geography of Africa.

Africa falls roughly into the two major divisions of North Africa, the Arab-Berber realm of the continent, which is mostly desert with a fringe of mediterranean coast-lands; and Africa south of the Sahara, or Negro Africa, which is predominantly tropical and subtropical grassland and rain forest. Since North Africa has already been considered in some detail in Chapters 14 and 15, major attention in the present chapter will be focused on trans-Saharan Africa.

Historical Background

A well-known book about modern Africa is entitled *Africa Emergent*.[1] The term "emergent," applied to an area which has traditionally been considered the "Dark Continent," is descriptive of a region whose interior was mainly inhabited by primitive tribesmen as late as 1900, but which is to-day witnessing revolutionary changes introduced by the various Occidental nations which have dominated the political and economic life of Africa since the latter nineteenth century. At present the greater part of the African continent is included within the colonial empires of Great Brit-

ain, France, Belgium, Portugal, and Spain. Germany and Italy formerly held African colonies which they have now lost. The United States, though never a colonizing power in Africa, has shown a strong interest in this region for many years, particularly in the fields of missionary activity and trade.

By European or American standards most parts of Africa were still extremely backward at the end of the nineteenth century. This was least true of the northern and southern extremities. Parts of northern Africa have been civilized for thousands of

---

[1] W. M. Macmillan, *Africa Emergent: A Survey of Social, Political and Economic Trends in British Africa.* Harmondsworth, Middlesex, England: Penguin Books, 1938, 1949.

years, and by 1900 the more desirable parts of the present Union of South Africa had been occupied on a permanent basis by Europeans. However, at the dawn of the twentieth century the vast spaces of interior tropical Africa were still primitive and little known. The isolation of much of Africa from contact with more advanced areas until comparatively recent times seems to be based on a combination of factors. Among these were (1) the presence of the great Sahara Desert barrier in North Africa, making difficult the penetration of tropical Africa by land from the north, (2) the inhospitable character of the African shoreline, which is exceptionally regular, thus lacking protected harbors and is bordered in many places by extensive sandbars and/or thick tropical forests (including considerable stretches of mangrove swamp) or desert, (3) the character of African rivers, which are generally shallow and full of sandbars near their mouths and are blocked inland at varying distances by falls and rapids, thus rendering difficult penetration of the interior by water, (4) the hot, humid climate and the many tropical diseases encountered by outsiders in the coastal areas, and (5) the hostility of many native tribes, due in considerable part to extensive slave-trading activities by Europeans, Americans, and Arabs. Perhaps most important was (6) the lack of readily apparent sources of wealth in the interior which would justify the risks of penetration.

Although Westerners did not penetrate the interior of tropical Africa to any degree until the last half of the nineteenth century, a fringe of trading posts and way stations designed to service passing ships began to be established around the African coasts early in the colonial period. The articles of trade in greatest demand from the African interior were ivory and "black ivory," or Negro slaves. Traffic in African slaves began many centuries ago. Negro slaves were known in ancient Egypt, Greece, and Rome. In later times large numbers of Negroes were brought by European and American slave traders to labor in the mines and on the plantations of the New World. Probably the greatest of all slave-trading peoples have been the Arabs, who were exploiting the northern and eastern fringes of Negro Africa by caravan across the Sahara and by ship along the coast of East Africa centuries before the first European traders appeared. One of the motives which led several European governments to claim territory in the interior of tropical Africa during the last quarter of the nineteenth century was a desire to stop the slave traffic at its source. Penetration of the interior was pioneered by a series of important journeys of exploration which began in the 1850's. These expeditions were undertaken by missionaries, traders, adventurers of various sorts, and in some cases by government officials. Once the main outlines of inner African geography were revealed, a scramble for colonial territory took place among the European powers, beginning about 1881. By 1900 most of the present political boundaries had been drawn, and Africa had become, as it remains today, predominantly a region of European dependencies.

African Problems

Recent decades have witnessed notable changes in the general conditions of African life. Improved standards of health and literacy among the native peoples have resulted from the work of government agencies and Christian missions. Better transportation facilities, particularly a wide extension of highways and airways, have made possible the marketing of farm products, including perishable items, from formerly inaccessible areas. The development of village stores has made available to millions of Africans a variety of European and American manufactured goods. Modern factories employing African labor have been established in a considerable number of the larger urban centers, and improved agricultural techniques have been introduced in many areas. Today it is becoming increasingly difficult to find African peoples who are still essentially outside the range of Occidental influences.

The foregoing changes have affected some African peoples and areas much more than others. Not all of the effects have been favorable: for example, one result of better transportation and increased opportunities for employment in mines and factories has been a steady drift of Africans from tribal villages to overcrowded slum areas in the larger towns and cities, often in numbers too great for the local job market to absorb. African craftsmen exercising their traditional skills in textiles, wood, clay, leather, or metal have frequently found it difficult or impossible to compete with the influx of factory-made goods. Nor has the total impact of change yet been sufficient to lift Africa above its current status as one of the major underdeveloped regions of the world. Africa still shares

many of the customary problems of such regions, including (1) a high incidence of illiteracy, poverty, hunger, and disease, (2) native customs, attitudes, and forms of social organization which tend to hinder the development of a modern economy, (3) inadequate over-all facilities for transportation and communication and (4) a lack of domestic capital which could be used to foster increased agricultural and industrial production and thus to raise the material standard of living. Other problems arise from a heavy dependence on outside markets for the sale of African goods. Like most other underdeveloped regions, Africa's place in the commercial world is basically that of a producer of foodstuffs and raw materials for sale outside the region. In the world markets where African goods are sold, there is a considerable fluctuation in demand and in prices over a period of years. Whenever the market is glutted and prices are low, unemployment and severe distress may result in African producing areas where the natives have come to rely on cash returns from commercial production. Finally, there are problems of racial friction, which are among the most serious of all African problems at the present time, especially in certain areas such as Kenya and South Africa.

The Difficult African Environment

Many of the problems of Africa are due in considerable part to a natural environment which is difficult to manage, particularly by native peoples equipped with a primitive technology. This environment varies considerably from place to place, but its broad outlines are relatively simple.

▶ Surface Configuration

Most of the continent is essentially a vast plateau, or more precisely, a series of plateaus at successive elevations. The plateau

surfaces are predominantly level to rolling, and over considerable areas are hollowed by shallow river basins, particularly the basins of the Congo, upper Zambezi, and Orange Rivers. The principal areas of lowland plain in Africa are found in a narrow band around the coasts, averaging 20 to 100 miles in width, though in places considerably wider. Inland from the coast, abrupt or ragged escarpments mark the transition to the plateau, which customarily lies at an elevation of 1000 feet or higher. In southern and eastern Africa the general

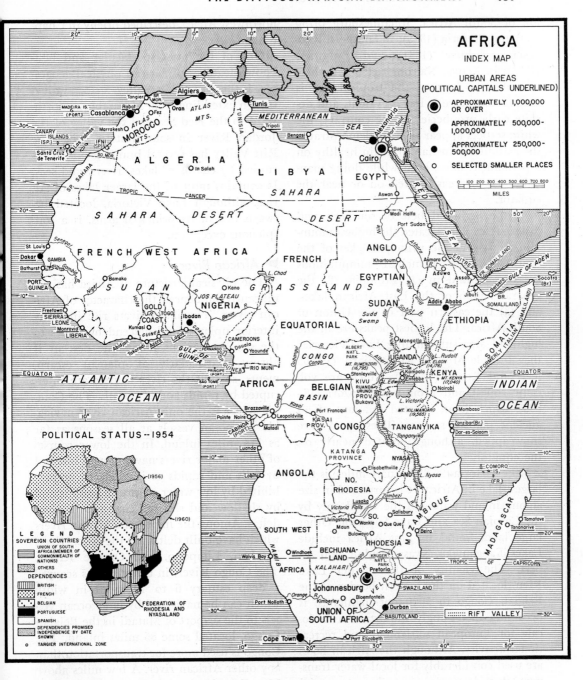

AFRICA
INDEX MAP

URBAN AREAS
(POLITICAL CAPITALS UNDERLINED)

APPROXIMATELY 1,000,000
OR OVER

APPROXIMATELY 500,000-
1,000,000

APPROXIMATELY 250,000-
500,000

SELECTED SMALLER PLACES

0 100 200 300 400 500 600 700 800
MILES

POLITICAL STATUS—1954

LEGEND
SOVEREIGN COUNTRIES
UNION OF SOUTH
AFRICA (MEMBER OF
COMMONWEALTH OF
NATIONS)
OTHERS
DEPENDENCIES
BRITISH
FRENCH
BELGIAN
PORTUGUESE
SPANISH
DEPENDENCIES PROMISED
INDEPENDENCE BY DATE
SHOWN
TANGIER INTERNATIONAL ZONE

FEDERATION OF
RHODESIA AND
NYASALAND

RIFT VALLEY

elevation rises to 2000 or 3000 feet, with considerable areas lying at 5000 feet or higher. The principal belt of highlands occupies roughly the eastern third of Africa, from the Union of South Africa northward to Ethiopia. It is in this area that the largest number of permanent European settlers are found. The majority of the Europeans live at altitudes of 4000 feet or higher, as indicated by the elevations of several important cities containing substantial European populations: in the Union of South Africa, Johannesburg (5750 feet) and Pretoria (4375); in Southern Rhodesia, Salisbury (4831) and Bulawayo (4393); in Kenya, Nairobi (5495). At these altitudes the heat of the tropical sun is tempered, disease is less prevalent, and despite early prophecies to the contrary, the white settlers appear to have demonstrated their ability to live and remain healthy on a permanent basis, even while doing manual work in areas located on or near the equator.

In the highland belt of southern and eastern Africa are located the highest mountain peaks and the principal lakes of the continent. The principal mountainous areas are found in (1) Ethiopia, (2) the general region of the East African lakes, and (3) the eastern part of the Union of South Africa. The loftiest peaks are in the highland area surrounding Lake Victoria: they include Mounts Kilimanjaro (19,565 feet) and Kenya (17,040), which are volcanic cones; and Mount Ruwenzori (16,795), which is an isolated remnant of an ancient plateau surface. These peaks are snowcapped, although located nearly on the equator.

Lake Victoria (26,828 square miles) is the largest lake in Africa. It is surpassed in size among inland waters of the world only by the Caspian Sea and Lake Superior. Other large lakes found in East Africa include Lakes Tanganyika, Nyasa, Rudolf, and Albert. The vicinity of the smaller Lake Kivu, located on the eastern border of the Belgian Congo in 5000-foot highlands, is becoming increasingly important as a locale for European settlement and recreational activity. Although the African lakes are used considerably for local water transport, they do not compare in commercial significance with the Great Lakes of North America.

Aside from the discontinuous mountain zone in eastern and southern Africa, the only other extensive area of high mountains in Africa is the Atlas Mountains of northwest Africa, described briefly in Chapter 14.

One of the most spectacular and best-known features of African physical geography is the Great Rift Valley, a steep-walled trough extending from Mozambique northward to the Red Sea and the valley of the Jordan River in southwestern Asia. The Rift Valley has several branches and is occupied by chains of lakes, rivers, and seas. It contains most of the larger lakes of Africa, although Lake Victoria, located between two of its principal arms, is a conspicuous exception.

▶ *African Rivers*

The physical structure of Africa has significantly influenced the character of African rivers. The main rivers rise in rainy interior uplands and descend by stages to the sea. At various points the descent is abrupt, particularly at plateau escarpments, so that the river courses are interrupted by rapids and waterfalls. The Gambia River is the only African river navigable for ocean vessels at all seasons as far as 175 miles inland. In the lower courses of other major rivers navigation is blocked by falls and rapids or is hindered or prohibited by low water at certain seasons and by shallow and shifting channels in river deltas. Among the important African rivers which have built deltas are the Nile, Niger, Zambezi, Limpopo, and Orange Rivers. The Congo River, in contrast, has scoured a deep estuary 6 to 10 miles in width which can be navigated by large ocean vessels to the seaport of Matadi in the Belgian Congo, located some 85 miles inland. The Congo is used more for transportation than any other African river. A few miles above Matadi navigation is blocked by rapids, and goods must be transshiped by rail a distance of 230 miles to Leopoldville. Above the latter city, the Congo and its major tributaries are navigable for long distances by river steamers and barges, although the continuity of transportation is broken in places by falls and rapids which are bypassed by rail or road. The character of water transport on the Congo system is generally representative of African inland waterways, which are discontinuous and interconnected by rail or highway in a manner not duplicated in any other continent.

The frequent falls and rapids of African rivers have a more positive side. They represent a great potential reservoir of hydroelectric energy. The hydroelectric power potential of Africa is estimated to be more than a third of the world total. The Congo River alone between Leopoldville and Matadi is estimated to have a greater power potential than the entire North American continent. However, less than 1 percent of the potential power of African rivers has been developed up to the present.

▶ Climate and Vegetation

Africa is bisected by the equator. It is approximately 2580 miles from the equator to the northernmost point of Africa, and 2400 miles to the southernmost point. Thus most of Africa lies within the low latitudes and is characterized by tropical climates. One of the most striking characteristics of the climatic pattern of Africa is its symmetry or regularity. This is mainly due to the position of Africa athwart the equator, coupled with the generally level character of the surface and the absence of extensive chains of high mountains.

• *Types of Climate.* The major pattern of climates is simply stated. Areas of *tropical rain forest climate* in central and western Africa near the equator gradually merge into *tropical savanna climate* on the north, south, and east. The savanna areas, in turn, trend into areas of *tropical steppe* and *desert* on the north and southwest. Along the northern and southern fringes of the continent are found relatively small but important areas of *mediterranean* and *humid subtropical* climates in which the majority of the European settlers live.

Tropical Rain Forest Climate. In Africa rainfall is heaviest, generally speaking, in areas near the equator in Central and West Africa. In these areas abundant moisture and continuously high temperatures produce tropical rain forest as the characteristic type of climate and associated vegetation. The main area of rain forest occurs in a broad band along the equator from the Gulf of Guinea eastward to the highlands of East Africa. It includes most of southern Nigeria, all of Spanish Guinea, and extensive portions of the Cameroons, French Equatorial Africa, and the Belgian Congo. Smaller areas are found on the tip of West Africa in Liberia, Sierra Leone, and a part of French West Africa. A third area remote from the main body occurs along the eastern, windward side of Madagascar. These areas have the characteristic climatic features of the wet tropics: constant, monotonous heat, with little variation in the average temperature from month to month, and only a few degrees change in temperature between day and night; considerable rain in every month of the year; and high humidity. Some areas of this climate type, as in Sierra Leone and Liberia, have a dry season of a few weeks but have enough total rainfall to support rain forest vegetation. Temperatures are not excessively high as a rule, seldom rising to much above 90°F., but the constant moist, steamy warmth is very enervating. Such conditions produce the luxuriant, tangled vegetation of the rain forest. This part of Africa has been highly publicized, but actually occupies only about a tenth of the continent.

Tropical Savanna Climate. The areas of tropical savanna climate are far more extensive than the areas of tropical rain forest climate in Africa. The most characteristic feature of this climate is the alternation of well-marked wet and dry seasons. The most common type of natural vegetation is tall tropical grass, which sometimes occurs in pure stands, but more often is intermixed with scattered trees. In some places within the realm of savanna climate trees become relatively more abundant than grass over considerable areas; therefore, the vegetation is properly classed as dry forest or tropical scrub. However, such forests are generally more open and easier to traverse than the tropical rain forest. Near the desert margins of the savanna climate the rainfall is lighter and there is characteristically a belt of shorter grass or bushland which is often referred to as tropical steppe. Avenues of closely spaced trees, known as *gallery forests,* extend along the banks of streams in many parts of the African savannas.

A broad belt of tropical savanna and steppe bordering the Sahara Desert on the south is known as the Sudan. Only the eastern margins of this belt line lie in the political unit of the Anglo-Egyptian Sudan. The remainder lies principally in French Equatorial Africa, French West Africa, and Nigeria.

Desert Climate. Deserts border the tropical savannas and steppes on the north and southwest. The great Sahara Desert, the world's largest, extends completely across the north of Africa from the Atlantic Ocean to the Red Sea. In the Union of South Africa and South West Africa, a narrow coastal desert, the Namib, borders the Atlantic. The "Kalahari Desert," which lies inland from the Namib, has a considerable growth of low grasses and shrubs, and it is better described as steppe or semidesert than as true desert.

Mediterranean and Humid Subtropical Climates. The coastal areas bordering the Mediterranean Sea in northwest Africa and the southwestern tip of the continent around Cape Town have a mediterranean or dry-summer subtropical climate characterized by rainy winters and almost complete drought during the midsummer

months. The extreme southeast coast of the continent in Natal Province of the Union of South Africa has rain at all seasons and is classed as humid subtropical. The high interior grasslands of the Union of South Africa, or High Veld, also have a subtropical climate, but one which resembles the tropical savanna climate in having a well-marked dry season during the period of low sun.

Climatic data for selected African stations are given in Table 22.

► *Water Resources and Problems*

Africa possibly receives enough total rainfall to provide amply for the needs of the whole continent, were the water more evenly spread in time and space. Unfortunately however, the available moisture is poorly distributed. Some parts of Africa receive too much rain, whereas other areas have scarcely any rain at all. Even in the rainier parts of the continent large areas have a dry season of considerable length, and wide fluctuations occur from year to year in the total amount of precipitation. Throughout most of Africa the precipitation comes mainly in heavy erosive downpours rather than in the form of a steady, soaking rain. In places considerable areas are inundated by waters which gather in swamps or marshes such as the Sudd Swamp along the Nile River in the Sudan. One of the major needs of Africa is a better control over the available water, involving irrigation projects in some areas, drainage projects elsewhere, conversion of marshes and swamps to rice fields or pastures, and the development of a system of dams along both the major streams and small tributaries to control floods, regularize the flow of water between seasons, and provide hydroelectric power in a continent which is poorly provided with the mineral fuels and in most places outside the rain forest is short even of fuel wood.

In the typical African village household water is carried laboriously by hand from

TABLE 22

CLIMATIC DATA FOR SELECTED AFRICAN STATIONS

STATION	POLITICAL UNIT	LATITUDE TO NEAREST WHOLE DEGREE	ELEVATION ABOVE SEA LEVEL (FEET)	TYPE OF CLIMATE	AVERAGE TEMPERATURE (DEGREES F. TO NEAREST WHOLE DEGREE)			PRECIPITATION	
					ANNUAL	COOLEST MONTH	WARMEST MONTH	ANNUAL AVERAGE TO NEAREST INCH	NUMBER OF MONTHS WITH LESS THAN 1.5 INCHES OF RAIN
Casablanca	French Morocco	34°N.	56	Mediterranean	63°	53°	73°	16"	6
In Salah	Algeria	27°N.	919	Desert	78°	55°	99°	0.1"	12
Jibuti	French Somaliland	12°N.	20	Desert	86°	78°	96°	5"	12
Dakar	French West Africa	15°N.	131	Tropical Steppe	78°	73°	82°	23"	8
Kano	Nigeria	12°N.	1539	Tropical Savanna	80°	71°	89°	35"	7
Accra	Gold Coast	6°N.	88	Tropical Savanna	80°	76°	82°	27"	6
Lagos	Nigeria	6°N.	10	Tropical Rain Forest	81°	78°	83°	72"	2
Douala	French Cameroons	4°N.	26	Tropical Rain Forest	78°	75°	81°	159"	0
Nairobi	Kenya	1°S.	5495	Tropical Savanna (Upland)	65°	61°	68°	35"	3
Elisabethville	Belgian Congo	12°S.	4035	Tropical Savanna (Upland)	69°	61°	75°	45"	6
Salisbury	Southern Rhodesia	18°S.	4831	Tropical Savanna (Upland)	65°	57°	71°	33"	7
Beira	Mozambique	20°S.	30	Tropical Savanna	75°	68°	81°	56"	3
Maun	Bechuanaland	20°S.	3090	Tropical Steppe (Upland)	72°	59°	80°	16"	7
Port Nolloth	Union of South Africa	29°S.	22	Desert	57°	55°	61°	2.4"	12
Cape Town	Union of South Africa	34°S.	40	Mediterranean	63°	55°	71°	25"	5
Durban	Union of South Africa	30°S.	50	Humid Subtropical	70°	63°	76°	45"	0
Johannesburg	Union of South Africa	26°S.	5750	High Veld	61°	49°	69°	30"	5
Tamatave	Madagascar	18°S.	20	Tropical Rain Forest	75°	70°	80°	123"	0

a near-by stream or lake or a shallow, polluted well—a task ordinarily performed by women. Especially in the seasonally rainy areas, education is needed in the construction and use of small dams to provide water storage throughout the year, coupled with development of simple pipelines or flumes to carry water by gravity to village households or the fields. "The African can be taught to dig and line wells, and such a primitive device as an endless porous rope of fibers absorbing water and passing through two wooden rollers to squeeze out the supply is within the power of any African to make and maintain. Unfortunately, over so much of Africa with its underlying complex of ancient rocks the water table behaves irregularly, and a well is both difficult to dig and uncertain of its supply. There is much to be said, in hilly or rolling country, for horizontal 'wells' into the hillsides from which water would flow by gravity as an artificial spring. It should be noted that artesian conditions are rare in Africa."[2]

▶ African Soils

The scientific study of African soils is still in an early stage. This represents one of the critical frontiers of human endeavor in Africa at the present time, inasmuch as further significant advances in the utilization of African lands for agriculture must be founded in large part on a better knowledge of the soils. Based on present knowledge, the following general observations regarding African soils can be made.

Among the most productive soils of the continent are the alluvial soils found on river plains. The soils along the Nile River in Egypt, for example, are especially noted for their fertility, and have supported agriculture for thousands of years. Other especially fertile soils are found in parts of the East African highlands where certain

types of volcanic material have weathered into excellent soil. A third group of better than average soils is the grassland soils found in the tropical steppes and in the temperate grasslands of the High Veld in the Union of South Africa. These soils, however, do not appear to be entirely comparable to the chernozems, prairie soils, and chestnut soils of North America. They tend to be less durable, and seem to lose their fertility more quickly under continuous cultivation.

Soils of the deserts and regions of mediterranean climate are generally thin and immature; over broad areas of desert, true soils of any type are lacking. In the mediterranean areas fertile soils are found in some valleys where transported materials from adjoining slopes have collected and accumulated.

In the tropical rain forests and savannas reddish tropical soils are generally dominant. There is a common idea that these soils are exceptionally fertile when cleared of their natural vegetation and used for agriculture. This idea is apparently based on the luxuriant plant growth which such soils often support in their natural state. However, the truth appears to be that they are rather poorly supplied as a rule with plant nutrients and tend to lose their fertility quickly when used for crops. They are usually low in humus and deficient in lime. These disadvantages of tropical soils are at least partly due to the rapid chemical action induced by the abundant heat and moisture of tropical climates. Such conditions promote rapid leaching of nutrient materials by percolating waters, and cause organic matter exposed to the air to combine with oxygen rather quickly and thus to be lost into the atmosphere in the form of carbon dioxide rather than being converted to humus and plant food by the soil bacteria.

[2] L. Dudley Stamp, *Africa: A Study in Tropical Development.* New York: John Wiley and Sons, Inc.; London: Chapman and Hall, Ltd., 1953. P. 89. Used by permission of the author and the publishers.

▶ Native Animal Life

Perhaps no aspect of Africa has been so well publicized as African wildlife. Thanks to innumerable movies, illustrated lectures, and popular books and magazine articles by explorers, naturalists, and professional big game hunters and guides, Africa is often thought of as a sort of giant zoo, tenanted by large numbers of elephants, lions, giraffes, zebras, hippopotamuses, rhinoceroses, apes, crocodiles, pythons, and other exotic and dangerous species. To a limited extent this conception is correct, for no other large area still exhibits such an abundant and varied fauna. However, it is easy to overstate the abundance and significance of African animal life at the present time. While reptiles, monkeys, and tropical birds are still relatively numerous, the total numbers of most of the larger animals have declined. The latter has been partly the result of unrestricted hunting by white market hunters and sportsmen as well as by natives equipped in recent decades with guns as well as the traditional spears, poisoned arrows, and traps. Partly, however, the decline in animal populations has been due simply to encroachment by an increasing human population on the habitat of the wild species. Whatever the cause, the numbers of many species have now declined to the point that they are protected by law from excessive hunting. In some parts of Africa the remaining wildlife is being conserved in large game reserves or national parks. The two best-known areas of this type are the Albert National Park, located in a volcanic highland region in the eastern part of the Belgian Congo, and the Kruger National Park, in the extreme northeast of the Union of South Africa. Lions and other game may be seen in their habitats from the park roads.

The tropical grasslands and open forests of Africa have been the principal habitat of the larger herbivorous animals, such as the elephant, buffalo, antelope, zebra, and giraffe, and also of carnivorous and scavenging animals, such as the lion, leopard, and hyena. The tropical rain forests have been much more deficient in the larger species of game than is commonly realized. In the rain forest the most abundant animal species have been birds, monkeys, and snakes, together with hippopotamuses, crocodiles, and fish life inhabiting the streams.

▶ Diseases and Parasites

A high incidence of diseases and parasites affecting people, domestic animals, and cultivated crops has been one of the main hindrances to African development. Certain parts of tropical Africa, particularly the rainy lowlands of West Africa, long had a reputation as a "white man's graveyard." Even today, despite recent advances in tropical medicine, the available evidence would suggest that it is diseases and parasites rather than the tropical climate *per se* which constitutes the principal barrier to permanent settlement by Europeans in the tropical lowlands of Africa. Among the native Africans, diseases and parasites take a heavy toll of strength and energy, even when not causing death. Many of the major diseases are carried by insects. Those carried by mosquitoes include malaria, yellow fever, dengue or "breakbone fever," and elephantiasis. Sleeping sickness is carried by the tsetse fly, which also transmits nagana, a destructive disease affecting cattle and horses. Bubonic plague is spread by fleas and relapsing fever by ticks and lice. Tuberculosis, according to some authorities, is responsible for more African deaths than any other disease. Large numbers of Africans are afflicted by diseases and parasites of the digestive tract, including dysentery, bilharzia, and hookworm and other types of intestinal worms. "In East Africa it has been established that over 90 per cent of the population are infected with one or more kinds of worms, and frequently as many as six kinds have been found in

Improved health services are gradually being brought to tropical Africa. The government nurse above is instructing a group of expectant mothers in the Gold Coast regarding the proper care of the newborn child. (*British Information Services.*)

the same individual."[3] The majority of digestive diseases appear to result from the use of contaminated water, and the incidence could undoubtedly be greatly reduced by the application of sanitary measures on a broad scale. Other diseases which are relatively common in Africa include yaws, leprosy, influenza, polio, trachoma, and the venereal diseases. Pneumonia is often devastating to undernourished and poorly clad Africans, particularly children, during sudden changes of weather.

Conditions with regard to health, sanitation, and disease in some of the more

backward areas have been described as follows: [4]

It is . . . clear from the statistics given in connection with the organization of health services that large numbers of the African people . . . are still beyond the reach of medical and health services in the ordinary sense. It is safe to conclude that in many districts such services consist of the limited facilities of a mission dispensary or a small supply of medicines and "first-aid" material at a government station, possibly dispensed by a half-trained African orderly. . . . Opinions with regard to

[3] Lord Hailey, *An African Survey*. London, New York, Toronto: Oxford University Press, 1938. P. 1146. Used by permission of the author and the publisher.

[4] Lord Hailey, *op. cit.*, pp. 1205–1206. Used by permission of the author and the Oxford University Press.

the incidence of the more typical African diseases may vary, but it is clear that in many rural areas the mortality from malaria is high and that sources of malarial infection exist in most villages; that intermittent fevers are prevalent; that helminthic diseases [caused by intestinal worms] are almost universal, the filthy state of the villages being conducive to their spread; and that few village children are free from sores, and many adults are undernourished and have little stamina. An examination of a typical Central African village would show that the sick, especially old persons and children, are neglected or unwisely treated, the elements of hygiene are lacking, the wearing of unhygienic and dirty clothing is usual, food is prepared in dirty vessels, flies swarm on garbage thrown near the village, and huts are often unswept and infested with parasites. . . . Little can be done to improve such conditions until the Africans themselves are conscious of a need for betterment, or at least until the native authorities themselves are aware of their responsibilities, and the health services have sufficient staff at their disposal to enforce sanitary measures.

Despite the miserable conditions which still prevail in some areas, much progress has been made in recent decades toward the conquest of disease in Africa. The efforts of medical men and women connected with Christian missions have been especially noteworthy. At the present time enough is known about the control of tropical diseases and parasites to greatly reduce the incidence of many of these afflictions if means were available for the technical knowledge to be applied. But Africa is a vast land, and as yet neither the money nor the personnel are available to fully cope with the situation.

▶ *Mineral Resources and Production*

Africa has become increasingly important in recent times as a producer of minerals. Most of the production is exported, principally to Europe and the United States. In world terms, Africa is particularly important as a producer of (1) precious metals and precious stones, (2) ferroalloys, (3) copper and tin, and (4) phosphates. Table 23 shows African production as a percentage of world production for a number of important minerals and indicates the principal African producing countries for each mineral. It is apparent from this table that four general areas in Africa are of primary importance in mineral production at the present time. These are (1) the Belgian Congo-Rhodesian region, (2) the Union of South Africa and South West Africa, (3) the Guinea Coast of West Africa, and (4) northwest Africa, in Morocco, Algeria, and Tunisia.

The *Congo-Rhodesian region* is one of the richest mineralized areas on earth. In few areas do sizable deposits of so many important minerals occur in such close proximity. In the Belgian Congo mineral production is mainly centered in the Katanga region of the southeast. The Congo leads all countries in production of diamonds and the important ferroalloy cobalt, is possibly the largest producer of uranium, is the fourth-ranking country in tin production, and is sixth in copper production. Northern Rhodesia exceeds the Congo in production of copper, and it ranks third among the world's countries in that metal. The value of copper produced in Northern Rhodesia is several times as great as that of all other minerals combined. The principal mining district borders the Congo and is an extension of the Katanga area. Besides copper, Northern Rhodesia is an important producer of cobalt and vanadium. These ferroalloys are in demand for the manufacture of special steels, but are produced in only a few of the world's countries. In Southern Rhodesia gold, chromium, and coal lead in value of production. Both Northern and Southern Rhodesia have sizable deposits of iron ore. An iron and steel plant has been erected at Que Que in Southern Rhodesia. The plant utilizes local

An open-pit phosphate mine in French Morocco about 80 miles southeast of Casablanca. The mining industry of Africa is dominated by large corporations utilizing heavy equipment such as that shown in this view. (*French Embassy Press and Information Division.*)

sess substantial coal deposits. The African continent is very poor in mineral fuels, being even more deficient in petroleum and natural gas than in coal

In the *Union of South Africa* gold is by far the leading mineral in value of production. The principal gold-mining district is the Witwatersrand, in which the city of Johannesburg (largest in Africa south of the Sahara) is located. South Africa is the world's leading gold-producing country, and is second to the Belgian Congo as a producer of diamonds. It has the largest deposits of bituminous coal in Africa, and also has deposits of iron ore. The coal and iron have provided the basis for a steel-milling industry that has made South Africa nearly independent of foreign imports of iron and steel. South West Africa is the world's second largest producer of vanadium.

In *West Africa* the principal minerals currently produced are manganese, gold, and diamonds in the Gold Coast, tin in Nigeria, and iron ore in Sierra Leone and Liberia. This region also has extensive de-

iron ore and limestone, and secures coking coal by rail from a field at Wankie, 500 miles to the northeast. Southern Rhodesia is one of the few African countries to pos-

TABLE 23

PRODUCTION DATA FOR TWELVE IMPORTANT AFRICAN MINERALS

MINERAL	PERCENTAGE OF WORLD OUTPUT PRODUCED IN AFRICA, 1951	LEADING AFRICAN PRODUCING COUNTRIES, 1951 (FIGURES REPRESENT PERCENTAGE OF TOTAL AFRICAN PRODUCTION)
Diamonds	98.2	Belgian Congo, 64.1; South Africa, 13.7; Gold Coast, 9.7
Gold	39.9	South Africa, 86.1; Gold Coast, 5.2; Southern Rhodesia, 3.6
Platinum	29.2	South Africa, 99.9
Manganese	24.7	Gold Coast, 47.3; French Morocco, 21.5; South Africa, 15.0
Chromite	30.2	South Africa, 64.5; Southern Rhodesia, 35.5
Cobalt	87.4	Belgian Congo, 82.9; Northern Rhodesia, 10.8; French Morocco, 6.3
Vanadium	Approx. 20–25	South West Africa, 77.5; Northern Rhodesia, 22.5
Copper	20.6	Northern Rhodesia, 58.5; Belgian Congo, 35.4; South Africa, 6.1
Tin	13.7	Belgian Congo, 57.2; Nigeria, 37.7; South Africa, 3.2
Phosphate rock	33.1	French Morocco, 60.8; Tunisia, 21.6; Algeria, 10.0
Iron ore	2.7	Algeria, 35.7; South Africa, 18.0; Sierra Leone, 15.0; Spanish Morocco, 12.0; Tunisia, 11.7; French Morocco, 6.8
Coal	1.5	South Africa, 87.7; Southern Rhodesia, 7.6; Nigeria, 1.8; French Morocco, 1.3

Source: Calculated from table in 1953 *Encyclopaedia Britannica Book of the Year*, pp. 461–462. World total for vanadium was not available. Africa is known to be an important producer of uranium, although exact figures are not available. The Belgian Congo is thought to be the leading African producer and possibly the leading world producer of uranium.

posits of bauxite which are to be utilized for the manufacture of aluminum at a new plant on the Volta River in the Gold Coast.

In *northwest Africa* two minerals—phosphates and iron ore—lead all others by a wide margin in value of production. The deposits of both minerals occur in Morocco, Algeria, and Tunisia. The phosphate deposits are among the most extensive in the world. Most of the production is exported to various European countries. The iron deposits, while smaller in size, contain considerable reserves of high-grade hematite ore, mainly exported to France and Britain to supplement the lower-grade domestic ores of those countries.

East Africa has been relatively unimportant in the production of minerals. However, Tanganyika has large diamond mines;

large deposits of copper are known to exist in Uganda; and both Kenya and Uganda have substantial, though undeveloped, deposits of iron ore.

Taken as a whole, Africa would appear to have a sufficient base of minerals for a considerable industrial development. The Congo-Rhodesian region and the Union of South Africa seem especially promising in this respect. Both of the latter areas have coal in addition to a variety of other important minerals.

Mineral production in Africa has rested primarily in the hands of large European corporations. Modern, large-scale methods are employed in extracting and processing the ores for export. Managers and overseers at the mines are mainly Europeans, and native Africans are employed as laborers.

The African Peoples and Their Economy

In a sense, none of the present African peoples is really "native," since all of the ancestral populations are thought to have entered the continent from outside, principally from Asia. Beginning in the remote past, northeastern Africa appears to have been a corridor through which successive peoples have entered Africa and then have drifted, or been pushed, into all parts of the continent. In the process considerable biological and cultural mixing has occurred.

Nevertheless, certain broad divisions can be discerned within the native peoples. Perhaps the most fundamental distinction is between the Negroid and non-Negroid peoples. The latter include mainly the Arabs, Berbers, and other basically Caucasoid peoples of North Africa. These peoples are lighter skinned on the average than the Negro races, have straight or wavy rather than fuzzy hair, and straight, narrow and often hooked noses in contrast to the broad flat nose of the typical Negro. Another important distinguishing characteristic is lan-

guage. Most of the non-Negroid peoples speak Semitic or Hamitic languages which are quite distinct from the native languages of Negro Africa. In the east-west grassland belt known as the Sudan there has been considerable mixing of Negroid and non-Negroid peoples over a long period. Among the peoples exhibiting both Negroid and non-Negroid characteristics in varying proportions and speaking Hamitic languages are the Fulani of the western Sudan and the Ethiopians, Galla, Somali, and Masai of East Africa.

The dominantly Negroid peoples of Africa include three principal groups: (1) the relatively primitive Pygmy Negrillos, Bushmen, and Hottentots, (2) the Guinea and Sudanese Negroes, and (3) the Bantu.

The *Pygmies,* as their name implies, are short in stature, averaging around $4\frac{1}{2}$ feet. They chiefly inhabit the tropical rain forests of the Congo Basin. Formerly the Pygmies lived exclusively by hunting, using poisoned arrows, and by gathering roots, nuts, fruits, and other food in the forest.

However, they have now mainly taken up agriculture, although their food supply is still augmented by gathering and products of the chase. The *Bushmen,* found primarily in the Kalahari region of southwestern Africa, are also below average in height, although a little taller than the Pygmies. They are nomadic hunters, using poisoned arrows, and constructing crude temporary shelters as they move about in search of game. They are expert trackers and stalkers of wild animals, and are also skilled in finding water. The latter is of vital importance in the semi-desert country which they inhabit. Like the Pygmies they are gatherers as well as hunters; their diet includes such items as roots, honey, gum from acacia trees, ant eggs, ostrich eggs, lizards, and locusts.

The *Hottentots* have nearly been eliminated as a separate people. The remnants live mainly in South West Africa north of the Orange River. They are primarily herdsmen, raising long-horned cattle and fat-tailed sheep. Their principal foods are milk products and meat. They live in semi-permanent villages of oval huts built about a central open space. The village is surrounded by a fence of thorn, and the animals are driven within the enclosure at night for protection. This type of village, known as a *kraal,* is often found among pastoral peoples of trans-Saharan Africa. The Hottentots formerly ranged widely over southern Africa, but most of their lands were taken either by the Europeans or by Bantu tribes pushing in from the north at roughly the same period that the Europeans began to move inland from the Cape of Good Hope. The Pygmies, Bushmen, and Hottentots are relatively unimportant numerically, and are gradually declining in numbers.

Far more numerous and important are the *Guinea and Sudanese Negroes* and the *Bantu.* Each of the two groups is estimated to number at least 40 or 50 million. Most of the Bantu are found south of the equator; the Guinea and Sudanese Negroes inhabit the West African coastlands and the Sudan. The Bantu peoples speak languages belonging to the same language family, though individual languages may often be different enough to be mutually unintelligible. The Guinea and Sudanese Negroes, in contrast, speak a great variety of unrelated tongues; in fact, the area they inhabit has often been termed a linguistic "shatter belt," comparable to parts of Melanesia in the confusion of languages. The Guinea Negroes, who mainly inhabit forested areas bordering the Gulf of Guinea, display in relatively unmixed form the dark brown to black skins, woolly hair, broad noses, wide nostrils, thick everted lips, and projecting jaws which are accepted as characteristic Negro traits. The Sudanese Negroes and some of the Bantu, on the other hand, often show evidence of a certain amount of non-Negroid blood in having lighter skins, thinner lips, and a tendency toward narrow or aquiline noses. The Guinea and Sudanese peoples have attained a somewhat higher level of development than most other Negroid peoples of Africa, and today are in general the farthest advanced toward self-government.

A small but increasing number of Africans have now become thoroughly Westernized in speech, clothing, education, and general way of life. Others are partially Westernized, while still clinging in various respects to the old tribal ways. Among these first two groups are the converts of Christian missions. The remainder adhere mostly to the old ways. Among them superstition and witchcraft are often rife. Polygamy still flourishes, although the missions stand resolutely against it, and governments tend to discourage it by increased taxes for additional wives. The missions also frown on the practice of *lobola* or giving of presents by a suitor to the father of his intended bride.

► African Agriculture

The Guinea Negroes live principally by tilling the soil. Some tribes among the Sudanese Negroes are also cultivators, others are herdsmen, and many are both. The same is true of the Bantu. Some of the chief characteristics of the native agricultural and pastoral economy of Africa have been described as follows by L. D. Stamp: [5]

Along the Mediterranean borders we find an agriculture established from very early times, with cattle, the plow, cereals and Mediterranean fruits—especially barley, wheat, olives, figs and the grape. Southward towards the desert margins nomadic pastoralism based on sheep replaces cultivation; in the deserts cultivation is limited to oases, and human life depends on date palms and camels.

South of the deserts in the semi-arid open lands of the Sudan are again pastoralists depending for their livelihood on cattle and sheep. Southward, with increasing rainfall and a modest rainy season, there is again some cultivation, precarious, and dependent mainly on sorghum and millet. Cultivation is by the hoe; use of the plow remains unknown.

The area of intermediate rainfall of the savanna between the steppes of the desert margins which are too dry and the forests of the equatorial margins which are too wet is favorable to cultivation. Large villages are the rule; there have been in the past empires of considerable size. Dependence for food is on millet and corn (maize); latterly on groundnuts [peanuts] on the uplands and rice along the rivers. Tobacco is grown, sometimes cotton; kola nuts are gathered. Often cattle are bred, sometimes sheep and horses, and among the cultivators or mixed farming communities are tribes almost exclusively pastoral.

Unfortunately, where the rainfall becomes more reliable and where mixed farming should reach its maximum intensity, we encounter the "fly belts" where the tsetse fly virtually eliminates domestic animals. Here the basis of life becomes the yam, manioc, banana, and palm oil, with cocoa as a "cash crop" now developed to a great extent in the Gold Coast and elsewhere.

As the closer forest is reached, villages are smaller, population sparser and patches of cultivation (shifting cultivation) more scattered.

On the plateaus of East Africa, and formerly in South Africa, the balance is somewhat different. The settled cultivators tend to be less numerous and subordinate to the aggressive, often warlike, pastoral tribes. It is here that wealth has come to be measured in head of cattle, independently of quality; indeed the cattle have little more practical value than the gold bars we civilized people bury in our vaults. Madagascar differs somewhat from the continental mainland in that cattle breeding is there associated with rice cultivation. . . .

• Shifting Cultivation

The system of agriculture commonly though somewhat misleadingly known as "shifting cultivation" is practiced through a very large part of tropical Africa. As a system it is better described as "land rotation" or "bush fallowing." In those areas inhabited by sedentary farming peoples, each village or settlement has proper to it a tract of surrounding land. The tract is probably only loosely defined except where settlements are close and population dense. In a given year the villagers working together as a community will clear a part of this village land, cutting and burning the woodland or scrub and then planting the crops appropriate to the climate and soil of the area. In due course the crops are harvested communally and the land used for a second and perhaps a third year. It is then abandoned, and a fresh tract of the village land is cleared. The abandoned land

[5] L. Dudley Stamp, *Africa: A Study in Tropical Development*. New York: John Wiley and Sons, Inc.; London: Chapman and Hall, Ltd., 1953. Pp. 147–151. Used by permission of the author and the publishers.

quickly becomes covered with a second-growth woodland or scrub. In due course the clearings reach a full cycle, and if a given tract has been allowed to "lie" fallow for about fifteen years it may be regarded as fully rested. Bush clearing is largely man's work. There is also surrounding the village itself, often as a series of enclosed gardens or "compounds" attached to individual huts, the "women's land," cultivated regularly to afford a supply of vegetables for the pot. Often the kokoyams, peppers, beans, melons, bananas, etc., are scarcely grown at all in the open farmland. The women's land is enriched by house sweepings, ashes, refuse and manure afforded by chickens, goats and human beings.

The system has often been condemned as wasteful of natural forest, of land and of labor. But it has many good points. The natural forest is probably second growth of little value anyway. The land cleared in small patches protected by surrounding woodland escapes the evils of soil erosion, and its nutrient status temporarily enhanced by the ashes of the burnt bush is maintained by the fallowing, the soil not being exposed to the atmosphere long enough for serious oxidation. Expenditure of labor is minimized by burning, and no attempt is made to remove large stumps. The cultivation is by hand—by hoeing—so the stumps do not constitute the obstacles there would be if the plow were used. We may accordingly agree with Lord Hailey when he says that shifting cultivation is "less a device of barbarism than a concession to the character of a soil which needs long periods for recovery and regeneration."

It has been estimated that in 1948 approximately 74 percent of the total population of Africa was directly dependent on some form of agriculture for a livelihood. This compares with 70 percent for Asia, 60 percent for South America, 33 percent for Europe, 31 percent for North and Central America, and 40 percent for Oceania.[6]

In the future, as industry and transportation become more fully developed in Africa and the standard of living slowly improves, it is logical to expect that the economy of the continent will become more diversified than at present and that the percentage of people engaged in agriculture will drop. However, it seems more than probable that large sections of Africa will continue to be basically agricultural at least for several decades to come.

At present the great bulk of crops produced by native Africans are grown for the use of the cultivator and his family, or for a purely local sale. In other words, the native farm economy is still mainly on a subsistence basis. However, the proportion of cash crops destined for export or for sale in the larger urban centers has been increasing in recent years. This has been partly the result of taxation and other governmental pressures, and has partly resulted simply from the desire of Africans to obtain cash with which to purchase manufactured goods and foodstuffs in the stores. In some parts of the continent, particularly in Nigeria and the Gold Coast, a class of peasant cultivators has developed which is heavily dependent on the sale of cash crops, especially cacao and palm oil. Around two thirds of the total world production of the latter two commodities normally comes from Africa, mainly from small farms in western and central Africa. Often the cacao trees and oil palms are interplanted. Large quantities of cotton and peanuts are produced for cash sale on native farms in various parts of the savanna lands. Cotton comes principally from Uganda, the Anglo-Egyptian Sudan, the Belgian Congo, French Equatorial Africa, Nigeria, Tanganyika, and French West Africa. More peanuts are produced in French West Africa, Nigeria, and the Cameroons than in all other African countries combined. Other cash crops of considerable impor-

[6] United Nations Department of Economic Affairs, *Review of Economic Conditions in Africa.* New York: 1951. P. 9.

tance grown by individual African cultivators include coffee, tobacco, and some
rice.

► Commercial Plantation Farming

Only in scattered areas of Africa have
large commercial plantations become well
established. Some of the largest plantations
are corporate enterprises in the Belgian
Congo, with palm oil as the major product.
The Firestone Company, an American concern, has developed large rubber plantations in Liberia. On the whole, however,
commercial plantations owned and operated by Occidentals have been little developed in West Africa. In British East Africa
sisal is an important plantation crop. Africa normally accounts for half or more of
the total world production. Tanganyika
is the major producing country. Considerable quantities of tea are produced
on European estates in the highlands of
Kenya and Nyasaland; however, African
production of this crop is less than 5 percent of the world total. Coffee is widely
grown in tropical Africa, both on European holdings and on native farms. Total
production has more than doubled since
the beginning of World War II, and Africa
accounted for 15 percent of the world production in 1952.

► The Importance of Livestock

Many Africans are pastoral. However,
most Africans who live by tilling the soil
also keep some animals, even if only goats
and poultry. The significance of livestock
in the life of the African is portrayed in the
following selection: [7]

Many races rely largely on cattle. This is
especially true of the Kaffirs, Basutos, Bech-
uanas, Hereros, Watusi, Masai, Gallas, Ni-
lotic Negroes, and Fulbes, some of whom
have become so dependent on cattle that
if the latter were destroyed their whole

economic and social order would be disrupted and even their religion affected.

It is difficult to overestimate the importance of domestic animals in the lives of
the African natives. While wives represent
to some extent real property or estates, cattle, sheep, and goats represent currency. In
many tribes wives are secured only by the
payment to the woman's family of a certain
number of animals, say 30 goats or sheep or
10 cattle. . . . This is even the practice in
the essentially crop-producing tribes of the
Bantu peoples. Among the tribes such as
the Watusi, Masai, and others which are
dependent on cattle for their daily food,
the whole social, economic, and religious
pattern of their society is dependent on cattle. . . . These are extreme cases, but even
in a crop-raising tribe such as the Kikuyu
sheep or goats constitute the basis of the
most important social and economic events
in the life of the individual. . . .

Cattle, sheep, and goats occupy the
greater part of the African continent. They
are absent or scarce in the extreme deserts
. . . and the heavy tropical forest or coarse
high grass savannas of the Congo, and the
Guinea Coast. With these exceptions, they
are distributed over the remainder of the
continent. . . .

The great grasslands between the tropical rainforests and the deserts and the
mountain grasslands of central and southern Africa were occupied by cattle-raising
peoples. They dominate the adjacent agricultural tribes and often hold within their
organization a dependent group of soil till-
ers. The Masai of East Africa depend entirely on cattle which they milk and bleed
for their daily food. So close is this relationship that they cannot migrate without
their herds. Moreover, they regard these
cattle as almost a divine gift and husband
them as carefully as they would their own
children. The same can be said of the
Banyoro and the Watusi. Each animal has
a name, the herds are often carefully sorted
as to color, and the greeting of the nobles
of the tribe asks first about the welfare of

the cattle, then about the welfare of the wives and children.

The great grasslands support the herds throughout the year in most places, and there is no set migration. In the drier portions migrations are often forced by lack of grass for the herds. . . .

Sheep and goat herdsmen have ranged nearer the deserts and been probably more nomadic than the cattlemen. . . . The goat and the chicken have been a boon to the less favored races. Everywhere, even in the dense forests of tropical Africa, these animals constitute a part of the diet of the agricultural races. . . . One seldom sees a native moving without the accompanying coop with chickens inside or tied to the outside, and goats are generally tethered also.

One of the major needs of Africa is the development of strains of grasses suited to African conditions which will be more nutritious for stock than the native grasses now present. The latter are often coarse, tough, and not very nutritious, so that the carrying capacity of the native grasslands is relatively low. Considerable work with grasses has been done by government experiment stations in Africa, with results that seem promising. It is conceivable that Africa may eventually become a major exporter of livestock products, provided better grasses can be widely introduced, the menace of the tsetse fly brought under control, and the tribesmen be induced to take an interest in improving the quality of their herds, rather than thinking of them in terms of mere numbers. At present the largest exports of livestock products are from European farms and ranches in the Union of South Africa.

The Europeans in Africa

We may now turn to the outsiders who have introduced such important changes in Africa during recent decades. The Europeans in Africa number only about 5 million, but they exercise a controlling influence in most African countries. The only countries that were entirely independent of political control by Europeans in 1954 were Egypt, Libya, Ethiopia-Eritrea, and Liberia.

The Major Centers of European Settlement

The most important center of European settlement and influence in Africa is the Union of South Africa. About half of the total European population of the continent lives in the Union. Although a member state of the Commonwealth of Nations, it is self-governing in every respect. The Union of South Africa is the most Westernized country on the continent, possessing types of city development and the general range of occupational groups which one might expect to find in an advanced country of Europe, or, for that matter, in the United States. It contains the only really important concentrations of factory industry in Africa, and is by far the leading

A view of Johannesburg. Heaps of waste material from old gold mining operations appear at the right of the view. The downtown office buildings of the city rise against the distant skyline. (*Union of South Africa Government Information Office.*)

country in total foreign trade. Only a fifth of the total population is European, but this is a much larger proportion than is found in any other African country.

The second most important area of European settlement, in terms of total numbers, is northwestern Africa, where approximately 1½ million Europeans, mostly French, with some Spanish and Italians, are found in the coastal sections of Algeria, Morocco, Tunisia, and Libya. Some of the Europeans in this area are agricultural colonists growing products of mediterranean agriculture, but the majority prefer to live in the cities, especially the larger seaports such as Casablanca, Algiers, Tunis, and Oran.

In tropical Africa the number and proportion of Europeans is small. According to recent estimates there are approximately 320,000 Europeans in eastern and central Africa, and 80,000 in western tropical Africa.[1] Countries of tropical Africa containing the largest numbers of Europeans include Southern Rhodesia, Belgian Congo, French West Africa, Northern Rhodesia, Kenya, French Equatorial Africa, and Tanganyika. Among the prominent occupational groups are government officials, missionaries, mining employees, traders, and

owners or managers of plantations or estates.

In tropical Africa, and the Union of South Africa as well, the Europeans have developed an economy based essentially on the employment of large numbers of unskilled or semiskilled African laborers working under European supervision. Much of the labor employed, especially by the mining companies, is migrant labor, often drawn from a radius of hundreds of miles. Among the principal magnets for such labor are the Witwatersrand gold fields of the Union of South Africa, the Katanga-Rhodesian mining belt, the tin mines of the Jos Plateau in Nigeria, and the European plantation areas in East Africa. It is customary for the native laborers, who are almost exclusively male, to leave their families in the native villages, sometimes for as long as three years, and to live in special enclosures or "compounds" at the place of work. Some companies, especially those engaged in secondary types of industry, have now begun to provide company housing for African workers and their families, hoping thereby to assure a more stable and permanent labor force. In the Belgian Congo this practice has been generally followed even by the mining companies, with apparently good results.

The Colonial Powers

Five European nations have colonial possessions in Africa at the present time: Britain, France, Belgium, Portugal, and Spain. Italy holds Somalia (formerly Italian Somaliland) as a United Nations Trust Territory pending independence to be granted in 1960. In the past each nation has tended to govern its African colonies as it saw fit, with no particular interchange of views or attempts at cooperative action with the other colonial powers. Since World War II there has been some evidence of a more coopera-

tive attitude, but relations have been disturbed by important differences in the colonial policies of the various nations. Britain, for example, proposes to foster the political and cultural development of the native Africans along lines chosen in a considerable measure by themselves, with the end result to be full self-government and a choice between complete separation from Britain and dominion status in the Commonwealth of Nations. France, on the other hand, visualizes the gradual integration of

[1] United Nations Department of Economic Affairs, *Review of Economic Conditions in Africa.* New York: 1951. P. 9.

her African colonies into a closely knit French Union, with native peoples pursuing essentially a French way of life and possessing the political rights of French citizens. Belgium, which has only one colony, the Belgian Congo, is pursuing still a third policy of postponing political development toward self-government, while attempting to build a sound economy in the colony and thus to raise the standard of living. Portugal and Spain, likewise, have done little toward developing African participation in government, but in contrast to Belgium have given relatively little attention to economic and social development

in their colonies. To a considerable degree their colonial policy has been one simply of relative neglect, and their colonies have long been considered among the most backward, underdeveloped, and poorly managed of all colonial possessions.

Since World War II the colonial powers have shown a marked upsurge of interest in their African possessions. Heavy investments of money have been made, both by governments directly and by private investors, and the pace of African economic, social, and political development has been considerably accelerated over that of prewar years.

Spanish and Portuguese Africa

Portugal and Spain were the earliest of the colonial powers to obtain holdings in Africa. Portugal, particularly, was active in African exploration and trade by the mid-fifteenth century. The epochal voyage of Vasco da Gama to India in 1498 via the Cape of Good Hope was the culmination of several decades of Portuguese exploration along the African coast. Today, however, the African possessions of Portugal are of minor importance as compared with those of Britain, France, or even Belgium.

The same is true, to an even greater degree, of Spain's African holdings. The latter include Spanish Morocco, Spanish Sahara, and Spanish Guinea. Of these possessions the most important is Spanish Morocco. It is divided into a Northern and a Southern Zone separated by French Morocco. The Northern Zone, which borders the Strait of Gibraltar and the Mediterranean Sea, has around a million people, mostly Moslem Arabs and Berbers. There is a considerable export of iron ore. The climate and vegetation are mediterranean in character, and agriculture, the principal occupation, is mainly of a subsistence nature.

The Southern Zone of Morocco is administered with Spanish Sahara, as is the enclave of Ifni on the coast of French Morocco. All of the latter areas consist of desert or semi-desert and had a total estimated population of only 95,000 in 1952. They have been briefly described as follows: [2]

Ifni consists of largely sterile steppe country where a few sheep are raised and such hardy trees as the olive grow. Fishing is the greatest source of income and most of the natives on the coast engage in it. But Ifni is a land of milk and honey compared to Spanish Sahara. This desolate region comes by its name quite honestly, for here the Sahara comes right down and spills into the sea. The natives are, with few exceptions, nomads, and their wealth—using that term very loosely—consists of camels, sheep, asses and some scrawny cattle. They represent varying degrees of mixture among Arab, Berber and Negro elements. They all profess Islam, though hardly an orthodox brand. Anthropologists would doubtless find their social and economic organization into four castes to be most interesting. In the world's economy these people play no role whatsoever.

[2] Robert Gale Woolbert, "Spain as an African Power." *Foreign Affairs,* v. 24 (1946), p. 731. Used by permission of *Foreign Affairs.*

The tiny colony of Spanish Guinea is located in the rainy tropics of West Africa bordering the Gulf of Guinea. It includes a bit of mainland (Rio Muni) plus the island of Fernando Po and some smaller islands. This colony, particularly Fernando Po, which is a rather fertile volcanic island, yields cacao, coffee, palm oil, hardwood lumber, and other tropical exports.

Spain also holds the Canary Islands, off Spanish Sahara. These are pleasant, scenic, rather productive islands which are administered as part of Spain. The Canaries are essentially mediterranean rather than African in environment and culture.

The African possessions are all that remain of the great empire, mainly in Latin America, that Spain held in former times.

The Portuguese holdings in Africa are considerably larger and more important than those of Spain. There are two main Portuguese dependencies: Angola, or Portuguese West Africa; and Mozambique, or Portuguese East Africa. These are located on opposite coasts of southern Africa.

Mozambique is mainly tropical lowland with some interior areas of low plateau and limited areas of higher plateau in the northeast, where elevations rise to 6000 feet. The climate is tropical savanna. The country is divided into two fairly equal parts by the Zambezi River. There are two important port cities, Beira (43,000) and Lourenço Marques (94,000). The former is an important outlet for trade from the Rhodesias, Nyasaland, and the Katanga mining region of the Belgian Congo; while the latter port handles a considerable volume of trade from the Witwatersrand mining district of the Union of South Africa. The Portuguese ports are connected by rail

with the respective areas which they serve. British capital has been chiefly instrumental in development of the port facilities and the connecting rail lines.

Angola, likewise, has an important seaport which draws much of its trade from outside the country. This is the port of Lobito (24,000). It is an important outlet for the Katanga region, with which it is connected by rail. Angola is mainly tropical savanna country, with a fringe of tropical steppe and coastal desert in the southwest. A small coastal exclave of Angola known as Cabinda lies north of the Congo River estuary.

Both of Portugal's large African colonies are relatively undeveloped. Native subsistence agriculture and cattle raising are the rule, although there are some areas of European plantations in Mozambique producing sugar and bananas. Coffee is the main export of Angola, amounting to nearly half the total exports by value in 1951.

Other Portuguese holdings in Africa include the small mainland colony of Portuguese Guinea and the islands of São Tomé and Principe in the Gulf of Guinea. These areas yield a small export of tropical agricultural commodities. The Portuguese also hold the Cape Verde Islands, in the Atlantic about 370 miles west of Dakar. They are mainly inhabited by a mixed Negro-European population, and are of some importance as a fueling station for ships. The Madeiras, which are essentially mediterranean in character, though located in the Atlantic Ocean off northwest Africa, are administered as a part of Portugal. The African dependencies of Portugal are now officially termed "overseas provinces."

The Belgian Congo

The Belgian Congo is Belgium's only colony. However, it is an extremely valuable possession. Although it would doubt-

less be outranked by the British and French colonial empires in total world importance, it seems doubtful that any single colony belonging to a European nation has quite so great a potential for future development as does the Congo. The Belgians appear to be operating their colony in an efficient manner, with considerable regard for the welfare of the native Africans, and there have been few reports of serious native discontent in recent years. With the Congo is governed the small United Nations Trust Territory of Ruanda-Urundi, a densely populated highland area which adjoins the Congo on the east.

The Belgian Congo is almost entirely contained within the drainage basin of the Congo River. This immense shallow basin hollowed in the surface of the African plateau has a general elevation of 1000 to 2000 feet, but is rimmed on the south and east by higher land.

Europeans in the Congo, numbering 69,-000 in 1952, are found principally in the larger urban places. The two largest cities, with 1951 estimated populations, are Leopoldville, the capital (232,000), and Elisabethville (110,000), the main urban center of the Katanga mining region. These cities have European-style commercial cores with wide streets and a number of tall buildings. The visitor may find good hotels, taxis, restaurants serving European food, moviehouses showing European and American films, and other amenities. The four-lane boulevard which serves as the main street of Leopoldville would do credit to any European or American city. All of the larger places in the Congo are reached by regular air services, and external flights, particularly to Brussels and Johannesburg, tie the colony to the outside world.

▶ Variety of the Congo

The Belgian Congo exhibits more variety in relief, climate, and vegetation than is commonly realized. Most of the northern half of the country is an area of tropical rain forest. Aside from a few urban centers on the Congo River and scattered mission stations, this hot, damp, malarial area has mostly been avoided by the permanent European settlers, and even the native population is relatively sparse. Extensive areas of tall grass savanna are found in the southern third of the country, and also in a narrow strip north of the rain forest. The

A street corner in Luluabourg, in the southern Belgian Congo. (*Belgian Tourist Bureau.*)

savanna areas have a dry season in winter, lasting in general from 2 to 6 months. In general the rainy season comes at the time of high sun; since the Congo is bisected by the equator, the northern savanna is experiencing the high sun rainy season at the same time that the southern savanna is having the low sun dry season, and vice versa. Since the tributaries of the Congo River drain considerable areas both north and south of the equator, the flow of the main river tends to be reasonably constant throughout the year. In this respect the Congo is a great contrast to the Niger or the Zambezi, which are often very low at the height of the dry season in their respective hemispheres. In the extreme east of the Belgian Congo proper, and in Ruanda-Urundi, are volcanic highlands with sizable areas lying at 5000 feet or higher. In this region there is considerable vertical zonation of climate and vegetation according to altitude. Here are found Lakes Kivu, Albert, Edward, and Tanganyika. In the vicinity of the lakes there has been a considerable development of resort facilities, including some hotels, and bungalows used by Europeans part time or throughout the year. Among the attractions of this region for Europeans are the highland climate, considerably cooler and more pleasant than the climate in most other parts of the Congo, and, in addition, some of the finest natural scenery in Africa. In this area the mountainous and scenic wildlife sanctuary of the Albert National Park has been established. The southeastern part of the Congo, in the Katanga, is an upland region ranging in elevation from about 3000 to 6000 feet. Temperatures here are considerably moderated by the altitude, though not so much as in the eastern lakes region.

▶ Historical Background

The Belgian Congo first began to be developed under the auspices of Leopold II,

King of the Belgians, in the last quarter of the nineteenth century, following exploratory journeys by the American, Henry M. Stanley. During this early period the colony was virtually a personal possession of Leopold, under whom it was vigorously exploited for wild rubber, ivory, and other tropical products gathered by the natives. In the 1890's a railroad was built connecting the port of Matadi with Leopoldville, thus avoiding a 200-mile stretch of rapids on the Congo River and providing a means of ready access to the interior of the colony from the sea. In 1908 the Congo was formally annexed by Belgium.

▶ Commercial Economy of the Congo [3]

From the beginning of administration by the Belgian government the economic life of the colony has been dominated by large corporations licensed by the government to carry on business in certain lines. Often these companies have been given concessions covering certain geographical areas and lines of business, so that in many sectors of the Congo economy the result has been monopoly control rather than competition. The government has kept a close watch, however, over the activities of these corporate groups, and in many cases economic development has been carried on jointly by the government and the corporations. The large corporations own and operate plantations, factories, mines, smelters and concentration plants, stores, hotels, railroads, river boats, and port facilities. They operate banks, serve as representatives of European insurance companies, and deal with real estate. They collect, process, and market the palm oil, cotton, cacao, and other commodities produced on native farms. These companies pay taxes to the Congo government which are used exclusively to meet the expenses of the government, including investment in projects designed to further the economic and

---

[3] The discussion under this heading is based principally on two articles, "The Congo Is in Business" and "Colonial Big Five," by Herbert Solow, in *Fortune* (November, 1952).

social development of the colony. None of the tax returns go to Belgium. However, the companies are mostly owned in Belgium, and dividends from company earnings go principally to Belgian shareholders.

The Congo government is headed by a governor-general appointed by the government of Belgium and directly responsible to it. Subordinate officials, likewise, are appointed. Even the native chiefs are appointees. Neither whites nor Africans are allowed to vote; however, both groups have recourse to a system of courts of justice. The Belgians have taken the position that the first requirement for the colony is a sound economic base and an acceptable standard of living for both whites and Africans, with political development to come later. Attempts are being made to draw the Africans more fully into the general economic life of the Congo than has been the case in most African colonies. The Africans are not confined to unskilled labor, but through education and on-the-job training have been gradually brought into many occupations requiring considerable skill. Today without white assistance they operate trains, river boats, steam shovels, bulldozers, and electric furnaces, work as carpenters, masons, telegraphers, and typists, and serve as postal clerks, nurses, elementary school teachers, and pastors of native Christian churches. However, as yet they do not qualify as doctors, lawyers, engineers, or higher educators. In their school system the Belgians have emphasized elementary education, and a larger proportion of the children attend elementary school than in most other African colonies. However, comparatively few Congo natives have attended a college or university, as compared with a considerable number in the British and French colonies.

Employers of African labor in the Congo are required to conform to minimum wage scales set by the government. Workers receive most of their pay in the form of rations, clothing, housing, and social services, such as free medical care and education. Actual cash wages are low. However, the Belgians hope to gradually stimulate among the Africans a desire for material possessions and thus bring them more fully within a money economy. It is hoped, in other words, that the ideal of leisure can be replaced to some degree by the ideal of consumption, so that the Africans will come of their own volition to do regular and steady work in order to accumulate money with which to buy goods. In this way a large internal market will be developed, production of a variety of goods will be stimulated, and thus the colony will come to have a more balanced economy and be less dependent on export of a few primary products.

The mining companies are the largest employers of labor. Unlike the South African companies, employers in the Congo have tended to avoid the use of compounds at the mining sites in which native men are housed apart from their families. The practice has been to provide company housing for African families, thus assuring a smaller turnover and more general stability in the supply of labor. Even so, however, it has often proved difficult to induce the Africans to work steadily over long periods. It is estimated that three fourths of the native people still live in tribal villages and that 6.5 of every 10 Africans on the average are engaged in growing food. In recent years there has been an almost constant labor shortage in the expanding commercial economy of the Congo, and considerable numbers of workers have come into the colony from outside.

The Congo has experienced a modest development of manufacturing plants mainly producing the simpler types of goods. Typical commodities are cheap cotton textiles, shoes, bricks, cement, and various types of processed foods. There is some shipbuilding, cigarette manufacture, chemical manufacture, and metalworking. As yet, how-

TABLE 24

BELGIAN CONGO AND RUANDA-URUNDI
PRINCIPAL EXPORTS, 1951

MINERALS	PERCENT OF TOTAL EXPORTS BY VALUE
Copper	24.9
Tin Ore and Ingots	9.4
Cobalt, Granulated and White Alloys	5.8
Zinc Concentrates	3.4
Diamonds	3.0
AGRICULTURAL COMMODITIES AND TIMBER	
Palm Oil, Cabbage Palm Oil, and Cabbage Palm Nuts	18.9
Raw Cotton	11.0
Coffee	9.0
Crude Rubber	3.6
Timber	1.2
All Other Exports	9.8

Source: *United Nations Yearbook of International Trade Statistics,
1951.* Figures shown do not include exports of uranium.

ever, the Congo is mainly important in the economic world as an exporter of minerals and tropical agricultural products. The principal exports of the Congo together with Ruanda-Urundi in 1951 are shown in Table 24. It will be noted from the table that ten primary commodities or commodity groups constituted nine tenths of all announced exports by value. Among the minerals, uranium, copper, cobalt, and zinc come principally from Katanga Province, tin from Katanga and Kivu Provinces, and diamonds from Kasai Province. Palm products, crude rubber, and timber come from the areas of tropical rain forest, and cotton from the savannas and the drier fringes of the tropical forest. The main producing area for coffee is the eastern highlands.

The port of Matadi (43,000) normally handles well over half of the total foreign trade of the Congo. The principal port outside of the Congo is Lobito in Angola, which handles more of the colony's trade than all other foreign ports in Africa combined.

French Africa

The French possessions in Africa are the largest in total area of those held by any European country, although the total estimated population is somewhat less than the population of Britain's African possessions.

Most of French Africa is concentrated in the northwestern quadrant of the continent. Morocco, Algeria, and Tunisia have been discussed in Chapter 15. The principal French-held areas in tropical Africa are French Equatorial Africa, French West Africa, the Cameroons, and the large island of Madagascar.

▶ *French West Africa and French Equatorial Africa*

French West Africa and French Equatorial Africa are federations composed of several subordinate colonial territories. French West Africa lies mainly in the Sudan and the Sahara Desert, but includes fringes of tropical rain forest along the Gulf of Guinea. Dakar (330,000), a seaport which had considerable strategic importance during World War II, is the capital. Abidjan (160,000) is an important seaport on the Gulf of Guinea. French Equatorial Africa, extending nearly 1500 miles from north to south, is divided about equally between the desert, the Sudan, and the tropical rain forest. No other country of Africa displays so well the transition from tropical forest through tropical savanna and steppe to desert. Brazzaville (84,000), the capital, is located in the far south on the Congo River opposite Leopoldville, the capital of the Belgian Congo. Brazzaville is connected by rail with Pointe Noire (22,-000) on the Gulf of Guinea. The latter city has one of the best artificial harbors in West Africa. The Cameroons adjoins French Equatorial Africa on the west. Former German territory, it is divided between

France and Britain for administration as a United Nations Trust Territory. The same is true of the smaller and less important Togoland. French West Africa, French Equatorial Africa, the French Cameroons, and French Togoland are less developed in an economic sense than the Belgian Congo or several of the British colonial possessions in Africa. Possibly one reason can be that the French territories are relatively lacking in proven mineral resources as compared with the Belgian and British possessions. The quest for minerals in Africa has been perhaps the single most important factor leading to over-all economic development, and areas lacking in mineral deposits have definitely tended to lag behind. However, there are indications of greater mineral reserves in the tropical mainland territories of French Africa than those now known. These may be of considerable significance in the future.

▶ Madagascar and Réunion

Madagascar, known to the French as "La Grande Île," is one of the largest islands in the world. It is nearly 1000 miles long and about 350 miles wide. It lies off the southeast coast of Africa and has geological formations similar to those of the African mainland. However, it has been separated from the latter for a very long period, so that it has developed a distinctive flora and fauna.

Madagascar is unique among African areas in that it appears to have been originally settled by Malays and kindred peoples from Southeast Asia. The first migrations occurred perhaps as far back as 2000 B.C. More recently, there has been a considerable influx of Bantu peoples from the mainland, and the present native population is a fairly complex racial mixture. There are about 50,000 white Frenchmen and 20,000 recent Asian immigrants, most of them being Indians of the Hindu faith or Chinese.

The east coast of Madagascar rises steeply from the Indian Ocean to heights of over 6000 feet. Since the island lies in the path of trade winds blowing across the Indian Ocean, the east side receives the heaviest rain. Rice, the main crop, is raised here in terraced fields. Tamatave (36,000), the main seaport, is located roughly midway down the east coast. Tananarive (183,000), the capital, is located on a plateau, mostly lying at 3000 feet or higher, in the central part of the island. Madagascar has a much smaller degree of economic development than such tropical islands as Java, Formosa, or Ceylon.

The island of Réunion in the Indian Ocean east of Madagascar is a volcanic tropical island with a population mainly of French descent. It was uninhabited prior to the coming of the French in the seventeenth century. Elevations on the island reach 10,000 feet. The soils are fertile, and a great variety of tropical crops are grown. Sugar and rum are the main exports. Sugar is also the mainstay of the economy on the larger British island of Mauritius which lies near by. The latter island includes a larger proportion of lowland than Réunion. Its population is mainly composed of immigrant Indians. There are, however, a considerable number of Creoles, who are descended from eighteenth-century French planters, and in addition, some Negroes, Chinese, and mixed bloods. A number of small island groups in the Indian Ocean are administered as dependencies of Mauritius.

British Africa

By almost any standard except that of total area held, the United Kingdom is the leading colonial power in Africa. Although the French possessions are larger in total area, the British territories are more productive, more densely populated, and more

An African village in the oil palm belt of Nigeria. The oil, used for making such commodities as soap, oleomargarine, and candles, is secured from clusters of fruit found among the branches at the top of each palm. Most of the production is exported, although some is used as a cooking fat in village households. (*British Information Services.*)

economically developed than the French areas.

▶ British West Africa

The British colonial possessions in Africa are found in several different parts of the continent. The West African possessions are spaced at intervals along the Guinea Coast. They include Nigeria, the Gold Coast, Sierra Leone, and Gambia. It is in this area that the Negro has advanced farthest toward self-government in colonial Africa. In 1951 the Gold Coast witnessed the first election of Negroes to ministerial office in a British colonial territory. The number of Europeans in the four West African possessions is extremely small.

• *Nigeria.*[4] Nigeria is the largest of Britain's West African possessions, being indeed the largest in both area and population of any political unit still included within the British colonial empire.

Nigeria exhibits in an excellent manner the transition in environments, peoples, and ways of life which one encounters in proceeding northward from the tropical forests of the Guinea Coast through the grasslands of the Sudan to the fringes of the desert.

The rainy, forested south is inhabited by Negro tribes, largely pagan, who rely on cassava, yams, maize, and palm oil as subsistence crops and palm oil and cacao as cash exports. In recent years this area has

---

[4] The discussion under this heading is based principally on Keith Buchanan, "Nigeria—Largest Remaining British Colony." *Economic Geography,* v. 28 (1952), pp. 302–322.

accounted for about half of the world's palm oil exports and a sixth of the cacao exports. The principal belt of oil palms lies in the denser rain forest of the east, parts of which receive up to 100 inches of rain per year. Local population densities reach 500 to 1000 per square mile in the more highly developed areas of commercial palm oil production. The main cacao belt is found in the drier, more open forests of the west. Here, in extreme southwestern Nigeria, are two of the largest cities in tropical Africa: the important seaport and capital of Lagos (230,000) and the inland city of Ibadan (335,000), located 70 miles to the northeast.

The open, drier, seasonally rainy Sudan grasslands of northern Nigeria are a different world from that of the extreme south. Here Mohammedan Hamitic-Negro peoples are dominant, nomadic or semi-nomadic cattle and goat raising is of major importance, and grains (millets, sorghums, maize) rather than roots are the basic subsistence crops. Peanuts are of major significance both as a subsistence crop and as a cash export. Nigeria supplies two fifths of the world's exports of peanuts in some years. The old caravan city of Kano (107,-000), today served by an international airport, is the largest city and principal administrative and trading center of northern Nigeria.

The 4000-foot Jos Plateau in central Nigeria is one of the more important tin-mining areas of the world, supplying an eighth of world exports of this metal in some years. A government-sponsored dairy industry on the high grasslands of the plateau utilizes milk purchased from nomadic herdsmen to produce butter and cheese for urban markets.

The British portion of the Cameroons Trust Territory is administered with Nigeria. Here, under the auspices of the Nigerian government, a number of commercial plantations (formerly German) produce bananas, cacao, palm oil, and rubber.

They represent the only important development of this type of production in Nigeria.

• *The Smaller West African Dependencies.* The Gold Coast, although far smaller than Nigeria in both area and population, ranks second in size and importance among the British West African dependencies. It is predominantly an area of tropical savanna climate, although the rainfall is sufficiently great in the southwest to produce a natural vegetation of broadleaf evergreen forest. In this forested area is grown the major export crop—cacao. The Gold Coast normally supplies a third to half of the total world exports of cacao beans, which are roasted and then ground to a powder in overseas processing centers to produce cocoa. Nearly all of the cacao trees are grown by African farmers on small individual plots of land. The inland city of Kumasi (78,000) is located in the major cacao-producing district. Accra (136,000), southeast of Kumasi, is the colony's capital and an important seaport. However, like many other West African ports, it lacks deep-water harbor facilities, and cargo must be transferred between ship and shore by surf boats or lighters. A modern deep-water port has been developed on the southwest coast at Takoradi (18,000). Through the latter port move exports of cacao and manganese. Manganese is one of the two main minerals exported from the Gold Coast, the other, not illogically, being gold.

The remaining West African dependencies deserve briefer mention. In Sierra Leone a hot, damp, forested coastal lowland rises to a savanna upland in the extreme north and east. Long notorious as one of the most unhealthful areas in Africa, Sierra Leone has gained considerable note in recent years as an exporter of high-grade iron ore. Freetown (70,000) is the capital, largest city, and main port. An analogous position is held by Bathurst (20,000) in the remaining dependency, Gambia. The latter

Preparing cacao for export on a family farm in the Gold Coast. The cacao pods are cut open with machetes preparatory to removing the beans, which are embedded in a mass of pulp. After being dried in the sun, the beans will be packed for shipment to overseas processing centers. (*British Information Services.*)

is a narrow strip of tropical savanna extending inland along either side of the Gambia River. The major commercial product is peanuts, furnishing more than nine tenths of all exports by value.

► British East Africa

The dependencies of British East Africa include Kenya, Tanganyika, Uganda, and Zanzibar. Kenya and Tanganyika contain a considerably greater number and proportion of Europeans than the West African dependencies. However, in neither of these does the European population amount to even 1 percent of the total.

The largest number of Europeans (30,-000 in 1948) are found in Kenya. In this dependency the main area of European settlement is in the highland savannas of the southwest, where the land rises to more than 5000 feet over an extensive area. Nairobi (134,000), located toward the southeastern edge of the area of European set-

tlement, is the capital of Kenya and the largest city of British East Africa. It is connected by rail with the seaport of Mombasa (85,000) on the Indian Ocean.

Kenya has attracted much notice in recent years as a result of terrorist activities by a secret native society, the Mau Mau, whose avowed purpose is to oust the European population. The Mau Mau are members of the Kikuyu tribe of cultivators, who along with the Masai tribe of herdsmen, constitute the principal African population. Numerous atrocities, not only against the European settlers, but also against Africans friendly to Europeans, created a state of emergency in the early 1950's, and British troops were brought in to restore order. The situation with respect to the Mau Mau society was not yet fully resolved at the time of writing.

Tanganyika is a United Nations Trust Territory administered by Britain. Dar-es-Salaam (69,000) is the capital, largest city, and main port. Tanganyika has a considerably smaller European population than Kenya (16,000 in 1948), a fact due at least in part to a natural environment which is less favorable for European settlement. In Uganda the number of Europeans is even smaller, amounting in 1948 to 3500 out of a total population of about 5 million. Uganda, a protectorate, is being administered with native interests paramount, and European settlement is highly restricted. The country is dominated politically by the relatively advanced and prosperous Buganda kingdom.

Asians, mostly Indians, are more numerous than Europeans in each of the four East African dependencies. They are especially active in business in the towns. Their economic and political influence is particularly strong in Tanganyika, where the British government is obligated to give them equal opportunity with Europeans under the terms of the trusteeship. The British island protectorate of Zanzibar, ruled by a Moslem Sultan, is a remnant of former extensive Arab holdings along the East African coast.

The Anglo-Egyptian Sudan, administered jointly by Britain and Egypt pending self-government in 1956, and the small protectorate of British Somaliland have been discussed in Chapter 15.

▶ British Dependencies in Central and Southern Africa

British-held areas in Central Africa include Southern Rhodesia, Northern Rhodesia, and Nyasaland. The mineral wealth and relatively high elevation of the Rhodesias have been described in Chapter 23. In Southern Rhodesia an estimated 6.4 percent of the population is European—the highest proportion for any British possession in Africa. Europeans numbered 135,600 in 1951. Southern Rhodesia is almost completely self-governing. Salisbury (160,000 with suburbs), and Bulawayo (125,000 with suburbs) are the largest urban places. In 1953 the two Rhodesias were joined with Nyasaland to form the new Federation of Rhodesia and Nyasaland.

The three British High Commission Territories of Basutoland, Swaziland, and Bechuanaland, enclosed by or bordering the Union of South Africa, are of minor importance. They are a source of friction between Britain and South Africa, since the latter nation has openly expressed a desire to govern them. The population of these territories is almost solidly African.

The Union of South Africa

The Union of South Africa, occupying the far south of the African continent, is unquestionably the most powerful and influential African country. This is, of course, partly because of its position as a self-governing member state of the Commonwealth of Nations. Even more, however, it is because South Africa represents the leading center of permanent European settlement and modern industry in an underdeveloped continent dominated by Europeans, but mainly populated by non-Europeans.

The population of the Union includes about half of all the Europeans in Africa, and perhaps 85 percent of the Europeans in Africa south of the Sahara. Lying almost entirely in middle latitudes, the country has mean annual temperatures ranging generally between 60° and 70°F. except in the higher mountains, and most places have a period of frost in winter. Thus from the standpoint of temperature the Union is well suited to European settlement, though it should not be forgotten that the temperatures have also proved favorable for Africans. It cannot be claimed as a "white man's land" simply on the basis of climate.

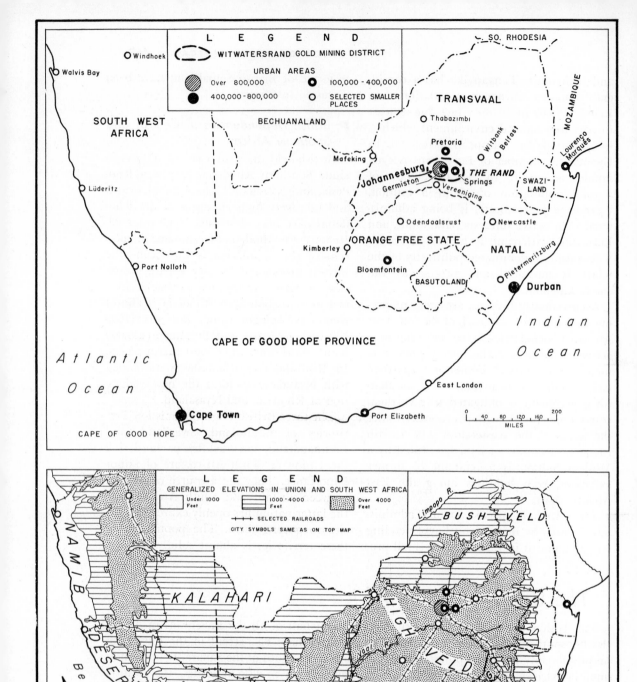

LEGEND

WITWATERSRAND GOLD MINING DISTRICT

URBAN AREAS

Over 800,000   100,000 - 400,000

400,000 - 800,000   SELECTED SMALLER PLACES

SO. RHODESIA

TRANSVAAL

Windhoek

Walvis Bay

SOUTH WEST AFRICA

BECHUANALAND

Thabazimbi

MOZAMBIQUE

Pretoria

Witbank   Belfast

Lourenço Marques

Mafeking

Johannesburg   *THE RAND*

Germiston   Springs

SWAZI-LAND

Lüderitz

Vereeniging

Odendaalsrust   Newcastle

ORANGE FREE STATE

NATAL

Port Nolloth

Kimberley   Pietermaritzburg

Bloemfontein

BASUTOLAND

Durban

Indian Ocean

Atlantic Ocean

CAPE OF GOOD HOPE PROVINCE

East London

Cape Town

CAPE OF GOOD HOPE

Port Elizabeth

0   40   80   120   160   200

MILES

LEGEND

GENERALIZED ELEVATIONS IN UNION AND SOUTH WEST AFRICA

Under 1000 Feet   1000 - 4000   Over 4000 Feet

SELECTED RAILROADS

CITY SYMBOLS SAME AS ON TOP MAP

Limpopo R.

BUSH VELD

NAMIB DESERT

KALAHARI

HIGH VELD

Orange R.

Vaal R.

Benguela Current

UPPER KARROO

Orange R.

DRAKENSBERG

GREAT KARROO

LITTLE KARROO

In practice, however, the Europeans, who have had virtually complete control in political and economic affairs, have developed the country according to their own conceptions. Mostly a frontier area a century ago, South Africa is today a land where the visitor from Western Europe or Anglo-America will find modern factories, fast trains, up-to-date resorts and hotels, substantial homes and schools, and most of the other institutions and facilities to which he is accustomed. Johannesburg and Cape Town, the largest urban places, are imposing cities of over half a million; the former has a number of towering office buildings which might have been transplanted from an American city of similar size. Hundreds of smaller places manifest the European or

if South West Africa is counted as part of the Union; see page 477) and twelve times the population of South Africa. The difference in population is even more striking when Europeans alone are considered. The United States has more than fifty times as many people of European descent as does South Africa. Instead of being overwhelmingly the majority group, as in the United States, the Europeans in South Africa represent only a fifth of the total population, being outnumbered more than three to one by the Bantu. In addition, there are two other sizable racial groups, the Coloured, of mixed origin, and the Asians, who are mostly Indians. Numbers and proportions of the four major population groups are given in Table 25.

TABLE 25

POPULATION ELEMENTS OF THE UNION OF SOUTH AFRICA

RACIAL GROUP	NUMBER (1951 CENSUS— FOUR PROVINCES)	PERCENT OF TOTAL POPULATION
European	2,643,187	20.9
African	8,535,341	67.5
Coloured	1,102,323	8.7
Asian	365,524	2.9
Total, four provinces	12,646,375	100.0
South West Africa	430,354	(European 49,641 or 11.5%; African 380,686 or 88.5%; Malay 16; Asian 11)

Source: *1954 Britannica Book of the Year*. Figures for Coloured include 63,557 Cape Malays

American influence in the arrangement of their business districts and residential sections.

▶ Comparison with the United States

Visitors to South Africa often say that they are reminded of the United States. However, such impressions are apt to be superficial, and comparisons between the two countries should not be pushed too far. For one thing, they are not in the same class with respect to size. The United States has roughly six times the area (four times

• The Africans. It is the existence of the large African majority in South Africa which provides perhaps the most essential point of difference between that country and the United States. There is, of course, a substantial Negro minority in the United States, but only in the South and the larger metropolitan centers outside of the South do Negroes form a large enough proportion of the population to be of major political, social, and economic significance. In South Africa, by contrast, the African is almost omnipresent.

You meet the African everywhere in South Africa. There is no farm or factory or town where he is not to be found. Where building and road-making are in progress; where European-owned shops and offices are being run; where ships are being loaded and unloaded, there the African will be. The traveler by train will see Africans at every station and siding; the traveler by road will, from time to time, pass an African who is walking hundreds of miles to a town or city. And when the traveler stays at a hotel for the night he will probably find Africans waiting on him at table and waking him with an early-morning cup of tea.[5]

An estimated 3 million Africans in the Union live on European-owned farms, which are vitally dependent on them for labor. Another 2.5 million live in towns and cities, where they are mainly employed as unskilled or semiskilled laborers in mines and factories, or as house servants. The remaining 3 million live on tribal reserves, which are comparable to the Indian reservations of western United States, though much larger in relative scale. Tribalism among the Africans has been gradually breaking down, although a semblance of the old ways is still maintained in the reserves. In the towns and cities many Africans have discarded their tribal allegiance and customs.

The Europeans in the Union have placed legal restrictions on the African population which have no real parallel in the United States. The Africans are excluded from voting, are prohibited by law from owning land outside the reserves, and are required to live in designated areas. They may not intermarry with Europeans. Even their freedom of movement is restricted in various ways.

In the Orange Free State and the Transvaal all African males must have a pass to move from district to district. They must have one to enter or leave Natal. They must have another to enter or to leave a reserve. And everywhere in the country they must have a pass to enter a proclaimed labor area.

Africans living in the cities must have a special pass to be in the European area after curfew. Entry into an urban area requires a local permit. At all times the receipt for the current poll tax must be carried. Failure to produce any of these passes or permits upon demand anywhere by the police means arrest and a fine or imprisonment. Furthermore, Africans must use separate buses and go to separate movies, restaurants, and hotels. In public buildings and public gatherings, in the shops, and on the beaches, they must use separate facilities.

Though the Coloureds and Indians are included in many of these rules and regulations, their movements are less restricted than those of the Africans. Nevertheless, limitations on ownership of land and other social and political ordinances cause mounting resentment.[6]

• *Unbalanced Economy of the Union.* A further significant point of difference between South Africa and the United States is revealed when the resources and economies of the two countries are compared. The United States has far more diversified and abundant resources, and the American economy is much more solidly based. Probably the United States comes closer than any other country to a completely balanced economy with a full development of all the principal types of economic activity. South Africa, in contrast, appears excessively dependent on a single economic activity, gold mining.

---

[5] Leo Marquard, *The Peoples and Policies of South Africa.* London, New York, Cape Town: Geoffrey Cumberlege, Oxford University Press, 1952. Pp. 33–34. Used by permission of the publisher.

[6] Samuel Thorne, Jr., and Alice Taylor, "Union of South Africa." *Focus*, v. 4, no. 2 (1953), pp. 5–6. Used by permission of *Focus* and the American Geographical Society of New York.

The Union's economy was originally based on extensive agriculture and grazing, but since the discovery of diamonds and gold it has really been founded on mining. Gold mining is the basic South African source of wealth. No matter where one begins a study of the South African economy, sooner or later one comes back to gold. Today agriculture and grazing are both artificially sustained by tax monies derived from the gold-producing industry. The bulk of the manufacturing activity is also fundamentally tied up with gold production. All students agree in calling the South African economy one of the most rigid, artificial and precariously balanced in the world today.[7]

Should the world demand for gold suddenly decline, or the deposits become exhausted, South Africa would be in a serious plight. However, there is no evidence that either of these contingencies is about to happen; furthermore, trends in recent years suggest that South Africa is slowly lessening its dependence on gold by improvement of agriculture and grazing and development of diversified types of manufacturing.

In trade emphases the United States and South Africa are opposites. The United States is predominantly an importer of raw materials and foodstuffs and an exporter of manufactured goods. In contrast, more than nine tenths of South African imports are manufactured commodities, and exports mainly consist of a few primary products of the mining and grazing industries. The leading exports in order of importance are gold, wool, and diamonds.

▶ South African Regions

Most countries in the world are characterized by a certain degree of physical, cultural, and economic regionalism. In South Africa this characteristic is very pronounced. To gain much of an insight into the geography of the country, it must be considered not only as a whole, but in terms of regional units. The latter may be delimited in various ways according to the purpose in view. For an introductory overview, as in this book, the provincial divisions of South Africa will serve reasonably well as major units for study. This is essentially due to the fact that South Africa exhibits a closer correspondence than most countries between major political divisions and regions defined in other terms.

Although the provincial divisions of South Africa are distinct from each other in various respects, they have a tendency to fall into three groups: (1) the Transvaal and Orange Free State, (2) Natal, and (3) the Cape of Good Hope Province and South West Africa. Such a threefold grouping has advantages from the standpoint of simplicity and eliminating unnecessary repetition, and will be adhered to in the following discussion.

▶ Transvaal and Orange Free State

The interior of South Africa is a plateau lying at a general elevation of 3000 to 6000 feet. It represents the southernmost extension of the interior plateaus which occupy most of the African continent. In South Africa the plateau surface is highest at the east and tapers off gradually toward the west. Three rivers, the Orange, Vaal, and Limpopo, drain most of the plateau area. At the extreme east of the plateau is the *High Veld,* a rolling expanse of open grassland somewhat similar to the original prairies of midwestern United States. The general elevation of the High Veld is 4500 to 6000 feet. It occupies most of the Orange Free State and the southern third of the Transvaal and extends into the adjoining native territory of Basutoland. The northern two thirds of the Transvaal is primarily a savanna with scattered trees—the "Bush Veld."

---

[7] C. Hartley Grattan, "The Future of Africa." *Harper's Magazine,* v. 186 (1943), p. 493. Used by permission of the author.

• *Gold and Diamond Mining.* The gold mining industry of the Union is almost entirely confined to the High Veld. The main workings are located on the Witwatersrand (Rand), a gold-bearing formation in the Transvaal about 110 miles long. Johannesburg (880,000 including suburbs), the largest city in Africa south of the Sahara, is located about in the center of the Rand. The city is directly on the gold field, and the workings extend underneath it. To the east and west are a number of smaller mining cities and towns, the largest of which are Germiston (150,000) and Springs (119,-000). Johannesburg and its suburbs and satellite cities make up a conurbation of roughly 1½ million people.

The Rand has been the principal area of gold mining since the original discovery of gold in 1886. It is by far the leading gold-producing area in the world, normally supplying between one third and one half of the estimated annual world production. Immense amounts of capital are invested in the Rand mines, which are operated exclusively by large corporations. In a few places mining operations have now reached depths of more than 9000 feet— among the deepest mines in the world. The Bantu laborers employed in the mines are recruited from native reserves in the Union or from other African political units. It is estimated that about three fifths of the total number now come from outside the Union.

It is thought that the Rand mines have now passed their peak of production, but sufficient gold reserves probably remain to support large-scale operations for several more decades. In addition to the Rand production, South Africa will be able to rely increasingly on gold deposits discovered in 1946 near Odendaalsrust in the Orange Free State. The latter deposits may in time rival those of the Rand in importance. Beside the value of the gold itself, recovery of uranium from mine tailings promises to be increasingly profitable. In 1953 several uranium extraction plants were being built at mines on the Rand and in the Free State.

Since 1867 the Union has been an important producer of diamonds. Formerly the major production was from diamond-bearing volcanic intrusions which were mined at Kimberley, Pretoria, and a number of other places. Since 1927, however, production from alluvial deposits in the Transvaal, Cape Province, and South West Africa has given increasing competition. Kimberly (59,000) in the Orange Free State is the principal administrative center for the diamond industry, although actual production of diamonds in the vicinity of the city has declined. In recent years the Belgian Congo has greatly surpassed South Africa in total production and exports of diamonds.

• *Coal and Steel.* The mining industry in South Africa requires large quantities of electricity, most of which is supplied by steam electric plants. These plants are powered by coal, which is present in the Union in vast quantities. Only five countries have a greater estimated reserve: the United States, USSR, China, Canada, and Germany. The coal deposits are of immense importance to South Africa, since the Union possesses little or no petroleum or natural gas and only a modest hydroelectric potential. Most of the important known deposits exist in the southern Transvaal and northwestern Natal; they include various grades of bituminous and some anthracite coal. Coking coal secured at Witbank (Transvaal) and Newcastle (Natal) has made possible the only sizable iron and steel industry in Africa. The industry is mainly concentrated within a radius of about 40 miles from Johannesburg. Blast furnaces and steelworks are located at Pretoria (283,000 including suburbs) and at Vanderbijl Park, near Vereeniging, and additional steelworks are found at Vereeniging and Johannesburg. Iron ore comes by rail from deposits of high-grade hematite in the vicinity of Thabazimbi, north-west of Pretoria.

• **Manufacturing.** The government of South Africa, which is anxious to foster a greater self-sufficiency in manufactured goods, has given assistance in various ways to the iron and steel industry and to other manufacturing industries as well. Besides iron and steel making and processing, the principal types of manufacturing include food processing; textile milling, mainly based on South African wool; and the manufacture of shoes and other leather goods. The greatest concentration of manufacturing plants is in the southern Transvaal, with Johannesburg as the main center. Outside of the Transvaal, manufacturing is mainly localized in or near the seaports of Durban, Cape Town, Port Elizabeth, and East London.

• **The Agriculture of the High Veld.** The High Veld is not only the principal focus of mining and manufacturing in the Union, but is also the leading area of field agriculture. The main field crop in acreage and value of production is maize. Around 85 to 90 percent of the maize acreage of the Union is located in the Orange Free State and Transvaal, mainly on the High Veld. Most of the production is fed to livestock, although a certain amount of maize is exported to the United Kingdom and other West European countries. The principal farm animals are beef cattle, dairy cattle, and sheep. The High Veld is the only part of the Union where commercial crop and livestock farming has been developed on an extensive scale. Individual farms are large, averaging between 500 and 1000 acres. Farmsteads are widely spaced and customarily include a number of planted shade trees around the house. Windmills are extensively used to pump water from wells for stock and household use.

Some parts of the Transvaal, mostly outside of the High Veld, have a more specialized agriculture based on tobacco, wheat, alfalfa, fruit, and vegetables. These districts, which often depend on irrigation water from the rivers to supplement the summer rains, are generally at a lower elevation than the High Veld and have a longer frost-free season. The northern half of the Transvaal, in fact, is essentially an area without frost. Under these conditions extensive production of citrus fruits has been possible, and the Transvaal now has around half of the total citrus acreage in the Union.

• **The Moisture Problem.** Although temperatures nearly everywhere in South Africa are favorable for agriculture, much of the country is too dry for nonirrigated farming. Most of the western half of the Union and virtually all of South West Africa receives less than 15 inches of rainfall annually. Due to the high rate of evaporation, this amount is too small for most types of nonirrigated field agriculture. The High Veld gets about 20 to 30 inches of precipitation on the average. But the total amount varies considerably from year to year, and there are frequent periods of drought even during what would normally be the rainy season. Fortunately for agriculture, the High Veld receives most of its precipitation during the summer half year, when it is most needed for crop growth.

Precipitation in South Africa is mainly derived from the Indian Ocean. Moisture-bearing winds blowing off the sea beat against the mountainous eastern escarpment of the plateau, are forced upward and cooled, and produce an annual rainfall of 40 inches or more in most of Natal, northeastern Cape Province, and Basutoland. As the winds move westward they become steadily drier. As a result western Cape Province and South West Africa are mainly semi-desert or desert.

Climatic data for some representative South African stations are given in Table 26.

TABLE 26

CLIMATIC DATA FOR SELECTED STATIONS IN THE UNION OF SOUTH AFRICA AND SOUTH WEST AFRICA

STATION	CLIMATIC AREA	ELEVA-TION (FEET)	AVERAGE TEMPERATURE		AVERAGE PRECIPITATION		
			JAN. °F.	JULY °F.	ANNUAL (INCHES)	PERCENT OCT.–MAR.	PERCENT DEC.–FEB.
Cape Town (Cape Province)	Mediterranean Region	40	71°	55°	24.7″	23.1%	8.5%
Port Nolloth (Cape Province)	Namib Desert	22	60°	55°	2.5″	28.0%	12.0%
Walvis Bay (South West Africa)	Namib Desert	24	66°	58°	0.3″	. . .	. . .
Windhoek (South West Africa)	Upland Steppe	5463	75°	55°	13.6″	86.8%	57.4%
Mafeking (Transvaal)	High Veld	4173	74°	52°	22.1″	85.5%	50.2%
Pretoria (Transvaal)	High Veld	4375	72°	51°	28.3″	76.3%	49.5%
Belfast (Transvaal)	High Veld	6135	62°	42°	31.2″	85.9%	46.8%
Pietermaritzburg (Natal)	Humid Subtropical Upland	2243	71°	56°	36.1″	81.2%	44.8%
Durban (Natal)	Humid Subtropical Coast	50	76°	63°	45.1″	68.5%	33.5%

▶ Natal

Natal occupies a hilly belt between the Indian Ocean and the Drakensberg, a bold escarpment marking the edge of the interior plateau. Seen from the east, the escarpment appears as a spectacular, rocky mountain wall. The highest elevations in the Union are found in the Drakensberg. Several peaks exceed 10,000 feet.

The leading commercial crop of Natal is sugar cane, most of which is grown in a narrow coastal lowland bordering the Indian Ocean. Nearly all the cane sugar produced in the Union comes from Natal.

• *The Indians.* Today, sugar cane is grown mainly on European farms worked by Bantu labor. Formerly, however, the majority of workers in the cane fields were indentured laborers brought from India. The latter began coming to Natal in the 1860's. The majority chose to remain in South Africa when their terms of indenture were ended, and the total number of In-

dians has steadily increased. No new immigration has been permitted since 1913, and internal migration of Indians from one province to another is now severely restricted by law. About nine tenths of the total Indian population is found in Natal, mostly in Durban or its vicinity. Today they are usually employed as market gardeners and small tradesmen; few are employed in the cane fields. The presence of this racial group is an important distinguishing characteristic of Natal.

Outside of Natal the main concentrations of Indians are found on the Rand and in Cape Town. In these places they are employed almost exclusively as tradesmen. The Indians of South Africa do not have equal political and economic rights with the Europeans, although ranking somewhat above the Africans in these respects.

• *The Specialized Agriculture of Natal.* In certain respects Natal is the Florida of South Africa, as the Cape Region is its California.

Like Florida, Natal is an important specialized producer of winter vegetables, sugar cane, citrus fruits, and other subtropical crops. In both cases the physical and economic factors favoring such production are essentially the same—a climate combining adequate rain with an extremely long growing season, coupled with accessible and dependable markets in areas where a competing type of production is prevented by winter frosts. The principal market area for Florida products is the large cities of northeastern United States; for Natal it is the mining and industrial centers of the High Veld.

Both Florida and Natal have a thriving cattle industry, though the emphasis is more on beef cattle in Florida and more on dairying in Natal. Most of the cattle in Natal are raised in the hills which lie between the coastal lowland and the Drakensberg. Maize is the principal field crop of the hilly belt, with the specialized subtropical crops being mainly confined to the coastal region.

Durban (475,000 including suburbs) is the largest city and main seaport. It handles a larger tonnage of freight than any other South African port, although Cape Town is more important as a passenger port. The harbor facilities can accommodate the largest vessels using the Indian Ocean. Durban is an important port for the High Veld as well as Natal itself. It is growing in importance as a manufacturing center, and has in addition a thriving resort business. Some visitors to Durban are reminded of Miami, although the total resort trade of the latter city is many times greater.

▶ Cape Province

The Cape of Good Hope Province, like Natal, is distinct in various ways from the rest of the Union. It is by far the largest in area of the four provinces, being half again as large as the other three provinces combined. It is also the most deficient in rainfall. Except for a humid fringe along the southern and southeastern coasts, nearly all of the Cape Province is semi-desert or desert. Parts of the province adjoining Natal share the humid subtropical climate of the latter area. The vicinity of the Cape of Good Hope has a mediterranean type of climate, being the only African area south of the Sahara where this climatic type occurs. Average temperatures at Cape Town are very similar to those of Los Angeles, in the mediterranean climatic zone of southern California. The annual rainfall at Cape Town is greater, however, and the tendency to summer drought is less pronounced.

Cape Town (572,000 including suburbs) is the principal city of the Cape Province and the second largest city of the Union. Of the four main ports of the Union, it is the only one which fronts on the Atlantic. The others, including Durban in Natal and Port Elizabeth (189,000 with suburbs) and East London (91,000 with suburbs) in Cape Province, are Indian Ocean ports. As in the case of southern California, the climate and scenery of Cape Town and its vicinity have been an important attraction for tourists and retired folk, and have stimulated resort development.

• The Cape Coloured. The Cape Province, like Natal, has a distinctive racial group, the Cape Coloured. Around nine tenths of the total Coloured population of the Union is found in the province, mostly in or near Cape Town. The Coloured had their origin in the early days of white settlement as a product of miscegenation among Europeans and their African and Asian slaves. Non-European racial stocks represented include Hottentot, West African Negro, Bantu, and East Indian. In South Africa the term "Coloured" is reserved for these mixed-blood people, the Bantu being referred to as "Natives" or "Africans." The Coloured vary in appearance from persons with pronounced Negroid features to oth-

A pleasant agricultural landscape in a valley of the Cape region. Regularly spaced rows of grape-vines in the foreground give evidence of the mediterranean climate of this area. (*Union of South Africa Government Information Office.*)

ers who are indistinguishable from Europeans. Included among the Coloured are some 64,000 Mohammedan Cape Malays.

Most of the Coloured work as house servants, farm laborers, factory operatives, or perform other types of unskilled or semi-skilled labor. As a group they are far more Europeanized than the Bantu and have enjoyed a higher social standing and greater political and economic rights, although ranking considerably below the Europeans in these respects.

• *The Distinctive Agriculture of the Cape Province.* Within the area of mediterranean climate, agriculture is adjusted to the characteristic regime of winter rain and summer drought. The early settlers established viti-

culture, for which the climate proved well adapted. Today, grape growing and wine making are a characteristic form of production helping to distinguish the Cape Province from the rest of the Union. The province contains 99 percent of the total acreage in vineyards in the Union.

Besides grapes, the Cape Province also produces a variety of other fruits. Of the total acreage in fruit in the four provinces, Cape Province has about two fifths of the citrus acreage, three fifths of the acreage in deciduous orchards, and more than four fifths of the acreage in pineapples. There is also a small production of bananas, although the banana acreage of the Union is primarily confined to Natal.

The principal field crop of the province

is winter wheat. The production is dependable, and Cape Province regularly harvests at least half of the wheat acreage of the Union. The proportion may rise to two thirds of the total when a drought year restricts production in the neighboring Orange Free State.

Production of wheat and grapes is mainly concentrated within 100 miles of Cape Town. The farm lands are found on small plains separating the low coastal ranges. Most of the grape acreage and some of the wheat acreage is irrigated. Irrigation is especially important in the drier western part of the Cape region. Citrus production is not so localized, being fairly well spread along the southern coast of the province.

• The Inland Districts. Most of the population of Cape Province resides in a band of relatively continuous settlement within 100 miles of the southern coast and extending from the Cape region to the border of Natal. Inland, the surface of the province rises by stages to the escarpment of the interior plateau, which is lower and less spectacular here than in the Drakensberg. Between the coast and the escarpment is an irregular assemblage of hills and low mountains interspersed with valleys, two of which are especially large and well known. These are the Little Karroo and the Great Karroo, respectively. Both are semi-desert areas, with a vegetation chiefly composed of scattered gray shrubs. This type of vegetation is known as "karroo" (a Hottentot word meaning dry), and extends onto the western part of the interior plateau or Upper Karroo. Most of interior Cape Province is so dry that field agriculture is confined to scattered irrigated districts. However, sheep are able to forage on the sparse vegetation, and thus sheep ranching has become the major pursuit. The province has about two thirds of the total sheep population of the Union. Many sheep are raised on farms in the coastal areas as well as on the larger ranches in the interior districts. Sheep are predominantly of the Merino breed, raised for their fine grade of wool. South Africa is second only to Australia in production of Merino wool. The Cape Province also has about a third of the cattle in the Union, mostly raised in the more humid eastern areas.

Aridity in the province increases toward the west, and northwestern Cape Province is desert. Most of the Atlantic shore of the province is barren and sparsely settled. Aridity here is due not only to distance from the Indian Ocean, the main source of moisture for South Africa, but also to the effects of the cool Benguela Current. Air drifting inland from the offshore waters brings cool temperatures and much fog to the coastal areas but produces little rain.

▶ South West Africa

The coastal desert extends northward into South West Africa. This former German colony was overrun by South African forces during World War I, and following the war it was mandated to South Africa by the League of Nations. The terms of the mandate called for administration of South West Africa as an integral part of the Union. Since World War II the United Nations has repeatedly called upon South Africa to place South West Africa under the trusteeship system, but the South African government has refused. In 1949 the legislature of the Union enacted a bill to incorporate South West Africa into the Union. At the time of writing this action seemed an accomplished fact, although the new status of South West Africa had not been officially recognized by the United Nations.

The desert extends the full length of South West Africa in the coastal areas. Inland is a broad belt of semi-arid country furnishing a certain amount of sparse forage for stock. It is mainly peopled by tribal remnants of the Hottentot population, for whom South West Africa has become a last refuge. The European population (50,000 in 1951) is mostly found on an interior plateau lying at a general elevation of 5000 feet or higher. Export production in South West Africa is mainly confined to minerals, including lead, zinc, diamonds, vanadium, manganese, and other minerals.

▶ The South African Economy and the Racial Problem

It has been previously indicated that in certain respects the economy of South Africa rests on an insecure base. The country appears excessively dependent on mining and underdeveloped with respect to manufacturing and agriculture. For labor with which to operate the mines, factories, and farms, the Europeans rely mainly on low-paid African workers who are often inefficient, have little economic or social incentive to improve, and seem likely to become increasingly dissatisfied with their lot. Throughout the Union manual labor is looked on by most whites as "Kaffir's work," an attitude common among Europeans in a tropical plantation area, but unusual in a middle latitude country. Both custom and law relegate the Africans to the less desirable types of employment.

• The British-Afrikaner Division. There is every evidence that the great majority of white South Africans are in favor of the general policy of white supremacy, at least in political affairs. Or to put the matter another way, the whites as a body are not prepared to yield political power to the extent that they might be outvoted by any combination of the other racial groups. In matters considered less fundamental, however, there is a division within the white population between the British South Africans and the Afrikaners, or Boers. The latter speak Afrikaans, a derivative of Dutch, as a preferred language. They outnumber the British approximately three to two.

• Early Boer Settlement at the Cape. The Afrikaners are the descendants of Dutch, French Huguenot, and German settlers who began coming to South Africa three centuries ago. The earliest permanent settlement, at Cape Town, was established by the Dutch East India Company in 1652 as a way station to provide water, fresh vegetables, meat, and repairs for company vessels plying the Cape of Good Hope route to the Orient. Although it had not been the intention of the company to annex large areas of land, settlement slowly expanded in the hinterland of the Cape, and a pastoral frontier society developed in the back country. Most of the original Hottentot and Bushman inhabitants were killed or driven out; the survivors were put to work as servants or slaves. However, their numbers were not adequate for the labor requirements of the colony, and from the very beginning slaves were brought in from other areas. The earliest group of slaves were brought from West Africa; later arrivals came from East Africa, Malaya, Madagascar, India, and Ceylon.

The Boer colonists were Calvinists and based many of their social and legal arrangements on the teachings of the Old Testament. They held a firm belief in the God-given inequality of different races, and thus could see little or nothing that was reprehensible in the institution of slavery. Particularly in the frontier districts, they became hardy individualists with an active dislike for central authority. During the Napoleonic Wars the Cape Colony was acquired by Great Britain. Occupation by the British on a permanent basis began in 1806, although a temporary occupation had taken place in 1795. Friction developed almost immediately between the Boers and the British authorities. In 1833 the tension came to a head when slavery was officially abolished throughout the British Empire. Thereupon the Boer leaders decided to escape from effective British control by moving northward out of reach.

• The Great Trek. In 1836 began the Great Trek, an epic migration by horse and ox wagon, which resulted in the founding of Natal, the Orange Free State, and the Transvaal as Boer republics. Natal was annexed by Britain in 1845, but Boer sovereignty in the Transvaal and Orange Free State was officially recognized in 1852 and 1854, respectively. The northward migration of the *voortrekkers* (pioneers) is a dramatic and colorful story comparable to the settling of the American Far West. An estimated 12,000 Boers—men, women, and children—were involved in the movement during the decade following 1835. As a result of the Great Trek, roughly a fourth of the Boer population was withdrawn from the Cape Colony. The advancing Boers clashed with Bantu tribes—the Zulus, Matabele, and others—who had begun to occupy South Africa from the north at roughly the same period that the Europeans were moving in from the south. Warfare with the "Kaffirs" was nothing new to the Boers, who had endured many decades of intermittent fighting on the frontier of the Cape. The Bantu tribesmen, though well organized, were equipped only with spears and shields, and since they owned no horses, were obliged to fight on foot. Eventually they proved no match for mounted Europeans equipped with guns, and the Boers were able to take firm possession of the High Veld. On the broad grasslands they pastured their flocks and herds and re-established their traditional way of living.

• **The Boer War.** Meanwhile, British settlers were coming to South Africa in increasing numbers. Port Elizabeth and East London were founded as British towns, and British influence also became dominant in Cape Town and Durban. It is conceivable that the British colonies and the Boer republics in South Africa might have developed peaceably side by side had not diamonds been discovered in the Orange Free State in 1867 and gold in the Transvaal in 1886. These discoveries set off a rush of prospec-

tors and other fortune hunters from outside, and mining camps sprang up at Kimberly, Johannesburg, and other places. The Boers possessed little or no capital with which to work the deposits, but British capital soon poured in. The conservative Boer leaders did not welcome the influx of outsiders ("uitlanders"), the majority of whom were British. Bad feeling led to the Boer War in 1899. It was an unequal contest since the British were able to draw support from the homeland and the Empire, whereas the Boers had to depend entirely on their own resources. After some early successes the Boer forces were decisively defeated, and the war ended in 1902. The present Union of South Africa was formed in 1910, following a display of constructive statesmanship by both sides. Afrikaans was recognized as an official language on a par with English, and Pretoria, in the Transvaal, was made the administrative capital as a concession to Boer sentiment. However, the national legislature meets at Cape Town, and the supreme court sits at Bloemfontein (109,000 with suburbs).

Since 1910 the Afrikaners have tended to dominate the political life of the Union by virtue of their greater numbers and cohesiveness. Their greatest political strength is in the rural districts. Roughly 85 percent of the farm population is Afrikaner, and election laws are written in such a way as to favor the rural areas at the expense of urban constituencies, in which the majority of the British South Africans live.

The South African problem of race relations is undoubtedly one of the most difficult in the world. It would be a mistake to suppose that thinking Europeans in South Africa do not realize the deeper implications of their situation, or that they are unconcerned with the welfare of the other racial groups. Probably a substantial majority of white South Africans would be found to favor a gradual advancement of the other groups in such matters as health, education, standard of living, and general welfare. However, the whites seem determined not to grant them the voting privilege on terms of full equality. They are resolved to preserve South Africa as a white man's country, and rightly or wrongly, they assume that the only way to secure this end is for them to keep a permanent superiority at the polls. They regard South Africa as a home, not only for themselves, but for their children and children's children, and they are afraid of being overwhelmed by numbers. It has been suggested that the racial problem of South Africa might largely disappear if there could be an immigration of enough Europeans to give the whites a numerical majority. However, this seems quite unlikely to happen, and so South Africa must continue to struggle with a problem which is full of explosive possibilities. By and large, it seems a problem which must be resolved by the South Africans themselves, but since the South African situation is but one facet of a larger world problem of race relations, other nations and peoples will continue to view events in South Africa with a deep interest and concern.

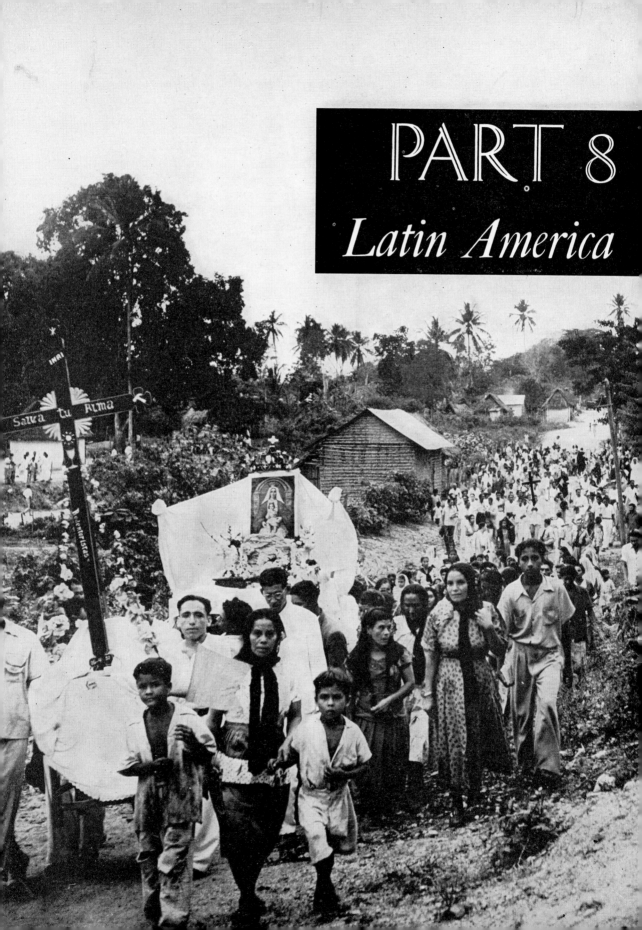

PART 8

Latin America

Introduction to Latin America

The land portion of the Western Hemisphere to the south and southeast of the United States has come to be known as Latin America. Both the name of this region and its ways of life reflect the importance of culture traits inherited from the Latin-European nations of Spain, Portugal, and France. Spanish is the prevailing language in 18 of the 20 Latin American republics, the exceptions being Brazil and Haiti where, respectively, Portuguese and French are used. Roman Catholicism, also a heritage from Mediterranean Europe, is widely accepted, and is the official religion in some nations. The feudalistic *hacienda,* or large estate, transplanted from Spain and Portugal, is perhaps better preserved in parts of Latin America than in the countries of origin. Nor are all the ties with Latin Europe indirect: newcomers from Spain and Portugal, as well as from Italy, dominate the Latin American immigrant lists.

It should not be assumed that the transplanting of European cultures to Latin America has been achieved without essential modification or that a uniform culture prevails today throughout the region. Many

Native Indians constitute a major population element in several Latin American countries. These Indian coffee-pickers in Guatemala are engaged in separating the ripe, red coffee berries from the immature green ones. (*Foreign Agricultural Service, U. S. Department of Agriculture.*)

483

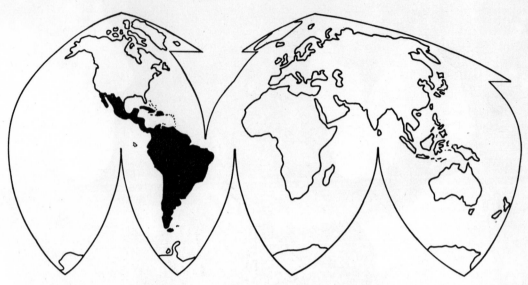

World location of Latin America. (*Boggs Equal Area Projection, copyright A. J. Nystrom & Co.*)

Latin American culture traits are a heritage from native Indians, imported Africans, or other non-European groups, and the cultural impress of these groups has varied unequally from one part of Latin America to another. Nevertheless, many features of a common Latin culture are discernible in most parts of the region, and the civilization of Latin America as a whole stands in recognizable contrast to that of Anglo-America, which has primary roots in Great Britain and in Germany, the Scandinavian countries, and other countries of northwestern continental Europe.

Physical Dimensions

With a land area of slightly more than 7.9 million square miles, Latin America is outranked in size by Africa, the Soviet Union, Anglo-America (including Greenland), and the Orient. However, its maximum latitudinal extent of more than 85 degrees or nearly 5900 statute miles is greater than that of any other world region, and its maximum east-west measurement, amounting to more than 82 degrees of longitude, is by no means unimpressive. Yet Latin America is not so large as these figures might suggest, for the region is not a uniformly-dimensioned block of the earth's surface. It is, instead, an "offset" area, in which Caribbean America trends sharply northwest from the north-south oriented continent of South America. The latter continent is therefore thrust into the Atlantic Ocean much farther than is the Caribbean realm or its northern neighbor, Anglo-America. In fact, the meridian of 80°W., which intersects the west coast of Ecuador and Peru, passes through Pittsburgh, Pennsylvania. Africa lies less than 2000 statute miles east of Brazil.

Diversity of Latin American Peoples and Cultures

Statistics on physical size and shape, however, do not answer the basic questions of significance. What is Latin America? How many people live there and what are they like? What is their political, economic, and social viewpoint—or viewpoints? Are they

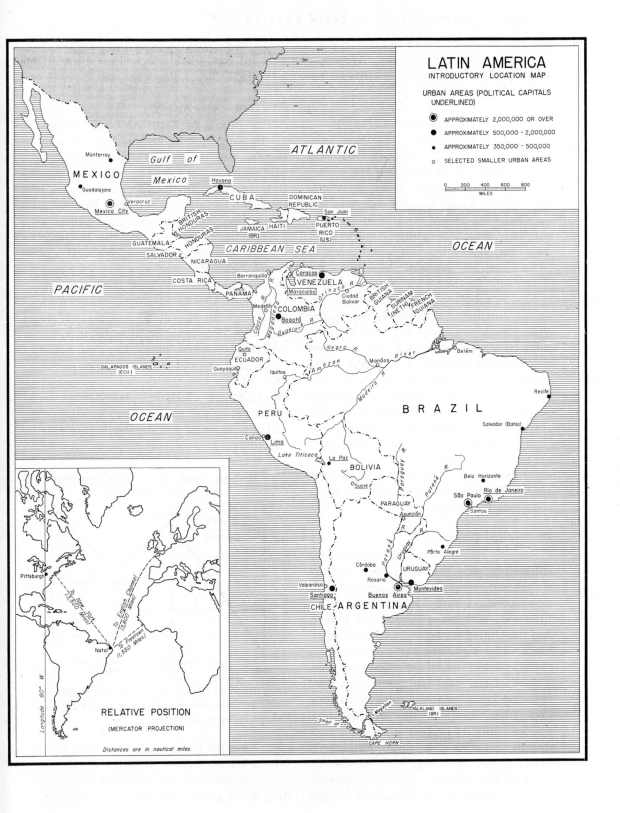

LATIN AMERICA
INTRODUCTORY LOCATION MAP

URBAN AREAS (POLITICAL CAPITALS UNDERLINED)

◉ APPROXIMATELY 2,000,000 OR OVER

● APPROXIMATELY 500,000 - 2,000,000

• APPROXIMATELY 350,000 - 500,000

○ SELECTED SMALLER URBAN AREAS

0 200 400 600 800
MILES

Monterrey

MEXICO

Gulf of Mexico

Guadalajara

Veracruz

◉ *Mexico City*

ATLANTIC

Havana

CUBA

DOMINICAN REPUBLIC

JAMAICA (BR) **HAITI**

San Juan

PUERTO RICO (US)

OCEAN

BRITISH HONDURAS

GUATEMALA HONDURAS

SALVADOR NICARAGUA

CARIBBEAN SEA

PACIFIC

COSTA RICA

PANAMA

Barranquilla

Caracas

VENEZUELA

Maracaibo

Orinoco R.

Ciudad Bolivar

BRITISH GUIANA

SURINAM (NETH)

FRENCH GUIANA

Medellín

COLOMBIA

Cauca R.

Magdalena R.

Bogotá

Guaviar R.

Quito

ECUADOR

Negro R.

GALAPAGOS ISLANDS (ECU.)

Guayaquil

Iquitos

Amazon

Manáos

River

Belém

Madeira R.

PERU

OCEAN

Callao *Lima*

Lake Titicaca

La Paz

BOLIVIA

○ *Sucre*

Paraguay R.

B R A Z I L

Recife

Salvador (Bahia)

Belo Horizonte

Paraná R.

São Paulo

Rio de Janeiro

Santos

PARAGUAY

Asunción

Paraná R.

Uruguay R.

Pôrto Alegre

Córdoba

URUGUAY

Valparaíso

Rosario

Paraná R.

Santiago

Buenos Aires

Montevideo

CHILE **ARGENTINA**

Magellan

FALKLAND ISLANDS (BR)

Strait of

CAPE HORN

RELATIVE POSITION
(MERCATOR PROJECTION)

Pittsburgh

To New York (3,500 Miles)

To English Channel (3,800 Miles)

To Freetown (1,550 Miles)

Natal

Longitude 80° W

Distances are in nautical miles.

the masters of their own destiny? What is the character of the land they live upon? In short, how does Latin America fit into the world pattern of major regions?

▶ Variations in Population Density

The total population of Latin America was estimated at 172 million in 1952–1953, as compared with an estimated 160 million for continental United States in August 1953. But as Latin America embraces well over twice the area of the United States, its over-all population density is correspondingly less, amounting to approximately 22 per square mile as compared with 53 per square mile for the United States. However, the Latin American population is more unevenly distributed than that of the United States. Some sections of Latin America exhibit rural population densities which are much heavier than any to be found within areas of comparable size in the United States. On the other hand, a much larger proportion of Latin America is sparsely peopled. At present, the populations in both Latin America and the United States are growing through natural increase at an exceedingly rapid rate, with the estimated rate of increase in Latin America being somewhat the higher.

▶ Political Diversity

Beneath their veneer of a common Latin culture, the peoples of this region evidence a marked diversity that is apparent in their many political units—20 republics, 8 political dependencies of Britain, 3 of France, 3 of the United States, and 2 of the Netherlands. The republics vary in size from gigantic Brazil, which occupies more than a third of the total Latin American land area and boasts nearly a third of its total population, down to tiny Haiti, which possesses only .14 percent of the land area, though containing a disproportionately high 2 percent of the aggregate population. Most of the colonies and other dependencies are even smaller than Haiti in both

area and population. Area and population data for the individual political units are given in Table 27, pages 488–489.

▶ Economic Diversity

The people of Latin America are primarily supported by various forms of subsistence and commercial agriculture, supplemented in some areas by mining, manufacturing, and trade. Approximately two thirds of the total population live on a subsistence, hand-to-mouth basis within a self-contained economic orbit that has little contact with foreign commerce and exchange. However, the economy of Latin America also reflects—with marked variations from area to area—the presence of the foreign investor. Large amounts of foreign capital have been invested in commercial plantations, mines, factories, transportation lines, and other sources of profit Most of the invested capital is from the United States, which has placed about 30 percent of its private long-term investment in Latin America. Britain and France also have large investments; however, invest-

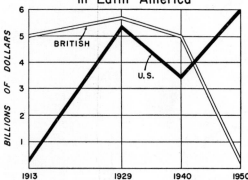

Comparison of United States and British investments in Latin America. (*From a graph by the Foreign Policy Association.*)

ment from the United States has risen rapidly in recent decades while European investment has declined. Industries financed directly by Latin American entrepreneurs or governments, often with borrowed capital, represent still a third ingredient in the economic structure of the region.

▶ Ethnic Diversity

The Latin Americans themselves do not evince much ethnic uniformity. In only three nations—Argentina, Uruguay, and Costa Rica—have European strains been preserved on a large scale with little admixture by Indians or Negroes. (Scattered districts in other political units are predominantly European.)

Native Indians comprise more than half of the total population in the highland nations of Guatemala, Bolivia, Ecuador, and Peru, as well as in the lowland country of Paraguay. They are also a major population element in southern Mexico and El Salvador. In outlying areas, especially in the basin of the Amazon River and in Panama, scattered lowland Indian tribes live more or less apart from the world about them.

The Negro is found in greatest numbers on the islands and along the hot, wet coastal lowlands of Caribbean America and areas near by. Except in Puerto Rico, Cuba, and the Dominican Republic, nearly all of the Caribbean islanders are Negroes. On the mainland, the east coast of Brazil between Cape São Roque and Salvador and the northern hinterland of Rio de Janeiro have sizable Negro populations, as do small districts in French Guiana, Surinam (Dutch Guiana), British Guiana, Venezuela, and Panama. A major concentration of Negroes is found along the lower valley of the Magdalena River and Caribbean coast of Colombia.

In most of Latin America, however, mixed bloods predominate. Most of the region exhibits a primary mixture of Spanish and native Indian stocks, resulting in a heterogeneous group known as *mestizos.* Mixed bloods of Negro-native Indian ancestry are usually termed *zambos.* European-Negro mixtures, or *mulattoes,* are fewer in number and are found chiefly in the Caribbean dependencies.

Similarities and Differences Between Latin America and Other Major World Regions

From the foregoing description one can infer that Latin America is an unusual amalgam of ideas, pursuits, and men. Yet this region is very much a part of the world geographic pattern, possessing characteristics which, however altered, tend to recur in other parts of the world. In fact, a comparison of Latin America with each of the other world regions considered in the present volume reveals many interesting and significant similarities and differences.

▶ Latin America and the Soviet Union

In over-all political and economic organization Latin America is unlike the Soviet Union. It is not, in other words, a unitary block of land controlled by a single dictatorial government and undergoing rapid and sometimes ruthless economic development according to a preconceived plan. Yet certain instructive comparisons can be made between recent economic developments in Latin America and the USSR. For example, in Mexico a government-enforced program of land reform has been introduced during the past four decades. Its primary objective has been the breaking up of large estates and redistribution of the property among the many landless peons.

By subdividing large holdings Mexico is making an appeal to man's inherent love of the land and is trusting that the new responsibility will, with government aid

TABLE 27

LATIN AMERICA: AREA AND POPULATION DATA

POLITICAL UNIT	POLITICAL STATUS	AREA (THOUSAND SQUARE MILES)	POPULATION (EST. MILLIONS)	DENSITY (PER SQUARE MILE: TO NEAREST WHOLE NUMBER)
CARIBBEAN AMERICA		*2045.9*	*72.71*	*36*
Mexico	Independent Republic	760.4	28.05 (1953)	37
Guatemala	Independent Republic	42.0	2.94 (1952)	70
El Salvador	Independent Republic	13.2	1.99 (1952)	151
Honduras	Independent Republic	59.1	1.51 (1952)	26
Nicaragua	Independent Republic	57.1	1.13 (1952)	20
Costa Rica	Independent Republic	19.7	0.85 (1952)	43
Panama [a]	Independent Republic	28.6	0.84 (1952)	29
Total: Central American Republics		219.7	9.26	42
Colombia	Independent Republic	439.8	12.03 (1953)	27
Venezuela	Independent Republic	352.1	5.44 (1953)	15
Panama Canal Zone	United States Military Reservation	0.55	0.06 (1952)	105
British Honduras	British Colony	8.9	0.07 (1952)	8
British Guiana	British Colony	83.0	0.44 (1952)	5
Surinam (Dutch Guiana)	Netherlands Overseas Territory	55.1	0.23 (1952)	4
French Guiana	French Overseas Department	34.7	0.026 (1951)	0.75
Total: Mainland Dependencies		182.3	0.83	4.5
Cuba	Independent Republic	44.2	5.81 (1953) [b]	131
Haiti	Independent Republic	10.7	3.20 (1952)	299
Dominican Republic	Independent Republic	19.1	2.24 (1952)	117
Total: Island Republics		74.1	11.25	152
Puerto Rico	Self-Governing Commonwealth of the United States	3.4	2.24 (1952)	652
U. S. Virgin Islands	United States Dependency	0.13	0.024 (1952)	180
Jamaica and Dependencies	British Colony and Dependencies	4.7	1.47 (1952)	315
Bahama Islands	British Colony	4.4	0.08 (1952)	19
Barbados	British Colony	0.17	0.22 (1952)	1301
Trinidad and Tobago	British Colony	2.0	0.66 (1952)	335

Country / Territory	Status	Area	Population (year)	Density
Windward Islands	British Colony	0.82	0.29 (1951)	349
Leeward Islands	British Colony	0.42	0.12 (1952)	284
Guadeloupe [c]	French Overseas Department	0.69	0.29 (1951)	425
Martinique	French Overseas Department	0.43	0.28 (1952)	660
Netherlands Antilles	Netherlands Overseas Territory	0.37	0.17 (1952)	470
Total: Island Dependencies		*17.5*	*5.85*	*334*
NATIVE INDIAN COUNTRIES OF SOUTH AMERICA		*1169.5*	*16.77*	*14*
Bolivia	Independent Republic	424.2	3.09 (1952)	7
Peru	Independent Republic	482.3	8.86 (1952)	18
Ecuador	Independent Republic	106.0	3.35 (1952)	32
Paraguay	Independent Republic	157.0	1.46 (1952)	9
BRAZIL	Independent Republic	*3287.8*	*55.77 (1953)*	*17*
COUNTRIES OF THE SOUTHERN MID-LATITUDES		*1442.9*	*26.43*	*18*
Argentina	Independent Republic	1084.4	18.06 (1952)	17
Chile	Independent Republic	286.4	5.93 (1952) [b]	21
Uruguay	Independent Republic	72.2	2.45 (1951)	34
Grand Total		*7946.1*	*171.68*	*22*

Note: Apparent discrepancies in totals are due to rounding of figures.
a Figures do not include Canal Zone.
b Census figures.
c Includes two main and five lesser islands.

and advice, result eventually in higher yields per unit of area and a higher standard of living per person. In the Soviet Union, where the former private holdings have been amalgamated into large collective farms or state farms, the ultimate objective—higher agricultural production—appears to be the same as in Mexico. The methods, however, are quite different. The Soviet leaders have placed their dependence in a collectivized system of agriculture controlled from above and fitted into an overall economic plan for the entire nation. Private ownership of farm land has been abolished, and farming has been made to resemble a factory type of enterprise so far as possible. Land reform in Mexico has also proceeded according to a plan—but a plan which depends for success upon giving each peon access to land—*his* land. He may or may not own it outright and he owns neither the water nor mineral rights to it (these are reserved by the government), but he has the right of access to it as long as he cares for it properly. Over 2.3 million peons have thus been granted access to land within the past 40 years. Some have acquired private holdings. Most, however, are members of *ejidos*—communities whose members may till, but, in most cases, not own, their individual plots of land.

▶ Latin America and Europe

In political organization Latin America bears a certain resemblance to Europe. Each of these world regions contains a large number of individual political units which vary widely in population, area, mode of governance, and other respects. However, unlike the leading nations of Europe, no Latin American country can boast a worldwide political and economic system with lifelines reaching over the globe toward

raw materials and markets in outlying nations and political dependencies. Several of the Latin American republics have small island possessions,[1] but these are trivial when compared with the overseas dependencies of Britain, France, or Belgium. Far from being generators of economic power, the republics of Latin America, as well as the colonial possessions, exhibit a high degree of economic dependence on the United States and Europe. Most of the trade of Latin America, for example, is with the latter two areas.

▶ Latin America and Anglo-America

Latin America bears a certain resemblance to Anglo-America in the nature and arrangement of its major topographic features. The major land mass within each of these world regions exhibits a gross physical pattern of high rugged mountains with associated plateaus and basins at the west, lower and generally older highlands and uplands at the east, and broad plains in the center. In each case more than half of the central region of plains lies within the drainage area of a single river system—the Amazon system in Latin America and the Mississippi-Missouri system in Anglo-America.

In political and economic respects, however, these New World regions are very different. The two massive, stable political units of Anglo-America—the United States and Canada—stand in marked contrast to the fragmented political order and notorious governmental instability of Latin America. The tremendous economic productivity and general prosperity of the Anglo-American nations places them in a different class from the underdeveloped and often poverty-stricken political units which comprise Latin America.

---

[1] The principal island possessions of the Latin American republics include the Galapagos Islands (Ecuador) and Easter Island and Sala y Gomez (Chile), all in the Pacific Ocean. In recent years Argentina has contested British claims to the Falkland Islands, in the Atlantic. Argentina and Chile also have claims to portions of Antarctica.

► Latin America and the Orient

Latin America, like the Orient, is in part a region of heavy population pressure, primitive or intensive subsistence agriculture, poverty, and hunger.

• **Population Density.** At first glance the region does not appear overpopulated, for its average population density of 22 per square mile is several times less than the average density in Europe or the Orient. Yet the tiny British island possession of Barbados contains an average of 1301 persons, chiefly rural, per square mile—a density comparable to that of the more heavily populated rural areas in the Orient. Also in the Caribbean realm are found other, although not so extreme, examples: Martinique, a French possession, contains 660 and Puerto Rico, a United States territory, 652 persons per square mile. Additional political units whose population densities exceed the over-all average in the Orient include the Netherlands Antilles; the French isles of Guadeloupe; the British colonies of Trinidad, Jamaica, Windward Islands, and Leeward Islands; the United States Virgin Islands; and the Negro republic of Haiti. There are, of course, political units in Latin America which are very sparsely populated: French Guiana, for example, has an average of less than 1 person per square mile. Between these extremes, the larger countries occupy a position resembling that of the region as a whole: Brazil has approximately 17, Argentina 17, Chile 21, and Mexico 37 inhabitants per square mile.

• **Population Distribution.** In its general pattern of population distribution Latin America differs somewhat from the Orient and from all other world regions. The Latin American pattern is that of heavy density in and around coastal cities (if local climatic handicaps, insects, diseases, and other liabilities are not too serious), a marked pressure in and near high mountain urban centers—in many cases, the capital of a country—and corridors of moderate to heavy concentration along the outlet routes from the mountains to the sea. There are, of course, variations and exceptions; yet the pattern is sufficiently consistent that nearly every political unit consists of a well-defined population core (or cores) with an outlying sparsely populated hinterland.[2] In other words the total area of each country differs considerably from the total *occupied* area, with exceptions in the case of Uruguay, El Salvador, Haiti, Puerto Rico, and most small island colonial possessions. In Brazil over three fourths of the total land area is essentially without inhabitants other than aboriginal tribes. Most Brazilians live along the eastern seaboard south of the city of Recife. Nearly seven tenths of the Argentine population is clustered in Buenos Aires or the adjacent humid pampa—an area containing slightly more than one fifth of Argentina's total land. Almost one half of Mexico's population is found in several mountain basins and valleys clustering about Mexico City—a district representing less than one seventh of the country's entire area.

• **Poverty of the Average Inhabitant.** Like most inhabitants of the Orient, the typical Latin American is poor. An inadequate, yet noteworthy, indicator of this poverty is the average per capita cash income of selected countries. According to one source—and sources differ appreciably—this amount is about $171 per year in Argentina, $133 in Chile, $84 in Costa Rica, $50 in Mexico, $49 in Brazil, $25 in El Salvador, and $15 in

---

[2] More detailed treatment of this idea, with excellent maps, may be found in R. S. Platt, *Latin America: Countrysides and United Regions.* New York and London: McGraw-Hill Book Company, Inc., 1942.

Haiti.[3] The general level of incomes is far below that of the United States, which had an average per capita income of $1525 in 1948.[4] In fact, a citizen of Haiti may work an entire year for what in the United States might be considered a day's wages. Such comparisons must be used with caution, however. Roughly two thirds of all Latin Americans seldom see money. Instead they tend to grow or make or barter their necessities. Hence their actual status cannot be measured by money income. Moreover, prices vary quite sharply among the Latin American countries and the differing values of units of currency (here translated into dollars for easy comparison) will buy markedly different amounts of merchandise in two separate countries.

▶ Latin America and the Pacific World

Like the Pacific World, Latin America is comprised of a series of islands and a major landform area supporting, all in all, a comparatively sparse population. The com-

---

[3] Preston E. James, *Latin America*, rev. ed. New York: The Odyssey Press, 1950. *Passim.*

[4] W. S. Woytinsky and E. S. Woytinsky, *World Population and Production: Trends and Outlook.* New York: The Twentieth Century Fund, 1953. P. 392.

The rural poverty which afflicts much of Latin America is well exemplified in this view, taken in Venezuela. The farm family in the picture is engaged in planting a field of upland rice. With a sharpened stick the farmer digs holes into which his wife drops the rice seeds. [*Standard Oil Company* (N. J.)]

parison can be carried still further. Like Australia, the largest land unit of the Pacific World, South America is a continent in which the most densely populated areas are situated on or near coasts, the interior being sparsely peopled. However, the settlement possibilities of the two continents differ. Australia possesses neither an Amazon River providing easy access to the interior, nor a natural environment over most of its area which, by present standards, can be occupied successfully by more than small numbers of people. In short, Australia's unpopulated expanses are chiefly desert. In contrast, over 80 percent of Brazil, a country somewhat larger than Australia, may eventually be occupied, although at present only about 25 percent is used effectively—even for such extensive practices as the pasturing of livestock.

Ethnically, Latin America and the Pacific World offer some interesting contrasts. The islands of Latin America are occupied almost wholly by descendants of immigrants from Europe or Africa, the native Indians having been driven off or exterminated long ago. The islands of the Pacific World, however, are settled principally by native peoples who have lived for centuries in their present habitats. The mainland of Latin America is populated by an amalgam of native Indians, Africans, Europeans, and other ethnic groups; but the mainland of the Pacific World—Australia—is occupied almost entirely by descendants of European, mainly British, immigrants, the aborigines having been killed or driven to inaccessible places by the early European settlers.

There are also political and economic similarities between these two world regions. Both are governed, with few excep-

tions, by Europeans or descendants of Europeans. In each case most of the inhabitants are citizens of independent countries and yet must depend economically upon foreign commerce—primarily with Anglo-America and Europe—to take away surplus raw materials (chiefly from the farm or mine) and to supply certain manufactured goods. Each is an outlying part of the commercial world, the cores of which are found in the industrialized areas lying on either side of the North Atlantic Ocean.

▶ Latin America and the Middle East

Like the Middle East, Latin America is a region that derives much of its regional unity from the nigh-omnipresence of a single religion—Mohammedanism in the Middle East and Roman Catholicism in Latin America. Each faith is dominant throughout essentially the entire extent of its region. In Latin America, Roman Catholicism is the accepted religion of the upper classes, and is the official state religion in some countries. In somewhat altered form it filters down to the majority of the people, who tend to observe not only Catholic rites, but also those learned from their native Indian or African forebears. This is particularly true in the communities of the native Indian.

The relationships between church and state in Latin America vary from country to country. The basic issues appear to be (1) the control of educational facilities, (2) the control of the marriage ceremony, and (3) continued exercise by the church of certain rights and property titles held during the colonial period—rights and titles whose validity has been challenged, with varying degrees of vigor, by the various national governments since independence.

Comparisons Between Latin America and Africa

Although Latin America contains features or combinations of features which have counterparts in the Soviet Union, Europe, Anglo-America, the Orient, the Pacific World, and the Middle East, the region in general resembles Africa more closely than any other major world region.

▶ Similarities in Shape and Location

Perhaps the most apparent similarity between Latin America and Africa is that of general shape. The major land mass of each assumes the form of a triangle with the apex pointing toward the South Pole. Moreover, the major continent of each is connected to an even larger continent to the north—*i.e.,* to North America and Eurasia respectively—by an isthmus which man has found it advantageous to canalize. There are also other similarities of location: north of the major continent in each region is a sea—the Caribbean and the Mediterranean—which tends to separate that continent from, and concomitantly to provide shipping lanes to, its poleward neighbor. And, in either case, that northern continental neighbor is the home of a busy industrial society which has established definite political and/or economic ties with the region to the south. Thus Latin America tends to lie predominantly within the overseas economic orbit of the United States and Africa within that of northwestern Europe.

The economic ties between Latin America and Africa and the industrialized regions to the north are associated with the fact that both Latin America and Africa are located predominantly in the lower latitudes, and hence are able to produce tropical crops which are in demand in Anglo-America and Europe but cannot be produced in quantity in the latter regions because of climatic handicaps.

▶ Similarities and Differences in Landforms

Both Latin America and Africa are characterized by pronounced differences in elevation from one part of the region to another. However, contrasts in elevation are much greater in Latin America than in Africa. Nowhere in the latter continent is there a prominent low-lying plain series like that of the Orinoco-Amazon-Paraná-Paraguay—the river plains which dominate the interior of South America and separate effectively the older, lower highlands of the east from the rugged Andes of the west. With high landforms, too, Latin America is the more generously endowed. This is evidenced by the nearly continuous Andes, Sierra Madre, and associated mountains which extend from northern Mexico to Tierra del Fuego. Between the latitudes of 30°N. and 40°S. these mountains reach prevailing heights of at least 5000 feet above the sea. Within the Andes proper the highest crests exceed 9000 feet for over 3500 miles from northern Colombia and Venezuela to central Chile and Argentina. The latter's Mount Aconcagua—with an altitude of 22,830 feet that marks the highest point of the Western Hemisphere—is in the southern portion of this more rugged Andean belt. Among the irregular mountains of Caribbean America, elevations of 9000 feet or higher are found in Costa Rica, Guatemala, and Mexico—in the last of these, especially near the capital city. In contrast, mountains of comparable elevation in Africa are limited to a few comparatively small and erratically distributed ranges or isolated peaks.

▶ Similarities in Types of Climate

In general, the types of climate and associated vegetation in Latin America as recognized in climatic classifications duplicate those of Africa. The differences most readily apparent are the much larger proportion of desert climate in Africa and the greater prevalence of middle latitude and high highland climates in Latin America.

• *Humid Tropical, Subtropical, and Marine Climates of Latin America.* The *tropical rain forest climate* in the massive center of Latin America tends to be—like its African counterpart—located at or near the equator. However, the Latin American area of this

A clearing in tropical rain forest on the Pacific lowlands of Ecuador. Subsistence crops are grown among the stumps in front of the house, while pigs and chickens find shelter under the house. The family food supply is rounded out from a small orchard of orange trees in rear of the house, and by hunting, fishing, and gathering nuts, fruits, and other foods in the forest. (*Foreign Agricultural Service, U. S. Department of Agriculture.*)

climate type is somewhat larger than the African area, reaches farther poleward in the Northern Hemisphere, and its coastal segments are mainly found on the east coast, rather than on the west coast as in Africa. On either side of this tropical rainy climate—as in Africa—is found the *tropical savanna climate,* which in Latin America extends erratically to the vicinity of the Tropic of Cancer in the Northern and the Tropic of Capricorn in the Southern Hemisphere. Still farther poleward in the eastern portion of South America is found a sizable area of *humid subtropical climate.* Its Northern Hemisphere counterpart lies north of the Mexican border in southeastern United States. These three climate types—tropical rain forest, tropical savan-

na, and humid subtropical—characterize most of Latin America. Of the others, perhaps the most idyllic is a small strip of *mediterranean* or *dry-summer subtropical climate* in central Chile. To the south in Chile is a strip of *marine west coast (humid marine) climate* bordered by bleak, rainy, windswept, glaciated, essentially uninhabited mountain country.

• *Dry Climates of Latin America.* The Latin American climates discussed above are those of more or less orderly, repetitious arrangement. One may expect to find generally similar climates in generally similar positions on all major land masses of the world. However, there are also in Latin America climates which are due at least partially to the presence there of high land-forms. To a certain extent some of the region's dry climates and, to a much greater degree, its mountain highland climates may be so considered.

The dry climates, especially those of the arid and semi-arid sections of Mexico (and southwestern United States) are to be associated partially with the global pattern of orderly climate arrangement, and partially with local mountains and uplands. A glance at a climate map will reveal dry lands in generally similar positions in Africa (both north and south of the equator) and in Australia. However, the high mountain ranges on either side of the northern Mexican peninsula, meeting in the vicinity of Mexico City, cannot be entirely overlooked in a consideration of causes for this particular area of dry land. The aridity of the dry lands of Argentina, Paraguay, and southern Bolivia is largely the result of their location in the rain shadow of the Andes. They have counterparts in other sections of the world only where high

ranges of mountains happen to block the path of prevailing winds and hence to cause a deficiency of rainfall on the lee side. In the west coast tropics and subtropics of South America, the Atacama and associated deserts cannot be explained so simply; for shifting winds, cold offshore currents, and other complexities—as well as the Andes Mountains—are important to climatic conditions there. However, the mountains serve to restrict this area of desert to the coastal strip.

• *High Upland and Highland Climates of Latin America.* Although the lowlands and low uplands of Latin America are extensive and support sizable populations in some countries, the highlands and high uplands are also very important to man's use of this region. They are significant not only for the natural resources they contain but also —chiefly because of their cooler temperatures—as habitats for settlement, particularly in the otherwise persistently hot lands. To immigrants or descendants of immi-

Sparsely settled ranching country in the tropical savannas of eastern Colombia. The isolated *mestizo* family on this cattle ranch may not see other human beings for months at a time, aside from the relatively primitive Vichada Indians who come to the ranch to trade. [*Standard Oil Company (N. J.).*]

grants from the middle latitudes such conditions have been especially attractive, for they resemble somewhat the climates from which the settlers came. However, the annual range of temperatures is much lower than in the middle latitudes. For example, Quito, Ecuador—an extreme case—records average temperatures as follows: January 54.7°F.; April 54.5°F.; July 54.5°F.; and October 54.7°F.

These upland and highland climates change markedly with increased elevation, and hence are subject to classification into vertical zones. Although each of the four basic weather and climatic elements—temperature, pressure, humidity, and winds—varies with altitude, temperature is the primary criterion for zonal classification. At least three major zones are commonly recognized in the higher lands of Latin America: the *tierra caliente* (hot country); the *tierra templada* (cool country); and the *tierra fria* (cold country).

Rising from the previously discussed lowland climates, the *tierra caliente* zone of hot, wet conditions reaches to approximately 3000 feet above sea level at or near the equator, and to slightly lower elevations in a subtropical country like Mexico. It is, in effect, an upward projection of these lowland climates, from which it has never been satisfactorily isolated by geographers and climatologists. Thus it is the environment of nature's rain forest or tropical savanna and man's rice, sugar cane, and cacao. It tends also to be the zone of the truly tropical plantation—whether owned locally or abroad—and of the Negro, zambo, and mulatto worker. In the islands of Caribbean America, it is the zone of major urban units, containing all of the cities of 100,000 or over.

The *tierra caliente* merges almost imperceptibly into the *tierra templada*. Although sugar cane, cacao, bananas, oranges, and other lowland products reach their respective uppermost limits at some point in this higher level, the *tierra templada* is

most notably the zone of the coffee tree. Indeed, some scholars use the criterion of effective coffee culture as the dividing line from the *tierra caliente*. In the *tierra templada* coffee can be grown with relative ease; at lower altitudes the crop encounters difficulties occasioned by excessive heat and/or moisture. The upper limit of this zone—approximately 6000 feet above sea level—tends also to be the upper limit of European-induced plantation agriculture in Latin America. In its distribution the *tierra templada* flanks the rugged western mountain cordilleras and, in addition, is the uppermost climate in the lower uplands and highlands to the east. The broad-leaved evergreen trees of its moister, hotter sections tend to resemble those of the *tierra caliente*. This is especially true of the eastern flanks of the high mountains. In its poleward margins, however, broadleaved trees are replaced to some degree by coniferous evergreens. In such places as the highlands of Brazil or Venezuela where there is less moisture, scrub forest or savanna grasses appear—the latter generally requiring the more water.

In brief, the *tierra templada* tends to be the zone of European-induced settlements and of commercial agriculture, especially in the low latitudes. Urban as well as rural settlement is very much in evidence: of Latin America's 73 cities of 100,000 or over 14 are in or very near the *tierra templada*. Two of the region's metropolises exceeding 1,000,000—Mexico City and São Paulo—are likewise in or near this zone. Others, like Rio de Janeiro, which are themselves situated at lower elevations, maintain close ties with predominantly residential or resort towns found in these cooler temperatures.

The *tierra fria*, or cold country, may be distinguished from the other zones by two criteria. First and perhaps most important in an agricultural region like Latin America, it is a zone where frost occurs. As one might expect, frosts are only occasional in the zone's lower reaches at approximately 6000 feet above the sea, but are much more frequent at higher elevations. The second criterion refers to type of economy: in contrast to the Europeanized *tierra templada,* the *tierra fria* tends to be the habitat of a subsistence, native Indian economy—best developed in Peru and Bolivia, but also present in Ecuador, Colombia, Guatemala, El Salvador, and Mexico. The upper limit of the *tierra fria* is generally placed at about 10,000 feet above sea level for locations near the equator, and at lower elevations toward either pole. This line is usually drawn on the basis of two criteria: (1) the upper limit of agriculture, as represented by such hardy crops as potatoes, barley, or the locally important cereal quinoa; and (2) the upper limit of natural tree growth. Above are the alpine meadows,

sometimes called *paramos;* still higher there may or may not exist barren rocks and snow or ice.

The *tierra fria* tends to be a last retreat and the major home of the native Indian and is characterized by small permanent settlements and by what Europeans or Americans might consider rather primitive ways of life. It is chiefly rural, containing only six of Latin America's cities numbering 100,000 or over. However, nature has placed here certain valuable minerals like tin, vanadium, and copper which have attracted modern types of large-scale mining enterprise into the *tierra fria* of Bolivia and Peru, as well as some other Latin American countries.

Climatic data for representative Latin American stations are given below in Table 28.

TABLE 28
CLIMATIC DATA FOR SELECTED LATIN AMERICAN STATIONS

STATION	COUNTRY	LATITUDE TO NEAREST WHOLE DEGREE	ELE-VATION ABOVE SEA LEVEL (FEET)	TYPE OF CLIMATE	AVERAGE TEMPERATURE IN DEGREES F. (UPPER FIGURE); AVERAGE PRECIPITATION IN INCHES (LOWER FIGURE)				
					AN-NUAL	JANU-ARY	APRIL	JULY	OC-TOBER
Chihuahua	Mexico	29°N.	4669	Steppe	64.6° 15.4″	50.0° 0.2″	66.4° 0.2″	76.6° 3.6″	64.8° 0.9″
Medellín	Colombia	6°N.	5000	Tierra Templada	70.5° 58.8″	70.9° 2.7″	70.7° 6.6″	70.5° 4.1″	69.4° 6.9″
Ciudad Bolivar	Venezuela	8°N.	125	Tropical Savanna	80.7° 34.3″	78.8° 0.5″	82.2° 0.9″	79.7° 6.2″	81.7° 3.4″
Manáos	Brazil	3°S.	147	Tropical Rain Forest	81.0° 69.8″	79.9° 9.2″	79.9° 8.5″	80.6° 2.2″	82.8° 4.1″
Goiaz	Brazil	16°S.	1706	Tropical Savanna	75.1° 66.4″	74.6° 12.1″	76.0° 4.9″	71.9° 0.0″	77.8° 4.9″
São Paulo	Brazil	24°S.	2690	Tierra Templada	65.4° 56.0″	70.6° 9.1″	66.6° 3.0″	59.4° 1.3″	64.8° 4.5″
Montevideo	Uruguay	35°S.	82	Humid Subtropical	61.0° 38.6″	72.0° 2.6″	63.0° 4.6″	50.5° 2.4″	58.1° 2.5″
Santiago	Chile	33°S.	1706	Mediterranean	57.0° 13.7″	68.7° 0.0″	56.7° 0.6″	46.2° 2.8″	56.8° 0.5″
Puerto Montt	Chile	41°S.	33	Marine West Coast	51.8° 85.7″	59.5° 4.6″	52.3° 7.4″	45.9° 10.8″	51.1° 5.5″
Lima	Peru	12°S.	512	Desert	66.8° 1.8″	72.6° 0.0″	70.2° 0.0″	61.2° 0.2″	63.0° 0.4″
La Paz	Bolivia	17°S.	12001	Tierra Fria	48.7° 22.6″	50.4° 3.8″	48.4° 1.5″	43.5° 0.2″	50.0° 1.3″
Quito	Ecuador	0°	9350	Tierra Fria	54.6° 44.3″	54.7° 4.2″	54.5° 7.4″	54.5° 0.9″	54.7° 3.7″

▶ Latin American Minerals

Latin America, like Africa, can claim only a moderate proven supply and variety of important economic minerals when viewed in a world perspective. Of course, these and other outlying regions have not been combed so thoroughly as have the more industrialized nations, and therefore it is possible that their full endowment in minerals is not yet appreciated. Currently, however, Latin America's known mineral resources that bulk large in a world-wide inventory of key minerals include only iron ore, petroleum, bauxite, tin, copper, nitrate, and silver. Supplies of good coal, especially coking coal, are almost entirely lacking.

Deposits of high-grade *iron ore* in the eastern highlands of Brazil and Venezuela are the largest known in the Western Hemisphere and are very possibly the largest in the world. Lesser and yet noteworthy deposits occur in northern Mexico, south-central Chile, and southern Cuba.

Petroleum is significant in the Caribbean Sea–Gulf of Mexico area, particularly in northern Venezuela, northeastern Colombia, the central coast of Mexico, and the island of Trinidad. Smaller reserves exist along the Peruvian-Ecuadorian coast, in the Andes of northern Argentina, and along the Atlantic margins of Patagonia, also in Argentina. Furthermore, the large sedimentary basins east of the Andes Mountains of South America may contain sizable petroleum supplies not currently known.

Most of the region's *bauxite*—the major source material for aluminum—is in the eastern section of South America. The deposits are situated not far from the seacoast in Surinam and British Guiana, but farther inland in Brazil.

Most of the known reserves of *tin* in Latin America are in the Andes of Bolivia. Small deposits have also been found at similar elevations in Peru. Like the iron ore to the east, however, these highland reserves are very difficult to reach by adequate transportation.

Low-grade but comparatively abundant *copper* deposits occur in the dry Atacama Desert of northern Chile and the arid and semi-arid sections of Mexico. Additional reserves are found in the Andes, especially in the mountainous sections of Bolivia, Peru, Chile, and Argentina.

Chile contains the only sizable reserves of natural *nitrate* that have ever been exploited commercially on a grand scale. Like the lower grades of copper, these are in the Atacama Desert.

The *silver* of Mexico, Bolivia, and Peru is principally found in mountains or rough plateau country. The deposits in Mexico, by far the most extensive, are mainly in the dry northern and north-central sections of the country.

▶ Similarities in Economic Activities

Since both Latin America and Africa are outlying regions in the world's economy, their basic industries serve principally to supply the wants of their own inhabitants insofar as is possible, and to send needed commodities to more highly industrialized areas insofar as demand exists for such commodities. In both areas agriculture is the leading livelihood industry.

• *Latin American Agriculture.* In Latin America agriculture employs between 50 and 60 percent of the total labor force. There is an appreciable range in the proportionate importance of agriculture among the various countries: for example, of those political units reporting statistics, Argentina has only one fourth of its total labor force engaged in agriculture, whereas approximately three fourths of the total workers are so engaged in Colombia, Nicaragua, the Dominican Republic, and El Salvador. The other countries range between these extremes.

The systems of agriculture vary. In political dependencies, commercial plantations—many of them absentee-owned and mulatto-managed—tend to dominate the rural scene. Native subsistence agriculture on individually controlled plots (often by "squatters") or on land furnished by the plantation owner, is an important source of local food.

Especially along certain hot, wet, but relatively hurricane-free coasts, company-owned banana plantations are also important—particularly so in Caribbean America. Most such plantations are now on the mainland. Many are shifting to the Pacific coast to avoid hurricanes and disease.

Particularly on the mainland are found community-owned and individually owned agricultural holdings belonging to citizens of the respective countries in which these properties are located. Community-owned lands, reflecting native Indian traditions, are especially well represented by the previously described *ejidos* of Mexico (see page 490) and by some community settlements in the two major Latin American concentrations of native Indians—one in northern Central America and southern Mexico inhabited by descendants of the Mayas, Aztecs, and neighboring peoples, and the other in the middle Andes of Peru and neighboring countries, containing descendants of the Incas. Unlike the *ejidos,* most of the native Indian communally held lands support a predominantly subsistence form of agriculture.

The individually owned holdings are of Latin-European origin. They may be large *haciendas* (Spanish) or *fazendas* (Portuguese) such as are found in some form in nearly all Latin American nations, or they may be small holdings like those of Costa Rica. Agricultural production on the large estates, whether called *haciendas, fazendas,* or by some other name, involves the employment of large numbers of landless, often illiterate, workers. In some areas these workers are traditionally bound to the estate, and in others they are free to move at will. In actual fact, most of them remain on the estate. The estate owner is well educated—often in Europe. He is usually a citizen of the country in which his property is located. He may have a residence in a city in addition to that on the estate. He may also be engaged in business, or one of the professions, leaving the direction of the estate to a carefully chosen manager. Although one estate may produce several commodities commercially, there is a tendency toward specialization in only one or two. All in all, such estates produce a sizable proportion of the coffee, sugar, cotton, henequen, livestock products, and other Latin American agricultural commodities entering world markets.

Types of production on small individual holdings vary with owner and place. The more active small farmers, like those of Costa Rica, tend to grow coffee, cotton, and other commercial specialties as well as subsistence crops of corn, beans, sorghums, and vegetables. Other, more inefficiently managed holdings tend to concentrate on subsistence crops only.

Not only does agriculture employ the majority of Latin America's people; it is also responsible for most of the region's exports. Of the 20 independent countries in the region, all but Venezuela, Peru, Bolivia, and Chile now export a larger value of agricultural commodities than of products from other livelihood industries. Coffee, sugar, cotton, meat, cacao, wheat, bananas, wool, and corn are among the major agricultural products leaving the region.

• *Mining as a Source of Livelihood.* The significance of mining to Latin America is not easily appraised. In terms of labor force it is comparatively unimportant, for the highly mechanized mining industry seldom employs more than 4 percent of the total labor force of a Latin American country. Since mining ventures are largely financed and usually managed by outside interests in order to get raw materials for the industrial economies of Anglo-America and Europe, few of the extracted products reach the Latin American people. However, the revenue from mining—whether in the form of income, property, export tariff, or other taxes—is very important to some Latin American governments.

Some of Latin America's mining activities are of major importance on a world basis. Over 15 percent of the world's annual output of petroleum originates in Venezuela, and 5 percent in Mexico. Between 30 and 40 percent of all mined silver, approximately 14 percent of all mined lead, and nearly 10 percent of all mined zinc is extracted in Mexico. Nearly 30 percent of all bauxite comes from Surinam, and over 20 percent from British Guiana. Approximately 14 percent of all copper and essentially all natural nitrate comes from Chile. Over 30 percent of all vanadium is mined in Peru.

• *The Increasing Importance of Manufacturing.* In both Latin America and Africa but especially in the former, the local factory is assuming increasing importance. In fact, the industrial revolution which we so often place in the latter part of the eighteenth century is only now beginning to reach effectively to these outlying world regions. In a sense, a frontier—or a series of frontiers—of industrialization is migrating over these peripheral world regions just as the now legendary frontier of settlement in the United States once shifted westward. A leading authority on Latin America, Professor Preston E. James, has characterized this change as follows: [5]

The history of the Occidental world during the last few centuries has been chiefly involved with the impact of the new *industrial society* and the older *feudal society*. Beginning in Western Europe the new way of living, coupled with enormously increased productivity in all forms of eco-

nomic activity through the use of controlled inanimate power, has gradually transformed whole sections of Europe and America. In some instances the transformation has taken place by gradual evolution; in not a few instances it has been accompanied by violence and warfare, both civil and international. The rapid increase in the need for raw materials of all kinds has produced the present intense rivalry for the control of the productive regions, especially of the sources of power. The English-speaking peoples, who were the first to adopt the new way of living, were able to gain control of about 75 per cent of the developed power resources of the world; and the challenge to this control lies behind the present international turmoil. In Latin America, the impact of the industrial society with the traditional feudal society is now going on. Where the industrial way of living has become established, a new and still more profound line of cleavage has been formed across all the previous diversities of Latin-American society.

The fundamental characteristics of the industrial society should be reviewed briefly. The use of controlled inanimate power changes the emphasis from production by cheap labor to production by machines—or, in terms of economics, capital investment assumes a position of preponderant importance, and the owners of capital rather than the owners of land assume places of the highest prestige and political power. Production is enormously increased, not only total production, but also per capita production. This leads to specialization and exchange, and hence to interdependence over wide areas. Trade is transformed from a small-scale exchange of luxury goods or specialties to a large-scale exchange of staples, and as a result communities are no longer supported by the products of the territories immediately surrounding them, but from a wide variety of producing areas, most of them beyond the control of the community which absorbs the products. With life organized on such

[5] Preston E. James, *Latin America*, rev. ed. New York: The Odyssey Press, 1950. Pp. 36–39. Used by permission of the author and the publisher.

a pattern society reaches a much higher standard of material comfort than any previous society has been able to reach; but this standard can be maintained only if a nation accepts the fact of wide geographical interdependence, turns away from provincial isolation, and cooperates with other nations in the maintenance of a stable financial structure of money and credits.

The industrial society brings profound changes in the details of human life. Prestige, we repeat, is to be gained through the ownership of capital which brings power, rather than through the ownership of land which brings security. Life becomes more speculative, less certain, but with rewards for the successful which are in a material way far beyond anything the world has offered before. There comes a notable change in the time concepts. With the increased tempo of life the vague concepts of feudal society, such as *por la mañana, por la tarde,* must be given up for more precise concepts, such as 9:45 A.M. or 3:10 P.M. Behavior of all sorts becomes more standardized. The picturesqueness of provincial costumes disappears under a uniform cover of blue denim overalls; people from Patagonia to Labrador watch the antics of Popeye the Sailor; local differences in manners and customs are modified by the impact of the new patterns of life. In the big cosmopolitan centers of Latin America life follows the same routine as in North American or European cities—this uniformity is apparent in styles of architecture, styles of dress, forms of work and recreation—in short, the whole aspect of life is changed from its variegated feudal base to a uniformity repeated in all the Occidental urban centers.

These changes affect the distribution of people. As long as coal remains the chief source of power, manufacturing industry is carried on at the lowest cost in large concentrated units. People gather together in great cities—cities greater than any that the world ever knew before, cities of more than a million inhabitants. Although the use of electric power may have the effect of spreading manufacturing industry over a wider area, thus transforming the life in smaller towns and villages, the large concentrations of city people still perform more efficiently the urban functions of commerce and administration. These cities are still dependent on the productivity of the land for their support, but the land base has been greatly extended; and as a result the means of transportation which tie the cities together must be greatly elaborated.

The urban-industrial way of living has come to Latin America from outside, not by slow evolution from the earlier feudal base. In parts of Europe and in Anglo-America where the cities and the urban life developed out of the rural background there is a certain normal relationship between the size of the city and the productivity of its rural hinterland. . . . In Latin America one finds cities which have become industrial and commercial centers with an industrial way of living, but which bear little relationship in size or in function to the rural districts back of them. The contrast between the cities and the rural districts is enormous: the average tourist who journeys by boat or airplane from one city to another scarcely catches a glimpse of the Latin America which is traditional, and which is still dominant in terms of area and numbers of people.

Urban-industrial growth has appeared at various places in Latin America. The largest development of this cosmopolitan life centers in Buenos Aires, Rio de Janeiro, São Paulo, Santiago, and Mexico City—all cities of a million or more people, all thoroughly modern metropolises, with a way of living entirely familiar to metropolitan dwellers throughout the Occidental world. Smaller industrial development can be observed in Rosario, Tucumán, and Córdoba in Argentina, Pôrto Alegre and many of the smaller cities of Southeast Brazil and of São Paulo state, Valparaiso and Concepción in Chile, Lima in Peru, Medellín in Colombia, and Monterrey, Puebla, and Guadalajara in Mexico. Steel industries have been built in Volta Redonda, Brazil; Monterrey, Mexico; and Concepción, Chile. Yet the industrial productivity of all Latin America is very small compared with that of the United States or Western Europe.

Thus the Latin American countries which are trending most rapidly toward the factory system are Argentina, Brazil, Mexico, and Chile. Peru, Cuba, Uruguay, Colombia, and Venezuela are also increasing their factory output. Over 15 percent of the total labor force in the four most active nations is now composed of factory workers, engaged chiefly in the production of processed foods, fibers, and various forms of fabricated metal products for home markets.

► *Similarities in the Major Pattern of Settlement and Transportation*

Settlement in both Latin America and Africa is peripheral with respect to the relative newcomers from Europe. The interior of each region tends to be only sparsely occupied, and then by erratically distributed aboriginal tribes. This "rim" pattern of European settlement becomes apparent in the orientation of the component countries, of the cities, and of the major transportation features of both regions. The political units tend to cluster along seacoasts. Those few countries which lack a stretch of coast must seek access to the oceans by way of the coastal states. Thus, in Latin America, Bolivia and Paraguay must negotiate with their neighbors for access to the sea.

The major cities, with few exceptions, are also near the coasts or at high elevations. The exceptions tend to be the mining communities, which are located on or near mineral deposits, wherever found.

Until recently, the ocean vessel has been without serious competition in Latin American transportation. In fact, this situation still obtains, although the airplane is becoming increasingly important as a carrier—not only of specialty items, but also of meat, copra, and other staples. The railroads augment the ocean ship—connecting, in most instances, interior focuses of trade with oceanic outlets. Highways are in an immature stage of development. Few roads are hard-surfaced, and many are passable only with difficulty. This is particularly true in the rainier climates of the low latitudes.

Some Important Differences Between Latin America and Africa

Latin America and Africa are not, of course, completely alike. Of their many differences, perhaps the most significant is that of political status. Whereas all of the Latin American countries except the Caribbean dependencies are politically independent (however unstable their governments may be), only Egypt, the Union of South Africa, Libya, Ethiopia, and Liberia currently enjoy similar privileges in Africa. This is an important distinction, for despite the appreciable degree to which the political units of both major regions are dependent economically upon Anglo-America and/or Europe, independent nations can enter into negotiations on a free-and-equal political basis. They are thus in a better position to pursue their own best interests than are politically dependent governments.

Racial segregation and strife is much more of a problem in Africa than in Latin America, where many ethnic groups have tended to mingle through intermarriage.

There are also important environmental differences. Latin America has a larger area of mountain lands and of low-lying river plains and smaller areas of plateau and upland than does Africa. In addition, Latin America projects farther into the Southern

Hemisphere and thus gains access to a larger area of humid middle latitude climates. Africa has no effective counterpart of the rich pampas of Argentina, Uruguay, and southern Brazil, nor of the marine west coast climatic area of southern Chile.

Summary of Some Major Latin American Characteristics

Latin America is a highly diversified region. Particularly in its landforms, climates, political units, and population distribution, it is one of the most diverse of the eight world regions.

It is a region which does not use its natural and human resources as efficiently as do more highly industrialized regions elsewhere. Between 50 and 60 percent of its labor force depends upon some form of agriculture for existence, yet the region produces only about one tenth of the world's food and fiber. Many of its farmers have no knowledge of modern agricultural techniques, and most Latin American governments lack adequate capital to promote a revision of farming practices.

It is a region in which the population increase is pronounced—particularly in the poorer, less developed sections such as most islands in Caribbean America.

It is also a region which depends markedly upon the industrial societies of Anglo-America and Europe with respect to exports, imports, and investment of capital. This dependence is currently being decreased, especially in the economically stronger countries, by the development of local manufacturing plants—of which many are sponsored by the respective national governments. In these countries a long-established landed aristocracy now sees its traditional rights, privileges, and power threatened by a rising merchant and factory class.

Finally, it is a region with potentialities for further development. These potentialities tend to take one of four primary forms: (1) the establishment of more factories in the region; (2) the breaking up of large landed estates into smaller parcels which can be worked by owners or quasi-owners; (3) the opening up of new agricultural and grazing lands, particularly in the interior of South America; (4) the intensified utilization of mineral resources, for domestic consumption wherever possible. All of these potentialities are recognized by Latin Americans and by the mother countries of the political dependencies. Whether they can be realized at a rate concomitant with the extremely rapid increase in population numbers remains to be seen.

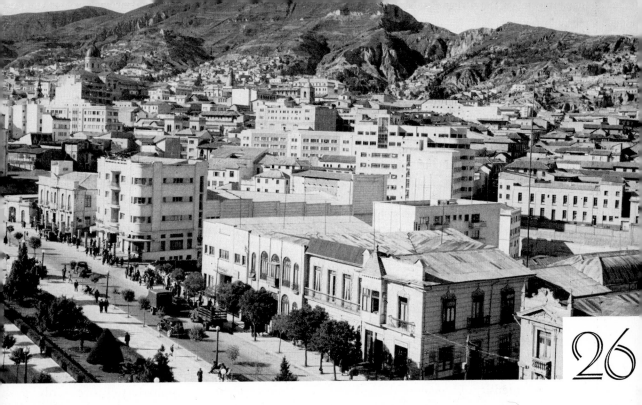

Latin American Regions

One of many possible ways of subdividing Latin America for purposes of study results in a major northern realm known as Caribbean or Middle America; a second region comprised of the predominantly native Indian countries of Ecuador, Peru, Bolivia, and Paraguay; a third consisting of giant Brazil; and, finally, mid-latitude South America—cored by Argentina, with the smaller country of Chile flanking its entire western border and still smaller Uruguay situated to the northeast. These regional subdivisions will be discussed in the order named—an arrangement which does not imply an order of importance, but continuity from the Rio Grande to Tierra del Fuego. Area and population totals for each regional group of countries, as well as for individual countries, are given in Table 27 on pages 488–489.

Caribbean America

The northernmost of the four major Latin American subrealms is Caribbean or Middle America. Broadly conceived, Caribbean America includes the large mainland nations of Mexico, Colombia, and Venezuela; the small Central American repub-

The downtown business and administrative district of Bolivia's largest city and *de facto* capital, La Paz. The city lies in a valley beneath the rim of the central Andean plateau or Altiplano, marked by the irregular skyline in the background. In the foreground is a spacious avenue—the only one in La Paz. Such a thoroughfare is frequently found in the central part of the larger Latin American cities. (*Foreign Agricultural Service, U. S. Department of Agriculture.*)

lics of Guatemala, El Salvador, Honduras, Nicaragua, Costa Rica, and Panama; the mainland dependencies of British Honduras, British Guiana, Surinam (Dutch Guiana), French Guiana, and the Panama Canal Zone; and the numerous islands, large and small, in the Caribbean Sea and the Gulf of Mexico. Among the insular political units, only Cuba, which encompasses all of the largest island, and Haiti and the Dominican Republic, which share the second largest, are independent.

▶ Diversity in Size and Population Pressures Among the Component Political Units

Caribbean America is comprised of 12 independent countries and 16 dependencies, all of pronouncedly varied size, shape, and intensity of human settlement and use. The largest nation, Mexico, contains over 760,000 square miles and an estimated 28 million people. The smallest independent country, Haiti, has only 11,000 square miles but has a population of over 3 million. The population density of Mexico—approximately 37 people per square mile—is only slightly higher than that of all Caribbean America. The density in Haiti, on the other hand, amounts to about 300 people per square mile. However, the real extremes in density are found in the political dependencies. British Guiana, the largest of these in area, has some 83,000 square miles, a population of over 440,000, and a density of only 5 persons per square mile. The Virgin Islands, a dependency of the United States—essentially the smallest organized dependency in area—include a total of 132 square miles, a population of some 24,000, and a density of 180 persons per square mile. There is still more to the story: French Guiana has a density of less than 1 per square mile, whereas the British colony of Barbados has 1300 per square mile. In appraising these statistics, the student should remember that the people of Caribbean America are primarily rural. By

way of comparison, the average population density of the highly industrialized United States is around 53 persons per square mile.

Despite its diversity, Caribbean America may be divided for closer examination into component regions—in this case, politically defined regions—as follows: Mexico; the Central American Republics; Colombia and Venezuela; the Mainland Dependencies; the Island Republics; and the Island Dependencies.

▶ Mexico

Four characteristics of Mexico are particularly striking: (1) nearly one half of its people live in, around, or between Mexico City (2,235,000) and Guadalajara (380,000); (2) almost one third of the total population is native Indian, and most of the rest is *mestizo;* (3) approximately two thirds of the total population depends for a living upon agriculture; and (4) over two thirds of all crop land grows corn—chiefly for human consumption.

• *Agriculture.* The Mexicans are a people who prize agricultural land. Three major types of land holding are represented.

1. Individual *haciendas,* the feudalistic, large-scale private holdings, contain upwards of 2500 acres and in some cases over 100,000 acres. These are scattered throughout the country, but the largest numbers are found in the northeast and in the Yucatan Peninsula. In 1940 *haciendas* encompassed over 60 percent of the total exploited land (crop land, forest, pasture, etc.) in Mexico.

2. The small private holdings have various names: *solar* (if containing fewer than $2\frac{1}{2}$ acres); *granja* (if involving from $2\frac{1}{2}$ to $12\frac{1}{2}$ acres); and *rancho* (if covering from $12\frac{1}{2}$ to 2500 acres). In 1940 such holdings comprised 16 percent of all exploited land in Mexico, with the smallest and most numerous holdings in and near the area of densest population.

3. Properties owned by entire commu-

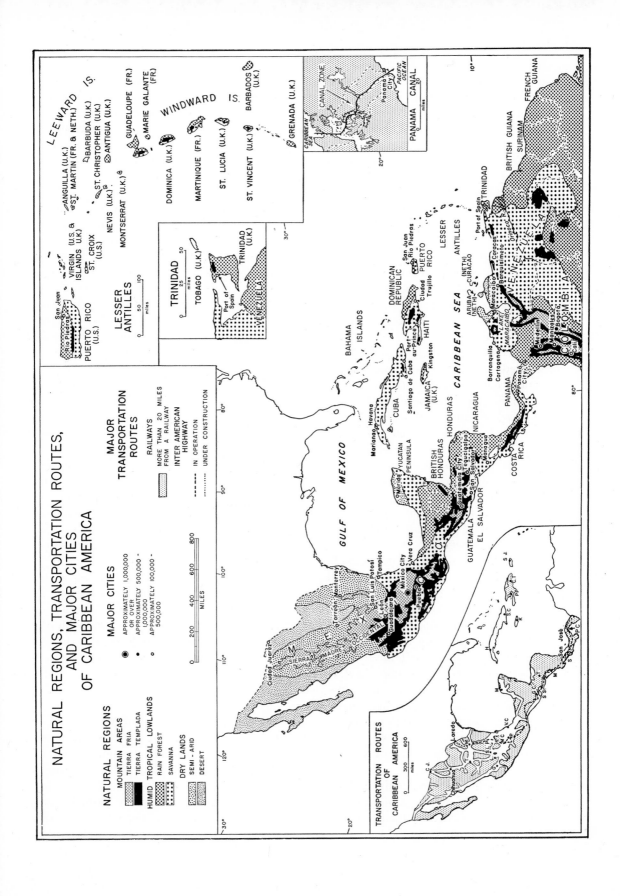

NATURAL REGIONS, TRANSPORTATION ROUTES,
AND MAJOR CITIES
OF CARIBBEAN AMERICA

NATURAL REGIONS

MOUNTAIN AREAS
TIERRA FRIA
TIERRA TEMPLADA

HUMID TROPICAL LOWLANDS
RAIN FOREST
SAVANNA

DRY LANDS
SEMI-ARID
DESERT

MAJOR CITIES
APPROXIMATELY 1,000,000
OR OVER
APPROXIMATELY 500,000 -
1,000,000
APPROXIMATELY 100,000 -
500,000

MAJOR
TRANSPORTATION
ROUTES

RAILWAYS
MORE THAN 20 MILES
FROM A RAILWAY

INTER AMERICAN HIGHWAY
IN OPERATION
UNDER CONSTRUCTION

MILES
0   200   400   600   800

TRANSPORTATION ROUTES
OF
CARIBBEAN AMERICA
0   300   600
miles

PUERTO RICO
(U.S.)
San Juan
Rio Piedras

LESSER
ANTILLES

TRINIDAD
25   50
miles
0   50   100
TRINIDAD (U.K.)
TOBAGO (U.K.)
Port of Spain
VENEZUELA

LEEWARD IS.
ANGUILLA (U.K.)
ST. MARTIN (FR. & NETH.)
BARBUDA (U.K.)
ST. CHRISTOPHER (U.K.)
ANTIGUA (U.K.)
GUADELOUPE (FR.)
MARIE GALANTE (FR.)
NEVIS (U.K.)
MONTSERRAT (U.K.)
VIRGIN (U.S. &
ISLANDS U.K.)
ST. CROIX
(U.S.)

WINDWARD IS.
DOMINICA (U.K.)
MARTINIQUE (FR.)
ST. LUCIA (U.K.)
ST. VINCENT (U.K.)
BARBADOS (U.K.)
GRENADA (U.K.)

PANAMA CANAL
CANAL ZONE
Panama
City
PACIFIC
OCEAN
CARIBBEAN
SEA
miles
0   10   20

GULF OF MEXICO

CARIBBEAN SEA

BAHAMA
ISLANDS

CUBA
Havana
Marianao
Santiago de Cuba

JAMAICA (U.K.)
Kingston

HAITI
Port-au-Prince

DOMINICAN
REPUBLIC
Ciudad
Trujillo

PUERTO
RICO
San Juan
Rio Piedras

LESSER
ANTILLES

Ciudad Juarez
Chihuahua
SIERRA MADRE OCCIDENTAL
Torreón
Monterrey
Tampico
San Luis Potosí
Guadalajara
León
Mexico City
Puebla
Vera Cruz
SIERRA MADRE

MEXICO
YUCATAN
PENINSULA
Mérida

BRITISH
HONDURAS
GUATEMALA
Guatemala City
EL SALVADOR
San Salvador
HONDURAS
Tegucigalpa
NICARAGUA
Managua
COSTA
RICA
San José
PANAMA
Panama
City

COLOMBIA
Barranquilla
Cartagena
Medellín
Manizales
Bogotá
Cali

VENEZUELA
Maracaibo
LAKE
MARACAIBO
Barquisimeto
Caracas
Valencia
Maracay

ARUBA
(NETH.)
CURACAO
(NETH.)

TRINIDAD
Port of Spain

BRITISH GUIANA
SURINAM
FRENCH
GUIANA

TRANSPORTATION ROUTES
OF
CARIBBEAN AMERICA
Laredo

nities, whether allotted to (but not owned by) individual heads of families or, in rare cases, worked communally, are called *ejidos*. Unlike the other holdings the *ejido* system can be traced to native Indian ways of life. An average *ejido* worker has at his disposal 45 acres of land, of which slightly less than one fourth is in crops. The *ejidos* are distributed throughout Mexico in a manner roughly similar to small private holdings. Although they occupy only approximately 24 percent of all exploited land, they encompass over one half of all cultivated land. This means that a very high proportion of the privately owned land in Mexico is in forest, pasture, and other noncrop use.

Shortly before World War I, Mexico instituted a state-enforced agricultural reform program which is still continuing. Its major objective has been the breaking up of *haciendas* into small units, chiefly *ejidos*. The estates are usually left with no fewer than 250 acres of land, including the original buildings. Over 2.3 million peons—almost one in ten—have been thus granted access to land. Although mistakes have been made—the initial subdivisions, for example, were too small—the program appears to have effected a wholesale transfer of land title without a serious decline in production and without major bloodshed.

In addition to corn, the primary subsistence crops include beans, wheat, and barley. In all, such crops occupy over 82 percent of Mexico's crop land—most of it in the *tierra templada* and lower *tierra fria* climates of the heavily populated central section. Yields per acre are low: the yield for corn, for example, averages fewer than 8 bushels, as compared with nearly 30 bushels for the United States—itself a country with only moderate agricultural returns per acre.

Cotton, grown principally under irrigation in the dry north, is of increasing importance to both the home and foreign markets. It is currently the leading export,

having quadrupled in export volume between 1948 and 1951. Other major agricultural exports include coffee (from the region east of Mexico City), henequen (from the semi-arid northern margin of the Yucatan Peninsula), and meat (from both the north and the central district).

• *Manufacturing.* Measured by labor force, manufacturing is far less significant than agriculture, accounting for only 11 percent of the nation's total employment. Many of the workers are in handicraft industries. The principal modern manufacturing plants are located in two general areas: (1) the central district, which is characterized particularly by labor-oriented and market-oriented industries (i.e., cotton, woolen, and rayon textile plants; tobacco-processing shops); and (2) the dry lands of the north, which contain chiefly raw material-oriented industries (*i.e.,* concentrating and smelting mills for the production of iron and steel, lead, zinc, copper, silver, and other metals). Except for iron and steel production, most of the latter operations are more a part of mining than of manufacturing, as their primary function is that of enriching the ores sufficiently so that they can be shipped elsewhere for further manufacture.

Of major importance to Mexico is the local iron and steel industry centered at Monterrey (330,000). Most of the iron ore and coal are brought from fields within a radius of 300 miles. The Monterrey district produces nearly three fourths of Mexico's iron and steel output—an output insufficient, however, for the country's needs.

• *Mining.* Only 2 percent of Mexico's labor force is engaged in mining. This figure does not convey accurately the importance of the mining industry, for many of the mines are highly mechanized and thus employ comparatively few workers. Mined products comprise a major portion of Mexico's exports. The leading commodities, of which most are exported in semi-finished form, are lead (refined), zinc (concentrates and refined), petroleum (crude and refined), silver (refined), and copper (crude and refined). The silver production, although not of paramount importance to Mexico, is the highest in the world—amounting to over one third of the average annual world production. At Tampico and lesser centers along the central Caribbean coast, petroleum recovery and refining plants are responsible for about 5 percent of the world's annual petroleum output.

• *Minor Livelihood Industries.* Among minor livelihood industries are commercial fishing (along both coasts) and tourism. Most of the tourists come from the United States. In return, a migratory counterflow occurs annually—not of tourists, but of laborers seeking farm work. Of the 50,000 to 200,000 such workers moving northward and returning each year, an estimated two thirds are "wetbacks" who cross the Rio Grande in a manner strictly informal. The strength of this movement indicates the disparity in standards of living between the United States and Mexico and dramatizes the key problems of Mexico—a low stand-

ard of living, a rapidly increasing population, and a dearth of local capital for exploitation of its natural resources.

The general economic status of Mexico is not unlike that of most other Latin American countries and dependencies, particularly those of the Caribbean realm. Nearly everywhere in the Caribbean area the bulk of the people support themselves by subsistence farming. A few commercial export

TABLE 29
DOMINANT EXPORT COMMODITIES OF THE CARIBBEAN AMERICAN REPUBLICS

COUNTRY	COMMODITY AND PERCENT OF TOTAL EXPORTS BY VALUE, 1951
Mexico	Cotton, 24; Lead, 10
Guatemala	Coffee, 77
El Salvador	Coffee, 89
Honduras	Bananas, 29; Coffee, 22
Nicaragua	Coffee, 40; Gold, 19
Costa Rica	Coffee, 56; Bananas, 27
Panama	Bananas, 37
Colombia	Coffee, 78; Petroleum, 16
Venezuela	Petroleum, 97
Cuba	Sugar and Molasses, 87
Haiti	Coffee, 52; Sisal, 24
Dominican Republic	Sugar and Molasses, 52; Coffee, 16; Cacao, 16

Source: *Foreign Commerce Yearbook*, 1951.

Large-scale commercial plantation agriculture in Central America. The photo shows a banana plantation of the United Fruit Company on the Pacific coastal plain of Guatemala. Barracks of workers front on the company-owned railroad in the center of the picture. (*Foreign Agricultural Service, U. S. Department of Agriculture.*)

crops or mined products are grown or extracted in scattered localities, mainly with the aid of foreign capital. In most countries one or two primary commodities dominate the export lists, as shown in Table 29.

▶ The Central American Republics

Economically, the Central American republics are miniatures of Mexico—except that they have even less local capital and fewer exploitable minerals. Systems of land use vary. The predominant subsistence farming is most evident in the native Indian settlements of northern Guatemala and adjacent areas and least perceptible in

A rural landscape in the Andean *tierra fria* of Colombia about 30 miles north of Bogotá. Level land is at a premium here, and fields and pastures are carried as far up the mountain slopes as possible. (*Foreign Agricultural Service, U. S. Department of Agriculture.*)

Costa Rica, where a society of small farmers—relatively unmixed descendants of Spaniards—works most of the land. Coffee, the predominant mainland crop for export, is grown on both small and large holdings, most of which are owned by citizens of the country involved. Banana plantations, found principally along the hot, moist, coastal lowlands, are in large measure under the control of the United Fruit Company, an American concern. Because careful management and precision timing are needed to market the ripening bananas (which are picked while still green), the company's own employees manage both the plantations and a fleet of specially built ships plying between Caribbean ports and wholesale markets, chiefly in coastal cities of Anglo-America.

The land problem in these countries is even more serious than in Mexico. Their average acreage of cultivated land per farm worker is less than half that of their northern neighbor—and, for comparison, less than one twelfth that of the United States. Moreover, they are the masters of their own destiny to a much more limited degree than Mexico. Catering to tastes in the world market, they manage as best they can by attracting foreign capital when possible and selling such tropically grown products of farm and forest as will be purchased by peoples with standards of living higher than their own.

▶ Colombia and Venezuela

The high landforms which dominate Mexico and Central America extend southward, with interruptions, through Colombia. An outlier reaches eastward in Venezuela to the offshore island of Trinidad. Population nuclei of these South American nations are distributed in the same erratic manner as are those of the northern mainland republics, with a preference for highlands and uplands very much in evidence.

In the two countries the basic geographic ingredients do not differ so much in nature as in distribution. Both have mountains, but Colombia is predominantly mountainous; both contain essentially *mestizo* populations, but that of Colombia is over twice as large and the ethnic divisions within the population are more pronounced; both contain a wide range of climates, but Colombia has more of the cool highland and upland types; both depend chiefly for livelihood on agriculture, but Colombia more so. They have about the same amount of cultivated land—and consequently Colombia, with the larger population, has fewer acres per farm worker. Currently of prime importance, both have mineral resources, but Venezuela has most of the known reserves and output of the most critical resource, petroleum.

Of Colombia's exports, nearly 80 percent by value is represented by coffee and 16 percent by petroleum. The coffee is grown principally along the mountainous middle sections of the Magdalena and Cauca River valleys. It is shipped northward by precarious rail-river routes or by air to such Caribbean ports as Barranquilla (285,000) or Cartagena (127,000), or westward to the smaller Pacific coast port of Buenaventura. The petroleum fields are chiefly extensions of those in Venezuela, and thus are located mainly in Colombia's northeast. Most petroleum leaves the country via small ports at or near the mouth of the Magdalena River.

The majority of Colombia's people, like their counterparts in Mexico and Central America, live in the highlands. Of the country's six cities of 100,000 or more, four are in the *tierra templada* or the *tierra fria* of the mountains. These are Medellín (355,000), Bogotá (643,000), Manizales (124,000), and Cali (259,000), each serving as a market center for an agricultural basin or series of basins. Medellín, with its predominantly European population, is somewhat more active economically than the capital, Bogotá, or the other two cities. The two remaining major cities, Barranquilla

and Cartagena, are break-of-bulk ports at the mouth of the Magdalena River.

In effect, Venezuela is composed of (1) a large, sparsely settled hinterland of tropical savanna climate in the Orinoco River Basin, (2) an irregularly settled east-west trending mountain cordillera of *tierra templada* country near the north, and (3) a petroleum-rich coastal lowland—particularly in and near Lake Maracaibo.

Except for the mining of iron ore by United States corporations in the Guiana Highlands—projects now getting under way effectively to supply tidewater iron and steel plants in the United States—the savanna country is essentially the domain of the livestock ranch. In contrast, the *tierra templada* zone contains two of Venezuela's three cities of over 100,000 (Barquisimeto (105,000) and the capital, Caracas (695,000 with suburbs); the remaining city is Maracaibo (232,000) on the northern coastal lowland), and has a diversified agricultural economy producing coffee, cacao, sugar, and other commercial export commodities in addition to food crops. The temperate grasses of this zone, more palatable and nutritious than the coarse savanna grasses, are used to fatten cattle from the savanna lands before they are slaughtered.

Petroleum, amounting to nearly 15 percent of the world's production, constitutes 97 percent of the country's exports by value. It is taken from the ground in Venezuela but refined, for the most part, on the Dutch-owned islands of Aruba and Curaçao by British and American firms. Most of Venezuela's oil comes from the Maracaibo area; however, petroleum extraction is also important in a rather wide area northeast of the Orinoco River delta. Refined products comprise nearly three fifths of all outgoing petroleum. Most of the petroleum exports move to Europe and Anglo-America.

In summary, Colombia and Venezuela may be viewed, in economic terms, as magnified counterparts of the Central American republics—plus petroleum.

Petroleum is the leading Latin American mineral in value of production. The photo shows oil being extracted from beneath the shallow waters of Lake Maracaibo in western Venezuela. [*Standard Oil Company (N. J.*).]

▶ The Mainland Dependencies

British Guiana, French Guiana, Surinam or Dutch Guiana, British Honduras, and the Panama Canal Zone are the mainland dependencies in Caribbean America. Of these, the first three are contiguous. Each of the last two is politically isolated, being bordered by republics.

The Panama Canal Zone is essentially a district 100 miles wide trending in conformance with the Panama Canal. Over one half of its component population of 58,000 lives in urban centers at either end of, or along, the canal. Unlike other Caribbean dependencies, it is an area with substantial economic support from abroad— *i.e.,* from the United States.

The remaining dependencies, however, are of a common stamp. They are among the farthest outposts of European colonialism in Latin America. Their physical environment is chiefly that of tropical rainy, disease-ridden lowlands. Unless they contain a resource which is currently exploitable, they receive comparatively little attention from the controlling nation. In Surinam and British Guiana bauxite is such a resource: the former supplies nearly 30 percent and the latter nearly 20 percent of the world's production of this aluminum-bearing ore. Local benefits are not numerous, however, as most of the work is done with machines.

Only a small fraction of the total land area of the three South American dependencies has been cleared for cultivation. Yet agriculture supports most of the people. Plantations, clustered along the coast, yield rice, coconuts, sugar, and bananas. Some subsistence farming is practiced, with rice and yams as the principal crops.

French Guiana is economically the poorest of the South American dependencies, partly because it exports in quantity no critical minerals, and partly because it has only recently been elevated from the status of a penal colony. The more docile prisoners were kept on the mainland and those more difficult to manage on Devil's Island, a few miles offshore. Most of the prisoners were from France. Many, now freed, still live in French Guiana.

In the Central American dependency of British Honduras, forest products replace those of the mine and farm as major exports. Lumber, both soft and hard, and chicle, the base for chewing gum, are of prime importance on the export list. Corn, grown by subsistence methods, is the principal agricultural crop. Some food is imported, chiefly flour and rice.

▶ The Islands

Caribbean islands are not unlike the mainland dependencies in some respects: politically and/or economically, they are outposts. As on the mainland, single-crop plantation agriculture is the principal means of population support and provides most of the exports. Particularly in the small islands, a single plantation may exercise much control over the economic and social life of the inhabitants. Coffee, the mainstay of agriculture on the continent, is replaced by sugar—with a few exceptions —in the islands.

• *The Island Republics.* In area the island republics of Cuba, the Dominican Republic, and Haiti fall into a general class with the independent countries of Central America. Population densities, however, are generally much higher than on the mainland, except in the case of El Salvador.

Cuba's is essentially a sugar economy. Annually approximately one fifth of the world's sugar is produced, and most of it is earmarked for export. Sugar and molasses represent more than 85 percent of the country's outgoing commodities, with the principal market being the United States. Both are produced from sugar cane, grown primarily by tenants working small parcels of land belonging to large estates. When harvested, the cane must be milled quickly or the juice will ferment and the sugar yield be lowered. Most tenants cannot afford mills; hence these are owned by those who can—chiefly foreign interests. Over one half of the sugar is refined in mills owned by citizens of the United States, who have invested more capital in Cuba than in any other Latin American country except Venezuela. Havana is the capital, largest city, and main port. Greater Havana has more than a million people.

Haiti and the Dominican Republic share uneasily the island of Hispaniola or Haiti. Although the diversity of natural features in this mountainous island is not inconsequential, that of culture and society is even more pronounced. Haiti is a Negro republic in which the rapidly growing population has already attained a density nearly twice as high as that of any other republic in Caribbean America. Its present-day subsistence agricultural economy reflects little influence from the French who once controlled the country. The Dominican Republic, though containing some Negroes and a larger number of people with some Negro blood, is proud of its Spanish cultural heritage. Its small farm-plantation economy supports a population which is only two thirds as large as that of its western neighbor.

The boundary line between these two countries is one of long-standing instability, and local border incidents have been rather frequent.

• *The Island Dependencies.* The statement that Caribbean America is not the master of its destiny is most applicable to the Caribbean island dependencies, where severe population pressures and poverty are almost omnipresent. In the larger members of this island series, such as Puerto Rico or Jamaica, determined local efforts are being made to improve the economic and social welfare of the inhabitants. These efforts are encouraged by the respective controlling nations. In the many smaller islands, however, such movements are essentially absent. The dominance of plantation agriculture built around the production of sugar; absentee ownership of land; restriction of suffrage rights (except in the American and French possessions, which have universal suffrage); and a prevalence of illiteracy and disease are characteristics which may be found, with comparatively minor exceptions, in most of the island dependencies.

▶ Transportation and Urbanization in Caribbean America

Caribbean America is not noteworthy for a highly developed system of transportation facilities or for a conspicuous degree of urbanization. However, connections with the outside world are afforded by the many important shipping lanes which converge on the region, partly attracted by the great interocean passageway across Panama. And a modest number of large cities exist, including one (Mexico City) with a population of more than 2 million, and three others (Havana, Caracas, Bogotá) with populations of more than 500,000.

• *The Panama Canal.* The Panama Canal is one of the two major man-made landform incisions which have caused a gross reorientation of the world's shipping lanes. Like its counterpart, the Suez Canal, its economic importance lies chiefly in the intensity of ocean traffic it attracts by providing a passage through a narrow land bridge connecting two continents. In this sense, it is only about 40 percent as important as the Suez channel: in 1950 it freighted approximately 28.8 million long tons of cargo as compared with 72.7 million long tons moving through the Suez. Nevertheless, it is a major focus of shipping lanes, being particularly important in the funneling of vessels from the Far East, the west coasts of the Americas, and other Pacific Ocean ports into the Atlantic. The return volume of cargo is less than one half as large as this prevailing west-to-east flow.

Again like the Suez, the Panama Canal has military as well as economic importance. Although the military implications vary with current events, they are never absent.

At the present time there is agitation for increasing the canal's present depth of 42 feet (actually, the minimum depth is now 37 feet at low tide in the harbor of Balboa) to 60 feet—thus permitting the largest naval and merchant ships, present and prospective future, to negotiate the channel. The possibility of converting the present vulnerable lock system into a sea level waterway is also under consideration.

Unlike the other transportation facilities of Caribbean America, the Panama Canal tends to be superimposed upon, rather than meshed into, the local economies. The traffic of most Caribbean countries would not be seriously altered if the canal were not used.

• *Local Transportation.* The remaining transportation facilities are, in the main, designed to serve Caribbean America. Mexico and Cuba have rather loosely woven rail networks with gauges similar to those of Anglo-America. A railway freight car can thus move from Canada to Mexico or (by car ferry) to Cuba.

Highway systems tend to parallel the railways. In Honduras, Panama, Haiti, the Dominican Republic, and most small islands, the highways take precedence in importance over the railroads. The Inter-American Highway is gradually reaching completion, although a few segments tend to be dry weather roads only, and a few breaks still remain.

The ocean ship and the airplane are of

primary importance as media of transportation within Caribbean America. Nearly every city of 100,000 or over has access to either one or the other. Only Puebla (210,000) in Mexico (situated fewer than 100 miles from the capital city), Marianao in Cuba (a suburb of Havana), and Río Piedras in Puerto Rico (a quasi-suburb of San Juan (357,000) are without such service.

• *Urbanization.* Few of Caribbean America's people live in major cities. In Venezuela, for example, approximately 1 inhabitant in 5 lives in a city of 50,000 or more. In Costa Rica the ratio is 1 in 14; in El Salvador, 1 in 10; and in Haiti, 1 in 20. These ratios are important indices of the comparative stages of economic development among the Caribbean American (and Latin American) countries, for the major cities have received the strongest impact from the factory system. Thus in Caribbean America, Mexico (with ten cities of 100,000 or over), Colombia (with six), Cuba (with three), and Venezuela (with three), have economies which are trending toward the factory system more rapidly than are those of the smaller nations in this generally agrarian region.

The Native Indian Countries of South America

Ecuador, Peru, Bolivia, and Paraguay are the predominantly native Indian countries of South America. Each has a high proportion—at least 50 percent—of native Indians in its total population. The ratio in Peru is the smallest, totaling 50 percent; in Bolivia, 57 percent; in Ecuador, 58 percent; and in Paraguay, 64 percent.[1] Except for Guatemala in Central America, no other Latin American nation contains a comparable proportion of native Indians.

These countries are further characterized by their very low income per capita—an income which ranges from $22 per year in Ecuador to $67 per year in Bolivia. They do not stand quite at the bottom of the Latin American scale in this respect, the average annual income in Haiti, for instance, being only $15 per person. Nevertheless, the cash income per capita in the four native Indian countries is lower than that of all but a handful of the other Latin American political units.

Still another distinctive feature of these four countries is the very small contribution they make to the total exports of Latin America. Peru, the most active commercially, is responsible for less than 3 percent of all exports from Latin America by value.

Furthermore, the native Indian countries have an unusually high ratio of rural to urban population. Only Quito and Guayaquil in Ecuador, Lima in Peru, and La Paz in Bolivia have populations exceeding 100,000.

In each of these countries, except Paraguay, a major segment of the total population resides in mountain valleys of the Andes. In Bolivia most of the people live at high altitudes; in Ecuador and Peru at high, intermediate, and low elevations; and in Paraguay at low elevations. Obviously the range from *tierra fria* through the *tierra templada* to the *tierra caliente* is well illustrated here.

▶ Bolivia

Of Bolivia's more than 3 million people, most live at or above the zone of the *tierra fria* of the Andes, which constitute the western third of the country. It is here that the Andean system reaches its widest extent—over 400 miles, if one includes the small portion to the west in Chile. Most of this

[1] Donald D. Brand, "The Present Indian Populations of Latin America." In *Some Educational and Anthropological Aspects of Latin America.* Austin: University of Texas Press, 1948. P. 51.

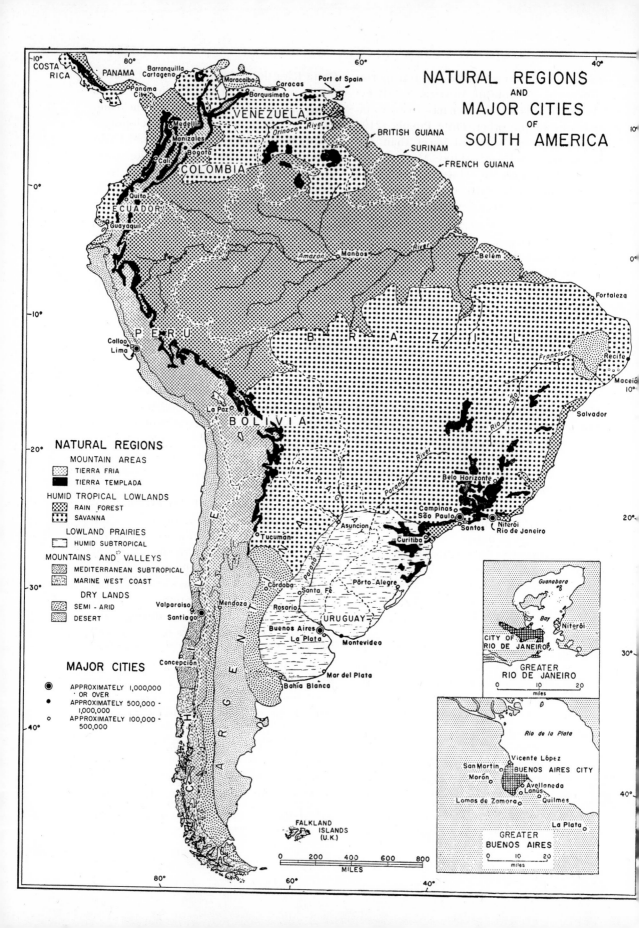

NATURAL REGIONS
AND
MAJOR CITIES
OF
SOUTH AMERICA

COSTA RICA
PANAMA
Panama City
Barranquilla
Cartagena
Maracaibo
Caracas
Barquisimeto
Port of Spain
VENEZUELA
Medellín
Manizales
Bogotá
Cali
COLOMBIA
BRITISH GUIANA
SURINAM
FRENCH GUIANA
Quito
ECUADOR
Guayaquil
Orinoco River
Amazon
Manáos
River
Belém
Fortaleza
PERU
Callao
Lima
B R A Z I L
Francisco
Recife
Maceió
La Paz
BOLIVIA
Rio São
Salvador
PARAGUAY
Paraná
Belo Horizonte
Campinas
São Paulo
Santos
Niterói
Rio de Janeiro
Tucumán
Asunción
Curitiba
Paraná R.
Córdoba
Santa Fé
Pôrto Alegre
Rosario
URUGUAY
Valparaiso
Mendoza
Santiago
Concepción
Buenos Aires
La Plata
Montevideo
Mar del Plata
Bahia Blanca
A R G E N T I N A

NATURAL REGIONS

MOUNTAIN AREAS
TIERRA FRIA
TIERRA TEMPLADA

HUMID TROPICAL LOWLANDS
RAIN FOREST
SAVANNA

LOWLAND PRAIRIES
HUMID SUBTROPICAL

MOUNTAINS AND VALLEYS
MEDITERRANEAN SUBTROPICAL
MARINE WEST COAST

DRY LANDS
SEMI - ARID
DESERT

MAJOR CITIES

⊙ APPROXIMATELY 1,000,000
   OR OVER
● APPROXIMATELY 500,000 -
   1,000,000
○ APPROXIMATELY 100,000 -
   500,000

FALKLAND
ISLANDS
(U.K.)

0   200   400   600   800
MILES

Guanabara
Bay
Niterói
CITY OF
RIO DE JANEIRO
GREATER
RIO DE JANEIRO
0   10   20
miles

Rio de la Plata
Vicente López
San Martin
BUENOS AIRES CITY
Morón
Avellaneda
Lanús
Lomas de Zamora
Quilmes
La Plata
GREATER
BUENOS AIRES
0   10   20
miles

highland country in Bolivia is above the level of the *tierra templada*. It is essentially comprised of two high mountain cordilleras, separated by a high intermontane plateau. The Western Cordillera, reaching elevations of 20,000 feet above the sea, is the most inhospitable of these areas to human settlement and the most formidable barrier to traffic routes. The intermontane plateau, the Altiplano, contains Lake Poopó, a salt water lake at an elevation of 12,120 feet above sea level; Lake Titicaca, a fresh water lake which Bolivia shares with its neighbor Peru at a height of 12,500 feet above sea level; and the Desaguadero River connecting the one lake to the other. The Eastern Cordillera, although attaining elevations of more than 20,000 feet, is more thoroughly dissected by streams than its western counterpart. In addition, it contains some very rich vein deposits of tin and other metals—metals which were sought and to some extent exploited by the Spanish, and which still form the principal exports of the country.

• *Settlement in the* **Tierra Fria**. Most of Bolivia's people live in either the Altiplano or the Eastern Cordillera. As has been stated, the majority of these are native Indians whose Inca ancestors have inhabited these highlands for centuries. The population density seldom exceeds 25 persons per square mile except around the shore of Lake Titicaca, which is surrounded by a closely spaced fringe of native Indian settlements. Although the lake with its attendant cluster of settlements is bisected by the political boundary line between Bolivia and Peru, the local inhabitants form a unitary community and customarily pay little heed to the boundary. Where left alone, they continue to live as their ancestors have done—grazing their sheep, llamas, and burros in the grassy areas of the Altiplano and on the *paramos* above, and growing their meager crops of potatoes, quinoa, and barley. Throughout the year temperatures re-

main surprisingly uniform—usually between 40°F. and 50°F. Rainfall varies greatly from valley to valley, with a rough average of perhaps 30 to 50 inches annually. It is a dreary life in a dreary land—a life which the native Indians ease somewhat by chewing leaves of the coca plant. This is a cultivated plant that contains the drug cocaine.

Tin is the most important product taken from Bolivian mines. In 1951 the country was responsible for slightly more than 20

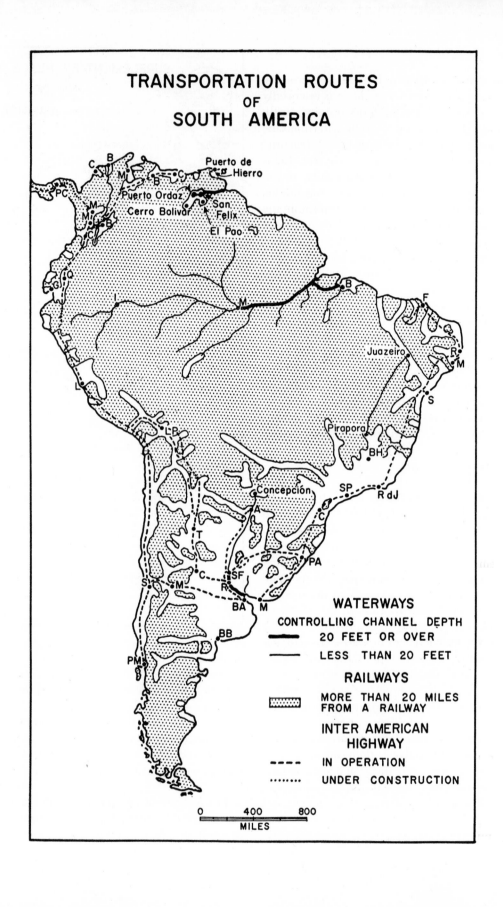

TRANSPORTATION ROUTES
OF
SOUTH AMERICA

Puerto de Hierro

Puerto Ordaz

Cerro Bolivar

San Felix

El Pao

Juazeiro

Pirapora

BH

Concepción

SP

R dJ

PA

SF

BA

BB

PM

WATERWAYS
CONTROLLING CHANNEL DEPTH
20 FEET OR OVER
LESS THAN 20 FEET

RAILWAYS
MORE THAN 20 MILES
FROM A RAILWAY

INTER AMERICAN HIGHWAY
IN OPERATION
UNDER CONSTRUCTION

0   400   800
MILES

percent of the total world mine production of this commodity. The leading mines are in the Eastern Cordillera and, to a lesser extent, in the Altiplano. In addition, silver, tungsten, antimony, lead, zinc, and bismuth are extracted in the same general areas—often from the same mines as the tin. Until recently the mines have been privately owned—in some measure from abroad and in some measure by Bolivian citizens. However, control over most of them has lately been assumed by the Bolivian government. The native Indians provide the principal labor force of the mines, being more effective in this capacity than are lowland dwellers, who soon find themselves short of breath because there is less oxygen at these heights.

• *La Paz.* Several urban settlements at varying altitudes are situated in valleys of streams which drain to the east away from the Eastern Cordillera. The most noteworthy of these is the city of La Paz (350,-000). Lying in a gorge immediately beneath the rim of the Altiplano, this unusually placed city is the *de facto* capital of Bolivia, although Sucre (40,000), 350 miles to the southeast, has long been officially designated as the capital, and the Bolivian Supreme Court actually sits there. La Paz is a true highland capital of a highland country. In addition, it is a redistribution point for agricultural products from the lower mountain valleys to the northeast and from the Altiplano, and for necessities brought by rail from either the Atlantic or the Pacific coast. Its manufacturing industries process food and make textiles, clothing, and other items needed by Bolivians.

• *Settlements of the Lower Tierra Fria and Upper Tierra Templada.* At lower elevations, especially to the south and east in the *tierra templada,* are found a number of settlements where European-induced forms of agriculture prevail. The most heavily populated of these is centered around Co-chabamba, a city of nearly 80,000 inhabitants. Food products from the small commercial agricultural district surrounding the city move chiefly to the mines in the highlands. In all of the four native Indian countries this district is the only sizable area within which the average population density exceeds 250 per square mile.

The eastern and northeastern wilds of Bolivia, a lowland countryside dominated by tropical savanna climate and ranging in vegetation from high forest near the Amazon to scrub forest on the Paraguay border, is as yet almost uninhabited.

▶ Peru

North and west of Lake Titicaca, the Altiplano comes to a rather abrupt end. The two cordilleras which have been distinct in Bolivia merge into a series of echelonlike ranges and groups of mountains. This series continues through Peru, where the Andean system becomes narrower until, at the Ecuadorian border, it is only about 150 miles wide.

• *The Tierra Fria.* The native Indians living in the high mountain valleys of Peru follow ways of life similar to those of highland Bolivia. Indeed, the highland Indians of both countries are descendants of the ancient Incas, who once controlled a considerable empire with its capital at Cuzco (45,000). As in Bolivia, the *tierra fria* supports primarily a subsistence agricultural economy, especially to the northwest and to the southeast.

In the center of the Peruvian Andes is a rich mining district in the vicinity of Cerro de Pasco (19,000), producing copper, silver, gold, zinc, bismuth, and more than one third of the world's output of mined vanadium. Some commercial farming is carried on in valleys not far from the mines. The wheat, corn, and other products grown here are shipped by rail to the mines or—farther downslope—to the capital city of Lima.

• *The Arid Coast.* The Andes drop sharply on the west to a narrow desert coast. Water from the numerous streams draining from the mountains into the Pacific provides irrigation for approximately 40 intermittently distributed oases. Some of these are the sites of commercial plantations specializing in cotton, others of similar plantations growing sugar cane. In still others the farming is predominantly of a subsistence character. Rice grown for local consumption is an important crop in most oases. No continuous rail route parallels the coast, and each oasis has its own seaport. Quality rather than quantity is emphasized in the production of both cotton and sugar. The cotton is chiefly a long staple variety similar to that of the Nile Valley in Egypt. Peru supplies approximately 1 percent of the total annual world production of both commodities.

Lima, the capital (about 1,000,000 including suburbs), is also on the arid coastal lowland. It was built by the Spanish and with its seaport Callao (100,000) became the focus of routes leading not only from nearby mines of the Andes, but also from more distant points. It is today an important manufacturing and university metropolis. Its manufacturing is mainly devoted to food, apparel, and other necessities for Peruvian consumption.

A series of small petroleum fields, situated at the northern edge of this arid coast, extends across the border into Ecuador. The wells are chiefly British controlled.

• *The Eastern* Tierra Caliente. The eastern part of Peru lies beyond the Andes and almost wholly within the Amazon Basin. Here is a broad lowland area of rain forest and sluggish river, of untamed Indian and venturesome trader. Iquitos (38,000), at the upper limit of effective steamboat navigation on the Amazon River, is the major focus of commerce and transportation. From the city move wild animal skins, crude rubber, certain gums (which form the base for chewing gum), tagua nuts, and other extracted forest and animal products.

Irrigated agriculture and sheep-raising in an oasis on the desert coast of Peru 150 miles north of Lima. The view shows a commercial sugar cane plantation owned and operated by an American corporation. In the foreground is the main control gate of the plantation's irrigation system. The Andes are visible in the distance. (*Foreign Agricultural Service, U. S. Department of Agriculture.*)

Some cotton is also shipped. In turn, the city acts as a primary trade center for a large, sparsely settled hinterland. Its traders sell to the natives and a few immigrant settlers such items as drugs, groceries, hardware, and buttons. Iquitos is connected to Callao and Lima by regular steamer service involving a total journey of over 6000 miles down the Amazon River, through the Panama Canal, and along the Pacific coast. Air service is also available.

▶ Ecuador

Ecuador, like Peru, has a lowland strip on its Pacific side, a high-mountain central segment, and a section of the Amazon River Basin. The Pacific lowlands are more hilly than their Peruvian counterparts. In climate, the coastal desert of the south gives way to tropical savanna and, in the north, to tropical rain forest.

The Andes Mountains, having narrowed increasingly from central Bolivia through Peru, are generally only 100 to 150 miles wide in Ecuador. They broaden again to the north in Colombia. Their areal arrangement in Ecuador becomes once again that of two rather distinct cordilleras, separated by a structural depression—or, more strictly, by a series of mountain valleys which together constitute such a depression. Volcanic peaks, very much present in Bolivia but relatively few in Peru, reappear conspicuously in either cordillera. The highest, Mount Chimborazo in the Western Cordillera, reaches 20,577 feet. The Amazonian lowland of Ecuador to the east of the Andes is not unlike that of Peru and southeastern Colombia in general character, but it is smaller in extent.

• **Settlement Pattern and Economy of the Highlands.** A majority of the people in Ecuador live in the Andean *tierra fria* at elevations higher than 7000 feet. They are clustered mainly in mountain valleys between the two cordilleras. Valleys of the far north, like their counterparts across the border in

Colombia, are mainly occupied by highland Indians, as are those of the south. Quito, the capital and second largest city (elevation about 9350 feet; population 210,000) lies in a high basin in the north central part of the country. In the surrounding countryside the subsistence economy of the native Indian gives place to commercial farming dominated by *mestizos* and whites, who also form a majority of the population in Quito itself. Barley, corn, quinoa, potatoes, and livestock are grown, chiefly for sale in Quito. The manufacturing industries of the city, like those in so many isolated Latin American urban centers, concentrate on the processing of locally grown agricultural produce for local consumption. Another valley characterized by commercial forms of agriculture and a dominantly *mestizo* or white population surrounds Ecuador's third city, Cuenca (40,000), approximately 300 miles south of Quito. The country's only noteworthy railroad connects Quito and Cuenca with the important seaport of Guayaquil on the Pacific.

The highland economy of Ecuador differs sharply from that of Peru and Bolivia in the comparative unimportance of minerals. Many different minerals are present, but few in deposits sufficiently large or rich to justify the costs of mining.

• **The Pacific Lowlands.** On the Pacific coast lives the other substantial portion of Ecuador's population. Here is found the port of Guayaquil (260,000), the largest city in Ecuador. A low alluvial area inundated regularly by the Guayas River surrounds the port. Here, under a tropical savanna climate, is grown rice—important not only as a food crop for Ecuador itself, but also providing the principal export of the country. Near by on slightly higher land, cacao—second in importance among Ecuador's exports—is produced. A few banana plantations are also in evidence. However, despite the importance of these commodities in volume of production, most of the land of the drier section along the west coast is devoted to the raising of livestock, mainly for consumption within the country.

▶ *Paraguay*

Paraguay is lowland. Only along its western margin and in a few scattered hills to the east does the elevation exceed 1000 feet. It is sparsely populated. The three fifths of the country situated to the west of the Paraguay River contains fewer than 2½ persons per square mile. Except for a corridor of settlement along the railway from the capital, Asunción (205,000 with suburbs), to Encarnación (16,000), the density to the east of the river does not generally exceed 26 persons per square mile. Effective Paraguay is, therefore, along the railway.

In perhaps no other country of South America has a not unfavorable physical environment been used so ineffectually as in Paraguay. Many of the soils, though not of the highest caliber, are reasonably fertile. The climate of the west, it is true, is a rather inhospitable, dry tropical savanna. To the east, however, where agricultural potentialities are much higher, are humid subtropical conditions where the annual precipitation, rather evenly distributed, ranges generally between 40 and 80 inches each year. Yet the country has lagged behind in the development of commercial forms of agriculture.

The Paraguayans themselves, like their Bolivian neighbors, ascribe much of their low economic status to an interior position. Of the 10 South American republics, only Paraguay and Bolivia are without a coastline. In 1865 Paraguay decided to remedy this situation by marching to the Atlantic Ocean. The latter proved a foolhardy undertaking resulting in war with Brazil, Argentina, and Uruguay. In five years of war a Paraguayan population numbering over 500,000 was reduced to approximately 300,000, of which only 22,000 were males. The country survives today primarily as a buffer state between Brazil and Argentina. It is strongly dependent on the seaports of Argentina for contact with world markets. In 1951 approximately one third of Paraguay's exports were consigned to Argentine ports for overseas shipment.

Present-day Paraguayans, chiefly Guaraní Indians and to a lesser extent *mestizos*, live in a semi-subsistence economy. Their small farms grow corn, cassava, beans, vegetables, some fruit—including citrus fruit—and cotton. The much larger land area that is not tilled is devoted chiefly to the raising of cattle. Meat and cotton are the principal agricultural exports.

Paraguay, however, sends two interesting forest products to the regional, and to a lesser degree, the world market. One of these is extract from the quebracho tree which thrives along the Paraná and Paraguay Rivers. The extract is used in the tanning of leather. The second product is comprised of leaves from a South American holly plant. These leaves are used to make yerba maté, a form of "tea" which is an important item of diet not only in Paraguay but also in other—especially near-by —sections of South America.

Brazil

Brazil, although a single sovereign nation, forms a major subdivision of Latin America comparable in extent and importance to regions containing several different countries. Both the area and the population of Brazil are impressive, especially in comparison with other Latin American nations. Its area exceeds that of continental United States. Its population, while only a third as large as that of the United States, is double that of Mexico, the second Latin American country in population. Brazil contains nearly a third of all the people in Latin America.

▶ Some Major Characteristics of Brazil

Brazil occupies a central position in Latin America. Situated on the equator, the country has extensive coastlines fringing the Atlantic Ocean in both the Northern and Southern Hemispheres. Its westernmost margin is not far from the Pacific. Smaller Latin American neighbors, including all of the other South American political units except Ecuador and Chile, flank its northern, western, and southern boundaries.

Much of its large area is undulating lowland or low upland. Unlike most other nations of comparable size, it is lacking in truly high mountains. At no place does it reach the Andes. Still, it has mountains and associated rough country in the Brazilian Highlands which flank most of the southeast coast; and, to the north across the Amazon River, in a small segment of the Guiana Highlands which reach over the border from Venezuela.

It encompasses nearly the whole of the drainage basin of the Amazon and its tributaries, one of the world's greatest river systems.

It includes the major portion of Latin America's tropical climates, vegetation, and soils. Except for the *tierra templada* of the highlands and the humid subtropical climate of the far south, Brazil is essentially a tropical nation.

It is the only Latin American nation in which Portuguese rather than Spanish is the official language.

Its people are predominantly rural dwellers, yet it contains Rio de Janeiro and São Paulo, two of Latin America's six metropolises that exceed one million in population. In addition, it possesses 12 cities with populations ranging from 100,000 to 550,000.

It is a nation in which manufacturing industries are growing rapidly in size and

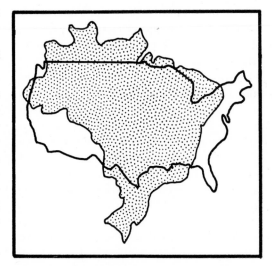

Brazil compared in area with the United States.

importance. During the decade after 1937 its manufacturing output quadrupled. In comparison that of the United States increased by about 70 percent.

It contains the largest expanses of uninhabited or sparsely settled and yet potentially productive land in Latin America. It is estimated that nearly four fifths of Brazil could be made productive and support at least a moderately dense population. At present, however, only about a fourth of the country is effectively occupied.

▶ Major Land Divisions

The land surface of Brazil falls generally into three major divisions: (1) the Atlantic coastal lowland strip; (2) the eastern highlands and uplands, sloping generally toward the continental interior; and (3) the lowlands of the Amazon, Paraná-Paraguay, and Uruguay Rivers.

• *The Atlantic Coastal Strip.* Although recognizable along the northeastern shorelines of Brazil, the Atlantic coastal strip is best developed on the country's southeastern margin between the cities of Recife (550,-000) and Pôrto Alegre (425,000). It is narrow, varying in width from almost nothing to about 100 miles. From Salvador (450,-

000) almost to Pôrto Alegre its western side is flanked by a steep series of terraces—or, in a few places, by a single terrace—customarily referred to as "the great escarpment." The coastal strip is predominantly a lowland of uneven surface, of tropical rainy or savanna climate and associated natural vegetation (much of which has been removed by man) and of rather infertile tropical soils. This coastal lowland is the most densely populated and intensively utilized of the three major surface divisions of the country.

The trend of the great escarpment is in conformance with that of the seacoast. Attaining elevations of 2500 feet—and, in isolated mountains up to 8000 feet—above sea level, this escarpment is the "height of land" in Brazil. It tends to separate headwaters of the numerous short rivers draining to the Atlantic Ocean on the east from those of longer arteries extending to the Amazon and Paraná-Paraguay systems on the west. The single major exception is the large São Francisco River, which reaches the Atlantic Ocean between Recife and Salvador.

• *The Brazilian Highlands.* The great escarpment forms the eastern edge of the Brazilian Highlands, which slope gently toward the interior. The irregular terrain has a tropical savanna climate, but with much variation in total rainfall from place to place and also in types of associated vegetation. Sparsely populated at present, this area contains much of Brazil's potentially productive land.

• *The Interior Lowlands.* In general the surface of the interior lowlands is uneven, although the flood plains proper are quite flat. To the north, the great Amazon system lies under tropical rainy climate, with tributary waterways extending into the adjacent tropical savanna—particularly that of the Southern Hemisphere. During the rainy summer months (December–February) these tributaries bring floods to the main river. Such floods are large enough to destroy sedimentary islands deposited the preceding year, together with the luxuriant jungle vegetation which establishes itself annually on these islands. Meanwhile, islands are again created, upon which the jungle will grow anew. Above the high-water mark are the tall broadleaved evergreen trees of the tropical rain forest proper.

To the south, the Paraguay, Paraná, and Uruguay Rivers also flow through uneven terrain. The climate varies from tropical savanna along the middle Paraguay to humid subtropical along the middle Paraná and upper Uruguay. Settlement of the river lowlands ranges from almost empty areas of rain forest in the Amazon River Basin to moderately peopled subtropical grasslands in the south.

▶ *Population Distribution*

Brazil is predominantly an area of sparse, unevenly distributed, rural population. The majority of the inhabitants are concentrated within two major clusters along the southeast coast. One of these lies around and between the cities of Recife and Salvador. The other extends from Rio de Janeiro (2,500,000) and its hinterland to São Paulo (2,300,000) and its hinterland. Smaller clusters are found around the other major cities and at other, less prominent places, of which most are near the sea. In no sizable area does the population exceed 250 persons per square mile.

▶ *Brazilian Agriculture*

The people of Brazil look primarily to agriculture and grazing for a livelihood. These engage some 70 percent of all workers, excluding 43 percent who are domestic servants. The principal farming areas are found along, or relatively near, the southeast coast. The coastal areas focusing on Recife and Salvador specialize primarily in cotton. Two varieties are produced:

(1) a long-staple "tree cotton" plant reaching 12 feet or more in height, and (2) of much greater importance, a short-staple plant generally resembling varieties grown in southeastern United States, although having shorter fibers. In this section of Brazil, where the prevailing climate is tropical savanna, is grown more than one third of the country's total cotton crop—a crop ranking second only to coffee in exports. Lesser crops include rice, corn, and manioc —all of which are cultivated principally for home consumption. In addition, tobacco and sugar—each of which was at one time the principal specialty of this district —are still produced.

These crops and, farther south, cacao, tend to be grown on *fazendas,* which are large holdings not greatly unlike the *haciendas* discussed elsewhere. The combination of these large holdings with a rather dense population results in a relatively high proportion of workers per *fazenda.* These may be tenants or hired employees, but are usually the former. Some are permanently attached to the land (more so by custom than by law), and others tend to move about. Although definitely subordinate to *fazendas* in extent and importance, subsistence farms are also present.

In the far north of this coastal strip the landowners are mainly of European descent. Around Salvador, however, Negroes and mulattoes constitute approximately two thirds of the total population and a sizable proportion of the property owners.

Agricultural activities of the hinterland of Rio de Janeiro are restricted quite closely to the coastal strip east of the great escarpment. Coffee, at one time very prominent here, is still in evidence northeast of the capital city—although short-staple cotton is receiving more and more attention. Beyond, in a sparsely settled coastal district extending toward Salvador, cacao assumes more significance. Brazilian cacao accounts for about 15 percent of the world's commercial output. Rice, oranges, vineyards,

and truck crops are also grown in this lowland landscape of tropical rainy or tropical savanna climate—especially important nearer the city. One of the major agricultural functions of the hinterland is that of supplying the people of Rio de Janeiro with food.

Still farther south in the *tierra templada* and tropical savanna hinterland of São Paulo nearly one half of the world's annual coffee crop is cultivated. Unlike Brazil's other agricultural districts, this area reaches far over the crest of the great eastern escarpment of the Brazilian Highlands. It is still moving outward. Each year tenant farmers are assigned virgin land to clear, upon which they grow food crops for the following two years. Subsequently, the land is planted to coffee, and the tenants move again to unbroken deciduous forest land. The secondary crop of this district is cotton, which is becoming increasingly important.

In contrast to areas near Rio de Janeiro and Salvador, this is chiefly a district of Europeans and *mestizos* (in Brazil called *mamelucos*). There are few Negroes or mixed Negroid types. The *fazendas* otherwise do not differ sharply from those farther north.

As one proceeds toward Uruguay into humid subtropical climate, he finds himself first in an area of coniferous evergreen forest—a general counterpart to the softwoods of southeastern United States. Beyond this is a discontinuous belt of semideciduous woods which quickly gives way to prairie grasses. Colonies of Slavs (mostly Poles), Germans, and Italians have developed in the forested areas—flourishing, after a slow start, in a diversified agricultural economy based on that of their homelands. The population of these immigrant communities is currently increasing biologically at a rate without parallel in most of Latin America.

To the south, long-established cattle ranching dominates the rolling prairie lands. Important on the leeward side—that is, on the western side—of all the Brazilian Highlands, this form of livelihood is perhaps the most picturesquely represented here where the Brazilian *gaucho*—in most cases, a *mameluco* or *mestizo*—rules supreme.

▶ Manufacturing and Mining

In two other livelihood industries—manufacturing and mining—Brazil is increasingly significant, although neither industry is yet very active when measured in terms of labor force. Manufacturing accounts for only about 6 percent and mining less than 2 percent of all workers. However, Brazil has important potentialities for future development in both fields.

As in other Latin American countries, manufactured products are made primarily for home consumption. This is true of even such finished items as fabricated steel. In addition to iron and steel made at the Volta Redonda plant (largest in Latin America) on the Paraíba River and at older, smaller mills in the Brazilian Highlands, there are major industries engaged in the production of foodstuffs, cotton textiles, leather and leather products, cement, and a substantial variety of other commodities.

The city of São Paulo leads in this industrial trend, employing over one third of all the country's manufacturing labor force, and producing more than 40 percent of all manufactured goods by value. There is a secondary concentration of manufacturing in Rio de Janeiro, and a scattering of industries among the other cities of the country, especially those exceeding 100,000 in population.

Brazil lacks supplies of good coal (although some deposits of low to medium grade exist in the southeast), but has substantial reserves of water power. There are a total of 1,813,000 generating plants in the country, of which approximately one half are hydroelectric. The latter are largely concentrated in the Brazilian Highlands. Unfortunately, much of the undeveloped hydroelectric power is along the Paraná River in southeastern Brazil, and therefore removed from many current industrial sites.

Both the foreign investor and the Brazilian government—the latter acting often with borrowed funds—have been active in developing Brazil's manufacturing industries. Most foreign capital has come from the United States and from Britain, with France a poor third. Especially in recent years, such government agencies as the Export-Import Bank of the United States and the International Bank for Reconstruction and Development of the United Nations have made funds available to the Brazilian government for development purposes, particularly for hydroelectric power.

Some Brazilian mines antedate European settlement. Yet, except for precious metals and stones, the mineral deposits of the country have not been exploited to the same degree as many deposits in other parts of Latin America. The most important concentration of minerals lies in the Brazilian Highlands, in the general district of Belo Horizonte (370,000). This area contains a reserve of high-quality iron ore which may be the world's largest. Manganese is also in good supply. Other Brazilian minerals include copper, bauxite, lead, zinc, nickel, chromium, quartz crystals, diamonds (chiefly for industrial purposes), and a few rare stones and gems.

▶ Transportation and Urbanization

In a country where most of the inhabitants live on or near the seacoast and where many live within the framework of an essentially subsistence economy, inland transportation routes are less important than might otherwise be the case. Nevertheless, the coffee, cotton, minerals, livestock, meat, and other commodities must get to market, and consumer goods and other necessities must be shipped back. Brazil's rather

An inland metropolis of southeastern Brazil—the city of Belo Horizonte in Minas Gerais State. The wide, parklike central boulevard is characteristic of the larger Latin American cities. (*Pan American World Airways System.*)

poorly developed railways assume most of the responsibility for such shipments. The networks tend to converge upon Rio de Janeiro and São Paulo. The highway pattern conforms generally to that of the railways, but is less extensively developed. The Amazon River system and the São Francisco River (the latter not navigable over the great escarpment) provide inland water transportation which varies in depth and therefore in utility with the season, for both river systems extend into the zone of seasonally rainy climate. The airplane is increasingly important as a means of quick access from the interior to the coast, where connections exist with the world's major air lanes.

Although a large proportion of Brazil's people live in a subsistence economy, there is a close coincidence between the general distribution of the country's population and that of its major cities. Brazil has 14 cities with populations of 100,000 or over. In areal distribution they form a sinuous

linear pattern beginning at Manáos (100,-000) in the central Amazon Basin, extending downstream to Belém (270,000), and thence southeastward along or near the coast. Each city tends to stand alone, acting as a manufacturing center and/or trade focus for a distinct hinterland.

The two metropolises of Rio de Janeiro and São Paulo, although separated by an approximate distance of only 250 miles, differ rather markedly. Rio de Janeiro is the nation's capital, as attested by its many beautiful government buildings. Although much has been said about moving the capital into the interior and although a general site has been chosen some 500 miles to the northeast, no real action has yet been taken to implement such a change. The city is a major tourist center, offering easy access to both the sea and a mountain countryside. It is particularly attractive during the drier winter months. It is also a major shipping, manufacturing, and trade center. Its port, which can accommodate ships drawing as much as 40 feet of water, accounts for nearly half of the nation's total imports and ranks second only to Santos in volume of exports. Its railroads reach toward São Paulo and Santos on the southwest, past Belo Horizonte and the mining district of the Brazilian Highlands on the northwest, and toward Salvador on the northeast. Therefore, its hinterland is sizable in area and population, and it is diversified in economic activity.

São Paulo and its port, Santos (200,000), depend chiefly upon an economic base of commerce and manufacturing. Much of the commerce involves coffee, shipped through São Paulo to ocean ships at Santos. The hinterland of these cities includes not only the major Brazilian coffee district, but also some of the lumber district to the southwest and the northern portion of the livestock ranching area beyond. To the north-

east, it merges with the trading area of Rio de Janeiro in the vicinity of the Volta Redonda steel mill. Through the port of Santos move nearly half of Brazil's exports by value and approximately 40 percent of its imports.

The manufacturing of São Paulo is comparatively new and growing rapidly, as, indeed, is the city itself. A major portion of the Volta Redonda iron and steel products come here for further fabrication into textile and electrical machinery, finished steel and wire, and railway rolling stock. Automobiles (final assembly only) are also produced. Textiles, including cotton, wool, rayon, jute, or silk, are important, as are leather products and processed foods. The factories of São Paulo produce principally for Brazilian consumption and operate chiefly on hydroelectric power from a large installation near by.

The Countries of the Southern Middle Latitudes

Argentina, Chile, and Uruguay are the Latin American countries of the southern middle latitudes. The populations of these countries live mainly in subtropical lowlands, although sparsely settled portions of Argentina and Chile extend poleward into cooler climates.

As is true elsewhere in Latin America, the economic structure of these nations is principally agricultural when measured by labor force. However, unlike most other Latin American countries, Argentina, Uruguay, and Chile must compete—chiefly because of their middle latitude climates—with the powerful agricultural economy of the United States as well as with agricultural systems in Canada, Australia, the Union of South Africa, and other mid-latitude nations which sell agricultural and pastoral commodities in world markets.

Despite competition from other temperate lands, these three nations are among the leaders in Latin American exports. In fact,

Argentina is the leader, with nearly 28 percent of the region's total, measured by value. Chile is outranked in total exports only by Argentina, Brazil, Cuba, Venezuela, and Mexico; Uruguay by these five countries plus Colombia.

The per capita cash income of these nations is among the highest in all of Latin America, that of Argentina being the highest. Chile's is exceeded only by that of Argentina and Panama—the latter a country which benefits financially from the presence of the Panama Canal. Uruguay ranks somewhat lower, behind Argentina, Panama, Chile, Venezuela, Cuba, and Costa Rica.

The countries of the southern middle latitudes have a further distinctive characteristic in their ethnic composition. Over 90 percent of the aggregate population in the three countries is either European or *mestizo*. In all of Latin America only Nicaragua, Costa Rica, Colombia, Venezuela, and Mexico approach this very high ratio. In Argentina and Uruguay approximately 90 percent of the people are of European descent. Chile, with 10 percent of its population native Indian and over 65 percent *mestizo,* is more diversified ethnically. In all three countries Negroes are few in number.

▶ Argentina

Of the three countries, Argentina is by far the largest. But, as for so many Latin American countries, effective Argentina is far smaller than total Argentina. Nearly 70 percent of the people live in the immediate hinterland of Buenos Aires (3,371,-000)—an area encompassing only slightly more than one fifth of the entire nation.

• *The Agriculture of the Humid Pampa.* The populous core of Argentina is essentially the humid pampa, a crudely circular district bordering on the Atlantic Ocean and extending outward from Buenos Aires as far as 350 miles. It is characterized by a humid subtropical climate that merges into drier conditions on the south and west. Precipitation ranges from 20 to 40 inches annually. Toward the west and south there is a tendency for a decrease in total amount, for a summer maximum, and for a great degree of unreliability in rainfall. The most highly prized farm land is found southwest of the Paraná River between Buenos Aires and Rosario (468,000). Temperatures are moderate; monthly averages vary within a general range of 45° to 75°F. The black, waxy, and highly fertile prairie and chernozem soils have developed over a nearly flat residual accumulation of wind-blown and stream-deposited materials—a mantle that is, in places, over 1000 feet deep.

Labor for the *haciendas* is supplied principally by tenant workers, who—like their counterparts in Brazil (particularly in São Paulo State)—are often utilized to open up new land. Upon this virgin land the tenant plants wheat for himself (although a part of the crop may be paid as rent) and alfalfa for the *hacienda* owner. After the initial wheat crop has been harvested, the alfalfa establishes itself firmly in the field—to be used in succeeding years as pasture or feed for livestock belonging to the landowner. Meanwhile, the tenant moves to another plot of land. In areas where no new land is available, the tenant is, of course, more closely bound to one section of the estate.

Extending outward from Buenos Aires are a series of districts, each characterized by a rather distinct type of rural land use. Near the city itself is a fruit and vegetable district supplying urban residents with garden produce. To the northwest, the fertile lands between Buenos Aires and Rosario are devoted chiefly to corn, alfalfa, and livestock. Most of Argentina's corn is grown here. Although its annual harvest of the grain is small compared to that of the United States, Argentina is the world's leading exporter of corn.

Farther to the north, west, and south, a combination of wheat and livestock becomes more important. These same commodities also are predominant in a coastal district somewhat removed from Buenos Aires, between La Plata (Eva Perón: 272,-000) and Mar del Plata (115,000). Argentina provides nearly 30 percent of all beef and 10 percent of all wheat entering world markets.

Between Buenos Aires and Mar del Plata are a series of swamps that have not as yet been drained sufficiently to be tilled. These soggy lands are devoted principally to the grazing of sheep, beef cattle, and dairy cattle.

Wheat, alfalfa, corn, truck garden products, and livestock are thus the principal agricultural commodities of the humid pampa. Except for the truck garden products (grown primarily for the Buenos Aires market) and the alfalfa (grown chiefly for livestock feed and pasture), these commodities are produced mainly for export. Products of lesser significance include barley and flax.

• *Agriculture in the Outlying Areas.* The outlying countryside of Argentina beyond the humid pampa is sparsely settled. The existing population is generally clustered into districts of agricultural specialization—districts that are superimposed upon an extensive livestock grazing economy. Thus, in the far northeast of the area between the Paraguay-Paraná and Uruguay Rivers, yerba maté—the tea of Argentina and near-by lands—is grown. In the north, along the Paraguay-Paraná River, the quebracho tree is cut—as it is in Paraguay—for its tannin. Low-latitude beef cattle, like those of the savannas of southern Venezuela, are also raised here. In the semi-arid west, and southward into even drier Patagonia, grazing is the characteristic land use, with the cattle of the west giving way to the sheep of Patagonia. Irrigated valleys support an intensive form of agriculture built around specialized crops. Tucumán (194,000) is the center of an irrigated sugar cane district, and Mendoza (105,000) has developed a reputation for its fine vineyards. Other, lesser, oases are scattered along the eastern piedmont of the Andes.

• *Manufacturing and Mining.* More workers are employed in manufacturing in Argentina than in any other Latin American country except Brazil. Over a million wage earners—approximately one in seven of the entire Argentine labor force—are so engaged.

Manufacturing has been stimulated not only by local investment, but also by a comparatively heavy influx of foreign capital—particularly from the United States and Britain. The former has invested heavily in manufacturing industries and the latter in communication and transportation facilities. In recent years, however, the Argentine government has been nationalizing more and more of the industries—especially the transportation and communication networks—heretofore supported by foreign capital.

Power is supplied mainly by imported coal and petroleum and by local hydroelectric facilities and petroleum. About one half of Argentina's fuel consumption comes from coal, mainly imported from Britain. About one half of its modest petroleum requirements also come from abroad—chiefly from the Caribbean realm. The heaviest concentration of local hydroelectric plants is near the city of Córdoba (370,-000). A secondary concentration is found in the vicinity of Mendoza. Argentine petroleum fields are located in the far northwest and along the seacoast in Patagonia.

The products of Argentine factories are intended chiefly for the home market: foodstuffs, textiles, cement, paper, boots and shoes, and other consumer items. Most of the factories are in greater Buenos Aires—an urban agglomeration involving 8 of the country's 15 cities of 100,000 or over.

Argentina is not rich in known minerals. In addition to the oil already mentioned, local deposits of copper, lead, silver, tin, manganese, and iron, as well as some low-grade lignite, are mined. Most of the deposits are in or near the Andes, in the northwestern portion of the country.

• *Transportation and Urbanization.* Reaching out well beyond the core of settlement in the humid pampa is the most extensive railway network in all of Latin America. It serves not only Argentina, but also Paraguay and much of Bolivia and ties into the railways of Chile, Brazil, and Uruguay. All major routes converge on Buenos Aires. Most of the key lines, built by the British, have been nationalized.

Highways are numerous, but poorly developed. This is due in large measure to the fact that the smooth pampa, with a surface conducive to such roads, is comprised of very fine clay and/or loess. It contains, therefore, neither a good base upon which roads can be built nor good materials for road construction. Even gravel is scarce. There are, however, a few hard-surfaced roads, including the Pan-American Highway, which reaches Buenos Aires. Steamship service and air service—both excellent—are, as elsewhere in Latin America, vital to the country's economy.

Argentina is without parallel in Latin America with respect to the number and close juxtaposition of major cities. Nearly one third of the total population lives in cities of 100,000 or over. Nearly one fourth lives in the cluster of major urban units comprising Greater Buenos Aires. It is in these and other sizable cities that most of Argentina's major industries are concentrated. Of these industries, many are either managed by, or provide employment for, Italians, Spaniards, and other recent European immigrants or descendants of immigrants. Although the main tide of immigration has waned, its effects are still felt in Argentina—particularly in the coastal cities.

▶ Chile

Across the Andes from Argentina lies Chile, which has the distinction of possessing the greatest latitudinal extent of all Latin American countries except Brazil. In width, however, it seldom exceeds 225 miles. To the north, more than one third of the country is the Atacama Desert—where, in places, no rain has ever been recorded. To the south, an even larger portion is comprised essentially of windswept, fiorded, inhospitable mountain country. In the center, primarily within an area of mediterranean climate, is effective Chile, where most of the people live. The summer deficiency and winter maximum of precipitation and the moderate temperatures resemble those previously described for the borderlands of the Mediterranean Sea. This district is bordered on the south by a habit-able section of marine west coast climate, with conditions not unlike those in Portland, Oregon, or Vancouver, British Columbia.

• The System of Agriculture. The populous middle section of Chile has traditionally been a land of the *hacienda*, with nearly 90 percent of all holdings so classified. Today, however, a rapid breakup of these large properties is increasing the number and proportion of small landowners.

Hacienda society in Chile has been characterized as follows by Preston E. James: [2]

The Chilean tenant, unlike the rural worker of countries like Bolivia and Peru, is not separated from the landed aristocracy by racial difference, for in racial make-up Chilean society is notably homogeneous. The Chilean tenant, also, is legally free to move about as he chooses. He is not a peon, for debt bondage is not recognized in Chile. Yet the fact remains that in few parts of Latin America is the tenant worker more closely bound to the land than in Middle Chile: he works on the land on which his ancestors have worked perhaps for centuries; he is conditioned from birth to regard the estate owner as his protector, his *patrón*. The landowner, who never undertakes manual labor even as a form of training for his position, is the manager, and the patriarch. He lives in a world apart: he is educated in Europe, he is widely traveled, he is familiar with the world's art and literature. The landowner would be ashamed to permit any of his inquilinos [tenant workers] actually to starve, but no pressure of opinion forces him to raise their miserable standard of living above the bare necessities which tradition accords them. Although the inquilino is held to the estate on which he was born only by custom, he would find it difficult to leave were he to attempt to do so. The other haciendas would not accept him, and there is no unoccupied land in this part of Chile [*i.e.,* Middle Chile] for him to claim by the

[2] Preston E. James, *Latin America,* rev. ed. New York: The Odyssey Press, 1950. Pp. 221–222. Used by permission of the author and the publisher.

time-honored method of squatting. Only the city would offer him a place.

The life of the Chilean inquilino contains few pleasures. He is given a house, usually built of mud, with a mud floor, and a thatch roof. There is no provision for heating, and the cooking is done outside, even in winter. About two acres of land around the house may be used in any way the tenant desires, and is generally used for gardens; and each tenant is given a small plot of land some distance away on which he may raise his own supply of grain. Around his house there are usually a few animals—dogs, chickens, and one or two pigs. The furnishings of the house are meager: a few crude chairs, a chest of drawers, a trunk, an iron bedstead, and, usually, a sewing machine. There are no provisions for sanitation. The water supply for all purposes is taken from an open irrigation ditch, common to the whole group and entirely unprotected from pollution. It is little wonder that of every thousand children born alive in Chile 248 die within the first year.[3] If the Chilean inquilino, on occasions, seeks the solace of the local vintages somewhat to excess, the remedy would seem to lie in a change of the system of which he is the traditional victim.

On these lands are grown wheat, livestock, vegetables, grapes, and other products characteristic of mediterranean climate. The major portion of these commodities do not reach the export market. In fact, despite its sparse settlement and its agricultural economy, Chile must import food.

• *Importance of Mining for the Export Trade.* Exports from Chile consist mainly of minerals. Of these, copper and nitrate are by far the most important. The primary deposits of both are in the Atacama Desert. Thus, the major exports of the country come from one of its most sparsely populated sections. The Atacama copper ore, located in the Andes on the eastern edge of

the desert, is poor in quality, averaging approximately 2 percent metal. Yet Chile contains over one third of the world's known reserves. Besides the desert production centered chiefly at Chuquicamata and Potrerillos, there is a third production center at El Teniente, in the Andes south and east of Santiago in Middle Chile.

Nitrate currently ranks next to copper in value of exports. The Atacama Desert contains the only extensive deposit of commercially recoverable nitrate in the world. It has been exploited for over a century. Yet, because of competition with synthetic nitrate—competition which first made itself felt effectively soon after World War I, and which was abetted by an export tax of nearly one third of the total sale price levied by the Chilean government—the mining of Chilean nitrate faces an uncertain future.

Chile is endowed with two other significant materials. Iron ore is mined at El Tofo, in the southern portion of the Atacama. Controlled by Bethlehem Steel Company, the ore taken from this deposit moves through the Panama Canal to Sparrows Point near Baltimore in Maryland. Ore from this district is also carried 500 miles southward to a small iron and steel plant in the Chilean city of Huachipato, a suburb of Concepción (120,000). Here it meets coal, which is Chile's fourth major mineral. This is a poor grade of coal that is mined still farther southward at Lota, a coastal location on the Lebu Peninsula, 50 miles southwest of Concepción.

• *Chilean Manufacturing.* The manufacturing industries of Chile, although less important on the basis of employment than those of Brazil, Argentina, Peru, Mexico, and Cuba, are currently receiving much attention. In 1939 the Chilean government established the Chilean Development Corporation for the express purpose of increasing the coun-

---

[3] The figure is from the 1930's. Since then the infant deathrates has been somewhat lowered. (Personal communication from Professor Preston E. James.)

try's manufacturing output. The primary industries are not unlike those mentioned elsewhere, ranging from foodstuffs and tobacco through textiles, metal and metal products, chemicals, leather and rubber goods, and lesser industries. Producing chiefly for home consumption, most are centered in and to the immediate south of Santiago (1,450,000 with suburbs) and Valparaíso (219,000).

• *Transportation and Urbanization.* With its 2600 miles of coastline and its narrow width, Chile is oriented toward the ocean. Ports along the Atacama Desert, however, are hampered by the fact that no good harbors exist in the northern third of the country. Steamers must anchor some distance offshore and accept or discharge cargo via smaller craft. Valparaíso in Middle Chile is the seaport for Santiago, the capital. Lesser ports stud the coast as far south as Puerto Montt (20,000).

A railway line trends along the central valley of the country from a point north of Iquique (32,000) to Puerto Montt. Its usefulness is somewhat limited, however, by the fact that it is narrow gauge (3.28 ft.) in the northern desert, and broad gauge (5.5 ft.) from Santiago southward. Thus goods shipped the length of the network by rail must be transferred from one freight train to another. From Santiago and Valparaíso a railway climbs over high Uspallata Pass in the Andes to reach the Argentine piedmont city of Mendoza. It is not a heavily traveled route. From the Atacama two small northern lines also reach into the Andes, in Bolivia.

Of the roads, the most noteworthy is the Pan-American Highway, which provides Santiago and Valparaíso with access to coastal Peru on the north and, over Uspallata Pass, to Mendoza on the east. The remaining roads tend to form a pattern not unlike that of the rail net.

Airways from Santiago lead not only to other major world cities, but also to Arica (14,000) on Chile's far north, to Punta Arenas (25,000) in the far south, and points in between.

Nearly one fifth of Chile's people live in the two major cities of Santiago and Valparaíso. Most of Chile's manufacturing industries are located in or between these two cities.

▶ Uruguay

Uruguay, like its large neighbors on either side, is primarily a rural country. It is also like Argentina and Brazil in that more of its land is pastured than is cultivated. The agricultural district is mainly a small crescent around the city of Montevideo (850,000). Here, under a humid subtropical climate that encompasses the entire country, are grown wheat, flax, barley, oats, and some truck crops. The pastoral section includes nearly all of the remainder of the country. From it come beef and wool amounting, respectively, to about 16 percent and 4 percent of the total world exports of these commodities.

About one third of Uruguay's people live in the capital city of Montevideo. The rest are distributed somewhat uniformly throughout the city's hinterland—which extends outward to the nation's boundaries. A railway network focusing on Montevideo connects with the rail systems of Brazil and Argentina. Steamship service, both passenger and freight, between Montevideo and Buenos Aires adds to the capital's commerce.

27

Introduction to Anglo-America

The colonizing activities of Great Britain have left a major imprint on the United States and Canada. Hence these two countries (including the United States territory of Alaska) are commonly distinguished, under the term "Anglo-America," from the rest of the Americas, which have received primarily the Latin imprint of Spain and Portugal. For some purposes the large Arctic island of Greenland is conveniently included in the concept of Anglo-America. This procedure is justified by Greenland's proximity to Canada and its strategic importance to both of the Anglo-American countries, but not by the island's culture (a blend of native Eskimo and imported Danish elements) nor by its present political status as an integral part of the Danish state. The same general considerations apply to the small French island possessions of St. Pierre and Miquelon, south of Newfoundland, except that the latter are French in culture and are administered as dependencies of France.

The massive towers of the financial district in lower Manhattan symbolize the great wealth and world-wide financial power of Anglo-America. [*Standard Oil Company* (N. J.).]

Ties with Britain

Effective British settlement of the present United States and of Newfoundland began in the early seventeenth century. Effective settlement of the Canadian mainland by Britain commenced in the later eighteenth century, after Canada had been wrested from France in the French and Indian Wars. Continued immigration from the homeland and a high rate of natural increase in the newly colonized areas led to a rapid growth in the number of British settlers. Consequently, a basically British form of culture became firmly established and has remained dominant in Anglo-America to the present day, despite the entry of large numbers of settlers from continental Europe and smaller numbers from Africa, Latin America, the Orient, and the Middle East. These non-British elements in the Anglo-American population have now been largely (though not completely) assimilated into the general culture of the United States and of Canada.

The most obvious and probably most important evidence of the cultural tie with Britain is the dominance of the English language in Anglo-America. Other evidences of the British heritage are found in the political and legal institutions of the Anglo-American countries, as well as in a multitude of everyday customs and practices among the people. Present-day cultural and political affiliations with Great Britain are closer and more openly acknowledged in Canada than in the United States, despite the large French element in the Canadian population. Canada retains membership in the Commonwealth of Nations and gives formal allegiance to the British Crown. The basic cultural bonds between the United States and Britain, on the other hand, were weakened by a long period of political antagonism beginning in colonial times and continuing for many years after the American Revolution. Indeed, this antagonism is still evident at times among some segments of the American and British populations, although the two peoples as a whole have been drawn closer together by the great world crises and military conflicts of the twentieth century.

Anglo-American Wealth and Power

In the twentieth century Anglo-America has become the main center of wealth and power in the world. Consequently, this region exerts an immense influence in world affairs. The United States, although hard pressed by the competition of the Soviet Union, is undoubtedly the world's most powerful nation. Canada, with a population of only fourteen and three-quarter millions (1953 estimate), is a less powerful nation in its own right but is an exceedingly valuable ally of the United States and wields an influence disproportionately greater than might be expected of a country with such a small number of inhabitants.

The material wealth of the Anglo-American countries finds an expression in their exceptionally high standards of living. Most estimates place the United States first and Canada second among the nations of the world in this regard.

Although the success of the Anglo-American nations in achieving such high levels of wealth, power, and influence is a matter too complicated to be fully explained, it is clear that these countries possess a number of rather specific assets on which they have

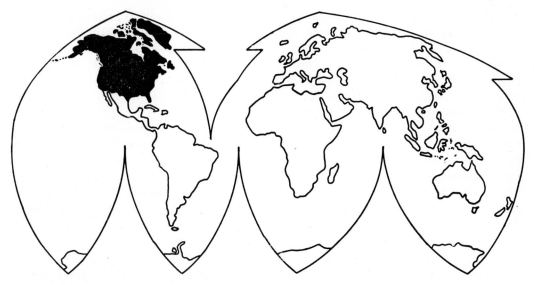

World location of Anglo-America. (*Boggs Eumorphic Equal Area Projection, copyright by A. J. Nystrom & Co.*)

been able to capitalize. Some of the more important assets may be stated as follows:

1. The Anglo-American countries are large in area.

2. They possess effective internal unity.

3. They are outstandingly rich in natural resources.

4. Their combined population is impressively large (the United States alone being the fourth most populous nation of the world), yet neither country is overpopulated.

5. They possess highly mechanized economies which lead the world in over-all production per capita.

6. They occupy a strong defensive position, due to relative isolation from other major centers of population and military power.

7. Their relations with each other are friendly and cooperative.

Each of the foregoing statements will be discussed at some length in the remainder of the present chapter. These points, when elaborated, not only help to explain the success of the United States and Canada in reaching their present enviable position in world affairs, but also throw much light on the general character of Anglo-America as a world region.

Large Area of the Anglo-American Countries

Possession of a large area assures a country of neither wealth nor power. But it does afford at least the possibility of finding and developing a wider variety of resources and, other things being equal, of supporting a larger population than might be expected in a small country. In the twentieth century two of the world's largest countries, the United States and the Soviet Union, have surpassed the older and smaller states of Western Europe as world powers. Both the United States and the Soviet Union have resources which are much superior to those of the West European nations, but until the twentieth century neither country had yet found the means to occupy and organize its national territory effectively and thus to take adequate advantage of its resources.

That there is no direct relationship between size of area on the one hand, and wealth and power on the other is amply attested by the comparative areas of the Anglo-American countries themselves. Canada is the larger country of the two, but is much the lesser in total wealth and political, economic, and military power. The United States, the world's wealthiest and most powerful nation, measures within its continental boundaries 3,083,000 square miles, while the area of Canada is 3,846,000 square miles. Canada's territorial extent is second in the world only to that of the Soviet Union and possibly China (see page 360) while the United States ranks behind the USSR, Canada, China, and Brazil. Even the United States, however, has a greater area than all of Europe outside the Soviet Union. France, the largest European country in area, is only a bit more than one fifteenth the size of the United States. And in Alaska, though it is little developed as yet, the United States controls another 586,000 square miles.

Internal Unity of the United States and Canada

The welding of their large national territories into effectively functioning units represents a major accomplishment by the Anglo-American countries and a major source of their wealth and power. They are not weakened by chronic political separatism in any of their parts. Their economic welfare and, indirectly, their political unity are promoted by constant and large-scale interchange of goods between sections far removed from one another.

Political separatism in the world's countries is often based on ethnic differences. The cultural unity of Anglo-America is strikingly in contrast to the large number of different ethnic groups found in such areas as Europe and the Orient. The aboriginal population of American Indians was overwhelmed by the tide of European settlement and has now been reduced to an insignificant minority concentrated mainly in the western and northern parts of Anglo-America. The Indian population is gradually being absorbed into the main stream of American and Canadian life. Non-British immigrants have been gradually absorbed also, though not without making valuable contributions to the Anglo-American society they have entered.

Each of the Anglo-American countries has one major ethnic minority, and in each case this minority has been the focus of serious problems of national unity. About 4.3 million Canadians, approximately 31 per cent of the total population, belong to the French-Canadian group, which is differentiated from the rest of the Canadian population not only by language but by religion, being overwhelmingly Roman Catholic while the rest of Canada's population is predominantly Protestant. The French-Canadians are concentrated, for the most part, in the lowlands along the St. Lawrence River in the province of Quebec, although they have also spread to some extent into adjoining areas. The ancestors of this group, some 60,000 to 70,000 strong, were left in British hands when France was expelled from Canada in 1763. They did not join the English-speaking colonists of the Atlantic seaboard in the American Revolution and by their abstinence laid the basis for the division of Anglo-America into two separate countries. Since the eighteenth century the French-Canadians have increased rapidly in numbers and have clung tenaciously to their distinctive language and culture. At times major controversies have arisen between this group and other Canadians, and separatist sentiments

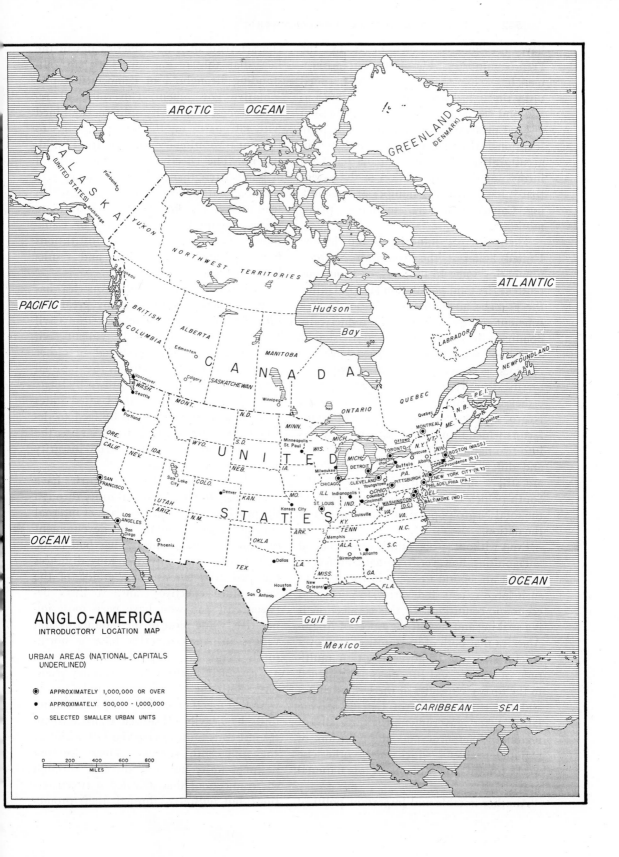

ANGLO-AMERICA
INTRODUCTORY LOCATION MAP

URBAN AREAS (NATIONAL CAPITALS
UNDERLINED)

◉   APPROXIMATELY 1,000,000 OR OVER
●   APPROXIMATELY 500,000 - 1,000,000
○   SELECTED SMALLER URBAN UNITS

0   200   400   600   800
MILES

have occasionally been voiced by the French minority. The Canadian governmen has achieved and preserved national unity through the recognition of French as a second official language and the provision of legal protection for French-Canadian institutions. Although not yet assimilated in a cultural sense, French Canada has been incorporated into the nation to the extent that it has provided a number of outstanding Canadian leaders, including prime ministers.

The principal minority group in the United States is the American Negroes, numbering some 15 millions, or about one tenth of the total population (1950). Unlike the French-Canadians they do not form a coherent minority which is numerically dominant in any major political division or section of the country. Neither have the Negroes as a group been an active force toward disunity in the United States. Nevertheless, a conflict of attitudes toward Negro slavery was among the important factors which nearly split the United States into two nations in the nineteenth century, and differing attitudes toward the Negro are still a source of friction between the South (which contains about two thirds of the total Negro population) and the rest of the nation.

Even without strong ethnic contrasts and antagonisms, however, regional conflicts of interest are bound to occur in countries of such large extent and varied physical and economic conditions. In this connection it is a striking and significant aspect of Anglo-America that both of its countries employ a federal structure of government. A multitude of powers and functions are assigned to the forty-eight states of the United States and the ten provinces of Canada, giving latitude for governmental expression of regional differences and the solution of regional problems which might otherwise work toward the disruption of national unity.

Another notable and important political characteristic of Anglo-America lies in the fact that this region represents an outstanding stronghold of democratic representative government. Governmental responsiveness to majority opinion, combined with safeguards for the minority, tends to prevent revolutionary pressures from building up. The effectiveness of the political system is strengthened by the fortunate economic circumstances of the region, which lead most of its inhabitants to congratulate themselves on being Americans or Canadians and to feel that their institutions have provided opportunities and results beneficial to themselves.

The result is that Anglo-America has been characterized thus far by great stability of government. The American Civil War is the only large-scale, violent civil conflict that has ever occurred in either nation. In neither country has the national government ever been overthrown by force. Thus the governments of the United States and Canada have not been obliged to devote large energies merely to preserving the state's existence or its territorial integrity against internal stresses.

The governments of both countries have assiduously fostered national unity through the provision of adequate means of internal transportation. In both, the development of transportation networks has had to be accomplished not only over long distances but primarily against the "grain" of the land, since effective transport links between east and west have been most imperative, while most of the mountains and valleys in Anglo-America have a north-south trend, thus opposing themselves as a series of obstacles to cross-country transport. Both the United States and Canada were tied together as effectively functioning units by heavily subsidized transcontinental railroads built during the latter half of the nineteenth century. These fostered national unity not only directly, through the connections they afforded between sections, but indirectly through their promotion of settlement and of general economic development. Later, automobile transportation on publicly constructed highway networks and, still later, the development of air transportation further solidified internal unity.

The Large and Diversified Natural Resources of Anglo-America

The natural resources which the Anglo-American countries have within their boundaries are outstanding in both variety and abundance. In part, this fact is simply a reflection of the large territorial extent of each nation. Countries of such magnitude are almost bound to contain a sufficient diversity of physical conditions to produce resources that are out of the ordinary in size and utility. Nevertheless, it is probable that no area of the earth's surface of comparable extent contains so much natural wealth as Anglo-America. The abundance of resources also reflects the inventiveness and skill of the Anglo-American peoples in the exploitation of nature, in the "making" of resources. It should not be forgotten, however, that the value of Anglo-American resources is partly due to scientific and technological advances in other lands. The usefulness of coal, for example, was discovered in England long before the superior coal resources of Anglo-America were more than vaguely known.

▶ Agricultural and Forest Resources

Large areas of Anglo-America are suited by topography and climate for cultivation. The United States, although the fifth largest country in total area, is second only to the Soviet Union in total area of arable land and is easily first in the world in arable land of high quality. A much smaller proportion of Canada is arable, but even in that nation the total arable acreage is still greater than that of any country except the Soviet Union, the United States, India, and China. With only 14.8 million people Canada is the world's richest country in arable land per capita (about 5½ arable acres per person). The United States, despite its much larger population (151 millions at the 1950 census; an estimated 160 millions in 1953), ranks behind only Canada and Australia in the amount of arable land it possesses per capita, which is about 3 acres. In contrast, no country in Europe has even 2 acres of arable land to support each member of its population. Furthermore, the United States ranks second only to Australia in total area of meadow and pasture land, while in Canada such lands, although much less extensive than in the United States, are sufficient to allow a perennially important export of meat and live cattle in addition to a high domestic consumption of livestock products.

Anglo-America has been estimated to contain almost a fifth of the world's total forested area. Canada and the United States rank third and fourth among the nations of the world in this regard, behind the Soviet Union and Brazil. The intensively exploited forests of the United States can no longer supply the needs of the country for wood, although American forest resources are still extremely large and varied. In fact, the United States has become the world's greatest importer of timber products, with Canada, the largest exporter of such commodities, being the main source of supply. Canadian forest resources are larger in extent than those of the United States, but are not so varied in type. For example, Canada has no forests comparable to the redwoods of California or the pine forests of southeastern United States, and is far behind the

An agricultural village in French Canada on the south shore of the St. Lawrence River about 200 miles northeast of Quebec City. The long, narrow farms extending back from the closely spaced farmsteads along the road are characteristic of this part of Canada. (*Canadian National Railways.*)

United States in both acreage and variety of deciduous hardwoods.

▶ Mineral Resources

Not only is Anglo-America rich in agricultural and forest resources, but estimates of mineral reserves give a picture of a region possessing outstanding mineral wealth, probably greater than that found in any part of the earth of comparable size.

Power resources are especially plentiful. The United States is estimated to possess about two fifths of the world's known coal of bituminous grade or better, ranking well ahead of any other country in total reserves. Canada, however, is relatively poor in coal, although not totally devoid of it. Various ways of defining and estimating petroleum resources lead to estimates which differ substantially, but most estimates credit the United States with something like a fifth or even a fourth of the world's petroleum reserves. It normally produces over half of the world's total output of petroleum, although even this immense production is

not sufficient to supply the nation's needs, and substantial imports are required. Canada has not been a major producer of petroleum in the past, but recent developments seem to indicate that that country also has large reserves. Northern Alaska is a further potential source of future production. The United States currently produces an estimated nine tenths of the world's natural gas, and has very large reserves. Estimates of the world's total hydroelectric potential do not give Anglo-America an outstandingly high proportion. Canada and the United States are each credited with about 5 percent of the world total. But they lead the world in *developed* water power, with the United States having about a quarter and Canada about one eighth of the world total, and neither country has developed more than a small fraction of its potential as yet.

With regard to metals the general picture is also one of outstanding wealth and great variety. Iron, the most useful metal, currently represents one of the weaker spots

TABLE 30

ANGLO-AMERICA'S SHARE IN THE WORLD'S KNOWN WEALTH AND PRODUCTION: SELECTED ITEMS

ITEM	APPROXIMATE PERCENT OF WORLD TOTAL [1]		
	UNITED STATES	CANADA	ANGLO-AMERICA
Area	5	7	13
Population	6	1	7
Agricultural resources and production			
Arable land	14	3	17
Permanent meadows and pastures	12	1	13
Production of:			
Wheat	20	7	27
Corn	58	—	58
Soybeans	40	—	40
Cotton	40	—	40
Tobacco	30	2	32
Apples	20	2	22
Oranges	41	—	41
Number of:			
Cattle	10	1	11
Hogs	22	2	24
Forest resources and production			
Area of forests and woodlands	7	9	16
All wood cut	22	6	28
Sawn wood production	35	7	42
Wood pulp production	40	22	62
Minerals, mining, and smelting			
Probable coal reserves [2]	41	1	42
Probable brown coal and lignite reserves	66	3	69
Coal production [2]	26	1	27
Proven oil reserves	28	1	29
Estimated potential oil reserves	17	I.D.	I.D.
Crude oil production	53	1	54
Crude oil refinery capacity	59	3	62
Natural gas production	90	—	90
Iron ore reserves, probable	6	4	10
Iron ore reserves, potential	20	2	22
Iron ore mined	40	1	41
Pig iron produced	44	2	46
Steel produced	46	2	48
Bauxite reserves	2	—	2
Bauxite mined	16	—	16
Aluminum produced	43	25	68
Copper reserves (copper content)	24	7	31
Copper mined (copper content)	32	10	42
Copper smelted	34	8	42
Lead reserves (lead content)	17	9	26
Lead mined (lead content)	23	10	33
Lead smelted	26	9	35

Source: A considerable number of sources were used in the preparation of this table, including the Encyclopedia Britannica books of the year, *World Population and Production* by W. S. and E. S. Woytinsky, the United Nations statistical yearbooks, the FAO yearbooks of production and forest products statistics, *Agricultural Statistics* (U. S. Department of Agriculture), *World Resources and Industries*, revised edition, by Erich W. Zimmermann, the United Nations publication entitled *World Iron Ore Resources and Their Utilization* (1950), and others. While the percentages used are believed to convey as accurate an impression as is possible with a single set of figures, the reader must be warned that such figures can easily give a false impression of stability, reliability, and detail. Actually, many of the percentages used in the table are subject in varying degree to (1) errors in estimation and compilation, (2) fluctuations from year to year or from one period of years to another (3) misinterpretations due to differences in quality or ease of exploitation of particular resources from one area to another, such differences not being revealed in the percentages given. The latter are based on *volume* rather than *value* of production or reserves. In general, percentages given for production were computed on the basis of two-year or three-year averages for the period 1949–1951.

[1] The notation (—) indicates none or no appreciable amount. The notation (I.D.) indicates insufficient data for a reasonably accurate percentage to be stated.

[2] Sub-bituminous and better grades.

TABLE 30 (Continued)

ITEM	APPROXIMATE PERCENT OF WORLD TOTAL		
	UNITED STATES	CANADA	ANGLO-AMERICA
Zinc reserves (zinc content)	12	I.D.	I.D.
Zinc mined (zinc content)	28	14	42
Zinc smelted	39	10	49
Nickel mined (nickel content)	—	94	94
Gold mined	6	13	19
Platinum produced	6	44	50
Phosphate rock mined	48	—	48
Potash produced (K$_2$O equivalent)	27	—	27
Sulfur produced	91	—	91
Asbestos mined	4	63	67
Water power			
Undeveloped water power	5	5	10
Capacity of existing hydroelectric plants	28	12	40
Manufacturing other than metals			
Raw cotton consumed	34	1	35
Raw wool consumed	24	1	25
Rayon produced	36	2	38
Sulfuric acid produced	45	2	47
Motor vehicle production	80	4	84
Production of all machinery and transportation equipment	Over 50	—	Over 50

in the resource position of the United States. The enormous scale of exploitation by the American iron and steel industry in the twentieth century has seriously depleted the nation's iron ore deposits of highest grade. Even so, however, the United States is estimated to have 6 percent of the world's "economic" reserves, that is, reserves of sufficient quality to be economically usable under present conditions. The country has an estimated one fifth of the world's "potential" reserves; in other words, reserves only approximately estimated as to extent, and often composed of lower grade ores than those being mined at present. Canada also has substantial deposits of iron ore. Canadian reserves are smaller in total quantity than those of the United States, so far as is known, but are larger per capita and are at a much earlier stage of exploitation. A selection of other important metals shows the following estimated percentages of world reserves in Anglo-America: copper, United States 24 percent, Canada 7 percent; lead, United States 17 percent, Canada 9 percent; zinc, United States 12 percent, Canada considerably less; nickel, United States little or none, but Canada well over half of the world total. Anglo-America is also outstandingly rich in a considerable number of important nonmetallic minerals other than power minerals: the list includes phosphate, potash, sulfur, industrial salt, gypsum, and asbestos. Anglo-American reserves and production of the latter minerals are concentrated mainly in the United States except for asbestos, of which Canada is the world's greatest producer.

Such is the wealth of the region that it is easier to summarize the gaps in the resource structure than to describe the resources themselves. Agriculturally, the lack of any truly tropical area is felt, necessitating the import of such commodities as coffee and tea, bananas, rubber, and tropical vegetable oils. The major mineral deficiencies are chromite, manganese, tungsten, tin, diamonds, graphite and high-grade bauxite. However, the industrial development of the

United States has progressed to the point that large imports are normally required even of minerals with which the United States is itself well endowed and of which it is a major producer. Canada is an important source of supply for some of these imported minerals. Certain important aspects of the world position of the Anglo-American countries with regard to resources and production are summarized in Table 30.

Such estimates as those given in the foregoing paragraphs and in Table 30 serve adequately to outline the general picture of Anglo-American advantages with respect to resources. However, these estimates should be understood as only approximations.

They are subject to a certain amount of error and change and tend to underemphasize the factor of quality. The contrasts and rankings they show are the result not only of differing natural conditions, but also of differences in technical knowledge and ability, in general economic conditions, and in cultural emphases among the countries concerned. Estimates of mineral reserves, in particular, must be used with caution, since the figures cited by various authorities often differ widely, and the known quantities and distributions of minerals are constantly changing as a consequence of new ore discoveries and the development of new processes for making use of ores previously considered to be substandard.

The Favorable Position of Anglo-America with Respect to Population

In 1950 the United States had a population of 151 million, while in 1951 Canada counted 14 million inhabitants. Thus at mid-century Anglo-America contained about 165 million people, Alaska's 130,000 being negligible in the total. Three of the world's countries—China, India, and the Soviet Union—overshadow all of Anglo-America in population. Nevertheless, the United States is fourth among all countries in population, containing more people than the combined total of approximately 143 million for the three major powers of Western Europe—the United Kingdom, West Germany, and France. Most of Anglo-America's people live in the southeastern quarter of the region, from the St. Lawrence Lowlands and Great Lakes south, and this part of Anglo-America is one of the world's four extensive areas of dense population, along with the continent of Europe, China, and the Indian subcontinent.

From the beginning of settlement Anglo-America has been a region of rapidly growing population, and this growth continues at the present time. By 1800, approximately two centuries after the first settlements were firmly established at Jamestown and at Quebec, there were over 5 million people in the United States and several hundred thousand more in Canada. Population growth since that time is summarized in Table 31. Continuing rapid growth is evident in an increase of about 19 million in the United States between 1940 and 1950, plus an estimated increase of 13 million more between 1950 and 1954.

The population of this region has been increasing at a rate more rapid than that of the world as a whole. Between 1900 and 1950 the increase in world population is estimated at around 50 percent, while that in Anglo-America was over 100 percent. Thus one element in the mounting world importance and power of Anglo-America, and particularly of the United States, has been its possession of an increasing share of the world's population. The older world powers of Western Europe, especially, have

TABLE 31

POPULATION GROWTH IN THE UNITED STATES AND CANADA, 1850–1950

YEAR	U. S. POPULATION (MILLIONS)	CANADIAN POPULATION (MILLIONS)	TOTAL (MILLIONS)	TOTAL INCREMENT	
				MILLIONS	PERCENT
1850	23.3	2.4	25.7		
1900 [a]	76.1	5.4	81.5	55.8	217
1950 [a]	151.1	14.0	165.1	83.6	103

[a] Actual dates for Canada are 1901 and 1951. The decennial census is taken one year later in Canada than in the United States.

been surpassed. In 1870, at the time of the Franco–Prussian War, the United States had almost exactly the same population as each of the two belligerents, Germany and France, but in 1953 it had 1.4 times as many people as the latter countries combined.

However, the Anglo-American share of the world's population is still not an excessively large one. The United States and Canada have together about 7 percent of the estimated world total. This compares with their possession of about 12 percent of the world's land area, or 13 percent if Alaska is included. Thus the population density of Anglo-America is below the world average, being 22 per square mile, as compared with 45 for the world as a whole, or 50 excluding Antarctica. However, the figure for average density obscures the con-

trast between the United States, with 53 persons per square mile, and Canada, with only 3½ per square mile. The very low figure for Canada is due to its tremendous expanse of sparsely settled northern lands, the effectively occupied parts of the country in the south being much more densely populated, although far smaller in areal extent.

It is evident that judged by the world as a whole even the United States is far from overpopulated, considering its exceptional resources and enormous production, and Canada, if anything, is underpopulated. Thus the Anglo-American countries have a combined population sufficiently large to exploit the resources of the region effectively but not so large as to press heavily on those resources and thus prevent surplus production to supply military strength when the latter is needed.

The Highly Mechanized and Productive Economies of the Anglo-American Countries

On the whole, economic production per person involved is higher in Anglo-America than in any other part of the world. This regional characteristic is reflected in, and to some extent can be measured by, the high per capita incomes of the United States and Canada. It is attested by the results of comparative studies of industries in the United States and in overseas coun-

tries, as well as by the efforts of other nations to learn American production methods. High production per worker is a basic factor leading not only to a high income level and high standard of living in Anglo-America, but also to military power, since it means that there is a large surplus of productive capacity available beyond that needed to supply the necessities of the people. This surplus capacity can be used to produce military equipment when the need arises.

Anglo-American production methods are not easy to imitate in the rest of the world because they are so closely related to other outstanding characteristics of the region and to its distinctive historical development. The use of machines and mechanical energy on a scale greater than anywhere else in the world is basic to Anglo-American productivity. But this superior mechanization has been achieved in a region which has had an abundance of resources and a shortage of labor throughout most of its history; which has possessed resources sufficiently large and rich both to attract foreign capital and, through large-scale and often wasteful exploitation, to make possible large domestic accumulations of capital; and which has been superlatively endowed with the necessary fuels to drive machinery. Furthermore, it has been achieved in a region where a free and fluid society has encouraged full development of the abilities of the people; where free and untrammeled economic progress has generally been encouraged, fostered, and subsidized by government; where the energies of the people have not had to be too much diverted into war; and where large segments of the population have subscribed with an almost religious fervor to the ideals of hard work and economic success since early times. Finally, in the United States, a large and unified internal market has allowed great economic organizations to specialize in the mechanized mass production of a few articles, thus lowering the unit costs of production. The foregoing combination of circumstances has been essentially unmatched in any other part of the world, much of which seeks mechanization under comparatively severe handicaps.

Defensive Advantages of an Isolated Position

Anglo-America is essentially a huge island, bordered on the east by the Atlantic Ocean, on the north by the Arctic Ocean and on the west by the Pacific. The only land connection with another world region is along the boundary between the United States and Mexico, which mostly runs through sparsely populated territory and is far removed from the core area of either country. No good land route yet connects the United States and Canada with South America, and most of Anglo-America's contacts with Latin America, as well as with other world regions, are made by sea and air.

The closest land approaches of Anglo-America to Eurasia are at the northeastern and northwestern corners of the region. A series of islands bridges the North Atlantic between Canada and Europe, and includes Greenland, Iceland, the Faeroes, the Shetlands, and Spitsbergen. Only the Bering Strait separates Asia from Alaska. The first historic contact between Europe and North America, that of the Vikings from the ninth to the eleventh centuries, was made via the island stepping stones of the North Atlantic. Contacts with Asia occurred earlier, since the North American Indians are thought to have entered the continent in prehistoric times from Asia via the Bering Strait area. In the eighteenth century Russian fur traders entered Alaska, which only passed from Russian to American control by purchase in 1867.

But harsh climatic conditions in the latitudes of these land approaches have prevented them from serving as major avenues of movement between Anglo-America and Eurasia during historic times. The North Atlantic approach is dangerous to navigate and leads, on the American side,

only to the wasteland of tundra and coniferous forest which occupies northern
Canada. Bering Strait is backed on both
sides by similar stretches of wasteland. Between the two approaches Eurasia and
North America are separated by the ice-
jammed Arctic Ocean, again backed by
tundra and taiga on both sides.

Consequently, the main connections between the two great land masses of the
Northern Hemisphere have lain across the
oceans farther south, although the routes
generally followed do swing north to approximate great circle courses. From the
Atlantic seaboard ports of Anglo-America
south of the taiga the sea distance to Britain is about 3000 miles (only about 2000
between the outer extremities of Newfoundland and Ireland), and from Puget
Sound to Japan is about 4000. If the Pacific
is crossed via Hawaii to Japan, the distance
becomes well over 5000 miles. These have
been the real distances separating the states
of Anglo-America from the world's other
centers of political and military power—
distances not over long for peaceful commerce, but constituting a major obstacle
to military operations. Such distances
(added to inherent strength) have so reduced the danger of a successful military
attack on Anglo-America that the region
has been able to proceed with its domestic
development while paying relatively little
attention to considerations of defense and
the entanglements of world politics.

However, three new factors have arisen
in relatively recent times to lessen the value
of Anglo-America's protected position and
to make the psychological attitude of iso-
lationism which it engendered a dangerous
one. In the first place, the destruction of
the balance of power in Eurasia has raised
the possibility that while no individual
Eurasian power could successfully overcome Anglo-America, a Eurasia united
wholly or in large part under one dominion might well aspire to do so. A united
Eurasia would change the position of
Anglo-America from that of an isolated
region protected by distance to that of an
area semi-surrounded by its possible antagonist. Secondly, the development of air
power has placed the core areas of Anglo-
America within range of attack from Eurasia via the northern areas of most direct
approach, which can be easily and rapidly
traversed by air if not by sea or land. Finally, the development of nuclear armaments has raised the possibility of devastating or even decisive effect by attack from
the air.

The relatively isolated position of Anglo-
America has allowed the region to develop
in relative peace and security, and remains
a valuable asset and source of strength,
since it is still harder to attack effectively
over long than over short distances. But the
protective value of this position has declined sharply in recent years, and the people of the region can no longer afford to
harbor such feelings of isolation, immunity,
and security as have been habitual in the
past. The world at large has been forcibly
brought to their attention.

Cooperative Relations of the Anglo-American States

For many years after the American Revolution the political division of Anglo-
America between the independent United
States to the south and a group of British
colonial possessions to the north was accompanied by serious friction between the
peoples and governments on either side of
the United States boundary. A heritage of
antagonism was present due to the failure
of the northern colonies to join in the Rev-

olution, their use as British bases during that war, the large element of their population which was composed of Tory stock driven from American homes during the Revolution, and uncertainty and rivalry as to ultimate control of the central and western reaches of the continent.

The War of 1812 was largely an American effort to conquer Canada. Even after the failure of this effort a series of border disputes occurred, and American ambitions to possess this remaining British territory in North America were openly expressed; suggestions and threats of annexation were made in official quarters throughout the nineteenth and into the twentieth century.

In fact, Canada as a unified nation is in good part a result of American pressure. After the American Civil War the military power of the United States took on a threatening aspect in Canadian and British eyes. Suggestions were made in some American quarters that Canadian territory would be a just recompense to the United States for British hostility toward the Union during the war. The British North America Act, passed by the British Parliament in 1867, brought an independent Canada into existence. Britain sought, and as the event has proved, successfully, to establish in Canada an independent nation capable of achieving transcontinental unity, of maintaining its independence and integrity, and of relieving Britain of some of the burden of defense in North America.

Hostility between the United States and its northern neighbor did not immediately cease with the establishment of an independent and unified Canada; in fact, a certain amount of friction is evident from time to time even today. Nevertheless, relations between the two Anglo-American nations have improved gradually to the point where these countries are often cited as an outstanding example of international amity and cooperation, and the frontier between them has ceased to be a source of mutual insecurity and weakness. This frontier, stretching completely unfortified across a continent, has become more a symbol of friendship than of enmity.

The bases of Canadian-American friendship are cultural similarities, the material wealth of both nations, and the mutual need for and advantages of cooperation. Despite certain vexatious tariff restrictions, a very large volume of trade moves across the frontier and strengthens both countries economically and militarily. Each country is the other's principal foreign market and source of supply, although Canada is much more dependent on the United States in this regard than is the United States on Canada. In 1950, for example, Canada supplied 22 percent of all United States imports by value and took 19 percent of all United States exports; while the United States supplied 67 percent of Canada's imports and took 65 percent of its exports. In addition, the United States supplies large quantities of capital which have been an important factor in the rapid economic development of Canada during recent decades. Major items moving from the United States to Canada include coal and oil; iron, steel, and machinery; other manufactures; and subtropical agricultural products, such as cotton and citrus fruits. Those moving from Canada to the United States include such vital items as lumber, wood pulp and paper, and a great variety of minerals.

Politically and militarily the two nations function to a certain extent as a unit. A permanent Joint Defense Board has been in existence since 1940, and joint Civil Defense was provided for in 1951. Cooperative military maneuvers in northern Anglo-America and cooperative arrangements for the production of military equipment are further evidences of the close working relationship which exists in matters of military preparedness and defense. The two nations are partners in several alliances and international organizations.

These cooperative efforts and relations mean essentially that Canada is protected by its more powerful neighbor, which would certainly regard any attack on Canada as an attack on itself, while at the same time Canadian resources and strategic assets greatly strengthen that neighbor. Meanwhile, Canada continues, as an independent nation, to develop its separate way of life and to maintain its ties with the United Kingdom and the other states of the Commonwealth of Nations.

Anglo-American Regions

28

Among the most notable characteristics of Anglo-America as a world region are a certain broad uniformity of culture and a simplicity of political organization which contrast sharply with the cultural and political complexity of such areas as Europe or the Orient. Nevertheless, even Anglo-America is sufficiently different from place to place that a multiplicity of cultural and political regions and subregions can be distinguished. The regional complexity becomes much greater when physical and economic factors are considered. Since a regional treatment of some type seems essential in presenting the geography of such a vast and varied segment of the earth's surface as Anglo-America, the problem arises as to what scheme, or schemes, of regional division should be chosen.

One possible solution to this problem is provided by certain grand divisions which are commonly recognized by scholars in various fields and the public generally: in the United States the Northeast (including its distinctive subrealm of New England), the South, the Middle West, and the West; in Canada the Maritime Provinces, Newfoundland, Quebec, Ontario, the Prairie Provinces, British Columbia, and the vast, empty Northern Lands; with Alaska and Greenland representing essentially continuations of the Canadian Northern Lands in

A landscape along the southern margin of the Dairy Belt section of the Interior Plains. This view was taken in southeastern Minnesota near the Wisconsin border. The tilled field in the foreground bordered by pasture contains, in order from bottom of photo, contour strips of hay, wheat (in shocks), and corn. The silo beside the large barn in the right foreground indicates a dairy operation. (*United States Information Service, Department of State*)

physical respects, though politically separate from the latter. But these grand divisions, defined essentially on a cultural and political basis, are cut across, subdivided, and given great internal variety by a series of major landform divisions and climatic regions, each of which tends to have certain characteristic economic activities associated with it. For example, one landform division, the Rocky Mountains, extends not only completely across Canada and nearly across continental United States, but also into Alaska. Yet throughout the Rockies there are certain broad similarities in the aspect of the land and a recurring pattern of economic development, whether the particular segment of the mountains be located in the American West, the Canadian West, or Alaska (although in northern Canada and Alaska a severe climate greatly restricts the range of economic opportunities). A somewhat comparable, though economically more complex, situation prevails with respect to the great Interior Plains of Anglo-America, which occupy portions of the American Middle West, South, and West, and extend into the Prairie Provinces of Canada and parts of Ontario and Quebec as well.

On the whole, the physiographic and associated climatic and economic complexity of Anglo-America appears sufficiently greater than the cultural and political complexity that a basic scheme of regions utilizing landform boundaries seems a suitable means of avoiding repetition and generally giving sharpness to an introductory discussion. Thus the regional treatment in the present chapter is organized under eleven major landform divisions: the Canadian Shield, the Gulf-Atlantic Coastal Plain, the Piedmont, the Appalachian Highlands, the Interior Highlands, the Interior Plains, the Rocky Mountains, the Intermountain Basins and Plateaus, the Pacific Mountains and Valleys, the Arctic Coastal Plains, and Greenland. The discussion of these divisions is prefaced by a brief survey of the major climatic regions of Anglo-America, whose boundaries only rarely coincide with those of the landform divisions, and which give much internal variety to the latter. Data with respect to regional economic and urban development are included in the discussion of the respective landform divisions, and the entire treatment is viewed, insofar as possible, against a general background of the grand cultural-political divisions, such as the South and Middle West, which have been outlined earlier.

Climatic Types and Regions

The climatic pattern of Anglo-America exhibits both diversity and largeness of scale. Every major nontropical type of climate is found within the region, usually over broad expanses. The United States includes a greater number of major climatic types within its boundaries than any other country of the world. Even Canada is more diversified in climate than is commonly assumed. The variety of economic opportunities and possibilities afforded by the wide range of climates in Anglo-America is one of the basic factors underlying the economic strength of this world region.

▶ Polar and Subarctic Climates

Northern Anglo-America is handicapped by cold. A belt of *tundra climate,* with its associated vegetation of mosses, lichens, sedges, hardy grasses, and low bushes, rims the coast from Alaska to Labrador and extends into the Arctic islands of Canada and the coastal sections of Greenland. In interior Greenland an *ice-cap climate* pre-

Identification map of Anglo-America showing major landform divisions, and other areas, places, and features referred to in the text.

Key: a, Superior Upland; b, Newfoundland; c, Maritime Provinces and southeastern Quebec; d, northern New England; e, southern New England; f, Hudson-Mohawk Valley; g, Adirondack Mountains; h, Champlain Lowland; i, Blue Ridge; j, Ridge and Valley Section; k, Northern Appalachian (Allegheny) Plateau; l, Cumberland Plateau; m, Ozark Plateau; n, Ouachita Mountains; o, St. Lawrence Lowlands; p, Unglaciated Southeastern Interior Plain; q, Mackenzie River Lowlands; r, Basin and Range Country; s, Colorado Plateau; t, Columbia Plateau; u, Snake River Plains; v, Fraser-Nechako-Stikine Plateaus; w, Yukon River Basin; x, California Central Valley; y, Sierra Nevada; z, Klamath Mountains; aa, Cascade Mountains; bb, Willamette-Puget Sound Lowland; cc, Olympic Mountains; dd, Kenai Peninsula; ee, Susitna River Valley; ff, Alaska Range; 1, Labrador-Quebec iron field; 2, Annapolis-Cornwallis Valley; 3, Aroostook Valley; 4, Sea Island District; 5, Black Belt; 6, Mississippi Lowland cotton district; 7, Black Waxy Prairie cotton district; 8, Texas-Oklahoma Red Prairies cotton district; 9, Texas-Louisiana rice lands (coastal prairies); 10, Arkansas rice district; 11, Mississippi Delta "sugar bowl"; 12, Lake Okeechobee sugar district; 13, Nashville Basin; 14, Kentucky Bluegrass Region; 15, Tri-State mining district; 16, Mesabi Range; 17, Steep Rock Lake; 18, Wisconsin unglaciated area; 19, Mount Mitchell (6711 feet); 20, Black Hills; 21, Yellowstone National Park; 22, Salt Lake oasis; 23, Gila-Salt River oasis; 24, Imperial Valley; 25, Hoover Dam; 26, Mount Elbert (14,430 feet); 27, Mount Whitney (14,495 feet); 28, Truckee Pass; 29, Shasta Dam; 30, Mount Hood (11,245 feet); 31, Bonneville Dam; 32, Mount Rainier (14,408 feet); 33, channeled scablands; 34, Grand Coulee Dam; 35, Matanuska Valley; 36, Mount McKinley (20,300 feet); 37, lower Rio Grande irrigated area; 38, central Florida citrus belt; 39, Georgia-Alabama-Florida peanut district; 40, Virginia–North Carolina peanut district. Physiographic boundaries after Fenneman, Lobeck, and others.

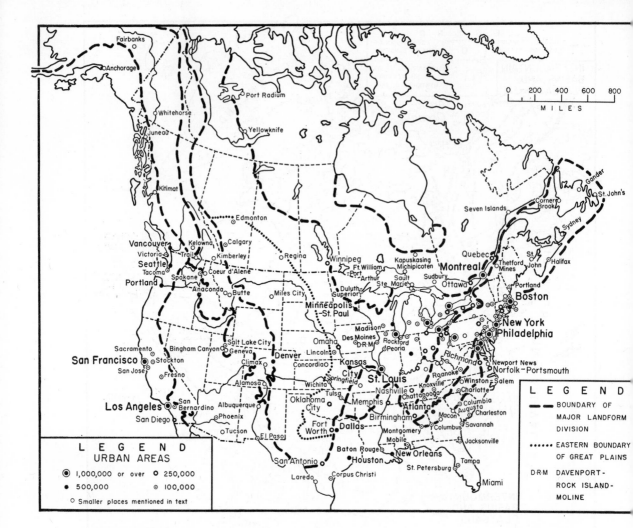

vails, and the land is covered by an enormous continental glacier. In the ice-cap climate every month has an average temperature below 32°F. In the tundra climate from 1 to 4 months average above freezing, although no month averages above 50°F. South of the tundra a vast expanse of *subarctic climate* spreads across most of Alaska and occupies about half of Canada. Like its counterpart in Eurasia, this belt extends completely across the continent between the Atlantic and Pacific Oceans. The subarctic region of Anglo-America, with its long, cold winters and short, cool summers, has a natural vegetation of coniferous snow forest resembling the Russian taiga. Population is extremely sparse in the zones of tundra and subarctic climate, and practically nonexistent in the ice-cap climate.

Small groups of people are supported by trapping, hunting, fishing, mining, and lumbering.

▶ Humid Continental and Humid Subtropical Climates

Approximately the eastern half of Anglo-America south of the subarctic zone is an area of humid climate which accounts for most of Anglo-America's agricultural production and within which most of the people of this world region are found. Temperature variations associated with a spread in latitude of more than 25 degrees provide the basis for a division of this humid eastern area into three climatic regions, each taking the form of an east-west belt. At the north is the region of *humid continental climate with short summers,* in the center is

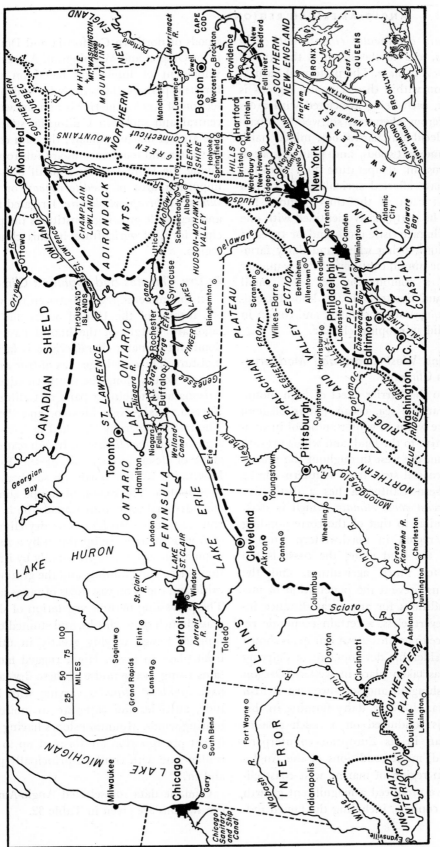

Northeastern United States and southeastern Canada. Map symbols follow those of the main Anglo-American maps.

the *humid continental climate with long summers,* and to the south is the *humid subtropical climate*. The pattern of natural vegetation within these climatic regions is complex, each being associated with areas of coniferous evergreen softwoods, broad-leaved deciduous hardwoods, mixed hardwoods and softwoods, and prairie grasses. Variations in temperature and growing season have affected agriculture in such a way that each of the three regions has come to be particularly identified with one or two characteristic crops and/or types of production: spring wheat and dairy farming in the humid continental short-summer climate; a combination of corn, small grains, and livestock in the humid continental long-summer climate; and cotton in the humid subtropical climate.

▶ Marine West Coast and Mediterranean Climates

Due to the barrier effect of high mountains near the sea, ocean waters offshore which are warm in winter and cool in summer relative to the land, and winds prevailingly from the west throughout the year, a narrow coastal strip from southern Alaska to northern California has a distinctive *marine west coast climate,* which is strikingly similar to that of the corresponding climatic region in northwestern Europe. Most of the land along the coast is too rugged for much agriculture, and the mountains prevent the penetration of marine conditions for any great distance inland. Nevertheless, a certain economic resemblance to northwestern Europe is shown in a considerable development of dairying which has taken place in western Oregon and Washington and southwestern British Columbia. However, dairy farming in this section is conducted on a much smaller scale than in its European counterpart. The mild, moist conditions of the Anglo-American region of marine west coast climate have produced a magnificent growth of giant conifers, including the famed red-

woods of northern California and Douglas fir of Oregon and Washington. A great development of lumbering based on these forests is perhaps the activity for which this section of Anglo-America is best known. In central and southern California, south of the area of marine climate, the rain comes in winter and temperatures are subtropical, giving the United States a small but very important area of *mediterranean* or *dry-summer subtropical climate*. Irrigated fruit and vegetable growing constitutes the principal form of agriculture in this climatic region.

▶ Dry Climates and Highland Climates

In the immense region between the western littoral of the United States and the landward margin of the humid East, the dominant climatic characteristic is lack of moisture. The only large area of true *desert climate* occurs along the southern edge, in Arizona and adjoining parts of California, Nevada, Utah, New Mexico, and Texas. The rest is generally classified as having a semi-arid *steppe climate,* although scattered areas of desert occur west of the Rocky Mountains as far north as southeastern Washington. The region of steppe climate extends northward into Canada both east and west of the Rockies. The dry climates of Anglo-America are inhabited by a sparse population supported principally by irrigation agriculture, mining, and the grazing of cattle and sheep on vast areas of range land. The prevailing natural vegetation of short grass, bunch grass, shrubs, and stunted trees supplies forage varying greatly in utility from place to place. High, rugged mountains rising in the midst of these dry lands have *highland climates* varying with latitude, altitude, and exposure to moisture-bearing winds. Mountain slopes having sufficient precipitation are forested up to the timber line with conifers, principally pine and fir.

Climatic data for selected Anglo-American stations are given in Table 32.

TABLE 32

CLIMATIC DATA FOR SELECTED ANGLO-AMERICAN STATIONS

STATION	REGION	ELE-VATION ABOVE SEA LEVEL (FEET)	TYPE OF CLIMATE	AVERAGE TEMPERATURE (DEGREES F. TO NEAREST WHOLE DEGREE)			AVERAGE ANNUAL PRECIPI-TATION TO NEAREST INCH
				AN-NUAL	JANU-ARY	JULY	
Barrow, Alaska	Arctic Coastal Plains	22	Tundra	10°	−16°	40°	4″
Fairbanks, Alaska	Yukon River Basin	436	Subarctic	26°	−11°	60°	12″
Kapuskasing, Ontario	Canadian Shield	752	Subarctic	32°	−2°	62°	28″
Regina, Saskatchewan	Interior Plains (Spring Wheat Belt)	1884	Humid Continental (Short Summer)	35°	−1°	65°	15″
Montreal, Quebec	St. Lawrence Lowlands	187	Humid Continental (Short Summer)	43°	14°	70°	41″
Portland, Maine	Northern New England	61	Humid Continental (Short Summer)	45°	22°	69°	42″
Des Moines, Iowa	Interior Plains (Corn Belt)	948	Humid Continental (Long Summer)	50°	21°	76°	32″
Concordia, Kansas	Interior Plains (Winter Wheat Belt)	1375	Humid Continental (Long Summer)	54°	27°	79°	26″
Lexington, Kentucky	Southeastern Interior Plains	979	Humid Subtropical	55°	34°	76°	43″
Norfolk, Virginia	Atlantic Coastal Plain	26	Humid Subtropical	60°	42°	79°	45″
Atlanta, Georgia	Southern Piedmont	977	Humid Subtropical	62°	44°	79°	49″
Miami, Florida	Atlantic Coastal Plain	8	Humid Subtropical	75°	68°	82°	55″
Houston, Texas	Gulf Coastal Plain	41	Humid Subtropical	69°	54°	83°	46″
Dallas, Texas	Gulf Coastal Plain	487	Humid Subtropical	66°	46°	84°	35″
Laredo, Texas	Lower Rio Grande Valley	500	Steppe	74°	57°	88°	18″
Denver, Colorado	Great Plains	5292	Steppe	51°	31°	73°	14″
Miles City, Montana	Great Plains	2629	Steppe	46°	17°	74°	13″
Calgary, Alberta	Great Plains	3540	Steppe	38°	13°	62°	17″
Spokane, Washington	Columbia Plateau	2357	Steppe	49°	27°	70°	16″
Tucson, Arizona	Basin and Range Country	2558	Desert	67°	50°	86°	11″
Los Angeles, California	Southern California Coast	312	Mediterranean	63°	56°	71°	15″
Sacramento, California	California Central Valley	25	Mediterranean	60°	46°	74°	18″
Seattle, Washington	Puget Sound Lowland	14	Marine West Coast	52°	40°	65°	34″
Juneau, Alaska	Southern Alaska Panhandle	15	Marine West Coast	44°	21°	60°	104″
Alamosa, Colorado	Rocky Mountains	7534	Highland	42°	25°	66°	6″

The Canadian Shield

The landform division called the Canadian Shield,[1] or sometimes the Laurentian Shield or Laurentian Upland or Plateau, occupies an immense area in northeastern Anglo-America. It extends from the Arctic Ocean to the line of the Great Lakes and the St. Lawrence Lowlands, and from the Atlantic to a line on the west traversing Great Bear Lake, Great Slave Lake, Lake Athabaska, and Lake Winnipeg. The Shield covers more than half of Canada, and extends into the United States to the west and south of Lake Superior; this American section is known as the Superior Upland. The Adirondack Mountains in New York State are geologically an extension of the Shield, but for most purposes they are more conveniently discussed with the Appalachian Highlands. In general, the topography of the Shield is that of a rolling plain or an endless succession of low, rounded hills. Its surface was repeatedly scoured by the continental glaciers which spread from both sides of Hudson Bay in the Great Ice Age. Thus the ancient crystalline rocks composing the Shield are generally exposed at the surface or covered by a very thin layer of poor soil. Glaciation disrupted the pre-existing drainage system, resulting in a plethora of lakes, swamps, and wandering streams with many rapids and waterfalls. Today this tangled wilderness area often seems to consist more of water than of land.

Much of the Shield has a rugged quality, and a few sections are mountainous. Most elevations are between 1000 and 2000 feet. The edge of the Shield north of the St. Lawrence Lowlands in Quebec rises rather abruptly to about 2000 feet and is called the Laurentide Mountains. The Torngat Mountains of northern Labrador exceed 4000 feet and are reported to be twice that high in their little-known extension in Baffin Island.

▶ Economic and Urban Development

Most of the Shield has either a tundra or a subarctic climate. Economic development is largely concentrated along the southern fringe, in the southernmost reaches of the subarctic climate zone, or in areas of humid continental short-summer climate. This more developed section of the Shield lies in relatively close proximity to densely populated areas of Canada and the United States farther south. The immense, cold, northern reaches are the home of a few thousand Eskimos, Indians, and whites who live mainly by trapping and fishing. Permanent settlements are mostly limited to tiny, widely scattered trading-post villages. Small, isolated commercial fishing villages dot the rocky coast of Labrador, where the eastern margins of the Shield reach the Atlantic. On the western side of the Shield there are two important mining settlements in the north. Yellowknife (3000) is a gold-mining settlement on Great Slave Lake, and Port Radium (200), on Great Bear Lake, is an important source of radium and uranium. The northern Shield is an area of critical importance to both of the Anglo-American nations from the standpoint of defense against air attack, and is increasingly the scene of joint operations and installations of the Canadian and American armed forces.

---

[1] "Shield" is a term applied to a number of different areas in the world that are underlain by extremely ancient crystalline types of rock. Such areas have remained above the level of the sea for most or all of their known geologic history. Hence they are devoid of sedimentary formations, or nearly so. Besides the Canadian Shield, prominent examples include the Fennoscandian Shield in northern Europe and the Angara Shield in Siberia.

A large aluminum works along the Saguenay River in Quebec Province. The aluminum plant, power dams, and forests in this view reflect three major aspects of the southern Canadian Shield. (Aluminum Company of Canada, Limited.)

• *Importance of the Forest Industries, Hydro-electricity, and Tourism in the Southern Shield.* The southern fringe of the Shield makes invaluable contributions to the Anglo-American economy, although it is still a thinly populated area. These contributions stem principally from its forests, its minerals, and its rivers. The Shield is forested, mainly with conifers, almost everywhere south of the tundra. But the best and most accessible stands are along the southern margins, and here the forest industries reach their maximum development, especially in Quebec and Ontario. Pulp and paper, destined mainly for United States markets, are the most valuable products, but large quantities of lumber are also produced. Most of the mills are scattered in small riverside communities near their sources of timber. Quebec and Ontario are responsible for over 60 percent of Canada's total forest production, and most of this comes from the southern Shield.

A multitude of hydroelectric plants are found along the rivers of the southern Shield. Water power is often regarded as Canada's most important natural resource. More than half of the country's installed hydroelectric capacity is located along or near the edge of the Shield in Quebec and Ontario. The Quebec Shield alone accounts for about 40 percent of Canada's developed water power. Shield power has been a key element in the development of manufacturing in the populous lowlands of Quebec and Ontario to the south.

Another industry which has been developing rapidly throughout the southern Shield is the tourist and resort business. This area offers both summer recreation and winter sports. Tourism has been fostered by public recreational developments on both the national and provincial level. Income from American visitors is an important factor helping Canada to achieve a balance in trade with the United States.

• *The Highly Developed Mining Industry.* The ancient and highly metamorphosed rocks of the Shield are rich in metallic ores. Iron, nickel, and gold are the principal metals extracted, but copper, zinc, silver, platinum, and a number of other metals are also produced in considerable quantities. Mining activity is found in scattered parts of the southern Shield from Labrador to Saskatchewan, but two mining districts are outstanding: the Sudbury district and the Superior Upland. Sudbury, Ontario (70,-000),[2] is the Shield's largest mining settlement. It produces most of the world's nickel, and large quantities of other metals, principally copper and platinum. From this single district, closely concentrated around the city, comes over a fifth of the total value of Canadian mine production. The Superior Upland has long supplied the great bulk of the iron ore used in the steel industry of the United States. Although mines are operated in all three states of the Upland (Minnesota, Wisconsin, Michigan), the Mesabi "Range" of Minnesota completely dominates production. A total of about 55,-000 people live in mining villages, towns, and small cities near the great open-pit Mesabi mines that have made this section of Minnesota the world's greatest iron mining district. The ore is shipped east on the Great Lakes, and the port which dispatches most of it, the twin-city district of Duluth, Minnesota, and Superior, Wisconsin (143,-000 for the combined cities), is the largest urban settlement on the Shield.

The best Mesabi ores are approaching exhaustion, and iron resources in the Canadian section of the Shield are becoming more significant. Two important Canadian iron mines are operating in southwestern Ontario, one near Michipicoten and the other at Steep Rock Lake, but the great field of the future will be the one recently opened in the interior of the Shield on the Labrador-Quebec border. Ore from the latter field is brought by rail to a shipping port at Seven Islands on the estuary of the St. Lawrence River.

• *Urban Development in the Shield.* Aside from mining towns, the principal urban places of the Shield are ports and manufacturing centers. In the east a cluster of small manufacturing towns and cities has developed in recent decades along the Saguenay River, a north bank tributary of the St. Lawrence. The tremendous power resources of the Saguenay have been harnessed to provide electricity for large-scale aluminum production based on ores brought in by ship. The urban centers of this district aggregate over 100,000 people. Farther west, along the "Soo" Locks connecting Lakes Superior and Huron, a pair of small Canadian and American cities with the identical name, Sault Ste. Marie, have grown to a combined population of about 50,000. The Canadian city, the larger of the two, is an iron and steel manufacturing center. On the northwestern shore of Lake Superior another twin-city district, Fort William and Port Arthur, Ontario (combined population 66,000) is the main Great Lakes shipping point for wheat from the Prairie Provinces moving toward the east and Europe.

• *Retarded Agriculture of the Shield.* Agriculture is little developed on the Shield, being hindered by short growing seasons and soils that are thin, low in fertility, and inadequately drained. The southern fringe has been penetrated by some agricultural settlement, especially in Quebec, where the rapid

---

[2] Wherever available, the population figure cited for an individual city in the present chapter is the "urbanized area" figure as reported in the 1950 United States census or the "greater city" figure as reported in the 1951 Canadian census. In other words, the figure includes not only the central political city, but also suburbs and immediate satellites lying outside its corporation limits. In general, figures cited for cities of less than 50,000 are for the political city alone. In the case of Sudbury, no "greater city" figure was reported by the 1951 Canadian census, but such a figure has been calculated roughly from the available census data.

natural increase of the French-Canadian population has pressed hard on the limited areas of cultivable land in the lowlands. A few outlying pioneer farming communities have been established farther north, generally in districts where the soil is formed on filled and exposed lake beds. Such ventures have not been notably successful, on the whole. Although a few dairy farming districts seem well established and moderately prosperous, many of these pioneer areas have the aspect of rural slums. Often the settlers farm part time and eke out the remainder of their livelihood by work in the mining or logging camps near which their farms are usually located.

The Gulf-Atlantic Coastal Plain

An extensive coastal plain occupies the seaward margin of Anglo-America from New Jersey to the Rio Grande River. North of New Jersey it appears in two disconnected sections, Long Island and Cape Cod, and south of the Rio Grande it continues into Mexico. On the landward side it is bordered by the higher ground of the Appalachian Highlands, the Piedmont, and the Interior Highlands, and merges in certain sections with the Interior Plains. The Coastal Plain is narrow in the northeast, but widens to the south and west. Beyond the Appalachians it extends northward along the line of the Mississippi River to the mouth of the Ohio before its margin again swings off southwestward toward the Rio Grande. The landward margin of the Plain may be traced through the states of Massachusetts, New York, New Jersey, Maryland, Virginia, North Carolina, South Carolina, Georgia, Alabama, Tennessee, Kentucky, Missouri, Arkansas, Oklahoma, and Texas. Four states—Delaware, Florida, Mississippi and Louisiana—lie entirely within the Coastal Plain. This extensive portion of Anglo-America includes a substantial part of both the South and the Northeast, and reaches the margins of the Middle West and the West.

▶ Physiography and Climate

The Gulf-Atlantic Coastal Plain is generally low in elevation. Few places exceed 500 feet above sea level, and most lie considerably lower. In general, the surface is relatively level, although there are a few belts of rolling hills. Most of the soils are sandy and of low to medium fertility. Especially fertile soils are associated, for the most part, with limited areas of river alluvium or of chalky limestone bedrock. The Plain is crossed by numerous sluggish rivers, and contains many swamps and marshes, especially along its seaward edge.

The climate of most of the Coastal Plain is commonly classified as humid subtropical. However, this rather broad category embraces some significant differences, as, for example, between Virginia and Florida. North of Chesapeake Bay the climate is humid continental with a considerable marine influence, and near the Rio Grande it is classed as steppe. Pine forest is the prevailing natural vegetation, except for stands of swamp hardwoods in poorly drained areas and prairie grasslands in certain belts underlain by limestone and along the coasts of Texas and southwestern Louisiana. The coastal prairies of Texas grade into a steppe vegetation in the vicinity of the Rio Grande.

▶ The Varied, Specialized Agriculture of the Coastal Plain

Long, hot summers, mild winters, and abundant, well-distributed annual precipitation, amounting to 40 inches or more in all areas except the extreme west, compensate to some extent for the poverty of Coastal Plain soils, and this area has long been important in American agriculture.

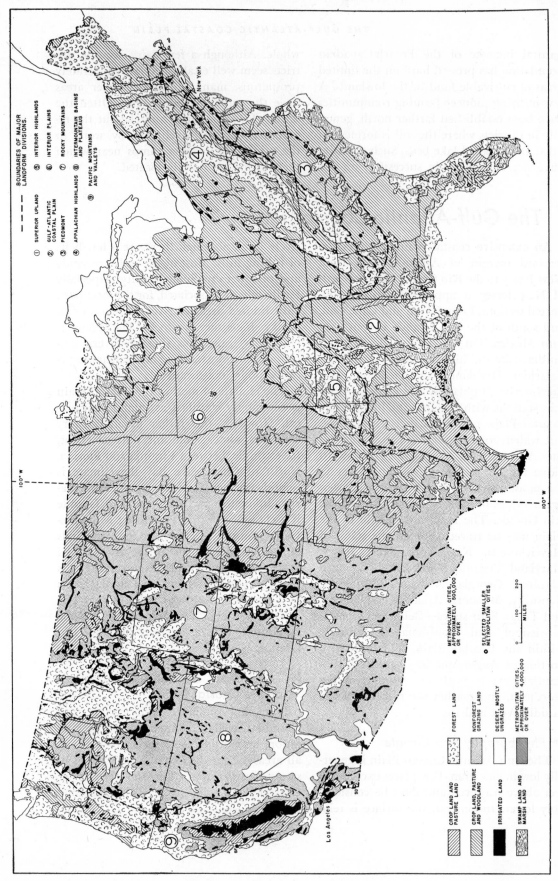

Major uses of land in the United States. (After a map by the Bureau of Agricultural Economics).

BOUNDARIES OF MAJOR
LANDFORM DIVISIONS.

① SUPERIOR UPLAND
② GULF-ATLANTIC
   COASTAL PLAIN
③ PIEDMONT
④ APPALACHIAN HIGHLANDS
⑤ INTERIOR HIGHLANDS
⑥ INTERIOR PLAINS
⑦ ROCKY MOUNTAINS
⑧ INTERMOUNTAIN BASINS
   AND PLATEAUS
⑨ PACIFIC MOUNTAINS
   AND VALLEYS

CROP LAND AND
PASTURE LAND

CROP LAND, PASTURE
AND WOODLAND

IRRIGATED LAND

SWAMP LAND AND
MARSH LAND

FOREST LAND

NONFOREST
GRAZING LAND

DESERT, MOSTLY
UNGRAZED

METROPOLITAN CITIES,
APPROXIMATELY 500,000
OR OVER

SELECTED SMALLER
METROPOLITAN CITIES

METROPOLITAN CITIES,
APPROXIMATELY 4,000,000
OR OVER

0   100   200
MILES

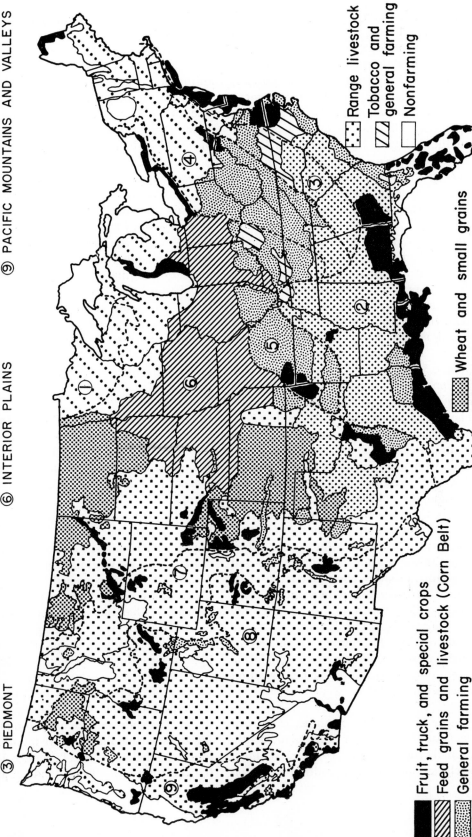

BOUNDARIES OF MAJOR LANDFORM DIVISIONS

① SUPERIOR UPLAND   ④ APPALACHIAN HIGHLANDS   ⑦ ROCKY MOUNTAINS
② GULF-ATLANTIC COASTAL PLAIN   ⑤ INTERIOR HIGHLANDS   ⑧ INTERMOUNTAIN BASINS AND PLATEAUS
③ PIEDMONT   ⑥ INTERIOR PLAINS   ⑨ PACIFIC MOUNTAINS AND VALLEYS

Fruit, truck, and special crops
Feed grains and livestock (Corn Belt)
General farming
Cotton

Wheat and small grains
Dairy

Range livestock
Tobacco and general farming
Nonfarming

Major types of farming in the United States. (After the Bureau of Agricultural Economics, Department of Agriculture.)

Even now, however, much of the Plain is in forest, and the general pattern is one of islands of intensive agricultural development scattered through a sea of pine woods. These intensively farmed areas vary greatly in size, productivity, and type of agricultural development. Most of them are rather highly specialized on one or a few products, but the variety of these specialties for the Coastal Plain as a whole is very great. Thus the over-all pattern of agricultural activity is most intricate. Only the major aspects of this pattern are discussed below.

• *Truck Farming.* The growing of vegetables and small fruits is important in many Coastal Plain communities, representing often the principal source of income. Most truck-farming communities are near the coast. They dot almost the whole of the coastal margin from Cape Cod, with its famous cranberries, to the lower Rio Grande Valley with its large irrigated production of early vegetables. Three general areas of truck growing are outstanding. (1) The *northeastern area* includes Long Island, southern New Jersey, the Delmarva Peninsula east of Chesapeake Bay, and extends with lesser intensity to the vicinity of Norfolk, Virginia. Nearness to the great urban markets of the industrialized Northeast is the principal advantage of truck farms in this section. (2) The *Florida Peninsula,* with its warm winters and consequent advantages for early harvesting and marketing, produces about one tenth of all United States truck crops by value. In truck growing Florida is second as a state only to California. (3) The *lower Rio Grande Valley* of Texas has climatic advantages for truck farming similar to those of Florida except that scanty rainfall makes irrigation a necessity.

• *Poultry Farming.* The northeastern part of the Coastal Plain, from Long Island southward through Virginia, is the most intensively developed area of poultry production in the United States. Poultry farming has risen rapidly in recent years to displace truck growing as the main type of agriculture in many communities. About two thirds of the total farm income of Delaware, for instance, generally comes from the sale of poultry products. As with truck farming, the major stimulus is the demand of near-by urban markets.

• *Peanuts.* Three-quarters or more of the peanut crop of the United States is grown on the Coastal Plain. Peanuts are the mainstay of agriculture in two widely separated sections—one on the Virginia–North Carolina border and the other in southern Georgia and adjoining parts of Alabama and Florida. Farmers in these areas grow peanuts mainly as a cash crop, but they are also used to some extent as forage for hogs. Peanuts are one of several major sources of vegetable oils used for making lard and butter substitutes, soap, and kindred products.

• *Tobacco.* Tobacco was established in early colonial times as the first great agricultural staple of the Coastal Plain. Today the Plain accounts for roughly a third of American tobacco production by volume. Practically all of this is raised in a discontinuous belt extending from the Maryland counties between the Potomac River and Chesapeake Bay to northernmost Florida. Soils on the coastal plain of Virginia, where American tobacco culture originated, were so depleted and eroded by a one-crop system of agriculture that this area produces almost no tobacco today. The major areas of present-day production on the Coastal Plain are in North and South Carolina.

• *Cotton.* Most of the American Cotton Belt is located on the Gulf-Atlantic Coastal Plain. The only important cotton-producing areas outside the Plain are found in the southern Piedmont, the Tennessee Valley, the northwestern Texas and adjoining

Oklahoma sections of the Interior Plains, and irrigated districts scattered from Texas to California. Within the Coastal Plain cotton is widely grown from southern Virginia to Texas, except that it is generally unimportant near the immediate coast. However, most of the annual harvest comes from limited areas of concentrated production within the main belt. Throughout the history of the American South the center of cotton production has tended to migrate toward the west. To a certain extent this migration has been merely a phase of the general westward expansion of American settlement. However, it has also been a response to progressive exhaustion of the soil and to the extensive ravages of the boll weevil, a remarkably destructive insect pest which thrives best in the more humid eastern sections of the Cotton Belt.

Areas of Concentrated Cotton Production.
The first great center of cotton production in the United States was the offshore islands and adjoining mainland sections of Georgia and South Carolina. This "Sea Island District" had lost its primacy by the time of the Civil War, but continued to be an important cotton producer until devastated by the boll weevil in the twentieth century. Very little cotton is now grown along this coast. By 1860 the Black

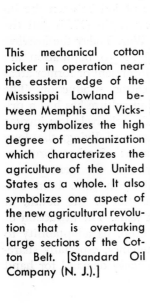

This mechanical cotton picker in operation near the eastern edge of the Mississippi Lowland between Memphis and Vicksburg symbolizes the high degree of mechanization which characterizes the agriculture of the United States as a whole. It also symbolizes one aspect of the new agricultural revolution that is overtaking large sections of the Cotton Belt. [Standard Oil Company (N. J.).]

Belt of Alabama and Mississippi had become the principal center of cotton production, although the crop had already reached the flood plain of the Mississippi River and spread beyond it into Texas. The Black Belt, so called for the color of its soils, is a crescent-shaped area extending east and west through central Alabama and then curving northward into northeastern Mississippi. The virgin soils of this belt, developed on limestone bedrock under a natural vegetation of prairie grasses, were exceptionally fertile, but were worn out by excessive cropping in cotton, which, like tobacco, is notoriously hard on soils. Exhaustion of the soil plus the ravages of the boll weevil ruined cotton production in the Black Belt almost as completely as it was ruined in the Sea Island District. In recent years the Black Belt has become increasingly important in the production of beef cattle—a phase of agriculture which is rapidly developing in the Southeast.

The only area of concentrated cotton production now found on the Coastal Plain east of the Mississippi Lowland is a long, curving arc of land which follows the inner margin of the Plain from southern Virginia into Alabama. The most important center of production on the Plain, however, lies in the alluvial lowland along the Mississippi River and the lower courses of its tributaries. This Mississippi Lowland, some 600 miles long from the mouth of the Ohio to the Gulf of Mexico and often over 50 miles in width between the bordering bluffs, is a remarkable feature in the physical geography of Anglo-America, comparable in many ways to the great flood plain and delta areas which support dense populations in the Orient. On its deep and fertile soils, shared by six states, close to a quarter of the American cotton crop and nearly 10 percent of the world's crop by volume is produced. Mississippi and Arkansas, whose principal cotton-growing areas are found in the Mississippi Lowland, are ordinarily the second and third ranking

states in cotton production. Another quarter of the American cotton crop generally comes from Texas, the state which ranks first. This state contains three outstanding areas of concentrated cotton production, two of which are on the Coastal Plain. The most important of the three is the Black Waxy Prairie, an area which resembles physically the Black Belt of Alabama and Mississippi, but which, unlike the latter, is still a major cotton producer. It extends as a belt some 50 miles wide from near San Antonio to the northern border of the state. The second most important Coastal Plain cotton district in Texas extends along the Gulf Coast from the Rio Grande Valley, where the crop is irrigated, to the vicinity of Houston. The third district, located in northwestern Texas and adjoining parts of Oklahoma, lies outside the Coastal Plain.

Effects of Cotton Growing on the Regional Life of the South. More than any other economic activity, cotton production has given distinctive regional qualities to Southern life. The large Negro population of the South, in many ways the most important element differentiating this section culturally and politically from the rest of the nation, is descended from African slaves who became mainly concentrated on cotton plantations in the period between the invention of the cotton gin (1793) and the close of the Civil War. Today the heaviest densities of rural Negro population are commonly found in present or former areas of concentrated cotton production. The prevalence of cotton culture has had a primary bearing on the relatively low income levels and standards of living, the long retarded development of other forms of economic activity, and the general economic difficulties which have been outstanding characteristics of the South, at least up to recent years. The attraction of cotton as a cash crop, its adaptability to systems of farm tenancy, especially sharecropping, and its heavy demand for hand labor, coupled with the poverty-stricken condition of the post-Civil War South and the lack of alternative sources of employment, created a situation which allowed a relatively small class of large landowners, cotton ginners and dealers, storekeepers, fertilizer merchants, and bankers to accumulate profits and even become wealthy, while at the same time the much larger group of actual cultivators, unable to acquire sufficient capital to improve their situation, were living fairly close to the margin of subsistence. Continuous cropping in cotton wore out the soil, and dependence on overseas markets resulted in increasing difficulties under the stress of a growing foreign competition. The depths of distress in the cotton South were reached in the Great Depression of the early 1930's, when the price of cotton sank to unprecedented lows and large numbers of cultivators and their families were forced to seek government relief in order to live. In the twentieth century, particularly since 1930, cotton culture in the South has experienced a relative decline in the face of these mounting difficulties and under the stimulus of a concentrated attack on Southern problems. Great acreages have been removed from cotton cultivation, although the over-all levels of production have been maintained by increased yields per acre. Communities which were formerly dependent on cotton have groped, with varying degrees of success, toward new types of agriculture and other means of support. Now the mechanical cotton picker is rapidly being adopted. What new economic revolutions the release of labor from cotton is going to bring in a Southern economy long nearly static, but now suddenly dynamic, is a subject of much speculation.

• *Citrus Fruit.* Most of the output of citrus fruit in the United States is concentrated in a few localities on the Gulf–Atlantic Coastal Plain. The danger of frost in areas farther north restricts citrus growing on the Plain to the extreme southern sections of the zone of humid subtropical climate. There is some production scattered along most of the Gulf Coast, but the southernmost areas, Florida and the lower Rio Grande Valley, contain the major producing districts. Florida, in which fruit growing is the most important type of agriculture, normally accounts for over half of the total United States output of citrus. Most of the Florida production comes from a belt in the center of the peninsula east of Tampa Bay. This part of Florida has many lakes and low hills which give a certain amount of added protection against frost damage. Citrus production is the principal element in the irrigated agriculture of the lower Rio Grande Valley. It is supplemented by truck farming, as in Florida, and by cotton. The only other major area of citrus growing in Anglo-America is found in southern California, principally around Los Angeles.

• *Sugar.* No part of the United States is sufficiently tropical for really efficient production of cane sugar. However, two districts specializing in this product have developed behind tariff protection. The larger and more important of the two is the so-called "Sugar Bowl" in the southern Mississippi Delta of Louisiana; the other is near Lake Okeechobee in Florida. Their combined production amounts to only a small percentage of American sugar consumption, considerably less than the percentage supplied by the beet-sugar industry, which is localized in other parts of the country. Most of the sugar used in the United States is imported cane sugar, principally from Cuba, Puerto Rico, the Philippines, and Hawaii.

• *Rice.* The United States supplies its own needs for rice and even exports a certain amount to the Orient. Rice consumption per capita in the United States is relatively small, and American rice is produced with extreme efficiency by machine methods. Over half of the American crop comes from the prairies along the coasts of Louisiana and Texas and another fifth from the Arkansas portion of the Mississippi Lowland, the remainder almost entirely from California. The total American production is quite small when measured on a world scale, but rice growing is an important phase of the economy in the areas where production is centered.

• *Other Crops.* In addition to the major specialties of Coastal Plain agriculture described above, many other crops are grown, sometimes as basic specialties in small areas, sometimes in combination (often in rotation) with the major crops. The most widespread and important of these secondary crops is corn. Among the others are soybeans, some wheat, sorghums toward the drier west, tree crops such as pecans and tung, and a variety of grasses and legumes grown as hay, forage, and soil-building crops.

• *The Growing Importance of Livestock.* A growing emphasis is being placed on livestock, principally beef cattle, in many parts of the Coastal Plain, and the amount and proportion of land devoted to feed crops and pasture has definitely increased in recent years. Ranching districts are found in south central Florida and along the Texas and Louisiana coasts. The Black Belt of Alabama and Mississippi has redeveloped from a cotton-growing to a livestock-farming area, and cattle are being emphasized along with soybeans in a movement toward greater diversification of the Mississippi Lowland cotton district.

▶ *Forestry, Tourism, and Fishing*

Three other important economic activities are widely scattered over the Coastal Plain or along its shores. These are the forest industries, the tourist and resort indus-

try, and commercial fishing. Most of the original natural forest of the Coastal Plain has been cut, but very large areas are in second growth timber of varying size and quality. One of the great natural assets of the southern Coastal Plain, as well as of other areas in the South, is the rapid growth of trees in the subtropical climate, some reaching saw-log size in 20 years or less. The forests of southeastern United States furnish approximately 40 percent of the country's total production of lumber and wood pulp, of which half or more comes from the Coastal Plain. Southern pine is the outstanding Southern source both of lumber and of pulpwood, and in addition supplies more than half of the world output of naval stores. But the production of hardwoods from river bottom lands is also important. Memphis, Tennessee, on the Mississippi, is the country's chief commercial center for hardwood lumber. Thus over wide areas of the southern Coastal Plain the wood industries vie with agriculture as the principal basis of economic life. Only in the areas of natural prairie and in the sections north of Virginia, where trees grow more slowly, are the forest industries absent or unimportant.

Resort establishments and fishing villages dot the shore from Cape Cod to Texas. Miami, Florida (459,000), St. Petersburg, Florida (115,000) and Atlantic City, New Jersey (105,000) are the largest cities of the United States that are primarily resort centers. However, many of the larger cities along the coast count the resort business as an important element in their economies, while many smaller settlements are primarily dependent on it. Commercial fishing is sometimes carried on in the same communities as the resort trade, sometimes in separate villages and towns. About 40 percent of the commercial fish catch of the United States by value is ordinarily landed along this coast. Major areas of concentration are found in Chesapeake Bay and off the

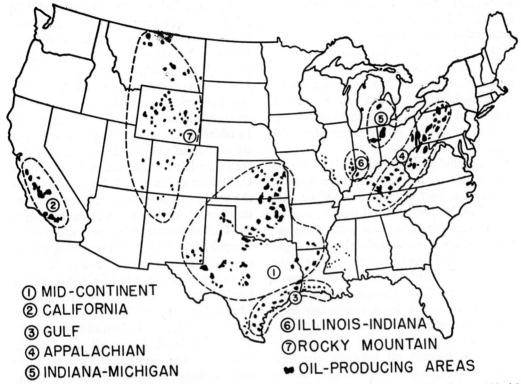

① MID-CONTINENT
② CALIFORNIA
③ GULF
④ APPALACHIAN
⑤ INDIANA-MICHIGAN
⑥ ILLINOIS-INDIANA
⑦ ROCKY MOUNTAIN
• OIL-PRODUCING AREAS

Major oil fields of the United States. (Modified from a map by W. S. and E. S. Woytinsky in World Population and Production: Trends and Outlook, New York: Twentieth Century Fund, 1953.)

Louisiana coast, where oysters and shrimp, respectively, are the main specialties.

▶ Mineral Resources

Most of the Coastal Plain is poor in mineral resources. A conspicuous exception is phosphate. Several parts of the Plain have phosphate deposits, but three quarters of the American production by volume, and about a third of the total world production, comes from a narrow belt inland and north from Tampa in western Florida. Much of the production is marketed in the South, which uses more chemical fertilizer than any other section of Anglo-America. A small area in central Arkansas near the Interior Highlands produces almost all the bauxite mined in the United States. This production, however, represents only a small percentage of the total American con-

sumption of bauxite ore, most of which must be imported.

• Superior Resources and Industrial Development of the Texas-Louisiana Coast. The most valuable mineral resources of the Coastal Plain are found in Texas and Louisiana. Areas of the Coastal Plain in these states produce an important share of the total American output of petroleum and natural gas. Major oil fields are widely scattered along the immediate coast and also inland in eastern Texas and western Louisiana. Increasing amounts of oil are being produced offshore from beneath shallow waters overlying the continental shelf. Texas, which has many fields outside the Coastal Plain, accounted for just under half of the total United States petroleum production by volume and Louisiana for another 12 or

13 percent during the early 1950's. The Coastal Plain contribution to American oil production can hardly be stated as less than 35 to 40 percent, which is about a fifth of the total petroleum production of the world. To its wealth in oil, coastal Louisiana adds large deposits of sulfur and salt. Around nine tenths of the total world production of natural sulfur comes from this area.

The abundant resources of oil and natural gas, which are important chemical raw materials as well as fuels, plus sulfur, salt, inland timber, agricultural wealth, and access to ocean and coastwise water transportation go far toward explaining the rapid development of industry along this coast in recent years, when most of the Coastal Plain has experienced only slight industrial development aside from processing local agricultural products or timber. The major industries of coastal Texas and southern Louisiana include oil refining, chemical and synthetic rubber production, aluminum manufacture from imported bauxite, and the smelting of other imported ores such as zinc and tin. However, a scattering of other types of factories exist, including even a small steel plant at Houston.

▶ *Urban Development*

That the Coastal Plain is not, on the whole, an outstanding industrial area is reflected in the size and functions of its major cities. Most of the main cities are either ports, commercial foci of especially productive agricultural areas, or resorts. The two largest, Houston and New Orleans, are ports. In addition to its port functions, Houston (701,000) is the major center of the Gulf Coast oil industry and is the most important manufacturing center of the Gulf Coast. New Orleans (660,000), the "natural" port for the Mississippi Valley, long ago lost most of the trade of the Middle West to East coast ports, but is still the fourth ranking port in the United States in tonnage of foreign trade (after

New York, Baltimore, and Philadelphia). Another major port of the Coastal Plain is the urban agglomeration of Norfolk-Portsmouth (385,000) and Newport News (42,000) surrounding the mouth of the James River estuary in Virginia. This group of cities collectively comprise the greatest coal-exporting center in the world. In addition, the district is one of the greatest centers of shipbuilding in the United States, and is a major Atlantic base of the United States Navy. It is located on one of the world's finest natural harbors. In total tonnage of foreign trade it ranks fifth in the United States. Other port cities of the Coastal Plain include Jacksonville, Florida (243,000), and Mobile, Alabama (183,000), as well as Tampa, Florida; Baton Rouge, Louisiana; Savannah, Georgia; Corpus Christi, Texas; and Charleston, South Carolina, all with populations of between 100,-000 and 200,000. All in all, 10 of the 20 largest cities of the Coastal Plain are ports, and the large resort centers such as Miami, St. Petersburg, and Atlantic City add further to the concentration of urban development on the coast.

Of the major inland cities, Dallas (539,-000) and Fort Worth (316,000), Texas, are in the Black Waxy Prairie, and San Antonio (450,000) lies between it and the cotton region of the Gulf Coast. All of these cities benefit from the oil wealth of Texas, and Fort Worth and San Antonio serve as major commercial foci for grazing areas west of the Coastal Plain. The only other relatively large interior city is Memphis, Tennessee (406,000), a major commercial center for the Mississippi Lowland.

While these cities do not bulk large in the total picture of urbanization in the United States, they are outstanding in one significant aspect. Practically all of them are among the most rapidly growing urban centers in the country, an indication of the sudden dynamic growth of the Southern economy since the Great Depression of the 1930's. The South seems at last to have broken the relative lethargy which has characterized this region as compared with other parts of the country. Most of the larger cities of the Coastal Plain experienced a population growth in their metropolitan areas of between 30 and 80 percent in the 1940–1950 census decade. Miami, Baton Rouge, Corpus Christi, and Norfolk-Portsmouth led this increase, none experiencing growths of under 70 percent in metropolitan population during the 10-year period.

The Piedmont

The Piedmont lies between the Coastal Plain and the Appalachian Highlands. Its elevation, varying generally between 400 and 1500 feet, is distinctly higher than that of the Coastal Plain, but lower than that of the Appalachians. Most of the surface is rolling to hilly. The northern end of the Piedmont is found in the vicinity of New York City, from which it extends generally southwestward, widening toward the south, until its southern end is reached in east central Alabama. Parts of nine states—New York, New Jersey, Pennsylvania, Maryland, Virginia, the Carolinas, Georgia and Alabama—lie within the Piedmont.

▶ Climate, Vegetation, and Soils

The climate of the Piedmont is similar to that of adjacent sections of the Coastal Plain, being humid continental in the north and humid subtropical in the center and south. This landform division was originally an area of mixed forest, with hardwoods, especially oak, predominating. Most of the forest has now given way to crop and pasture land, although there is still a considerable production of hardwood lumber from some sections. Piedmont soils vary greatly in fertility, depending largely on the character of the underlying rock and the kind of treatment received since the beginning of settlement. Certain limestone-derived soils of southeastern Pennsylvania, in the vicinity of Lancaster, are among the most productive in the United States. These naturally fertile soils are farmed largely by the "Pennsylvania Dutch" (of German extraction), long known as some of America's most skillful and industrious farmers. Lancaster County, the heart of the Pennsylvania Dutch country, is renowned as an outstanding agricultural area. But most Piedmont soils are derived from crystalline rocks, were never exceptionally fertile, and have been seriously depleted and eroded (especially in the central and southern Piedmont) as a result of forms of agriculture stressing the production of clean-tilled row crops—such as tobacco, cotton, and corn—in a hilly area subject to violent downpours of rain.

▶ Agriculture

The principal agricultural contributions of the Piedmont to the American economy are dairy products, tobacco, and cotton. Dairy farming is the principal type of agriculture as far south as Virginia, that is, in the section closest to the largest urban markets. Hay and feed grains, especially corn, barley, and wheat, are the principal crops grown on Piedmont dairy farms. Dairying is supplemented or supplanted in various areas by the production of tobacco, beef cattle, potatoes, or apples, or some combination of these. The Piedmont of southern Virginia and North Carolina is a major tobacco farming area. North Carolina, with its Piedmont and Coastal Plain production areas, is the leading American state in tobacco growing, accounting for about 40 percent of the national production by volume. The Virginia Piedmont adds another 7 percent. All in all, over 60 percent of this important American crop comes from Piedmont or Coastal Plain areas between northern Florida and Maryland. From North Carolina to Alabama the Piedmont is part of the Cotton Belt—an old section, but still a producing area of some importance. Corn is generally the leading secondary crop in the tobacco and cotton districts. Some progress is being made toward diversification of agriculture in the interests of soil conservation and of higher and more secure farm incomes.

▶ Urban and Industrial Development in the Northern Piedmont

The northern Piedmont is a very highly urbanized and industrialized area. New York City and its environs, which lie at the extreme northern end, are discussed in the section on the Appalachian Highlands. South of New York, five important cities, including three of the country's greatest metropolitan districts, are closely spaced in a northeast-southwest line of about 150 miles. They include Trenton, New Jersey (189,000), Philadelphia, Pennsylvania (2,-922,000), Wilmington, Delaware (187,000), Baltimore, Maryland (1,162,000), and Washington, D. C. (1,287,000). Washington is almost entirely a governmental city. The others are industrial and commercial centers.

It will be noted that each of these cities lies at or near the outer edge of the Piedmont. The zone of contact between this landform division and the Coastal Plain is known as the Fall Line, a name deriving from the falls and rapids which mark the course of rivers as the latter descend from the crystalline uplands of the Piedmont to the lower, sedimentary Coastal Plain. These falls and rapids mark the head of navigation on many rivers and have long supplied water power. Consequently, many urban areas originated and developed into cities at sites where a river crosses the Fall Line, and a line of cities may now be traced along the latter. Besides the five already mentioned, the Fall Line cities include Richmond, Virginia; Columbia, South Carolina;

Augusta, Macon, and Columbus, Georgia; and Montgomery, Alabama.

However, the only place where really large cities have developed along the Fall Line is in the north. Here the Delaware River, Delaware Bay, and Chesapeake Bay, combined with feasible passages through the Appalachians to the west, have provided a setting for the development of two of the country's major seaports. Baltimore, located near the head of Chesapeake Bay, and Philadelphia, located on the lower Delaware River, are, respectively, the second and third ranking United States ports as measured by tonnage of foreign trade handled. The cities of the northern Piedmont have developed extremely important and varied industries. It is estimated that together their production comprises some 10 percent of the total value of United States manufactures. Philadelphia, including its New Jersey satellite, Camden, is especially important in the manufacture of woolen textiles, apparel, magazines, ships, chemicals, and locomotives. In addition, one of the country's great concentrations of oil refineries is located along the Delaware River in this vicinity. In recent years several new steel plants, exemplifying a trend toward tidewater location in the steel industry, have been built along the river. Baltimore has important steel, apparel, aircraft, and shipbuilding industries. Wilmington is primarily a chemical manufacturing city, the administrative and research center of the Du Pont Company. Trenton's major products are pottery and rubber goods. In addition, there are automobile assembly plants in all of these centers except Trenton, and such other manufactures as sugar refining, canning, and copper refining, as well as a very large output of machinery and miscellaneous metal goods.

▶ Urban and Industrial Development in the Central and Southern Piedmont

South of Washington, D. C., the Piedmont has few large cities. Atlanta, Georgia

(508,000), a commercial center located in an area where railroads from the east skirt the southern end of the high Appalachians, is the largest. Richmond, Virginia (258,000) is next in size. Four other cities—Charlotte, Columbia, Columbus, and Montgomery—each have between 100,000 and 150,000 people.

Nevertheless, the central and southern Piedmont is an area of considerable importance with regard to manufacturing. Major stimuli to industrial development have been the water power of the Piedmont and the adjacent Appalachians, the surplus of cheap labor offered by overcrowded, eroded, and often poverty-stricken rural areas, and the availability of certain raw materials from both the Piedmont and the adjoining regions, notably tobacco, timber (both hardwood and softwood), and cotton. Much of the manufacturing is dispersed throughout a large number of small towns and mill villages.

The largest industry is the manufacture of cotton textiles. In the twentieth century the central and southern Piedmont has displaced New England as the leading area of cotton milling in the United States. North Carolina, now the leading textile-milling state, has over one quarter of the installed capacity of the American cotton textile industry, and the Piedmont between Virginia and Alabama over 80 percent.

However, in certain sections other industries are quite important. Virginia is the leading American state in the production of synthetic fibers, its Piedmont and Appalachian sections combined accounting for over one quarter of the total United States production. Rayon is the leading fiber produced. Another major American manufacturing industry, cigarette production, is almost entirely concentrated in a number of Piedmont cities and towns located in the Virginia–North Carolina tobacco-growing district. These cities include Winston-Salem, North Carolina, Richmond, Virginia, and others. This same Piedmont section in North Carolina and southern Virginia has developed a furniture-manufacturing industry, originally based on local resources of mixed woods, which now totals over 10 percent of the entire United States output by value. Other manufactures which have gained a foothold in various parts of the central and southern Piedmont are pulp and paper, chemicals, and boots and shoes.

The Appalachian Highlands

The Appalachian Highlands extend from Newfoundland to northeastern Alabama. On the east they face the Atlantic and the Piedmont, on the west the Interior Plains. The eastern boundary of the Highlands is the Atlantic shore as far south as the vicinity of New York City and then may be traced across the states of New York, New Jersey, Pennsylvania, Maryland, Virginia, North Carolina, South Carolina and Georgia into Alabama. The western boundary extends from Alabama through the states of Tennessee, Kentucky, Ohio, Pennsylvania, and New York and through the Canadian province of Quebec to the south shore of the St. Lawrence estuary.

The mountains which dominate the topography of this landform division are not very high. The loftiest summits are below 7000 feet, and most of the Appalachian area lies below 3000 feet. But the Highlands form a very extensive and complex system in which mountain ranges, ridges, isolated peaks, and rugged dissected plateau areas are interspersed with narrow valleys, lowland pockets, and rolling uplands. Climatic conditions range from subarctic in Newfoundland to humid subtropical in the south and some sections are high enough to experience abnormal cool-

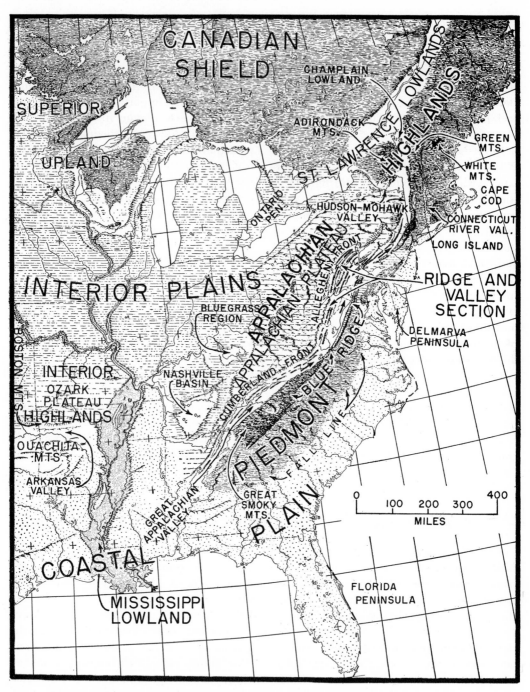

Major physiographic features of eastern United States and southeastern Canada. (*The base map is a portion of A. K. Lobeck's Physiographic Diagram of the United States, copyright, The Geographical Press, a division of C. S. Hammond & Company, Maplewood, N. J.*)

ness and precipitation. The natural vegetation is forest: coniferous and mixed coniferous and deciduous as far south as Pennsylvania, predominantly deciduous (though with some mixture of coniferous stands) south from Pennsylvania.

The Appalachian Highlands exhibit some very great internal contrasts in population density and economic development, often within short distances, but as a whole they have a surprisingly large population for a highland area and are of enormous importance in the Anglo-American economy. Many parts of the Highlands have a considerable rural population, farming such level lands as are available, and often extending cultivation up steep slopes better left in forest. A great variety of agricultural products and types of farming are found in different sections, although much of the land, perhaps most of it, is not farmed. But the principal significance of the Appalachian region lies in nonagricultural resources and activities: wood, coal, water power, metals, and manufacturing, especially the last.

Both the diversity and the economic importance of this landform division are brought out in the descriptions of the major subdivisions of the Highlands which follow. These subdivisions, as considered herein, are (1) Newfoundland, (2) the Maritime Provinces and Southeastern Quebec, (3) Northern New England, (4) Southern New England, (5) the New York Metropolitan Area (only partly within the Appalachians, but presented with this landform division for convenience), (6) the Hudson-Mohawk Valley and the Adirondacks, (7) the Northern Appalachian Plateau, (8) the Appalachian Ridges and Valleys of Pennsylvania, and (9) the Southern Appalachians.

▶ Newfoundland

Newfoundland became Canada's tenth province in 1949. As a province, it includes the dependent territory of Labrador on the mainland, but in common usage the name Newfoundland is restricted to the large island which lies opposite the mouth of the St. Lawrence. The island, which has an area of some 43,000 square miles, is rugged and rocky, although the highest elevation is only about 2600 feet. The climate is subarctic and the vegetation a spruce-fir forest, except for the higher areas, where considerable expanses of tundra occur. Although climate and soil have thus far conspired to make any extensive development of agriculture next to impossible, Newfoundland was the earliest center of permanent British settlement in Anglo-America. Today the island's population of 361,000 (1951 census) represents one of the largest population concentrations in the Anglo-American subarctic.

Since the beginning of European settlement in the sixteenth century, fishing has been the principal economic activity. Elevated portions of the sea bottom known as "banks" are found off the coast of Anglo-America from near Cape Cod to the Grand Bank, largest of all, which lies just off the southeastern corner of Newfoundland. The elevated, soft sea bottom and the mixing of waters from the cold Labrador Current and the warm Gulf Stream which occurs over the banks provides an excellent habitat for schools of cod and other economically valuable fish, and this part of the Atlantic has become one of the world's greatest centers of commercial fishing. Not only Newfoundland, but the Maritime Provinces, Maine, and Massachusetts send fishing fleets to the banks. However, in none of these other areas is fishing the basis of economic life to the same degree as in Newfoundland. Inshore fisheries supplement the catch from the banks in all of the areas mentioned.

In the twentieth century Newfoundland has developed a pulp and paper industry and a mining industry. The most valuable mineral product is iron ore, which is mined on Bell Island in Conception Bay, and shipped to steel-milling areas in Nova Scotia, the United States, and Europe. Most of the island's people live in small, often isolated, fishing villages. The interior is relatively empty. St. John's, the largest city and the capital, has only 68,000 people. It is also the chief port and is located on the southeast coast. Corner Brook (4000; including neighboring towns, 18,000) on the west coast is the largest center of paper milling. An important transatlantic airport has been developed at Gander (3000) in northeastern Newfoundland.

► The Maritime Provinces and Southeastern Quebec

Nova Scotia, New Brunswick, and Prince Edward Island are Canada's Maritime Provinces. Not only do these provinces border the Atlantic, but their traditional outlook is overseas rather than toward the rest of Canada. They are somewhat isolated physically by the mountains of northern New Brunswick and adjacent Quebec, politically by the northward projection of Maine, and socially by French Canada, which lies between the Maritimes and other dominantly British areas beyond Quebec. The Quebec French have been penetrating the Maritimes, and now make up over one third of the population of New Brunswick.

Prince Edward Island, the smallest Canadian province, has only about 2200 square miles and 106,000 people (1953 estimate). It is a lowland area which is almost completely in farms, and has little other economic activity besides some fishing. Dairying and potato growing are the main forms of agriculture. Nova Scotia and New Brunswick resemble Newfoundland in that their land is generally rugged, although the highest summit, found in northwestern New Brunswick, is only about 2700 feet. About four fifths of the land in the combined provinces is still forested, and lumbering and pulp and paper milling are of great importance in their economies. However, in Nova Scotia, the value of manufac-tured wood products is outranked by the value of steel produced at the seaport of Sydney. Coal, amounting to about a third of the total Canadian output, is mined here, and iron ore is brought from Newfoundland. The steel industry of Sydney is a small one when viewed against the background of Anglo-American production as a whole, but, nevertheless, the city ranks as one of Canada's three main centers of steel production, along with Hamilton, Ontario, and Sault Ste. Marie. Agriculture in New Brunswick and Nova Scotia is hindered by a cold climate and poor soils, as well as by the generally rugged character of the terrain. Many farms are part-time subsistence enterprises, although there are a limited number of commercial-farming areas specializing in dairy products, potatoes, or fruit. The Annapolis-Cornwallis Valley, a long narrow lowland just inland from the Bay of Fundy in southwestern Nova Scotia, is one of Anglo-America's main apple-growing districts.

The economic development of the Maritime Provinces has been hindered by relative remoteness from major markets—a remoteness partly physical, but partly economic owing to tariffs imposed by the United States. The population of the three provinces, totaling only 1,305,000 (1953 official estimates), has been growing more slowly for some time than that of the rest of Canada. The scale of their economic development is indicated to some extent by the respective sizes of their major cities, which include Halifax (134,000), a Nova Scotian port with a magnificent harbor but remote from interior Canadian centers of production; Sydney (86,000 with suburbs and satellites); and St. John (68,000), the largest city and main port of New Brunswick.

A strip of Quebec south of the St. Lawrence River lies within the Appalachians. It is generally similar to New Brunswick and Nova Scotia in physical character and economic development. A noteworthy element in its economy is the production of over half of the world's asbestos, and practically all the asbestos of Anglo-America, from mines in the vicinity of the town of Thetford Mines (15,000).

▶ Northern New England

Although New England is one of the most commonly recognized regional units in Anglo-America, there are actually sharp contrasts—physically, economically, and socially—between its three northern states and its three southern states. The three states of northern New England—Maine, New Hampshire and Vermont—contain more rugged and elevated land and more land considerably removed from the sea. Their economies are less intensively developed, they are less urbanized, and are not so densely populated as the states of southern New England—Massachusetts, Connecticut, and Rhode Island. In northern New England the native "Yankee" stock is a more distinctive element in the population than in southern New England, which has become one of the greatest "melting pots" of the United States.

Northern New England contains two major subranges of the Appalachians, each running in a general north-south direction. The Green Mountains occupy most of Vermont, although the state also contains a part of the Champlain Lowland to the west. Though generally somewhat subdued and rounded in shape, these mountains have some peaks reaching over 4000 feet. Most of New Hampshire is occupied by the White Mountains, which extend on the north into interior Maine. Northern New Hampshire, where Mount Washington reaches 6288 feet, contains the highest land in northeastern United States. The Green and White Mountains are separated by the upper valley of the Connecticut River. Northernmost Maine consists of a rolling upland which extends into adjacent New Brunswick. The coastal area of Maine and New Hampshire is a hilly, stony lowland which extends south along the Atlantic to the vicinity of New York City.

Maine and New Hampshire are basically industrial states from the standpoint of employment, income, and value of production, although their industries are only a small northward extension of the really intensive manufacturing development of southern New England. Most of the factories and main population clusters are found

Many aspects of rural New England are reflected in this view: the grazing dairy animals; the bedrock protruding at intervals through the thin soil; the large, neat frame structures of the village; the stone fences; the prominent spire of the church; the low, rounded uplands bearing a mixed second growth of coniferous and deciduous forest. The village in the picture is Tamworth, New Hampshire, located in the eastern foothills of the White Mountains. (A. Devaney, Inc.)

in small towns and cities in the coastal sections of New Hampshire and southern Maine. Wood industries, primarily pulp and paper milling, rank first in value of production. These states account for about 10 percent of the total United States production of wood pulp, with the major part coming from Maine. Textiles, both cottons and woolens, are a close second, followed by boots and shoes.

Relatively little of the rugged and rocky land which makes up Maine and New Hampshire is farmed, and many of the farms that do exist are part-time subsistence operations. The main types of commercial farming are dairying, poultry farming, especially in New Hampshire, and potato growing in Maine. The Aroostook Valley of far northern Maine is one of the most important areas of concentrated potato production in Anglo-America.

In contrast to its industrialized neighbors, Vermont is the only state in all New England which is to a large degree agricultural in its economy, although even in Vermont a variety of small industrial enterprises in small towns give employment to more people for the state as a whole than does agriculture. The state lies within the milkshed of New York City, and dairy farming is relatively more important in its economy than in that of any other American state. More than half of the land in the state is in farms, a great contrast to the situation in Maine and New Hampshire.

Throughout northern New England a noted and highly developed tourist and resort industry represents an important local supplement to the more widespread activities of manufacturing, agriculture, and forestry.

The total population of northern New England is only about 1,800,000. Despite the basic dependence on manufacturing in this region only one city, Portland, Maine (113,000), has over 100,000 people and only one other, Manchester, New Hampshire (85,000) has over 50,000.

► Southern New England

Very little of the land in the three states of southern New England is actually mountainous. Most of the area is hilly and rocky, however. The southern fringe of the White Mountains extends into Massachusetts, while the Green Mountains extend across Massachusetts into Connecticut. The southern section of the Green Mountains, generally called the Berkshire Hills, contains the highest elevations in southern New England, somewhat over 3000 feet.

Southern New England is an area of great industrial development, dense population, and a high degree of urbanization. Within a total area of about 14,500 square miles are contained some $7\frac{1}{2}$ million people, or about 5 percent of the population of the United States. The over-all density of population thus exceeds 500 per square mile. The metropolis of southern New England is Boston, which includes 2,233,000 people in its urbanized area.

The United States phase of the Industrial Revolution began in the late eighteenth and early nineteenth centuries with the rise of the mechanized cotton textile industry in southern New England, and the latter area has been an important manufacturing region ever since. Before machine production commenced, it was already the leading center of commerce and handicraft industries in the country. Rapid industrial development was facilitated by the accumulated capital of the area, its maritime location, its wood, its water power, and the surplus labor provided by an agriculture beginning to fail under competition from cheap and fertile lands beyond the Appalachians. Now the original forests of the area are largely gone, the available water power is inadequate for present needs, much of the plant equipment is out of date, both management and labor are often unduly conservative, and the region is in competition with newer industrial areas often better placed with regard to raw materials and markets. Similar difficulties are felt in northern New England. In recent years New England as a whole has come to be regarded as something of an industrial problem area in the American economy, and its industry and population have not grown as rapidly as those of other major sections of the United States.

Nevertheless, southern New England still produces something like 8 percent of the total value of manufactures in the United States, and is a leading region in several lines. Despite the twentieth century decline in cotton textiles as a result of Piedmont competition, southern New England still contains about 15 percent of the installed capacity of the United States cotton textile industry, in addition to about one third of its woolen and half of its worsted manufacturing capacity. Textiles as a whole continue as the region's leading form of industry. The main centers of production are Providence, Rhode Island (583,000), Fall River (118,000) and New Bedford (125,000) in southeastern Massachusetts, and Lawrence (112,000) and Lowell (107,000) in northeastern Massachusetts.

The region produces over 10 percent by value of all United States machinery and fabricated metal goods, offsetting its resource handicaps to some extent by specializing in highly finished products which have high value relative to their materials and weight, and which derive their value in good part from the expenditure of skilled labor. Machine tools, calculators, and cash registers, precision instruments and professional equipment, and watches and clocks are examples. The major centers of production for these miscellaneous metal goods include Boston and Providence as well as New Britain–Bristol (123,000), Bridgeport (237,000), and Stamford-Norwalk (174,000) in Connecticut.

Another major industry is shoe production. Southern New England turns out about one fifth of the United States output by value. Almost all of this is concentrated either in the Boston urbanized area or in Brockton, Massachusetts (92,000). Other sizable cities and urban areas include Hartford, Connecticut (301,000), a center of the aircraft industry and of the insurance business; Waterbury, Connecticut (132,000), in and around which most of the American brass industry is found; New Haven, Connecticut (245,000), a center of diversified manufacturing and education; Springfield-Holyoke, Massachusetts (357,000), producing metal products, textiles, and paper; and Worcester, Massachusetts (219,000), producing metal products, textiles, and shoes. In addition, Boston is an important center in the production of electrical equipment, ships, and leather, and is a major ocean port and the greatest fishing port on the Atlantic coast.

Agriculture in southern New England is overshadowed by other economic activities. However, it is often intensively developed and achieves a high output relative to the amount of farm land employed. The main forms of agriculture are part-time subsistence farming, dairy farming, and poultry farming, although the Connecticut River Valley is a leading specialty area producing truck crops and shade-grown tobacco. Agriculture in southern New England is oriented toward local urban markets, but the production falls short of the demand, and much food is brought into the region from other parts of the United States.

▶ The New York Metropolitan Area

The world's greatest city is not enclosed within the Appalachians, but is located where the Appalachians, the Piedmont, and the Coastal Plain converge. New York City proper centers on Manhattan Island. The latter is narrowly separated by the Harlem River from the southern tip of the mainland in New York State. On the east Manhattan is separated from Long Island by the East River; on the west from New Jersey by the lower Hudson River, here often called the North River. Manhattan is one of five boroughs composing the city proper. Of the remaining boroughs, the Bronx lies on the mainland to the north, Brooklyn and Queens are on the western end of Long Island, and Richmond is on Staten Island. The city proper contains some 7,892,000 people (1950 census), but the urbanized area contains a large number of suburban and satellite cities and towns lying to the north, east, and, especially, to the west in New Jersey. The population included within the urbanized area is about 12,296,-000, or about 8 percent of the total population of the United States.

New York owes its development in good part to the fact that it stands at the seaward end of the only continuous east-west lowland route through the Appalachians. This route follows the Hudson River Valley north to Albany, then runs west along the valley of the Mohawk River to the plain bordering Lake Ontario. Thus it affords an easy connection with the Great Lakes and the productive Interior Plains. The enormous and protected harbor of New York, fashioned by an intricate interpenetration of land and water, plus a central location between the agricultural South and the commercial and manufacturing region of New England, had already allowed the city to become the leading seaport of the United States before the trans-Appalachian route became of major importance. However, it was the completion of the Erie Canal along the Mohawk Valley in 1825, connecting Buffalo on Lake Erie with Albany on the Hudson and thus giving an all-water route from the Great Lakes to the port of New York, that provided the real impetus for the rise of New York to a position of clear and unchallenged commercial leadership among American cities. The New York Central Railroad now parallels the Erie Canal route, and this and other railroads through the Appalachians today far surpass the water route in the transportation of goods to and from New York. Today the Erie Canal, deepened and otherwise modi-

fied, forms a part of the New York State Barge Canal.

New York is still basically a commercial city. It generally handles approximately half of all United States foreign trade by value, although the proportion is less by bulk because the port specializes in relatively light and valuable freight. But from its commercial leadership has flowed pre-eminence in such fields as finance, business administration, advertising, and entertainment. And its enormous local market and population, its transportation facilities, and its wealth have made it the greatest manufacturing center in the United States, with over 10 percent of the country's total value of industrial production. Practically every manufacturing industry is represented to some extent in the metropolitan area, but the leading industry is the manufacture of clothing. Approximately three quarters of the national output of women's clothing and a third of the men's clothing comes from Manhattan, a concentration reflecting a number of factors but especially the prestige of New York as a style center. Other industries in which New York leads the nation are printing and publishing, chemical products, and, with Chicago, electrical machinery and equipment. A major share of the factories within the metropolitan area are located in the New Jersey section, where space is more abundant and cheaper and where the main rail freight terminals are located.

▶ The Hudson-Mohawk Valleys and the Adirondacks

The Hudson and Mohawk Valleys are lined with industrial towns and cities, mostly small and extremely varied in types of production. Three cities are outstanding in size and importance: Albany-Troy, Schenectady, and Utica. The twin-city district of Albany-Troy (292,000) occupies an especially strategic position with respect to natural transport routes: the Hudson Valley south to New York City, the Champlain

Lowland north to the St. Lawrence and Montreal, the Mohawk Valley west toward the Great Lakes, and, to the east, passes through the mountains followed by major rail lines to New England. Clothing and textiles lead the highly varied list of manufactures in these cities. Schenectady (123,-000), which is near Albany, is the headquarters and a major center of production for the General Electric Company. At the western end of the Mohawk Valley, Utica (117,000) manufactures textiles and clothing.

The circular mass of the Adirondack Mountains is geologically an upraised outlier of the Canadian Shield. The hard-rock formations which tie it to the main body of the Shield emerge in the St. Lawrence River as the picturesque "Thousand Islands" and are responsible for the rapids which block navigation on the St. Lawrence above Montreal. The highest peak of the Adirondacks exceeds 5000 feet in elevation. These mountains form an island of rugged, forested land and sparse population surrounded on all sides by more populous lowlands. The Adirondacks are important as a recreation area, however, and there is some production of pulp and paper around the margins, as well as a small production of iron ore.

▶ Physical Subdivisions of the Central and Southern Appalachians

South of the Hudson-Mohawk line the Appalachians fall into three major subdivisions. From east to west these are the Blue Ridge, the Ridge and Valley Section, and the Appalachian Plateau. Each of the three trends northeast-southwest, and they roughly parallel each other.

The *Blue Ridge,* long and narrow, can be traced from near the mouth of the Hudson to Alabama. Often it rises abruptly from the Piedmont to the east, and throughout much of its length it is but a single ridge. It has been given various local names. In some places, especially in the north, the Blue Ridge is discontinuous, and lowland gaps provide important east-west routes for transportation. It widens into several ranges and becomes higher and more continuous toward the south. Although the northern sections of the Blue Ridge often fail to reach 1000 feet in elevation, the section in western North Carolina known as the Great Smoky Mountains has a number of peaks over 6000 feet. Mount Mitchell in the Great Smokies, at 6711 feet, is the highest peak in the entire Appalachian system and in eastern United States.

West of the Blue Ridge, the *Ridge and Valley Section* of the Appalachians extends from southern New York to Alabama. Long, narrow, roughly parallel ridges trend generally north and south and are surrounded and separated by narrow valleys. The ridges are often 3000 to 4000 feet high, the valley floors 1000 to 2000 feet lower. On the east, immediately adjacent to the Blue Ridge, a valley somewhat wider than the rest extends almost continuously throughout the length of the Ridge and Valley Section. It is known in general as the Great Appalachian Valley, although it has many local names such as Shenandoah Valley in Virginia and Lehigh Valley in northeastern Pennsylvania. The Great Valley is a historic north-south passageway, and its productive limestone soils have provided the basis for an agricultural development superior to that of most parts of the Appalachians.

The *Appalachian Plateau* lies west of the Ridge and Valley Section. It covers most of southern New York State and extends southward into Alabama, narrowing toward the south. Although geologically a plateau (more precisely a series of plateaus), it is so deeply and thoroughly dissected in most places that it is actually an area of tangled hills and low mountains separated by narrow, twisting stream valleys. Most summit elevations are between 2000 and 3500 feet above sea level. The northern part is often called the Allegheny Plateau or Allegheny Mountains, and the southern

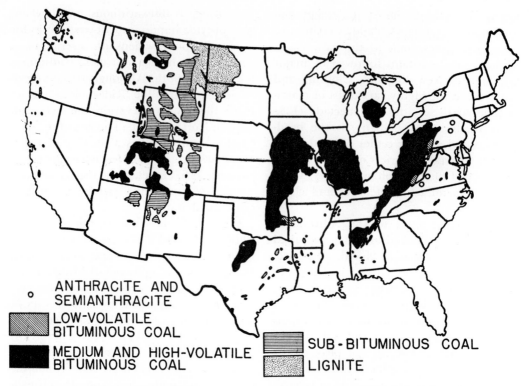

Coal fields of the United States. (*After a map by W. S. and E. S. Woytinsky in* World Population and Production: Trends and Outlook, *New York: Twentieth Century Fund, 1953.*)

part the Cumberland Plateau or Cumberland Mountains. Notable escarpments, the Allegheny Front in the north and the Cumberland Front in the south, mark the eastern edge of the plateau area, while the frayed western edge merges into the Interior Plains.

▶ The Northern Appalachian Plateau (Allegheny Plateau)

The Northern Appalachian Plateau occupies parts of the states of New York, Ohio, Pennsylvania, West Virginia, Maryland, Virginia, and Kentucky. It has important forest and water power resources and some oil and natural gas. But its greatest importance lies in the fact that it contains what is probably the world's best coal field, considering the quantity and quality of coal available and the extraordinary ease of working it. Among the states sharing the

Northern Appalachian Plateau, only New York has no noteworthy coal resources or production. About two thirds of the United States output of bituminous coal comes from the Northern Appalachian Plateau, or some 15 percent of the world's total production. The West Virginia, Pennsylvania, and Kentucky portions of the Plateau, ranking in that order, produce about 60 percent of the United States output, and the Ohio portion another 5 percent.

This enormous power resource drives industry and heats homes on the Atlantic Coast and in the Middle West, and it makes the Northern Appalachian Plateau itself a major center of heavy industry. Pittsburgh, Pennsylvania (1,533,000), strategically located where the navigable Allegheny and Monongahela Rivers flowing from the coal fields join to form the navigable Ohio River leading to the Midwest and South, is the world's leading center of primary iron and steel production. Although it has been declining in relative importance for some years the Pittsburgh district still possesses over 15 percent of the total United States steel capacity and well over 5 percent of that of the world. Other sizable steel centers in the Northern Appalachian Plateau include Youngstown (298,000) and Canton (174,000) in northeastern Ohio, Johnstown (93,000) in Pennsylvania, and Wheeling (107,000) in West Virginia. The whole area has about a third of the American steel industry. Its iron ore comes from the Superior Upland, and the industry could probably not have reached its present great development except for the fortunate interposition of the Great Lakes to enable cheap transportation of the ore.

Other important industries of the Northern Appalachian Plateau are those manufacturing secondary metal products, chemicals, glass and clay products, and rubber. Akron, Ohio (367,000), the original center, still retains about 20 percent of the country's rubber industry. A district extending along the valley of the Great Kanawha River in the vicinity of Charleston, West Virginia (131,000), and westward to Huntington, West Virginia–Ashland, Kentucky (combined cities 156,000) specializes in chemicals, though it also produces glass, rayon, and most of the world's nylon. The only sizable urban center in the New York portion of the Plateau is Binghamton (144,-000); being outside the coal area its industry is of a different type, principally shoe production.

Agriculture is overshadowed by industry and mining in the Northern Appalachian Plateau, although much of the land is in farms and there is a fair-sized farm population scattered along many of the valleys. Level land for crops is scarce, and farming is for the most part not a very rewarding or productive enterprise. West Virginia, where subsistence farming, often part time, is the major type of farming, and livestock the

principal source of cash income to farmers, is fairly typical. However, in the northern part of the region, especially in New York, the topography is somewhat more subdued and adequate markets more easily reached so that a considerable dairy industry has developed. As a state New York is second only to Wisconsin in dairy products, and its Appalachian Plateau section makes a considerable contribution to the state's total dairy production. The Finger Lakes district at the northern edge of the Plateau is a well-developed fruit- and truck-farming area.

▶ The Appalachian Ridges and Valleys of Pennsylvania

A small district in the Ridge and Valley Section of northeastern Pennsylvania produces almost the entire United States output of anthracite coal. Two main cities, Wilkes-Barre (272,000) and Scranton (236,-000) have developed on the anthracite field. Their principal business is mining, and with the twentieth-century decline in the demand for anthracite they have become two of the major problem cities of the United States, suffering chronic unemployment and a considerable decrease in population. Some apparel and textile firms have come in to take advantage of the surplus labor supply created by the decline of the anthracite industry.

The early development of the anthracite fields, plus small local deposits of iron ore, led to the rise of a sizable iron and steel industry in eastern Pennsylvania which far antedates the recent construction of tidewater plants in the Philadelphia area. Three urban areas in the Ridge and Valley Section of the state are still important steel producers: Allentown-Bethlehem (226,000), Harrisburg (170,000), and Reading (155,-000). These cities are all located in the Great Valley on rivers whose valleys provide superior passageways into the rugged country to the west and through the Blue Ridge to the east. Their steel industries have now remained relatively static for some time, and textile and clothing industries have developed which at present tend to overshadow steel. Allentown-Bethlehem has also had an extraordinary development of the cement industry. This industry has been favored by its access to coal, the limestone of the Great Valley, and the very large and easily-reached markets near by. Allentown-Bethlehem is now the foremost center of the cement industry in the United States and probably in the world.

The valleys of this section of eastern Pennsylvania are almost completely occupied by farms, primarily dairy farms, though livestock and subsistence farms are found in valleys more remote from markets.

▶ The Southern Appalachians

Most parts of the Appalachians south of the Potomac River and Northern Appalachian Plateau are still in the process of emerging from relative isolation and a poor agricultural economy. With the exception of the Great Valley, agriculture is largely on a subsistence basis, although commercial livestock production is increasing. The Great Valley has long been a superior agricultural section. It is now devoted principally to livestock and dairy farming or to general commercial farming. The Shenandoah Valley section is in addition one of the principal apple-producing areas of the United States. Alabama sections of the Appalachians are far enough south to have a considerable cotton production.

There is some coal production in Virginia, Tennessee, and Alabama, but the major stimulus to increased industrialization in recent decades has been water power, produced largely by the Tennessee Valley Authority (TVA) as a major aspect of its program to control the Tennessee River and its tributaries and to develop the resources of the Tennessee River Basin. The main industrial growth has been in the fields of chemicals, aluminum, rayon and other textiles, and atomic energy.

Only four cities in the Southern Appalachians reach 100,000 in population. Birmingham, Alabama (445,000), at the extreme southern end of the Appalachians, is by far the largest and is a special case. Here large deposits of coal and iron ore in close proximity present one of the world's most favorable natural situations for the development of an iron and steel industry, and the city is the main center of that industry in the southern part of the United States. The other sizable cities of the region are Chattanooga, Tennessee (168,000) located where the Tennessee River cuts a natural passageway through the southern end of the Appalachian Plateau; Knoxville (148,000), the main commercial center of the Tennessee portion of the Great Valley; and Roanoke, Virginia (107,000), a rail center and industrial city located at a gap through the Blue Ridge opposite the port of Norfolk.

The Interior Highlands

The Interior Highlands, often called the Ozark or Ozark-Ouachita Highlands, occupy most of southern Missouri, the northwestern half of Arkansas, and adjoining parts of eastern Oklahoma. They constitute an island of hill country and low mountains in the midst of a sea of plains: the Interior Plains on the north and west and the Coastal Plain on the east (Mississippi Lowland) and south. The Interior Highlands are divided into two major segments by the east-west valley of the Arkansas River. The northern segment consists of the Boston Mountains, overlooking the Arkansas Valley, plus the more extensive Ozark Plateau of northern Arkansas, southern Missouri, and northeastern Oklahoma. South of the Arkansas Valley are the Ouachita Mountains, constituting the other principal segment of the Highlands.

The Interior Highlands display a great deal of internal variety in form and relief. North of the Arkansas Valley most of the area consists of dissected plateau surfaces bearing a certain physical resemblance to the Appalachian Plateau. However, the plateau section of the Interior Highlands is lower in elevation and relief and lacks the coal deposits of the Appalachian area. The Ouachita Mountains consist of roughly parallel ridges and valleys resembling the Ridge and Valley Section of the Appalachians, except that in the Ouachitas the trend of the topography is east and west. The peak elevations in the Interior Highlands lie generally between 1000 and 2000 feet. No crest in the entire area reaches 3000 feet, although the highest summits of the Ouachitas approach that elevation. There are notable differences in local relief within the Highlands. A number of fairly level upland surfaces occur, but other areas are quite rugged. Most areas fall between these topographic extremes.

Farming and lumbering are the economic mainstays in most parts of this landform division. Much of the agriculture is of a subsistence character. On the better lands, especially where adequate transportation is available, an important commercial live-stock industry has developed, emphasizing dairying in some areas and the raising of beef cattle in others. A fruit farming district in northwestern Arkansas and adjoining sections of Missouri produces grapes, apples, and strawberries as major specialties. Cotton is the major crop of the Arkansas River Valley.

The Interior Highlands were originally in forest, and most parts are still forested, generally with a rather poor grade of second growth timber. Deciduous hardwoods predominate north of the Arkansas Valley and coniferous softwoods in the Ouachita Mountains.

Many deposits of minerals exist in the Interior Highlands, but most deposits are not of sufficient value to justify exploitation at present. Two areas, however, are important producers of metals. In the northeastern part of the Highlands, about 60 miles south of St. Louis, a small district supplies about a third of the annual United States production of lead. It is the leading lead-mining district in the country. In northeastern Oklahoma and adjoining parts of Kansas and Missouri is the Tri-State mining district, for many years the leading area of zinc production in the United States and still important, although declining as a mining area. A number of other mineral resources are exploited on a small scale in various parts of the Highlands.

Manufacturing is poorly developed, aside from sawmilling. A scattering of factories exist in a few towns and small cities. Springfield, Missouri (76,000), located in a well-developed dairy-farming area, is the largest city of the Highlands and the most important focus of highways and rail lines.

Recent years have witnessed a marked expansion in the tourist and resort industry. A considerable number of private resort developments cater to populations of the surrounding lowlands. In addition, state and federal government agencies have been active in the development of public recreational facilities. The impoundment of lakes behind federally built dams has been an important factor in increased tourist trade, and the electricity created in generating stations at these dams appears to offer a basis for increased industrial development in the Highlands.

The Interior Plains

The interior of Anglo-America, between the Rocky Mountains on the west and the Appalachian Highlands and Canadian Shield on the east, is essentially composed of a vast expanse of plains. These plains lie mostly within the drainage basins of four important rivers: the Mississippi, the Mackenzie, the Saskatchewan, and the St. Lawrence. Most parts of the Interior Plains are hundreds or thousands of miles from the sea; their location, in other words, is essentially continental rather than maritime. However, the Interior Plains reach the sea in the northwest and northeast of Anglo-America, respectively, along two narrow corridors—the Mackenzie River Lowlands and the St. Lawrence Lowlands. In the south the Interior Plains extend into Mexico, merge with the Gulf-Atlantic Coastal Plain, or abut against the Interior Highlands and Appalachian Highlands. The western edge of the Plains can be traced through the Northwest Territories, British Columbia, Alberta, Montana, Wyoming, Colorado, New Mexico, and Texas; their northeastern edge through the Northwest Territories, Alberta, Saskatchewan, Manitoba, Minnesota, Wisconsin, Michigan, Ontario, and Quebec; and their southeastern edge through Quebec, New York, Ohio, Kentucky, Tennessee, Alabama, Missouri, Oklahoma, and Texas. Besides parts of the states, provinces, and territories already mentioned, the Interior Plains include the whole of seven states: the Dakotas, Nebraska, Kansas, Iowa, Illinois, and Indiana. Approximately the western third of the Interior Plains, from Mexico north to the southern Prairie Provinces, is known as the Great Plains.

▶ Physiography, Climate, Vegetation, and Soils

The Interior Plains are seldom flat, although considerable areas are very nearly so. Most of the land is gently rolling, but some areas are hilly and occasional areas rather rugged. Most parts of the Interior Plains north of the Ohio and Missouri Rivers were covered with a mantle of glacial debris during the Great Ice Age and the topography was somewhat smoothed thereby. Thus the more hilly sections tend to be outside the area of glaciation, al-

though some unglaciated portions are also fairly level. The principal unglaciated hilly areas are in the southeast from southern Indiana across Kentucky into Tennessee, and in an "island" of unglaciated terrain in southwestern Wisconsin. Other areas of hilly terrain exist (1) in eroded strips along major stream courses, (2) in areas of terminal moraine deposition, (3) along cuesta escarpments separating different plain levels, (4) in fantastically eroded badlands of the western sections such as the famous ones in western South Dakota, and (5) in small, isolated mountain areas near the western border, of which the Black Hills of South Dakota are the most notable example. These various exceptions, however, do not essentially damage but only refine the over-all concept of a huge plains area with enormous expanses of land level enough for cultivation.

An interior area of this size extending from the margins of the low latitudes to the margins of the high latitudes naturally has a great range of climatic conditions, natural vegetation, and soils. The Mackenzie Delta is in the tundra zone, and the subarctic climatic zone with its coniferous forest reaches southward into central Alberta, Saskatchewan and Manitoba. Southern Alberta and Saskatchewan and areas west of approximately the 100th meridian in the Great Plains section of the United States are semi-arid and have a short grass, or steppe, vegetation. South of the general latitude of the Ohio River and east of the belt of steppe, considerable sections of the Interior Plains fall within the zone of humid subtropical climate. But the most important and productive agricultural areas of this landform division lie within the humid continental climatic zones: humid continental with short summers in a belt from Alberta to the Atlantic which includes southern Canada and large sections of the northern tier of states in the United States, and humid continental with long summers in a belt reaching from

Nebraska and Kansas to the Appalachians. Large areas within the humid continental zones were originally in forest, with deciduous hardwoods predominating in most places, but with a belt of mixed hardwoods and conifers in the north. However, tall grass, or prairie, vegetation occupied a roughly triangular area with its apex in Illinois and widening westward toward the steppe. The deep, black soils originally developed under a vegetation of tall grass are outstandingly fertile and some soils developed under the deciduous forest are above average in natural fertility, though not equal to the grassland soils. Such soils, combined with adequate rainfall and wide expanses of land sufficiently level for cultivation, have provided a natural setting for the development of one of the world's most important and impressive agricultural areas. All things considered, the Interior Plains represent the agricultural heartland of Anglo-America.

▶ Agricultural Regions

Relatively smooth topography, good soils and the existence of a number of major climatic regions, each occupying a broad area, has permitted the development of several large and rather distinct agricultural regions. These display considerable internal uniformity rather than the intricate and broken pattern of agriculture characteristic of many of Anglo-America's landform regions. The major agricultural regions of the Interior Plains, as considered herein, include (1) the Corn Belt, (2) the Dairy Belt, (3) the Spring and Winter Wheat Belts, (4) the Unglaciated Southeastern Interior Plain, (5) the Texas-Oklahoma Red Prairies, and (6) the Great Plains Region of Ranching and Irrigated Agriculture.

• **The Corn Belt.** The famous Corn Belt of the United States lies wholly within the Interior Plains. It extends from central Ohio to eastern South Dakota, Nebraska, and Kansas, and includes most of Indiana and Illinois, northern and western Missouri, all of Iowa, and southwestern Minnesota. It lies essentially within the humid continental long summer climatic zone of the Interior Plains, and except for its Indiana and Ohio sections is within the region of prairie soils. Physically its limits are set (1) on the east, by the more rugged land and poorer soils of the Appalachian Plateau, (2) on the south, by the eroded northern margin of the Ohio River Valley and by the Ozarks, (3) on the west, by semi-aridity (approximately the line of 20 inches average annual rainfall), and (4) on the north, by summers too short and cool to insure a mature corn crop.

The Corn Belt system of agriculture emphasizes the production of hogs and cattle for cash sale. The principal feedstuff is corn, which has a high feed value and grows exceedingly well in this region of fertile soil, long hot summers, and ample moisture. Most of the livestock are bred within the area, but many Western range cattle are brought into the Corn Belt for fattening before their final trip to the slaughterhouses. Oats, winter wheat, hay, pasture grasses and legumes, and soybeans are grown in a variety of rotations with corn. These latter crops contribute to livestock production, or they may, if the market favors it, be marketed as cash crops, especially the wheat and soybeans. In addition, corn is often marketed as a cash crop if the market is more favorable than for livestock. This practice is the usual one in some parts of the Corn Belt that are especially near major markets, as in large sections of Illinois where cash grain farming of corn has largely replaced livestock production.

Iowa and Illinois may be considered the heart of the Corn Belt. In total farm production, by value, Iowa ranks second among the states and Illinois fourth. Together these states account for about 12 to 14 percent of the country's total agricultural production by value. They produce almost a third of the nation's corn and hogs, and the Corn Belt as a whole accounts for well over half of the national output of these items. Although quite important within the Corn Belt, especially toward the west, the beef cattle industry of the United States is not so highly centered in the area as is the production of corn and hogs. Nevertheless, Iowa ranks second only to the much larger state of Texas in the production of beef cattle.

•*The Dairy Belt.* Dairy farming is the principal form of agriculture in those portions of the Interior Plains that lie in Wisconsin and adjacent parts of Minnesota, in Michigan, in New York, and in Ontario and Quebec. Outside the Interior Plains, dairy production is also important, though generally less intensive, in adjoining sections of the Appalachians and the southern margins of the Canadian Shield. Thus dairy farming is particularly an enterprise of the humid continental short summer climatic zone in Anglo-America. The southern limit of the Dairy Belt within the Interior Plains is set primarily by warmer summers that allow production of mature corn; its northern boundary is essentially the northern climatic limit of agriculture itself; and its western limit is set by semi-aridity and distance from adequate markets.

The principal items of sale from the dairy farms of this agricultural region are fluid milk, where city markets are sufficiently near, or butter and cheese in sections more distant from large cities. However, calves, nonproductive milk cows, hogs, and poultry are also marketed. The feed for these animals is supplied mainly by crops of hay, oats, and silage corn, by permanent and rotation pastures, and by creamery wastes and surplus milk. Approximately one quarter of all United States dairy products by value originate in the Interior Plains Dairy Belt, Wisconsin alone accounting for about 12 or 13 percent. Al-

most 40 percent of Canada's total agricultural production, by value, originates in lowland Ontario and Quebec, where dairying is the main type of farming. However, scattered throughout the Dairy Belt, and especially in this Canadian section, are small specialty areas producing such items as fruit and vegetables, tobacco, livestock, potatoes, and sugar beets. In the United States portion the principal specialty areas are fruit and truck districts located close to the shores of the Great Lakes, and thus benefiting climatically from the moderating influence of the lakes.

• *The Spring and Winter Wheat Belts.* Most of Anglo-America's large production of wheat originates in two zones of specialized wheat growing within the Interior Plains. One of these zones grows spring wheat, the other winter wheat. The Spring Wheat Belt occupies the western edge of Minnesota, practically all of North Dakota, northern South Dakota, northeastern Montana, and most of the plains area of the Canadian Prairie Provinces of Manitoba, Saskatchewan, and Alberta. It thus occupies the drier margins of the humid continental short-summer climatic zone and the wetter margins of the steppe. In general its limits are set by an increasingly short growing season on the north, sufficient moisture for more intensive forms of agriculture on the east, summers too warm for spring wheat on the south, and increasing aridity on the west. The Winter Wheat Belt centers in central and western Kansas and extends into adjoining parts of Nebraska, Colorado, and Oklahoma and into the Texas Panhandle. It thus occupies principally the drier margins of the humid continental long summer climatic zone and the wetter margins of the steppe. In general its limits are set by winters too cold for winter wheat on the north, adequate moisture for more intensive forms of agriculture on the east and insufficient moisture for wheat on the west and south. The actual limits of wheat growing undergo marked changes from one period of years to another due to severe climatic and market fluctuations.

Large-scale, highly mechanized commercial wheat production completely dominates the agriculture of these areas. The extensive use of machinery and the scale of operations tend to offset the disadvantage of crop yields that are generally low despite the excellent grassland soils. There is relatively little diversification, although small acreages are devoted to hay, oats, barley, rye, flax, and corn in the Spring Wheat Belt and to corn, sorghums, and hay in the Winter Wheat Belt. Fallow land, stubble, and some of these secondary crops provide forage for cattle, which represent a supplementary source of income and a means of avoiding disaster in case the wheat crop fails.

Statistics vary considerably from year to year, but in general the Winter Wheat Belt supplies close to 40 percent of the United States wheat crop, with Kansas (the leading wheat state) accounting for almost a fifth of the national output. The Spring Wheat Belt supplies approximately a quarter of the American crop, with North Dakota (the second ranking wheat state) accounting for about half of this. Practically all of the Canadian wheat crop is grown in the Spring Wheat Belt.

Commercial wheat farming in the Spring and Winter Wheat Belts is a risky and uncertain type of enterprise. These areas are climatically marginal, and relatively slight deviations from normal conditions can result in disastrous crop failures. The heavy dependence on one-crop farming makes it difficult for farmers to weather a year, often a series of years, of wheat failure. Most of the Canadian crop and a considerable share of the American are destined for export markets, in which the demand for Anglo-American wheat fluctuates considerably. The result of these factors is a great variation in farm incomes from year to year, often leading to the adoption of radical political programs by state and provincial governments in the wheat belts. North Dakota and the three Prairie Provinces of Canada are particularly known for such programs.

• *The Unglaciated Southeastern Interior Plain.* The Unglaciated Southeastern Interior Plain lies south of the Corn Belt. Its northern edge is found in dissected lands near the Ohio River in southern Indiana, and Illinois, and it extends southward to include those parts of Kentucky and Tennessee between the Appalachians and the Mississippi River embayment of the Gulf-Atlantic Coastal Plain. The topography of this southeastern section of the Interior Plains has not been smoothed by glaciation, and it is essentially a hilly area. The climate is mostly humid subtropical, albeit a cool phase of this climatic type.

The Unglaciated Southeastern Interior Plain is distinguished from other large agricultural regions of the Interior Plains by the fact that no well-established, highly developed, and specialized system of farming has evolved in the area as a whole. For the most part the type of agriculture resembles that of the Corn Belt, combining corn, winter wheat, and livestock production. But as the land is poorer than that of the Corn Belt, so is the agriculture poorer and less productive in almost every way. In addition, tobacco and, toward the Coastal Plain, a little cotton often enter the farming picture. Included within the general region, however, are two small but outstanding agricultural districts, both developed in basinlike areas where soils of more than average fertility have been derived from underlying limestone formations. These are the Bluegrass Region of north central Kentucky, specializing in tobacco production and also famous as the home of fine horses, and the Nashville Basin of central Tennessee, an area of livestock farming resembling that of the Corn Belt to the north.

• *The Texas-Oklahoma Red Prairies.* South of the Winter Wheat Belt in Texas and Oklahoma a major area of intensive cotton cultivation has developed on reddish prairie soils. Cotton can be grown without irrigation here, and extensive mechanization helps to compensate for low average yields. However, in recent years a considerable amount of irrigated cotton acreage has been developed. Until the comparatively recent development of large-scale cotton culture, this was principally a ranching district. Today some areas exhibit a mixture of cotton cultivation, ranching, and some wheat and sorghum production. However, cotton is the dominant agricultural interest for the region as a whole.

• *The Great Plains Region of Ranching and Irrigated Agriculture.* A north-south belt of country which is too dry for wheat except in abnormally wet years extends along the western edge of the Interior Plains from Alberta and Saskatchewan to the Mexican border. This area of steppe climate in the western portion of the Great Plains is culturally and economically a zone of transition between the farming country of the humid and subhumid East and the range livestock country of the West. Sheep and cattle ranches occupy most of the land, although goat ranching is important in the extreme south. The population is generally sparse, but islands of greater density are found in scattered irrigated areas. The largest of these are in Colorado, especially along the South Platte River. The agricultural mainstays of the Great Plains irrigated areas are hay, grown as supplemental feed for range animals, and sugar beets, which supply both a cash crop and fodder for livestock.

▶ *Urban and Industrial Development*

The Interior Plains are not only the leading agricultural area of Anglo-America, but contain many of the largest cities and much of the manufacturing industry of this world

region. Most of the urban and industrial development is found in the eastern half of the Plains. Of 46 metropolitan cities in the Interior Plains numbering 100,000 inhabitants or more, 35 lie either on the Mississippi or east of it. Eleven of the 12 cities numbering 500,000 or more are on the Mississippi or east of it, as are all six of the cities numbering more than a million inhabitants.

Most of the major cities in the eastern part of the Interior Plains lie within the American Manufacturing Belt, a zone of concentrated industrial activity extending eastward from the Mississippi River to the northeastern Atlantic seaboard. The western limit of the Belt lies in the vicinity of a line connecting St. Louis and Milwaukee; the northern limit along or near the line Milwaukee–Toronto–Montreal–Portland, Maine; and the southern limit along the general line St. Louis–Cincinnati–Charleston, West Virginia–Baltimore. The American Manufacturing Belt thus includes large portions of the American Middle West and Northeast, as well as several districts in southeastern Canada. It represents one of the two largest concentrations of relatively continuous industrial development in the world, the other being the great manufacturing region of Western Europe. In terms of major landform divisions, the American Manufacturing Belt lies partly in the Appalachian Highlands, partly in the northern Piedmont and adjacent Coastal Plain, and partly in the Interior Plains.

In general, the individual cities of the Interior Plains have been favored in their development by one or more of the following factors: (1) access to the agricultural wealth of the Plains; (2) access to coal, iron, and steel; (3) advantageous location with respect to transportation. Most of these cities began as commercial centers serving an agricultural hinterland. Many of them had particular advantages with respect to water transportation, which was of exceptional importance during the time they were first developing. Later the coming of railroads provided a further stimulus to growth, although many cities have continued to be important centers of water transportation as well as railroad centers. The manufacturing industries which have been developed in these cities of the Interior Plains fall under two main categories: (1) industries engaged in processing the agricultural products of the Plains and (2) industries manufacturing machinery, vehicles, and other secondary metal products from iron and steel produced in or near the Interior Plains. Position between the Appalachian coal fields and the iron ore resources of the Canadian Shield and its extension in the Superior Upland, with the Great Lakes–St. Lawrence Waterway providing cheap and efficient water transportation for both iron and coal, gives the manufacturing centers of the eastern Interior Plains a superior access to the basic raw materials needed by the iron and steel industry.

For purposes of description and analysis, the major cities and industries of the Interior Plains may be conveniently divided into the following four groups according to location: (1) cities and industries of the Ontario and Quebec lowlands, (2) United States cities and industries on or near the Great Lakes, (3) cities and industries of the southeastern section of the Interior Plains, and (4) cities and industries of the Interior Plains west of the Great Lakes.

• *Cities and Industries of the Ontario and Quebec Lowlands.* The core region of Canada is found in a group of lowlands bordering the Great Lakes or the St. Lawrence River from the vicinity of Detroit to Quebec City. The entire lowland area is often termed loosely the "St. Lawrence Lowlands," although the Ontario Peninsula between Lakes Huron, Erie, and Ontario is frequently recognized as a separate section. Well over half of Canada's manufacturing is carried on in the Ontario and Quebec lowlands,

and most of the large Canadian cities are found here. The industries of this Canadian section of the Interior Plains are very diversified, although generally smaller in scale than those found in the United States sections. The major manufactures include textiles; clothing; pulp and paper; shoes; rubber; flour, meat, and other food products; iron and steel; automobiles; machinery; and electrical equipment. Among the factors that have favorably influenced the development of these industries are (1) the availability of water power and minerals from the Canadian Shield, (2) the availability of coal from the Northern Appalachian Plateau, (3) access to good transportation facilities, especially water transportation, (4) the agricultural wealth of the surrounding lowlands, and (5) markets provided by the relatively large population of these lowlands.

Most of the main cities in the Ontario and Quebec lowlands are located either on the Great Lakes or on the St. Lawrence River. The St. Lawrence is navigable for large ships as far as Montreal, although blocked by ice for a considerable period in winter. Beyond Montreal, canals bypassing rapids on the river give small ships access to Lake Ontario. When the St. Lawrence Seaway is completed, relatively large ocean ships will be able to enter the Great Lakes. The obstacle of Niagara Falls, between Lakes Ontario and Erie, is circumvented on the Canadian side by the Welland Ship Canal.

The largest of Canada's cities, aggregating almost a tenth of the country's population in its urbanized area, is Montreal (1,395,000). Its transport advantages include not only its position at the head of navigation on the St. Lawrence, but also its access to the Champlain Lowland leading south toward New York City and to the Ottawa River Valley along which Canada's transcontinental railroads find a natural passage west and north into the Shield. It is the country's chief port and largest manu-

An air view of Montreal, Canada's largest seaport. Note the prominent grain elevators in the middle foreground. The St. Lawrence River appears at upper right. [*Photographic Services (Quebec)*.]

facturing center. Its industries are highly diversified, with the manufacture of textiles and clothing the most important. Quebec (275,000), on the St. Lawrence below Montreal, was the original center of French settlement and administration in Canada, chosen because of its fortress position at the head of the estuary where the river became narrow enough to be controlled by the cannon of the time. Its advantages for commerce, however, have proved far inferior to those of Montreal, though it, too, is an active ocean port.

Montreal's great rival among Canadian cities is Toronto (1,117,000), which has the finest natural harbor on Lake Ontario. Toronto has become the financial center of Canada and the commercial center of Ontario, as well as Canada's second city in population and manufacturing. Together Montreal and Toronto account for about a

third of the total value of Canada's manufactures. Toronto's manufacturing industries, like those of Montreal, are highly diversified.

Other Ontario cities include Ottawa (282,000), Canada's capital, which is located on the Ottawa River in the section where the river forms the boundary between the country's two largest provinces; Hamilton (260,000), a Lake Ontario port which is one of Canada's principal centers of iron and steel manufacture; Windsor (158,000), located opposite Detroit and thus favorably situated for its role as the greatest center of automobile production in the Commonwealth of Nations; and London (122,000), an inland commercial and industrial center in one of the most productive agricultural areas of lowland Ontario. In addition to the cities mentioned, a great deal of manufacturing is carried on in smaller industrial centers of the Ontario and Quebec lowlands.

• *United States Cities and Industries on or Near the Great Lakes.* Some of the largest cities in the United States, including the largest ones in the Interior Plains, are found along or near the southern shore of the Great Lakes. Their locations generally reflect past or present advantages deriving from such factors as natural harbors on the lakes, portages between rivers, river valley passageways leading from the lakes to the interior, or other factors bearing on water transportation.

Ready access to coal and steel has been an advantage of the greatest importance to the manufacturing industries of the lake cities. Most of the coal comes from the Appalachian Plateau, as does much of the steel. However, a number of the lake ports are themselves major steel producers. The leading ones in this respect are Chicago (where the industry is largely centered in the Indiana suburbs, especially Gary), Buffalo, Cleveland, and Detroit. The production in these four cities alone, not including smaller installations in other lake ports, represents about a third of the United States total. The Chicago urban area, the country's second greatest center of steel production (after Pittsburgh), contains about 15 percent of all United States steel-manufacturing capacity. The steel mills of the lake ports draw most of their ore from the Superior Upland via the lakes and their coal mainly from the Appalachians, but Chicago benefits also from relative proximity to the Eastern Interior coal field of central and southern Illinois and adjoining parts of Indiana and Kentucky. This field produces about 18 percent of the United States output of bituminous coal. Much of the coal can be used for coking when mixed with higher-grade Appalachian coal. Most of the lake cities are highly industrialized, and the group as a whole is of great importance in the iron and steel,

machinery, vehicle, and other metal industries. In addition, two cities in the group, Chicago and Buffalo, are major world centers of food processing, and another city, Rochester, is one of the world's greatest centers of the photographic equipment industry.

Chicago (4,921,000) is the second largest city of the United States and of Anglo-America. It is by far the largest city of the Interior Plains. The city has developed on a harbor formed by the mouth of the Chicago River at the southern end of Lake Michigan. Here the Great Lakes make their farthest penetration into the agricultural heartland of the United States. An old portage, first canalized a century ago, connects Lake Michigan drainage and Mississippi drainage in the vicinity of the city. Today a modern commercial waterway, following the old canal route, connects Chicago with the Mississippi and the Gulf of Mexico via the Illinois River. The city has become the world's greatest railway center, a result partly of the diversion of east-west tracks around the southern end of Lake Michigan, but more largely due to Chicago's original importance as a lake port. The relation of Chicago to the agriculture of the Corn Belt and the wheat belts is seen in its function as a major grain market and in its unquestioned world leadership in meat packing and the manufacure of agricultural machinery. However, most of the city's industries are engaged in producing a diverse array of metal products, including many different types of machinery.

Milwaukee (829,000), north of Chicago, is the second most important Lake Michigan port and industrial center. It has a better natural harbor than Chicago, but in other respects its location is less advantageous. Nevertheless it is a major industrial center, known for its large production of heavy machinery, beer (probably the result of its large population of German origin), automobiles, and a miscellany of other goods.

The second largest city of the Interior Plains, and second largest on the Great Lakes, is Detroit (2,659,000). Its position on the Detroit River linking Lakes Huron and Erie has long made it a city of considerable importance. However, its meteoric rise in the twentieth century into the top group of American population and industrial centers has been connected mainly with the equally meteoric rise of the American automobile industry. Despite some decentralization of the industry in recent years, Detroit still has no significant rival as a center of automobile manufacturing. Probably no city in the world of comparable size is so dependent on a single industry. Smaller cities around Detroit are also dominated by auto-making—either complete cars or components. The group includes Flint (198,000), Lansing (134,000), and Saginaw (106,000) in Michigan; Toledo (364,000) in Ohio; and South Bend (168,000) in Indiana, as well as many smaller places. Only two sizable cities between Lake Michigan and the western end of Lake Erie are not dominated by the auto industry. These are Grand Rapids, Michigan (227,000), and Fort Wayne, Indiana (140,000). Grand Rapids, located at a waterfall in an area originally in mixed forest, has become famous as a center of furniture manufacture, although that industry is now overshadowed by the manufacture of a variety of secondary metal products. Fort Wayne stands at a portage on a water route once affording an important connection between Lake Erie and the Ohio River. It, too, is mainly a producer of secondary metal wares. Even in these cities the motor vehicle industry is of some importance, as it is in most of the main manufacturing centers of the Great Lakes group outside the major areas of automobile production.

Two other major Great Lakes ports of the United States are Cleveland, Ohio, (1,384,000) and Buffalo, New York (798,-000). Between them lies the much smaller port city of Erie (152,000), the only Pennsylvania port on the lakes. Cleveland has a good harbor and lies in the path of rail lines skirting the Appalachian Plateau along the level coastal plain of Lake Erie, and others following relatively easy valley routes into the interior of the Plateau. The city is important in both the steel and automobile industries, but is most noteworthy for the production of machinery and assorted metal wares. Buffalo is pre-eminently the port where transportation along the Hudson-Mohawk Valley and the Lake Ontario Plain intersects that of the Great Lakes. Until the building of the Welland Canal it was the head of navigation on the upper Great Lakes, and it was the western terminus of the Erie Canal. Buffalo has important steel and automobile industries, and is the world's greatest center of flour milling. Hydroelectricity from Niagara Falls has provided a basis for a considerable development of electrochemical and electrometallurgical manufacturing. East of Buffalo, along the Erie Canal route, are two other important industrial centers, each connected by canal with a small port on Lake Ontario. Rochester (409,000) grew originally where the lowland route passed a waterfall on the Genessee River. It was primarily a flour-milling center in the early days, but it has now become the world's leading center for the production of photographic equipment. Its other manufactures are dominantly of a type requiring highly skilled labor. Syracuse (265,000) is located where the lowland route along the Mohawk Valley widens into the Lake Ontario Plain. Large salt deposits in the vicinity of the city have given rise to chemical manufacturing, but the chemical industry is outweighed in importance by a variety of secondary metal products.

• *Cities and Industries of the Southeastern Section of the Interior Plains.* During the early days of settlement in the Middle West, people and goods moved westward along three great routes issuing from the Appalachians into the Interior Plains. One of these routes was the Great Lakes, one was the Ohio River, and the other was the first land highway in the Middle West, the National Road, which pursued its westward course between the other two. Important cities are now found at intervals along each of these routes. Those along the Great Lakes have already been described. The principal Ohio River cities are Cincinnati, Ohio (813,000), located on the great northern bend of the river where tributaries enter from both sides; Louisville, Kentucky (473,000), located at a stretch of falls and rapids which long interrupted traffic until bypassed by a canal; and Evansville, Indiana (138,000), located not far from the mouth of the Ohio's major north bank tributary, the Wabash, which once carried a considerable amount of commerce. The main cities along the old National Road are Columbus, Ohio (438,000), located where the road issued from the Appalachian Plateau and intersected the Scioto River leading toward the Ohio; Dayton, Ohio (347,000), where the road intersected the Miami River leading southward to the Ohio at Cincinnati; and Indianapolis, Indiana (502,000), located at the intersection of the road with an Ohio tributary thought, erroneously, to be navigable at the time the city was founded. Despite the error with regard to the availability of water transport, Indianapolis became the capital of Indiana, for which its central location favored it, and also became a major rail center. The only large city in the southeastern part of the Interior Plains that is not on either of these old transport routes is Nashville, Tennessee (259,000), which lies considerably farther south and is the commercial center of the exceptionally fertile Nashville Basin, besides being the state capital and a minor center of chemical production.

With the exception of Nashville, each of the cities described in the preceding paragraph has an industrial structure dominated by the manufacture of ma-

chinery and other secondary metal products. In addition, some of them have secondary specialties such as beer and soap in Cincinnati, whiskey and tobacco products in Louisville, and drugs and meat products in Indianapolis. Cincinnati is the greatest single center of the machine tool industry in the United States, Columbus is noted for its mining machinery, and Dayton for light manufactures such as calculators, cash registers, and automobile ignition systems which require a high degree of skill to make.

• *Cities and Industries West of the Great Lakes.*

In the Interior Plains west of the Great Lakes cities are more widely scattered and smaller than farther east, and, in general, this becomes increasingly so the farther west one progresses. Most of the western cities of the Plains are basically commercial centers serving agricultural hinterlands, and such incidental manufactures as they possess ordinarily bear a close relation to their commercial functions. In the eastern part of this area the manufacture of machinery, especially agricultural machinery, continues to be of considerable importance, but farther west grain milling and meat packing become relatively more and more important.

The largest cities are on the Mississippi River. St. Louis (1,400,000), located near the junction of the Missouri, Mississippi, and Illinois Rivers, is the only one numbering more than a million inhabitants in its urban area. It has long been a famous and important river port, and has also become a major railroad center. It can draw on the coal of the Eastern Interior Field for power, and has developed a highly diversified list of manufactures, including machinery, clothing, chemical products, shoes, automobiles, meat, beer, steel, grain products, and alumina. It is also one of the country's principal markets for grain and livestock. The twin cities of Minneapolis and St. Paul (985,000), comprising the second largest urban center on the Mississippi, have developed at a point where rapids mark the head of navigation on the river and in addition furnish hydroelectric power. The Minneapolis–St. Paul urban district is primarily a commercial center for the Spring Wheat Belt and areas beyond. For years the Twin Cities led the world in flour milling, and are still of great importance in that industry. They are also of some importance in meat packing and in the manufacture of machinery, particularly agricultural machinery.

Important smaller centers of agricultural machinery production along the Mississippi, or between the Mississippi and Lake Michigan, include Peoria, Illinois (155,000), the headquarters of a large tractor company; the Davenport, Iowa-Rock Island-Moline, Illinois urban area (195,000), which is almost entirely specialized in the manufacture of agricultural machinery; Rockford, Illinois (122,000); and Madison, Wisconsin (110,000).

Toward the western edge of the Corn Belt three sizable cities have developed, primarily as market centers for adjoining sections of the Corn Belt and the Winter Wheat Belt. These are Kansas City, Missouri and Kansas (698,000), Omaha, Nebraska (310,000), and Wichita, Kansas (194,-000). Each is an important market and processing center for grain and livestock. Other industries are little developed except for automobile assembling and a small steel plant at Kansas City and a large aircraft plant at Wichita. Two other cities in the western Corn Belt, Des Moines, Iowa (200,-000) and Lincoln, Nebraska (100,000) are commercial, political, and educational centers with no significant industry.

The two largest cities of Oklahoma have a character somewhat different from that of the other cities of the western Interior Plains. Oklahoma City (275,000) and Tulsa (206,000) owe their growth largely to the oil industry. The Mid-Continent oil field extends in this part of the Interior Plains from Texas across Oklahoma and into southern Kansas. In addition to serving the oil industry as commercial, administrative, and refining centers, both cities are agricultural market centers, and Tulsa is the site of a large aircraft plant.

In the western Great Plains the thinning of urban development and manufacturing toward the west in the Interior Plains reaches its climax. Only one United States city in this area exceeds 100,000 population. This is Denver, Colorado (499,000), at the foot of the Rocky Mountains and economically as much a city of the mountains as of the plains. It is the commercial center for mining districts scattered through the Rockies to the west and for the irrigated areas and ranches of the plains to the east. The agricultural production of the Great Plains flows mainly toward the east and has not been intensive enough to stimulate the growth of large commercial centers within the Great Plains proper. Nor have the mineral resources of this area led to any large development of manufacturing. These mineral resources include oil and natural gas in the south, of which there is now a sizable production in western Texas and adjoining parts of New Mexico; enormous potash beds in New Mexico which furnish most of the United States supply; and considerable deposits of coal and lignite in a number of places. Most of the coal, however, is relatively low in quality.

The metropolis of the Canadian Prairie Provinces is Winnipeg, Manitoba (354,000), which is similar in function to such cities as Minneapolis–St. Paul, Omaha, and Kansas City. At Winnipeg the extensive rail network of the prairies focuses on two major lines which cross the Shield to the east. Consequently this city has become the principal market and distributing center for the three provinces. Toward the west, the Canadian part of the Great Plains has resources of coal and oil. In recent years oil production has increased rapidly in Alberta, and the two main cities of that province have experienced rapid growth. These cities are Edmonton (173,000) and Calgary (139,000). In their combination of oil and agricultural interests they somewhat resemble Tulsa and Oklahoma City in the United States.

The Rocky Mountains

The Rocky Mountains, broadly defined, may be regarded as extending from northwestern Alaska to northern New Mexico. Within the mountain area are many distinct ranges. Some of the latter are known locally as the Rocky Mountains while others are not, but the whole may be viewed as a single enormous system. On the north the Rockies are bordered by the Arctic Coastal Plains, on the east by the Mackenzie River Lowlands and Great Plains sections of the Interior Plains, and on the west and south by various sections of the Intermountain Basins and Plateaus. In Canada these mountains occupy the border zone between Yukon Territory and the Northwest Territories, and they extend south through eastern British Columbia and southwestern Alberta. In the United States they occupy northwestern Washington, northern and eastern Idaho, western Montana, western Wyoming, northeastern Utah, western Colorado, and north central New Mexico.

The Rockies are lofty, rugged mountains with many snowcapped peaks. The highest elevations are found in Colorado, which contains a number of summits above 14,000 feet. Mount Elbert, the highest peak in the entire system, has an elevation of 14,430 feet. Throughout the Rockies, peak elevations of 10,000 feet or higher are very frequent, and the valleys and passes are generally above 5000 feet. Elevations decline toward the extreme north, where the Brooks Range of Alaska rises to general summit levels of 5000 to 6000 feet. The mountains generally form series of linear ranges trending roughly in conformance with the system as a whole. Valleys of varying size and shape are enclosed between and within the ranges. Only in northern United States, north of Yellowstone National Park, does the linear outline break down. Here the mountains rise in jumbled masses.

Easy passes through the Rockies are almost nonexistent, and the system has been a major barrier to transportation. Seven east-west trunk railroads cross the mountains: the Canadian National, Canadian Pacific, Great Northern, Northern Pacific, Milwaukee, Union Pacific, and Denver and Rio Grande Western. The easiest route, followed by the Union Pacific, lies through southern Wyoming, where the Wyoming Basin almost breaks the mountain system in two, and thence through low passes in the Wasatch Range to the Great Salt Lake district. Elsewhere, three routes in Canada, three through Montana, and two through Colorado cross the Rockies via passes varying in elevation from 3700 to 10,000 feet.

▶ The Important Mining Industry of the Rockies

Mining is the most important economic activity of the Rocky Mountains from the standpoint of value of production. Scattered mining towns from New Mexico to British Columbia produce a variety of minerals, often from complex ores yielding several end products. The major minerals in terms of value are gold, silver, lead, zinc, copper, and molybdenum, but many others are produced. Among the many small and scattered mining communities, a few are of outstanding importance. They include Butte, Montana, where the famous copper mines also yield silver, lead, and zinc; Coeur d'Alene, Idaho, producing gold, silver, lead, and zinc; Kimberley, British Co-

Major physiographic features of western United States and southwestern Canada. (*The base map is a portion of A. K. Lobeck's* Physiographic Diagram of the United States, *copyright, The Geographical Press, a division of C. S. Hammond & Company, Maplewood, N. J.*)

lumbia, which mines most of Canada's lead and zinc; and Climax, Colorado, which normally produces four fifths or more of the world output of molybdenum. Some of the ores are refined and smelted in or near the mining districts. Anaconda, Montana, near Butte, and Trail, British Columbia, are among the world's greatest centers of nonferrous metallurgy. Many "ghost towns" in the Rockies tell of mineral deposits once important but now exhausted. Awaiting future exploitation, however, are widespread deposits of coal, now mined on a large scale only in the Wyoming Basin, and enormous reserves of phosphate and oil shale in the

central and northern United States Rockies and adjoining parts of the Intermountain Basins and Plateaus.

► *Economic Activities Other than Mining*

Ranchers graze sheep and cattle in many parts of the Rockies, and many valleys contain small agricultural communities. Agriculture is generally dependent on irrigation, however, and is limited by short growing seasons. Fodder crops are grown to supplement natural forage for grazing animals; and specialties such as tree fruits, potatoes, and vegetables have developed in some areas. The Rockies are forested, largely with varieties of pine, fir, and other coniferous softwoods, up to the tree line, and a certain amount of lumbering is found in various sections. However, large-scale lumbering has developed only in northern Idaho and adjoining areas. A very important and growing activity is the tourist and resort trade. Most of the land in the Rockies, in both the United States and Canada, is owned by the respective national governments. The latter exert control over the exploitation of mineral, timber, and water resources within their properties in the interests of conservation and sustained economic development of their countries. They have contributed to the growth of tourism by setting aside areas containing spectacular scenery or other natural or historical attractions as national parks or monuments. Tourist facilities have been developed in many of these recreational areas. In addition, a large number of privately owned resorts are found in the Rockies, often in close proximity to public recreational developments.

On the whole, the economy of the Rocky Mountains is handicapped by the relative isolation of much of the area. This isolation is partly a consequence of remoteness from important centers of population, and is partly due to the difficulty of constructing adequate transportation lines in such rug-

A roundup of range cattle in the Montana Rockies south of Butte. This semi-arid landscape in the upper valley of the Ruby River is characteristic in many ways of vast areas of range land in the Rocky Mountain and Intermountain West. Note the small trees lining the water course in the foreground. (*Charles W. Herbert from Western Ways.*)

ged terrain. The mountain area as a whole is sparsely populated, and urban development is very limited. The largest city, Butte, has only 33,000 people. The commercial capitals of the various sections of the Rockies generally lie just outside the mountains, in such cities as Denver, Colorado (499,000), Salt Lake City, Utah (227,000), Spokane, Washington (176,000), and Calgary, Alberta (139,000).

The Intermountain Basins and Plateaus

The Rocky Mountain System and the mountains near the western shore of Anglo-America are separated from each other, from Alaska to Mexico, by the Intermountain Basins and Plateaus. This landform division occupies an immense part of western Anglo-America. In general, while lower than the bordering mountains, the Intermountain Basins and Plateaus lie at comparatively high elevations above the sea. Few sections lie below 3000 feet, and very few below 2000. There is a great deal of variety in elevations, landforms, and local relief from place to place. Most of the land is composed of plateau surfaces in various stages of dissection so that rolling uplands and rugged hilly and mountainous sections are included, in addition to the large areas which are comparatively level or actually flat. Over much of the area the river valleys are deeply incised, forming spectacular canyons and gorges. The most famous of the latter, the Grand Canyon of the Colorado River, is an enormous gash cut in the surface of the Colorado Plateau in northern Arizona. In many places isolated mountain ranges project far above the general surface level.

Climatically, the Intermountain Basins and Plateaus are distinguished by low rainfall due to the position of this landform division between two shielding mountain systems. Most of the Intermountain area has a semi-arid (steppe) climate, although there are a number of sizable desert areas. The heaviest precipitation occurs on the higher surfaces. In the more northerly sections the effects of low precipitation are offset to some degree by the lessened evaporation attendant on lower temperatures. Temperature conditions range from subarctic in Alaska and northern Canada to subtropical along the Mexican border. Locally, there are great temperature as well as rainfall contrasts, due to differences in elevation.

▶ *Major Subdivisions*

The Intermountain area may be divided into a number of major subsections, as follows: (1) the Basin and Range Country, (2) the Colorado Plateau, (3) the Columbia-Snake Plateau, (4) the Fraser-Nechako-Stikine Plateaus, and (5) the Yukon River Basin.

The *Basin and Range Country* extends from southern Oregon and southern Idaho to the Mexican border. It includes parts of Oregon, Idaho, California, Utah, Arizona, New Mexico, and Texas, as well as practically the entire state of Nevada. The section lying between the Wasatch Mountains of Utah and the Sierra Nevada of California is often referred to as the Great Basin, although the latter includes many smaller basins. The basins of the Basin and Range Country, many of which have no external drainage, are often separated from each other by blocklike mountain ridges rising high above the general level. Semi-arid

climatic conditions produce such vegetation forms as short grass, bunch grass, and sagebrush, except in the southwestern part, where true desert with little vegetation of any sort prevails over a wide area in California, Nevada, and Arizona.

The *Colorado Plateau* occupies parts of Colorado, Utah, Arizona, and New Mexico. Rolling uplands lie at varying levels, often separated by steep escarpments. Mountain areas rise above the general surface in various places. Rivers, principally the Colorado and its tributaries, flow in deep canyons. The latter have been a great hindrance to transportation and have kept many sections extremely isolated. The climate is generally semi-arid, although some higher sections have sufficient precipitation to produce a forest growth.

The *Columbia-Snake Plateau* is found in eastern Oregon and Washington and southern and western Idaho. It is characterized by extensive areas of level land, the result of massive lava flows in the past which buried the previous topography. The soils formed from these volcanic materials are exceptionally fertile. Isolated mountains occur, and the streams often flow in canyons. The Columbia River, the master stream of the area, has cut many alternative channels in the past, which now form rugged "scablands" in parts of Washington. The Columbia's giant tributary, the Snake, flows along the border between Oregon and Idaho in a canyon rivaling the Grand Canyon of the Colorado. The climate is semi-arid.

The *Fraser-Nechako-Stikine Plateaus* of British Columbia form a more narrow and constricted section of the Intermountain region than their counterparts in the United States. The Fraser Plateau in the south is a deeply dissected and rugged area, but in the north the Intermountain section of British Columbia presents large areas of rolling upland, interrupted by several mountain ranges. The semi-aridity of the area is moderated by lower temperatures toward the north, where the grasslands and parklike forests of the south trend into the subarctic or taiga forest.

The *Yukon River Basin,* which occupies most of Canada's Yukon Territory and the greater part of Alaska, has a varied topography of rolling uplands, hill country, intrenched streams, and a few isolated mountain ranges. As the elevations decline toward the sea in the Alaska section of the Basin, marshy areas become more prominent. The extreme subarctic climate of the Yukon Basin sets it apart from other areas in the Intermountain Basins and Plateaus. Cold rather than aridity is the dominant climatic factor, and the subarctic taiga forest is the prevailing vegetation type.

► *Population, Economy, and Urban Development*

Population is very sparse in the Intermountain Basins and Plateaus, being almost nonexistent over wide stretches, especially in the north. The major economic activities are grazing, irrigation agriculture, and mining. Most of the land as far north

as the subarctic area of British Columbia is grazed, but the pasturage is generally poor. Ranches must perforce be large, and the ranching population, in consequence, is small and scattered. Here and there definite clusters of population are associated with irrigated areas or, to a lesser extent, with mining districts. Among the many scattered irrigated districts or oases, the following are outstanding in size and importance: (1) the Imperial Valley of California, watered by the lower Colorado River, (2) the Gila-Salt River Oasis around Phoenix, Arizona, (3) the Rio Grande Valley from Albuquerque, New Mexico, to El Paso, Texas, (4) the Utah Oasis (Salt Lake City area) at the western foot of the Wasatch Range, (5) the Snake River Plains in Idaho, and (6) a series of irrigated valleys along the eastern slopes of the Cascade Mountains in Washington and Oregon. There is much variety in types of production from one irrigated district to another. Different oases specialize in one or a combination of such crops as alfalfa, cotton, citrus fruits, early vegetables, sugar beets, potatoes, and apples.

A field of potatoes in the Yukon River Basin near Fairbanks, Alaska. Potatoes are one of the few crops that can be successfully grown in the subarctic climate zone. Vast areas of the Alaskan and Canadian subarctic are covered by a straggling growth of small trees, mainly conifers, such as cover the low uplands in the background. (*United States Information Service, Department of State*)

Mining activity characterizes almost the whole extent of the Intermountain area in greater or less degree, being least important in the Columbia-Snake Plateau and those of British Columbia. The leading minerals in value of production for the area as a whole are copper, gold, silver, lead, and zinc. Arizona and Utah are the leading American states in the production of copper. Most of their output comes from the Intermountain area. In the Yukon Basin gold mining is the mainstay of the economy. In addition to copper production from the great open-pit mines at Bingham Canyon, the state of Utah mines both coal and iron ore and has the only steel plant of the Intermountain area. The latter is located at Geneva, south of Salt Lake City.

Nonirrigated cropping is important in only one district, the Columbia Plateau, which is able to produce large quantities of wheat thanks to soils which are exceptionally fertile and water retentive. The tourist and resort industry is also limited mainly to one section—the southern deserts. Visitors are attracted to the latter for reasons of health as well as recreation. The intrenched rivers of the Intermountain area, flowing from adjacent mountain regions, produce a tremendous hydroelectric potential, much of which has been developed. The Columbia River and its tributaries have a greater hydroelectric potential than any other river system in Anglo-America. The largest and most famous power installations in the Intermountain area are Grand Coulee Dam on the Columbia River and Hoover Dam (formerly Boulder Dam) on the Colorado. Power from these dams is largely transmitted to points outside of the Intermountain Basins and Plateaus and has given rise to relatively little manufacturing within the area itself.

The general sparsity of population is indicated by the comparatively small size of the major cities: Salt Lake City (227,000), Phoenix (216,000), Spokane (176,000), El Paso (137,000), and Albuquerque (97,000). Each of these is identified with a major irrigated district except for Spokane, which serves the Columbia Plateau wheat belt. Each is the business center for a very large, but for the most part thinly settled hinterland. In British Columbia the largest Intermountain town, Kelowna, has about 9000 people; in Yukon Territory the largest settlement, Whitehorse, has 3000; while in the Alaskan section of the Yukon Basin, Fairbanks, with 6000 people, easily surpasses the other settlements in size.

The Pacific Mountains and Valleys

The Pacific shore of Anglo-America is bordered by a series of mountain ranges extending from Mexico to the Aleutian Islands. In the United States several large lowlands are included within this mountainous region.

► Physical Description of the Major Subdivisions

For purposes of introductory physical description, the Pacific Mountains and Valleys may be conveniently discussed in terms of the following major subdivisions: (1) the Coast Ranges of California, Oregon, and Washington, (2) the Sierra Nevada, (3) the Central Valley of California, (4) the Klamath Mountains, (5) the Cascade Mountains, (6) the Willamette–Puget Sound Lowland, (7) the Coastal Ranges of British Columbia and southeastern Alaska, and (8) the Alaska Range and other mountains of southern Alaska north of the southeastern "Panhandle."

The coasts of California, Oregon, and Washington are fronted by the *Coast Ranges*. The section in northwestern Washington known as the Olympic Mountains has peaks reaching approximately 8000 feet and in the south some sections east of Los Angeles exceed 10,000 feet. However, the peak elevations more commonly lie at 3000 to 5000 feet in California and at only 1000 to 3000 feet farther north. Along most of the western coast of the United States there is no coastal plain, or almost none, and even the lower parts of the Coast Ranges are often quite rugged. However, a few valleys are available for agriculture, especially in California; and from Los Angeles to the Mexican border the ranges lie a few miles inland and a lower, hilly district containing much of California's population fronts the sea.

The *Sierra Nevada* forms the inland edge of the Pacific Mountains and Valleys in central California, merging with the Coast Ranges north of Los Angeles and with the Klamath and Cascade Ranges in northern California. The Sierra Nevada is an immense upraised, tilted, broken, and eroded block presenting a long and comparatively gentle slope to the west and a precipitous face eastward toward the Basin and Range Country. It is very high and rugged, and constitutes a major barrier both climatically and with regard to transportation. Mount Whitney (14,495 feet) in the southern Sierra Nevada is the highest peak in the United States.

The *Central Valley*, a level-floored alluvial trough some 500 miles long by 50 miles wide, occupies the center of California between the Coast Ranges and the Sierra Nevada. It is completely surrounded by mountains except where San Francisco Bay breaks the continuity of the Coast Ranges and brings the Central Valley into contact with the Pacific.

The *Klamath Mountains* form a link between the Coast Ranges and the Sierra Nevada and Cascade Ranges, and separate the northern end of the Central Valley of California from the southern end of the Willamette Valley of Oregon. The Klamath Mountains are physiographically a dissected plateau. The valleys are deeply incised, giving an extremely rugged aspect to the terrain. Summit levels are frequently at 6000 to 7000 feet or higher.

The *Cascade Mountains* extend northward from the Sierra Nevada and the Klamath Mountains across Oregon and Washington and into British Columbia. Much of the area of the Cascades lies between 5000 and 9000 feet in elevation, and the mountains are surmounted by a series of volcanic cones reaching much higher elevations. Mt. Rainier (14,408 feet) and Mount Hood (11,245 feet) are probably the most famous of these. The Cascades are broken into two sections at the Oregon-Washington boundary by a spectacular gorge through which the Columbia River flows westward toward the Pacific.

The *Willamette–Puget Sound Lowland* lies between the Coast Ranges and the Cascades. Its Oregon section, from the Klamath Mountains in the south to the lower Columbia River in the north, is the valley of the Willamette River, while the northern section is commonly known as the Puget Sound Lowland. This latter section extends all the way across western Washington and north into British Columbia to include a small area along the lower course of the Fraser River.

In British Columbia and the southeastern "Panhandle" of Alaska a northward extension of the Cascades lies along the coast and is known as the *Coastal Ranges*. These Ranges are generally higher and more rugged than the Coast Ranges in the United States. Many peaks reach 9000 or 10,000 feet. The mountains rise abruptly from the sea and are penetrated by fjords, resembling in this respect the coasts of Norway and southern Chile. West of the Coastal Ranges a valley analogous in position to the Central Valley of California and the Willamette–Puget Sound Lowland has subsided below sea level and now forms the famous "Inside Passage" to Alaska. The mountains in British Columbia and southeastern Alaska which correspond in position to the Coast Ranges of the United States are partly submerged, and form a string of rugged islands along the outer edge of the Inside Passage.

Most of southern Alaska is mountainous. Just north of the Panhandle, spectacular glaciers descend the mountains to the sea. The highest mountains, however, are found farther to the north and west in the *Alaska Range,* where Mount McKinley reaches 20,300 feet, the highest elevation in Anglo-America. In a more subdued form the mountains continue from the Alaska Range into the Alaska Peninsula and the Aleutian Islands. A fair sized area of lower land is found south of the Alaska Range in the Susitna River Valley and along the western side of the Kenai Peninsula.

▶ Distribution of Population

From southern California to southern British Columbia the Pacific Mountains and Valleys contain a rather large population, especially considering that most of the included land is mountainous. This Pacific littoral forms an island of relatively dense population separated from the populous eastern areas of Anglo-America by the thinly peopled Intermountain, Rocky Mountain, and Great Plains regions. In the American section of the Pacific Mountains and Valleys are at least 13 million people, as compared with a total of some 5 million in all the interior states eastward to the western boundaries of the Dakotas, Nebraska, Kansas, and Texas. California is by far the largest center of population in the western third of Anglo-America. With an estimated 11 million people or more, it ranks second in population among the states. In Canada 75 percent of the 1,200,-000 people of British Columbia live in small lowland areas along or near the lower Fraser River and on the southern part of Vancouver Island. North of this southwestern corner of British Columbia there is little population in the Pacific Mountains and Valleys, but even so, the population is larger than in the adjacent regions of the interior. Two thirds or more of Alaska's estimated 182,000 people live along or near the Pacific Coast, the most concentrated area of settlement being in the Anchorage district.

▶ The Highly Developed Agriculture of California

The marked concentration of people along the Pacific littoral is partly due to the agricultural advantages of this area as compared with interior sections of the Anglo-American West. These advantages are much more pronounced in California than in any other section of the Pacific Mountains and Valleys. The lowlands of California are areas of mediterranean or dry-summer subtropical climate, except for especially sheltered spots in the southern part of the Central Valley, which grade into steppe and desert. The winter rains and mild winter temperatures permit non-irrigated grain farming to be carried on in the winter and spring, and there is enough moisture to provide fairly good pasturage for grazing. During the dry summers, near-by mountain pastures often provide valuable supplementary grazing for livestock. But the importance of California as an agricultural state derives mainly from the most extensive development of irrigation in the United States. This development has been made possible by the close proximity of high mountain ranges (especially the Sierra Nevada but also parts of the Coast Ranges) receiving very heavy precipitation. Rain and snow falling in these mountains provide large amounts of water for irrigating the lowlands of the Central Valley and southern California.

The principal products of California agriculture are a great variety of fruits. Citrus fruits, grown mainly in southern California, are the best known, and the state ordinarily accounts for over a third of the country's citrus production. However, California is also the leading producer

Mediterranean agriculture in southern California. The irrigated orange groves in this view lie at the foot of rugged mountains in the Coast Ranges east of Los Angeles. In the vicinity of Los Angeles is found one of the three greatest citrus districts of the United States. (*Los Angeles Chamber of Commerce.*)

of many other fruits, including apricots, dates, figs, grapes, olives, peaches, pears, and plums. It is also the leading state in vegetable production, usually accounting for between a fifth and a fourth of the country's total output by value. The Imperial Valley, located in the Intermountain area of southeastern California, plays an important part in the irrigated vegetable production of the state, along with the Pacific sections. The southern part of the Central Valley, known as the San Joaquin Valley, produces about a tenth of the American cotton crop, and the northern part (Sacramento Valley) about a quarter of the

country's rice crop. In addition, large dairy and poultry industries have developed in some sections, stimulated by the state's rapid growth in urban population. Grazing, dry farming, and irrigation farming combine to give California a remarkable diversity in agriculture and a production great enough to make it the leading state in total value of farm products.

► Agriculture in the Area of Marine West Coast Climate

North of California the lowlands of the Pacific area have a marine west coast climate characterized by mild, wet conditions similar to those of the corresponding climatic region in northwestern Europe. In the Willamette–Puget Sound Lowland, agricultural development has emphasized principally dairy farming and the production of tree and bush fruits, with some truck gardening. But agriculture has been handicapped, especially in the Puget Sound Lowland, by the difficulty and expense of clearing the land of immense stumps in cutover forest areas, and by soils which are often poorly drained and heavily leached. Nor does this section have a climate permitting it to produce specialties of the type which have allowed California to largely overcome its problem of great distance from major consuming centers in eastern United States. Consequently, agricultural development here is on a considerably smaller scale than in California, and there is much farming on a part-time subsistence basis. North of the Fraser lowlands and Vancouver Island, there is very little land sufficiently level for agriculture, and the largest agricultural area, found in lowlands north of Anchorage (Matanuska Valley), contains only a few hundred farms.

▶ Nonagricultural Resources of the Pacific Mountains and Valleys

The principal nonagricultural resources of the Pacific Mountains and Valleys are water power, oil, timber, and fish. Hydroelectricity is a major source of power for both domestic and industrial uses, and helps to overcome the region's shortage of coal. Electricity is supplied by many installations within the Pacific area, of which Bonneville Dam in the Columbia gorge and Shasta Dam on the Sacramento River in northern California are probably the outstanding examples. In addition, large amounts of power are transmitted from installations in the Intermountain Basins and Plateaus such as Hoover Dam and Grand Coulee Dam. The location of a large part of the United States aluminum industry in Washington and Oregon is closely related to the superior water power resources of these states. Now this industry is extending northward along the coast of British Columbia where the Kitimat installation will be the world's largest when fully completed.

Oil is another major source of power along the Pacific Coast, but its production is confined to California. Southern California and the southern end of the Central Valley supply about 15 percent of the national total, and California ranks second only to Texas as an oil-producing state. Los Angeles and San Francisco and their environs are major centers of oil refining.

The softwood forests which occupy the mountainous portions of the Pacific Coast region from the Sierra Nevada and San Francisco Bay northward are the most valuable in Anglo-America from the standpoint of size of trees and total reserves of saw timber. These large trees can be cut into long, high-quality boards, and represent the greatest reserve of saw timber in the United States. The famous Douglas fir of Oregon and Washington is the outstanding species, although the immense redwoods of northern California and various other species are important. Oregon, Washington, and California, in that order, are the first, second and third ranking American states in sawmilling, accounting together for 35 percent of the total United States production of sawn lumber, while British Columbia ranks first among Canadian provinces in this phase of the forest industries. Pulp and paper milling is relatively less important here than in most other forested areas in Anglo-America, but the Pacific area does produce more than 15 percent of all United States wood pulp. In fact, Washington is the leading American state in pulp and paper milling. In Alaska the forests are, on the whole, less impressive; nevertheless, they offer a major resource which has been very little exploited as yet. The first Alaskan pulp mills are now being built in the Panhandle section.

The fishing industry is important along the Pacific Coast from San Diego to the Aleutian Islands. In terms of value of catch, California is the leading fishing state with over a fifth of the United States total. Tuna and sardines are the principal species landed by the California fishing fleet. Oregon and Washington land almost 10 percent of the American catch, while the value of the catch in Alaska is about twice as great as that of Oregon and Washington combined. British Columbia is the leading Canadian province in total value of fishery production. Salmon, halibut, and herring are the major species landed by the Pacific fisheries north of California. The fishing industry is relatively more important as a phase of the total economy in northern British Columbia and Alaska than in areas farther south. Little other economic development has occurred in these more northerly sections, and fishing affords the principal support for most of the small and scattered coastal communities. The Anchorage area, dependent largely on United States military installations, is an exception to this generalization.

Finally, the scenery of the Pacific area and the climate of southern California must be considered as major resources since they afford the principal basis for a large and growing tourist trade.

▶ *Urban and Industrial Development*

The Pacific border from Vancouver southward includes an impressive number of large cities. In general, the importance of commerce seems somewhat greater than that of manufacturing in these cities, although a rapid development of industry has occurred in recent years. The six largest cities are all seaports. Their locations reflect advantages deriving from natural harbors or passes through the mountains to the east, or both. Los Angeles (3,997,000), the largest city on the Pacific Coast, is located in the northern and wider part of the coastal lowland of southern California,

west of passes over the Coast Ranges and south of passes leading to the Central Valley. It originally developed inland and had no first-rate natural harbor, but in the twentieth century it expanded to the coast and built a large artificial harbor. San Francisco (2,022,000 including suburbs east of San Francisco Bay) has developed on one of the world's best natural harbors. It lies west of the center of the Central Valley nearly opposite the important Truckee Pass over the high Sierra Nevada. Seattle, Washington (622,000), lies on a natural harbor on Puget Sound and west of passes through the Cascades. Vancouver, British Columbia (531,000), has an excellent natural harbor near the mouth of the Fraser River, whose valley affords a passageway through the mountains to the east. Among Canadian ports it ranks second only to Montreal, drawing products not only from its immediate hinterland but to some extent from the Prairie Provinces also. Portland, Oregon (513,000), is located on the lower Columbia River at the head of the Willamette Valley. Improvement of the channel of the lower Columbia has made it an ocean port and the gorge of the Columbia through the Cascades gives it access to the interior. San Diego, California (433,000), has developed on an excellent natural harbor, although it has suffered somewhat from inferior access to the interior as compared with the major cities farther north.

Several of the smaller cities of the Pacific area are interior commercial centers in California. They include San Bernardino (136,000) in southern California; Sacramento (212,000), Stockton (113,000), and Fresno (131,000) in the Central Valley; and San Jose (176,000) in an especially productive Coast Range valley south of San Francisco Bay. In each of these cities canning constitutes the principal industry. Farther north in the Puget Sound area are Tacoma, Washington (168,000), and Victoria (103,-000), the capital of British Columbia, both of which are minor seaports.

Los Angeles is the greatest manufacturing center of the Pacific area. The production of aircraft is its greatest industry, but one which is subject to extreme fluctuations due largely to variations from year to year in the demand for military aircraft. The area is the leading center of aircraft manufacture not only in the United States but also in the world, its output representing something like a third of the United States total. Aircraft production is also the major industry of San Diego and is important in the economy of Seattle. The other industry, in a sense a manufacturing industry, in which Los Angeles leads the world is, of course, movie making. The influence of motion pictures on clothing styles has been an important factor in a growing apparel industry in Los Angeles. In addition, the city serves as a major canning center for southern California's fruit and fish. Some miles east of Los Angeles, near San Bernardino, the only integrated steel mill in the Pacific area was built during World War II.

Like Los Angeles, San Francisco is an oil-refining and a canning center, but its major industry is shipbuilding, which is also important in the seaports of Washington and Oregon. The major industries of the latter states, however, are sawmilling and aluminum production. North of Vancouver almost the only manufacturing activities are sawmilling, pulp and paper making, and fish canning, although aluminum production will soon represent an important addition.

The Arctic Coastal Plains

Fairly extensive coastal plains fronting on Arctic waters are found in two distinct sections of Anglo-America, one north of the Brooks Range and the other along the southern shores of Hudson Bay. The Alaskan coastal plain is an area of tundra; while that along Hudson Bay is largely subarctic in climate and forested, though grading into tundra in some sections. These areas are extremely thinly populated and play almost no part in the economic life of Anglo-America, although there are a few fur-trading posts in the Hudson Bay section. Subsistence hunting and fishing are the principal means of support of the Eskimo population of the Alaska section. The considerable deposits of petroleum which are known to exist in the Alaskan coastal plain, however, may give it greater economic significance in the future.

Greenland

Greenland is the world's largest island, with an area of approximately 840,000 square miles. While not culturally or politically a part of Anglo-America, it may be regarded as a marginal part of the latter region from the standpoint of proximity and strategic geography. Almost the whole surface is covered by a permanent icecap and most of the island's 25,000 permanent inhabitants live in rugged strips of tundra along the southwestern and southeastern coasts. These people are primarily Eskimo but with a strong admixture of Scandinavian blood. Fishing (carried on both commercially and on a subsistence basis) and sheep herding are their chief means of livelihood. The population includes a few hundred Danes, mainly traders and government officials. The island is known to have considerable mineral wealth, but little of this has yet been exploited except for cryolite, a material useful in the glass, chemical, and aluminum industries. Greenland has practically a world monopoly of natural cryolite.

Politically, Greenland is an integral part of Denmark. The latter, a member of the North Atlantic Treaty Organization, has granted permission for the establishment of several NATO air bases along the Greenland coast. The United States has played a leading role in the development of these bases. The largest is located at Thule on the far northwestern coast.

Index

All page references to maps are in italics following general entry for topic.

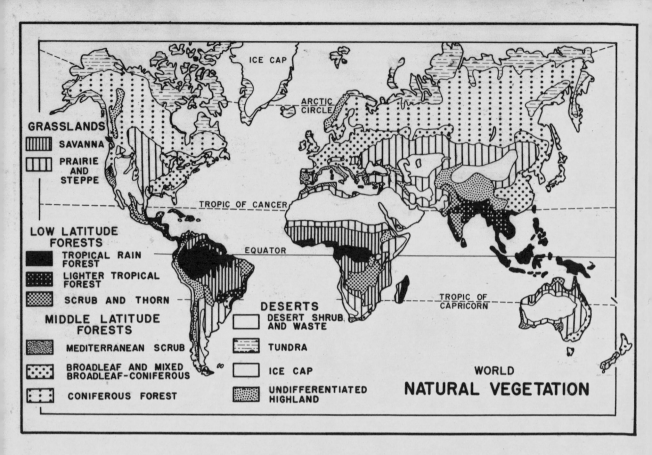

GRASSLANDS
SAVANNA
PRAIRIE AND STEPPE

LOW LATITUDE FORESTS
TROPICAL RAIN FOREST
LIGHTER TROPICAL FOREST
SCRUB AND THORN

MIDDLE LATITUDE FORESTS
MEDITERRANEAN SCRUB
BROADLEAF AND MIXED BROADLEAF-CONIFEROUS
CONIFEROUS FOREST

DESERTS
DESERT SHRUB AND WASTE
TUNDRA
ICE CAP
UNDIFFERENTIATED HIGHLAND

WORLD
NATURAL VEGETATION

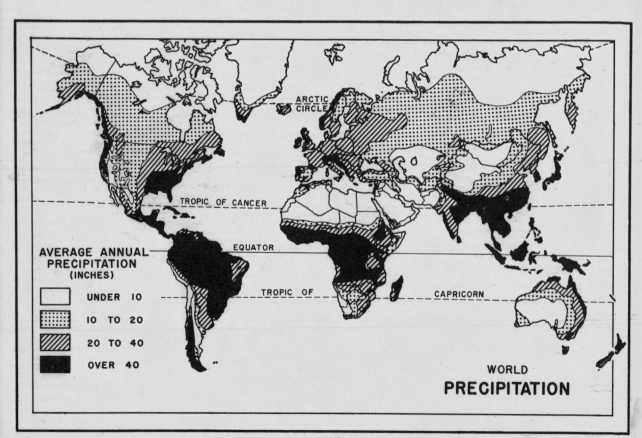

AVERAGE ANNUAL PRECIPITATION (INCHES)
UNDER 10
10 TO 20
20 TO 40
OVER 40

WORLD
PRECIPITATION